Collins

GCSE Maths
2 tier-higher
for AQA A

BRIAN SPEED

KEITH GORDON

KEVIN EVANS

William Collins' dream of knowledge for all began with the publication of his first book in 1819. A self-educated mill worker, he not only enriched millions of lives, but also founded a flourishing publishing house. Today, staying true to this spirit, Collins books are packed with inspiration, innovation and a practical expertise. They place you at the centre of a world of possibility and give you exactly what you need to explore it.

Collins. Do more.

Published by Collins
An imprint of HarperCollins*Publishers*
77–85 Fulham Palace Road
Hammersmith
London
W6 8JB

Browse the complete Collins catalogue at
www.collinseducation.com

ISBN-13 978-0-00-721578-2
ISBN-10 0-00-721578-9

British Library Cataloguing in Publication Data. A Catalogue record for this publication is available from the British Library

Commissioned by Marie Taylor, Vicky Butt and Michael Cotter

Project managed by Penny Fowler

Edited by Joan Miller and Peta Abbott

Additional proof reader: Ruth Burns

Indexer: Dr Laurence Errington

Internal design by JPD

Cover design by JPD

Cover illustration by Andy Parker, JPD

Page make-up by Gray Publishing

Page make-up of Really Useful Maths! spreads by EMC Design

Illustrations by Gray Publishing, EMC Design, Lisa Alderson (Advocate), Peter Cornwell, Bob Lea (Artists Partners), Martin Sanders (Beehive Illustration), Laszlo Veres (Beehive Illustration), Roger Wade Walker (Beehive Illustration) and Peters and Zabransky.

Production by Natasha Buckland

Printed and bound in Italy by Eurografica SpA

Acknowledgements

With special thanks to Lynn and Greg Byrd

The Publishers gratefully acknowledge the following for permission to reproduce copyright material. Whilst every effort has been made to trace the copyright holders, in cases where this has been unsuccessful or if any have inadvertently been overlooked, the Publishers will be pleased to make the necessary arrangements at the first opportunity.

AQA material is reproduced by permission of the Assessment and Qualifications Alliance. Please note that all questions used dated before 2003 are NOT from the live examinations for the current specification. New specifications for GCSE were introduced in 2003.

Grade bar photos © 2006 JupiterImages Corporation and Photodisc Collection / Getty Images

© 2006 JupiterImages Corporation, p1, p22 Main, p23 Middle and BR, p49, p67, p95, p143, p167, p195, p213, p257, p275, p299, p327, p355, p427, p453, p473, p483, p523, p549

© Bernd Klumpp / Istock, p22 TL

© Karen Town / Istock, p22 TR

© David Wall / Alamy, p22 BL

© Neale Haynes/Buzz Pictures, p23 TL

© Christian Kretz / Istock, p22 TR

© PCL / Alamy, p119

© Images Etc Ltd / Alamy, p225

© Dave Roberts / Istock, p373

© Michal Galazka / Istock, p505

© Agence Images / Alamy, p539

CONTENTS

Welcome to Collins GCSE Maths, the easiest way to learn and succeed in Mathematics. This textbook uses a stimulating approach that really appeals to students. Here are some of the key features of the textbook, to explain why.

Each chapter of the textbook begins with an **Overview**. The Overview lists the Sections you will encounter in the chapter, the key ideas you will learn, and shows how these ideas relate to, and build upon, each other. The Overview also highlights what you should already know, and if you're not sure, there is a short Quick Check activity to test yourself and recap.

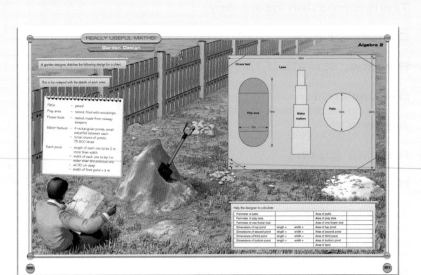

Maths can be useful to us every day of our lives, so look out for these **Really Useful Maths!** pages. These double page spreads use big, bright illustrations to depict real-life situations, and present a short series of real-world problems for you to practice your latest mathematical skills on.

Each **Section** begins first by explaining what mathematical ideas you are aiming to learn, and then lists the key words you will meet and use. The ideas are clearly explained, and this is followed by several examples showing how they can be applied to real problems. Then it's your turn to work through the exercises and improve your skills. Notice the different coloured panels along the outside of the exercise pages. These show the equivalent exam grade of the questions you are working on, so you can always tell how well you are doing.

Every chapter in this textbook contains lots of **Exam Questions**. These provide ideal preparation for your examinations. Each exam question section also concludes with a fully worked example. Compare this with your own work, and pay special attention to the examiner's comments, which will ensure you understand how to score maximum marks.

Throughout the textbook you will find **Activities** – highlighted in the green panels – designed to challenge your thinking and improve your understanding.

Review the **Grade Yourself** pages at the very end of the chapter. This will show what exam grade you are currently working at. Doublecheck **What you should now know** to confirm that you have the knowledge you need to progress.

Working through these sections in the right way should mean you achieve your very best in GCSE Maths. Remember though, if you get stuck, answers to all the questions are at the back of the book (except the exam question answers which your teacher has).

We do hope you enjoy using Collins GCSE Maths, and wish you every good luck in your studies!

Brian Speed, Keith Gordon, Kevin Evans

ICONS

 You may use your calculator for this question

 You should not use your calculator for this question

 Indicates a Using and Applying Mathematics question

 Indicates a Proof question

Number

This chapter will show you ...

- how to calculate with integers and decimals
- how to round off numbers to a given number of significant figures
- how to find prime factors, least common multiples (LCM) and highest common factors (HCF)

What you should already know

- How to add, subtract, multiply and divide with integers
- What multiples, factors, square numbers and prime numbers are
- The BODMAS rule and how to substitute values into simple algebraic expressions

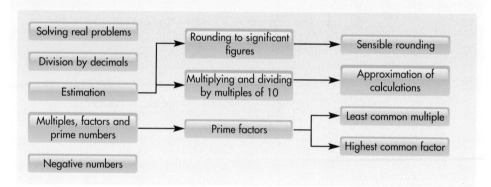

Solving real problems

Division by decimals

Estimation

Multiples, factors and prime numbers

Negative numbers

Rounding to significant figures

Multiplying and dividing by multiples of 10

Prime factors

Sensible rounding

Approximation of calculations

Least common multiple

Highest common factor

Quick check

1 Work out the following.

   a 23×167 **b** $984 \div 24$ **c** $(16 + 9)^2$

2 Write down the following.

   a a multiple of 7   **b** a prime number between 10 and 20

   c a square number under 80   **d** the factors of 9

3 Work out the following.

   a $2 + 3 \times 5$ **b** $(2 + 3) \times 5$ **c** $2 + 3^2 - 6$

Solving real problems

This section will give you practice in using arithmetic to:

● solve more complex problems

Key words
long division
long
   multiplication
strategy

In your GCSE examination, you will be given *real* problems that you have to *read carefully, think about* and then plan a **strategy** without using a calculator. These will involve arithmetical skills such as **long multiplication** and **long division**. There are several ways to do these, so make sure you are familiar with and confident with at least one of them. The box method for long multiplication is shown in the first example and the standard column method for long division is shown in the second example. In this type of problem it is important to show your working as you will get marks for correct methods.

EXAMPLE 1

A supermarket receives a delivery of 235 cases of tins of beans. Each case contains 24 tins.

a How many tins of beans does the supermarket receive altogether?

b 5% of the tins were damaged. These were thrown away. The supermarket knows that it sells, on average, 250 tins of beans a day. How many days will the delivery of beans last before a new consignment is needed?

a The problem is a long multiplication 235 × 24.

The box method is shown.

×	200	30	5
20	4000	600	100
4	800	120	20

```
  4000
   600
   100
+  800
   120
    20
  ____
  5640
```

So the answer is 5640 tins.

b 10% of 5640 is 564, so 5% is 564 ÷ 2 = 282

This leaves 5640 − 282 = 5358 tins to be sold.

There are 21 lots of 250 in 5358 (you should know that 4 × 250 = 1000), so the beans will last for 21 days before another delivery is needed.

EXAMPLE 2

A party of 613 children and 59 adults are going on a day out to a theme park.

a How many coaches, each holding 53 people, will be needed?

b One adult gets into the theme park free for every 15 children. How many adults will have to pay to get in?

a We read the problem and realise that we have to do a division sum: the number of seats on a coach into the number of people. This is (613 + 59) ÷ 53 = 672 ÷ 53

```
        1 2
   53 | 672
        530
        142
        106
         36
```

The answer is 12 remainder 36. So, there will be 12 full coaches and one coach with 36 people on. So, they would have to book 13 coaches.

b This is also a division, 613 ÷ 15. This can be done quite easily if you know the 15 times table as 4 × 15 = 60, so 40 × 15 = 600. This leaves a remainder of 13. So 40 adults get in free and 59 − 40 = 19 adults will have to pay.

EXERCISE 1A

1 There are 48 cans of soup in a crate. A supermarket had a delivery of 125 crates of soup.

   a How many cans of soup were received?

   b The supermarket is having a promotion on soup. If you buy five cans you get one free. Each can costs 39p. How much will it cost to get 32 cans of soup?

2 Greystones Primary School has 12 classes, each of which has 24 pupils.

   a How many pupils are there at Greystones Primary School?

   b The pupil–teacher ratio is 18 to 1. That means there is one teacher for every 18 pupils. How many teachers are at the school?

3 Barnsley Football Club is organising travel for an away game. 1300 adults and 500 juniors want to go. Each coach holds 48 people and costs £320 to hire. Tickets to the match are £18 for adults and £10 for juniors.

   a How many coaches will be needed?

   b The club is charging adults £26 and juniors £14 for travel and a ticket. How much profit does the club make out of the trip?

4 First-class letters cost 30p to post. Second-class letters cost 21p to post. How much will it cost to send 75 first-class and 220 second-class letters?

5 Kirsty collects small models of animals. Each one costs 45p. She saves enough to buy 23 models but when she goes to the shop she finds that the price has gone up to 55p. How many can she buy now?

6 Eunice wanted to save up for a mountain bike that costs £250. She baby-sits each week for 6 hours for £2.75 an hour, and does a Saturday job that pays £27.50. She saves three-quarters of her weekly earnings. How many weeks will it take her to save enough to buy the bike?

7 The magazine *Teen Dance* comes out every month. In a newsagent the magazine costs £2.45. The annual (yearly) subscription for the magazine is £21. How much cheaper is each magazine bought on subscription?

8 Paula buys a music centre. She pays a deposit of 10% of the cash price and then 36 monthly payments of £12.50. In total she pays £495. How much was the cash price of the music centre?

1.2 Division by decimals

This section will show you how to:
- divide by decimals by changing the problem so you divide by an integer

Key words
decimal places
decimal point
integer

It is advisable to change the problem so that you divide by an **integer** rather than a decimal. This is done by multiplying both numbers by 10 or 100, etc. This will depend on the number of **decimal places** after the **decimal point**.

EXAMPLE 3

Evaluate the following.   **a** $42 \div 0.2$ **b** $19.8 \div 0.55$

a The calculation is $42 \div 0.2$ which can be rewritten as $420 \div 2$. In this case both values have been multiplied by 10 to make the divisor into a whole number. This is then a straightforward division to which the answer is 210.

Another way to view this is as a fraction problem.

$$\frac{42}{0.2} = \frac{42}{0.2} \times \frac{10}{10} = \frac{420}{2} = \frac{210}{1} = 210$$

b $19.8 \div 0.55 = 198 \div 5.5 = 1980 \div 55$

This then becomes a long division problem.

This has been solved by the method of repeated subtraction.

$$
\begin{array}{rl}
1980 & \\
- 1100 & 20 \times 55 \\
\hline
880 & \\
- 440 & 8 \times 55 \\
\hline
440 & \\
- 440 & 8 \times 55 \\
\hline
0 & 36 \times 55 \\
\end{array}
$$

EXERCISE 1B

1 Evaluate each of these.

   a $3.6 \div 0.2$ **b** $56 \div 0.4$ **c** $0.42 \div 0.3$ **d** $8.4 \div 0.7$ **e** $4.26 \div 0.2$

   f $3.45 \div 0.5$ **g** $83.7 \div 0.03$ **h** $0.968 \div 0.08$ **i** $7.56 \div 0.4$

2 Evaluate each of these.

   a $67.2 \div 0.24$ **b** $6.36 \div 0.53$ **c** $0.936 \div 5.2$ **d** $162 \div 0.36$ **e** $2.17 \div 3.5$

   f $98.8 \div 0.26$ **g** $0.468 \div 1.8$ **h** $132 \div 0.55$ **i** $0.984 \div 0.082$

3 A pile of paper is 6 cm high. Each sheet is 0.008 cm thick. How many sheets are in the pile of paper?

4 Doris buys a big bag of safety pins. The bag weighs 180 grams. Each safety pin weighs 0.6 grams. How many safety pins are in the bag?

1.3 Estimation

This section will show you how to:
- use estimation to find approximate answers to numerical calculations

Key words
approximate
estimation
significant
 figures

Rounding off to significant figures

We often use significant figures when we want to **approximate** a number with quite a few digits in it.

Look at this table which shows some numbers rounded to one, two and three **significant figures** (sf).

One sf	8	50	200	90 000	0.00007	0.003	0.4
Two sf	67	4.8	0.76	45 000	730	0.0067	0.40
Three sf	312	65.9	40.3	0.0761	7.05	0.00301	0.400

The steps taken to round off a number to a particular number of significant figures are very similar to those used for rounding to so many decimal places.

- From the left, count the digits. If you are rounding to 2 sf, count 2 digits, for 3 sf count 3 digits, and so on. When the original number is less than 1.0, start counting from the first non-zero digit.

- Look at the *next* digit to the right. When the next digit is less than 5, leave the digit you counted to the same. However if the next digit is equal to or greater than 5, add 1 to the digit you counted to.

- Ignore all the other digits, but put in enough zeros to keep the number the right size (value).

For example, look at the following table which shows some numbers rounded off to one, two and three significant figures, respectively.

Number	Rounded to 1 sf	Rounded to 2 sf	Rounded to 3 sf
45 281	50 000	45 000	45 300
568.54	600	570	569
7.3782	7	7.4	7.38
8054	8000	8100	8050
99.8721	100	100	99.9
0.7002	0.7	0.70	0.700

1 Round off each of the following numbers to 1 significant figure.

    a 46 313   **b** 57 123   **c** 30 569   **d** 94 558   **e** 85 299

    f 0.5388   **g** 0.2823   **h** 0.005 84   **i** 0.047 85   **j** 0.000 876

    k 9.9   **l** 89.5   **m** 90.78   **n** 199   **o** 999.99

2 Round off each of the following numbers to 2 significant figures.

    a 56 147   **b** 26 813   **c** 79 611   **d** 30 578   **e** 14 009

    f 1.689   **g** 4.0854   **h** 2.658   **i** 8.0089   **j** 41.564

    k 0.8006   **l** 0.458   **m** 0.0658   **n** 0.9996   **o** 0.009 82

3 Round off each of the following to the number of significant figures (sf) indicated.

    a 57 402 (1 sf)   **b** 5288 (2 sf)   **c** 89.67 (3 sf)

    d 105.6 (2 sf)   **e** 8.69 (1 sf)   **f** 1.087 (2 sf)

    g 0.261 (1 sf)   **h** 0.732 (1 sf)   **i** 0.42 (1 sf)

    j 0.758 (1 sf)   **k** 0.185 (1 sf)   **l** 0.682 (1 sf)

4 What are the least and the greatest number of sweets that can be found in these jars?

    a   **b**   **c**

70 sweets (to 1 sf)   100 sweets (to 1 sf)   1000 sweets (to 1 sf)

5 What are the least and the greatest number of people that can be found in these towns?

    Elsecar   population 800 (to 1 significant figure)

    Hoyland   population 1200 (to 2 significant figures)

    Barnsley   population 165 000 (to 3 significant figures)

Multiplying and dividing by multiples of 10

Questions often use multiplying together multiples of 10, 100, and so on. This method is used in estimation. You should have the skill to do this mentally so that you can check that your answers to calculations are about right. (Approximation of calculations is covered on page 7.)

Use a calculator to work out the following.

    a $200 \times 300 =$ **b** $100 \times 40 =$ **c** $2000 \times 0.3 =$

    d $0.2 \times 50 =$ **e** $0.2 \times 0.5 =$ **f** $0.3 \times 0.04 =$

Can you see a way of doing these without using a calculator or pencil and paper? Basically, the digits are multiplied together and then the number of zeros or the position of the decimal point is worked out by combining the zeros or decimal places on the original calculation.

Dividing is almost as simple. Try doing the following on your calculator.

a $400 \div 20 =$ **b** $200 \div 50 =$ **c** $1000 \div 0.2 =$

d $300 \div 0.3 =$ **e** $250 \div 0.05 =$ **f** $30\,000 \div 0.6 =$

Once again, there is an easy way of doing these "in your head". Look at these examples.

$300 \times 4000 = 1\,200\,000$ $5000 \div 200 = 25$ $20 \times 0.5 = 10$

$0.6 \times 5000 = 3000$ $400 \div 0.02 = 20\,000$ $800 \div 0.2 = 4000$

Can you see a connection between the digits, the number of zeros and the position of the decimal point, and the way in which these calculations are worked out?

EXERCISE 1D

1 Without using a calculator, write down the answers to these.

a 200×300 **b** 30×4000 **c** 50×200

d 0.3×50 **e** 200×0.7 **f** 200×0.5

g 0.1×2000 **h** 0.2×0.14 **i** 0.3×0.3

j $(20)^2$ **k** $(20)^3$ **l** $(0.4)^2$

m 0.3×150 **n** 0.4×0.2 **o** 0.5×0.5

p $20 \times 40 \times 5000$ **q** $20 \times 20 \times 900$

2 Without using a calculator, write down the answers to these.

a $2000 \div 400$ **b** $3000 \div 60$ **c** $5000 \div 200$

d $300 \div 0.5$ **e** $2100 \div 0.7$ **f** $2000 \div 0.4$

g $3000 \div 1.5$ **h** $400 \div 0.2$ **i** $2000 \times 40 \div 200$

j $200 \times 20 \div 0.5$ **k** $200 \times 6000 \div 0.3$ **l** $20 \times 80 \times 60 \div 0.03$

Approximation of calculations

How do we approximate the value of a calculation? What do we actually do when we try to approximate an answer to a problem?

For example, what is the approximate answer to 35.1×6.58?

To approximate the answer in this and many other similar cases, we simply round off each number to 1 significant figure, then work out the calculation. So in this case, the approximation is

$35.1 \times 6.58 \approx 40 \times 7 = 280$

Sometimes, especially when dividing, we round off a number to something more useful at 2 significant figures instead of at 1 significant figure. For example,

$57.3 \div 6.87$

Since 6.87 rounds off to 7, then round off 57.3 to 56 because 7 divides exactly into 56. Hence,

$57.3 \div 6.87 \approx 56 \div 7 = 8$

A quick approximation is always a great help in any calculation since it often stops you writing down a silly answer.

If you are using a calculator, whenever you see a calculation with a numerator and denominator *always* put brackets around the top and the bottom. This is to remind you that the numerator and denominator must be worked out separately before they are divided into each other. You can work out the numerator and denominator separately but most calculators will work out the answer straight away if brackets are used. You are expected to use a calculator *efficiently*, so doing the calculation in stages is not efficient.

EXAMPLE 4

a Find approximate answers to   **i** $\dfrac{213 \times 69}{42}$ **ii** $\dfrac{78 \times 397}{0.38}$

b Use your calculator to find the correct answer. Round off to 3 significant figures.

a i   Round each value to 1 significant figure. $\dfrac{200 \times 70}{40}$

     Work out the numerator. $= \dfrac{14\,000}{40}$

     Divide by the denominator. $= 350$

ii   Round each value to 1 significant figure. $\dfrac{80 \times 400}{0.4}$

     Work out the numerator. $= \dfrac{32\,000}{0.4} = \dfrac{320\,000}{4}$

     Divide by the denominator. $= 80\,000$

b Use a calculator to check your approximate answers.

i $\dfrac{213 \times 69}{42} = \dfrac{(213 \times 69)}{(42)}$

So type in

    (2 1 3 × 6 9) ÷ (4 2) =

The display should say 349.9285714 which rounds off to 350. This agrees exactly with the estimate.

Note that we do not have to put brackets around the 42 but it is a good habit to get into.

ii $\dfrac{78 \times 397}{0.38} = \dfrac{(78 \times 397)}{(0.38)}$

So type in

    (7 8 × 3 9 7) ÷ (0 . 3 8) =

The display should say 81489.47368 which rounds off to 81 500. This agrees with the estimate.

EXERCISE 1E

 1 Find approximate answers to the following.

    a 5435×7.31 **b** 5280×3.211 **c** $63.24 \times 3.514 \times 4.2$

    d $354 \div 79.8$ **e** $5974 \div 5.29$ **f** $208 \div 0.378$

 2 Work out the answers to question **1** using a calculator. Round off your answers to 3 significant figures and compare them with the estimates you made.

 3 By rounding off, find an approximate answer to these.

    a $\dfrac{573 \times 783}{107}$ **b** $\dfrac{783 - 572}{24}$ **c** $\dfrac{352 + 657}{999}$

    d $\dfrac{78.3 - 22.6}{2.69}$ **e** $\dfrac{3.82 \times 7.95}{9.9}$ **f** $\dfrac{11.78 \times 61.8}{39.4}$

 4 Work out the answers to question **3** using a calculator. Round off your answers to 3 significant figures and compare them with the estimates you made.

 5 Find the approximate monthly pay of the following people whose annual salary is given.

    a Paul £35 200   **b** Michael £25 600   **c** Jennifer £18 125   **d** Ross £8420

 6 Find the approximate annual pay of the following people whose earnings are shown.

    a Kevin £270 a week   **b** Malcolm £1528 a month   **c** David £347 a week

 7 A farmer bought 2713 kg of seed at a cost of £7.34 per kg. Find the approximate total cost of this seed.

 8 A greengrocer sells a box of 450 oranges for £37. Approximately how much did each orange sell for?

 9 It took me 6 hours 40 minutes to drive from Sheffield to Bude, a distance of 295 miles. My car uses petrol at the rate of about 32 miles per gallon. The petrol cost £3.51 per gallon.

    a Approximately how many miles did I do each hour?

    b Approximately how many gallons of petrol did I use in going from Sheffield to Bude?

    c What was the approximate cost of all the petrol I used in the journey to Bude and back again?

 10 By rounding off, find an approximate answer to these.

    a $\dfrac{462 \times 79}{0.42}$ **b** $\dfrac{583 - 213}{0.21}$ **c** $\dfrac{252 + 551}{0.78}$ **d** $\dfrac{296 \times 32}{0.325}$

    e $\dfrac{297 + 712}{0.578 - 0.321}$ **f** $\dfrac{893 \times 87}{0.698 \times 0.47}$ **g** $\dfrac{38.3 + 27.5}{0.776}$ **h** $\dfrac{29.7 + 12.6}{0.26}$

    i $\dfrac{4.93 \times 3.81}{0.38 \times 0.51}$ **j** $\dfrac{12.31 \times 16.9}{0.394 \times 0.216}$

11 Work out the answers to question **10** using a calculator. Round off your answers to 3 significant figures and compare them with the estimates you made.

12 A sheet of paper is 0.012 cm thick. Approximately how many sheets will there be in a pile of paper that is 6.35 cm deep?

13 Use your calculator to work out the following. In each case:

   i write down the full calculator display of the answer

   ii round your answer to three significant figures.

a $\dfrac{12.3 + 64.9}{6.9 - 4.1}$ **b** $\dfrac{13.8 \times 23.9}{3.2 \times 6.1}$ **c** $\dfrac{48.2 + 58.9}{3.62 \times 0.042}$

Sensible rounding

In the GCSE you will be required to round off answers to problems to a suitable degree of accuracy. Normally three significant figures is acceptable for answers. However, a big problem is caused by rounding off during calculations. When working out values, always work to either the calculator display or at least four significant figures.

Generally, you can use common sense. For example, you would not give the length of a pencil as 14.574 cm; you would round off to something like 14.6 cm. If you were asked how many tins of paint you need to buy to do a particular job, then you would give a whole number answer and not something such as 5.91 tins.

It is hard to make rules about this, as there is much disagreement even among the experts as to how you ought to do it. But, generally, when you are in any doubt as to how many significant figures to use for the final answer to a problem, round off to no more than one extra significant figure to the number used in the original data. (This particular type of rounding is used throughout this book.)

In a question where you are asked to give an answer to a sensible or appropriate degree of accuracy then use the following rule. Give the answer to the same accuracy as the numbers in the question. So, for example, if the numbers in the question are given to 2 significant figures give your answer to 2 significant figures, but remember, unless working out an approximation, do all the working to at least 4 significant figures or use the calculator display.

EXERCISE 1F

1 Round off each of the following figures to a suitable degree of accuracy.

   a I am 1.7359 metres tall.

   b It took me 5 minutes 44.83 seconds to mend the television.

   c My kitten weighs 237.97 grams.

   d The correct temperature at which to drink Earl Grey tea is 82.739 °C.

   e There were 34 827 people at the test match yesterday.

   f The distance from Wath to Sheffield is 15.528 miles.

   g The area of the floor is 13.673 m^2.

2 Rewrite the following article, rounding off all the numbers to a suitable degree of accuracy if they need to be.

It was a hot day, the temperature was 81.699 °F and still rising. I had now walked 5.3289 km in just over 113.98 minutes. But I didn't care since I knew that the 43 275 people watching the race were cheering me on. I won by clipping 6.2 seconds off the record time. This was the 67th time it had happened since records first began in 1788. Well, next year I will only have 15 practice walks beforehand as I strive to beat the record by at least another 4.9 seconds.

3 About how many test tubes each holding 24 cm^3 of water can be filled from a 1 litre flask?

4 If I walk at an average speed of 70 metres per minute, approximately how long will it take me to walk a distance of 3 km?

5 About how many stamps at 21p each can I buy for £12?

6 I travelled a distance of 450 miles in 6.4 hours. What was my approximate average speed?

7 At Manchester United, it takes 160 minutes for 43 500 fans to get into the ground. On average, about how many fans are let into the ground every minute?

8 A 5p coin weighs 4.2 grams. Approximately how much will one million pounds worth of 5p pieces weigh?

1.4 Multiples, factors and prime numbers

This section will remind you about:
- multiples and factors
- prime numbers
- square numbers and triangular numbers
- square roots

Key words
factor
multiple
prime number
square number
triangular number

You should remember the following.

Multiples: Any number in the times table. For example, the multiples of 7 are 7, 14, 21, 28, 35, etc.

Factors: Any number that divides exactly into another number. For example, factors of 24 are 1, 2, 3, 4, 6, 8, 12, 24.

Prime numbers: Any number that only has two factors, 1 and itself. For example, 11, 17, 37 are prime numbers.

Square numbers: A number that comes from multiplying a number by itself. For example, 1, 4, 9, 16, 25, 36 … are square numbers.

Triangular numbers: Numbers that can make triangle patterns, For example, 1, 3, 6, 10, 15, 21, 28 … are triangular numbers.

Square roots: The square root of a given number is a number which, when multiplied by itself, produces the given number. For example, the square root of 9 is 3, since $3 \times 3 = 9$.

A square root is represented by the symbol $\sqrt{}$. For example, $\sqrt{16} = 4$.

Because $-4 \times -4 = 16$, there are always two square roots of every positive number.

So $\sqrt{16} = +4$ or -4. This can be written as $\sqrt{16} = \pm 4$, which is read as plus or minus four.

Cube roots: The cube root of a number is the number that when multiplied by itself three times gives the number. For example, the cube root of 27 is 3 and the cube root of -8 is -2.

EXERCISE 1G

1 From this box choose the numbers that fit each of these descriptions. (One number per description.)

 a A multiple of 3 and a multiple of 4.

 b A square number and an odd number.

 c A factor of 24 and a factor of 18.

 d A prime number and a factor of 39.

 e An odd factor of 30 and a multiple of 3.

 f A number with four factors and a multiple of 2 and 7.

 g A number with five factors exactly.

 h A triangular number and a factor of 20.

 i An even number and a factor of 36 and a multiple of 9.

 j A prime number that is one more than a square number.

 k If you write the factors of this number out in order they make a number pattern in which each number is twice the one before.

 l An odd triangular number that is a multiple of 7.

12			21
	8		15
13		17	
9			18
		10	
			6
14		16	

2 If hot-dog sausages are sold in packs of 10 and hot-dog buns are sold in packs of 8, how many of each do you have to buy to have complete hot dogs with no wasted sausages or buns?

3 Rover barks every 8 seconds and Spot barks every 12 seconds. If they both bark together, how many seconds will it be before they both bark together again?

4 A bell chimes every 6 seconds. Another bell chimes every 5 seconds. If they both chime together, how many seconds will it be before they both chime together again.

5 Copy these sums and write out the *next four* lines.

$$1 = 1$$
$$1 + 3 = 4$$
$$1 + 3 + 5 = 9$$
$$1 + 3 + 5 + 7 = 16$$

6 Write down the negative square root of each of these.

a 4		**b** 25		**c** 49		**d** 1		**e** 81	
f 121		**g** 144		**h** 400		**i** 900		**j** 169	

7 Write down the cube root of each of these.

a 1	**b** 27	**c** 64	**d** 8	**e** 1000
f −8	**g** −1	**h** 8000	**i** 64 000	**j** −64

8 The triangular numbers are 1, 3, 6, 10, 15, 21 …

    a Continue the sequence until the triangular number is greater than 100.

    b Add up consecutive pairs of triangular numbers starting with 1 + 3 = 4, 3 + 6 = 9, etc. What do you notice?

9 **a** $36^3 = 46\,656$. Work out $1^3, 4^3, 9^3, 16^3, 25^3$.

    b $\sqrt{46656} = 216$. Use a calculator to find the square roots of the numbers you worked out in part **a**.

    c $216 = 36 \times 6$. Can you find a similar connection between the answer to part b and the numbers cubed in part **a**?

    d What type of numbers are 1, 4, 9, 16, 25, 36?

10 Write down the values of these

a $\sqrt{0.04}$	**b** $\sqrt{0.25}$	**c** $\sqrt{0.36}$	**d** $\sqrt{0.81}$
e $\sqrt{1.44}$	**f** $\sqrt{0.64}$	**g** $\sqrt{1.21}$	**h** $\sqrt{2.25}$

11 Estimate the answers to these.

    a $\dfrac{13.7 + 21.9}{\sqrt{0.239}}$ **b** $\dfrac{29.6 \times 11.9}{\sqrt{0.038}}$ **c** $\dfrac{87.5 - 32.6}{\sqrt{0.8} - \sqrt{0.38}}$

This section will show you how to:
- write a number as a product of its prime factors
- find the least common multiple (LCM) and highest common factor (HCF) of two numbers

Key words
highest common factor (HCF)
least common multiple (LCM)
prime factor

Start with a number – say 110 – and find two numbers which, when multiplied together, give that number, for example, 2×55. Are they both prime? No. So take 55 and repeat the operation, to get 5×11. Are these prime? Yes. So:

$$110 = 2 \times 5 \times 11$$

These are the **prime factors** of 110.

This method is not very logical and needs good tables skills. There are, however, two methods that you can use to make sure you do not miss any of the prime factors.

The next two examples show you how to use the first of these methods.

EXAMPLE 5

Find the prime factors of 24.

Divide 24 by any prime number that goes into it. (2 is an obvious choice.)

Divide the answer (12) by a prime number. Repeat this process until you have a prime number as the answer.

2	24
2	12
2	6
	3

So the prime factors of 24 are $2 \times 2 \times 2 \times 3$.

A quicker and neater way to write this answer is to use index notation, expressing the answer in powers. (Powers are dealt with in Chapter 10.)

In index notation, the prime factors of 24 are $2^3 \times 3$.

EXAMPLE 6

Find the prime factors of 96.

2	96
2	48
2	24
2	12
2	6
	3

So, the prime factors of 96 are $2 \times 2 \times 2 \times 2 \times 2 \times 3 = 2^5 \times 3$.

The second method is called prime factor trees. You start by splitting the number into a multiplication sum. Then you split this, and carry on splitting until you get to prime numbers.

EXAMPLE 7

Find the prime factors of 76.

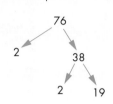

We stop splitting the factors here because 2, 2 and 19 are all prime numbers.

So, the prime factors of 76 are $2 \times 2 \times 19 = 2^2 \times 19$.

EXAMPLE 8

Find the prime factors of 420.

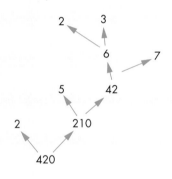

The process can be done upside down to make an upright tree.

So, the prime factors of 420 are

$$2 \times 5 \times 2 \times 3 \times 7 = 2^2 \times 3 \times 5 \times 7.$$

EXERCISE 1H

1 Copy and complete these prime factor trees.

a

b

c

C

d

20

2

220

e

28

4

280

f

128

4

4

4

g

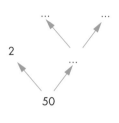

2

50

2 Using index notation, for example,

$$100 = 2 \times 2 \times 5 \times 5 = 2^2 \times 5^2$$

and $540 = 2 \times 2 \times 3 \times 3 \times 3 \times 5 = 2^2 \times 3^3 \times 5$

rewrite the answers to question **1** parts **a** to **g**.

3 Write the numbers from 1 to 50 in prime factors. Use index notation. For example,

$1 = 1$ $2 = 2$ $3 = 3$ $4 = 2^2$ $5 = 5$ $6 = 2 \times 3$ …

4 **a** What is special about the prime factors of 2, 4, 8, 16, 32, …?

   b What are the next two terms in this sequence?

   c What are the next three terms in the sequence 3, 9, 27, …?

   d Continue the sequence 4, 16, 64, …, for three more terms.

   e Write all the above sequences in index notation. For example, the first sequence is

   $2, 2^2, 2^3, 2^4, 2^5, 2^6, 2^7, …$

Least common multiple

The **least** (or lowest) **common multiple** (usually called the **LCM**) of two numbers is the smallest number that belongs in both times tables.

For example the LCM of 3 and 5 is 15, the LCM of 2 and 7 is 14 and the LCM of 6 and 9 is 18.

There are two ways of working out the LCM.

EXAMPLE 9

Find the LCM of 18 and 24.

Write out the 18 times table: 18, 36, 54, (72), 90, 108, ...

Write out the 24 times table: 24, 48, (72), 96, 120, ...

You can see that 72 is the smallest (least) number in both (common) tables (multiples).

EXAMPLE 10

Find the LCM of 42 and 63.

Write 42 in prime factor form. $42 = 2 \times 3 \times 7$

Write 63 in prime factor form. $63 = 3^2 \times 7$

Write down the smallest number in prime factor form that includes all the prime factors of 42 and of 63.

You need $2 \times 3^2 \times 7$ (this includes $2 \times 3 \times 7$ and $3^2 \times 7$).

Then work it out.

$2 \times 3^2 \times 7 = 2 \times 9 \times 7 = 18 \times 7 = 126$

The LCM of 42 and 63 is 126.

Highest common factor

The **highest common factor** (usually called the **HCF**) of two numbers is the biggest number that divides exactly into both of them.

For example the HCF of 24 and 18 is 6, the HCF of 45 and 36 is 9 and the HCF of 15 and 22 is 1.

There are two ways of working out the HCF.

EXAMPLE 11

Find the HCF of 28 and 16.

Write out the factors of 28.   1, 2, (4), 7, 14, 28

Write out the factors of 16.   1, 2, (4), 8, 16

You can see that 4 is the biggest (highest) number in both (common) lists (factors).

EXAMPLE 12

Find the HCF of 48 and 120.

Write 48 in prime factor form. $48 = 2^4 \times 3$

Write 120 in prime factor form. $120 = 2^3 \times 3 \times 5$

Write down the biggest number in prime factor form that is in the prime factors of 48 and 120.

You need $2^3 \times 3$ (this is in both $2^4 \times 3$ and $2^3 \times 3 \times 5$).

Then work it out.

$2^3 \times 3 = 8 \times 3 = 24$

The HCF of 48 and 120 is 24.

EXERCISE 1I

1 Find the LCM of each of these pairs of numbers.

a 4 and 5   b 7 and 8   c 2 and 3   d 4 and 7

e 2 and 5   f 3 and 5   g 3 and 8   h 5 and 6

2 What connection is there between the LCM and the pairs of numbers in question **1**?

3 Find the LCM of each of these pairs of numbers.

a 4 and 8   b 6 and 9   c 4 and 6   d 10 and 15

4 Does the same connection you found in question **2** still work for the numbers in question **3**? If not, can you explain why?

5 Find the LCM of each of these pairs of numbers.

a 24 and 56   b 21 and 35   c 12 and 28   d 28 and 42

e 12 and 48   f 18 and 27   g 15 and 25   h 16 and 36

6 Find the HCF of each of these pairs of numbers.

a 24 and 56   b 21 and 35   c 12 and 28   d 28 and 42

e 12 and 48   f 18 and 27   g 15 and 25   h 16 and 36

i 42 and 27   j 48 and 64   k 25 and 35   l 36 and 54

7 In prime factor form $1250 = 2 \times 5^4$ and $525 = 3 \times 5^2 \times 7$.

a Which of these are common multiples of 1250 and 525?

i $2 \times 3 \times 5^3 \times 7$ ii $2^3 \times 3 \times 5^4 \times 7^2$ iii $2 \times 3 \times 5^4 \times 7$ iv $2 \times 3 \times 5 \times 7$

b Which of these are common factors of 1250 and 525?

i 2×3 ii 2×5 iii 5^2 iv $2 \times 3 \times 5 \times 7$

Negative numbers

This section will show you how to:

- multiply and divide with positive and negative numbers

Key words

positive
negative

Multiplying and dividing with negative numbers

The rules for multiplying and dividing with negative numbers are very easy.

- When the signs of the numbers are the *same*, the answer is **positive**.

- When the signs of the numbers are *different*, the answer is **negative**.

Here are some examples.

$2 \times 4 = 8$ $\qquad 12 \div -3 = -4$

$-2 \times -3 = 6$ $\qquad -12 \div -3 = 4$

Negative numbers on a calculator

You can enter a negative number into your calculator and check the result.

Enter –5 by pressing the keys **5** and **+/–**. (You may need to press **+/–** or **–** followed by **5**, depending on the type of calculator that you have.) You will see the calculator shows –5.

Now try these two calculations.

$-8 - 7 \rightarrow$ **8** **+/–** **–** **7** **=** –15

$6 - -3 \rightarrow$ **6** **–** **–** **3** **=** 9

EXERCISE 1J

1 Write down the answers to the following.

a -3×5	**b** -2×7	**c** -4×6	**d** -2×-3	**e** -7×-2
f $-12 \div -6$	**g** $-16 \div 8$	**h** $24 \div -3$	**i** $16 \div -4$	**j** $-6 \div -2$
k 4×-6	**l** 5×-2	**m** 6×-3	**n** -2×-8	**o** -9×-4

2 Write down the answers to the following.

a $-3 + -6$	**b** -2×-8	**c** $2 + -5$	**d** 8×-4	**e** $-36 \div -2$
f -3×-6	**g** $-3 - -9$	**h** $48 \div -12$	**i** -5×-4	**j** $7 - -9$
k $-40 \div -5$	**l** $-40 + -8$	**m** $4 - -9$	**n** $5 - 18$	**o** $72 \div -9$

D

D

3 What number do you multiply –3 by to get the following?

    a 6   **b** –90   **c** –45   **d** 81   **e** 21

4 Evaluate the following.

    a –6 + (4 – 7)   **b** –3 – (–9 – –3)   **c** 8 + (2 – 9)

5 Evaluate the following.

    a $4 \times (-8 \div -2)$ **b** $-8 - (3 \times -2)$ **c** $-1 \times (8 - -4)$

6 Write down six different division sums that give the answer –4.

Hierarchy of operations

You will remember BODMAS (Brackets, Order, Division, Multiplication, Addition, Subtraction) which tells you the order in which to do mathematical operations in complex calculations. Many errors are made in GCSE due to negative signs and doing calculations in the wrong order. For example -6^2 could be taken as $(-6)^2 = +36$ or $-(6^2) = -36$. It should be the second of these as the power (order) would come before the minus sign.

EXERCISE 1K

D

1 Work out each of these. Remember to work out the bracket first.

    a $-2 \times (-3 + 5) =$ **b** $6 \div (-2 + 1) =$ **c** $(5 - 7) \times -2 =$

    d $-5 \times (-7 - 2) =$ **e** $-3 \times (-4 \div 2) =$ **f** $-3 \times (-4 + 2) =$

2 Work out each of these.

    a $-6 \times -6 + 2 =$ **b** $-6 \times (-6 + 2) =$ **c** $-6 \div 6 - 2 =$

    d $12 \div (-4 + 2) =$ **e** $12 \div -4 + 2 =$ **f** $2 \times (-3 + 4) =$

    g $-(5)^2 =$ **h** $(-5)^2 =$ **i** $(-1 + 3)^2 - 4 =$

    j $-(1 + 3)^2 - 4 =$ **k** $-1 + 3^2 - 4 =$ **l** $-1 + (3 - 4)^2 =$

3 Copy each of these and then put in brackets where necessary to make each one true.

    a $3 \times -4 + 1 = -11$ **b** $-6 \div -2 + 1 = 6$ **c** $-6 \div -2 + 1 = 4$

    d $4 + -4 \div 4 = 3$ **e** $4 + -4 \div 4 = 0$ **f** $16 - -4 \div 2 = 10$

4 $a = -2$, $b = 3$, $c = -5$.

Work out the values of the following.

    a $(a + c)^2$ **b** $-(a + b)^2$ **c** $(a + b)c$ **d** $a^2 + b^2 - c^2$

1 Frank earns £12 per hour. He works for 40 hours per week. He saves $\frac{1}{5}$ of his earnings each week.

How many weeks will it take him to save £500?

2 A bathroom wall measures 2.55 metres by 2.85 metres. It is to be covered with square tiles of side 15 centimetres. Tiles are sold in boxes of 24. How many boxes are needed?

AQA, Question 6, Paper 2 Intermediate, November 2003

3 As the product of prime factors $60 = 2^2 \times 3 \times 5$

a What number is represented by $2 \times 3^2 \times 5$?

b Find the least common multiple (LCM) of 60 and 48?

c Find the highest common factor (HCF) of 60 and 78?

4 a Write 28 as the product of its prime factors.

b Find the least common multiple (LCM) of 28 and 42.

AQA, Question 21, Paper 1 Intermediate, November 2004

5 Hannah, Gemma and Jo use their calculators to work out the value of

$$\frac{28.78}{4.31 \times 0.47}$$

Hannah gets 142.07, Gemma gets 14.207 and Jo gets 3.138

Use approximations to show which one of them is correct. You *must* show your working.

AQA, Question 16, Paper 1 Intermediate, November 2004

6 Use approximations to estimate the value of

$$\frac{212 \times 7.88}{0.365}$$

7 Tom, Sam and Matt are counting drum beats.

Tom hits a snare drum every 2 beats.
Sam hits a kettle drum every 5 beats.
Matt hits a bass drum every 8 beats.

Tom, Sam and Matt start by hitting their drums at the same time.

How many beats is it before Tom, Sam and Matt *next* hit their drums at the *same* time?

AQA, Question 14, Paper 1 Intermediate, June 2004

8 a You are given that $8x^3 = 1000$.
Find the value of x.

b Write 150 as the product of its prime factors.

9 a p and q are prime numbers such that $pq^3 = 250$
Find the values of p and q.

b Find the highest common factor of 250 and 80.

10 a a and b are prime numbers such that $(ab)^3 = 1000$
What are the values of a and b?

b p and q are integers such that $(pq)^3 = 216$
Explain why it is not possible to find values of p and q.

WORKED EXAM QUESTION

Estimate the result of the calculation

$$\frac{195.71 - 53.62}{\sqrt{0.0375}}$$

Show the estimates you make.

Solution

$$\frac{200 - 50}{\sqrt{0.04}}$$

First round off each number to 1 significant figure.

$$\frac{150}{0.2}$$

Work out the numerator and do the square root in the denominator

$$\frac{150}{0.2} = \frac{1500}{2} = 750$$

Change the problem so it becomes division by an integer

21

GRADE YOURSELF

D Able to recognise and work out multiples, factors and primes

D Able to multiply and divide with negative numbers

D Able to estimate the values of calculations involving positive numbers bigger than one

D Able to round numbers to a given number of significant figures

C Able to estimate the values of calculations involving positive numbers between zero and one

C Able to write a number as the product of its prime factors

C Able to work out the LCM and HCF of pairs of numbers

C Able to use a calculator efficiently and know how to give answers to an appropriate degree of accuracy

B Able to work out the square roots of some decimal numbers

B Able to estimate answers involving the square roots of decimals

What you should know now

● How to solve complex real-life problems without a calculator

● How to divide by decimals of up to two decimal places

● How to estimate the values of calculations including those with decimal numbers, and use a calculator efficiently

● How to write a number in prime factor form and find LCMs and HCFs

● How to find the square roots of some decimal numbers

Fractions and percentages

This chapter will show you ...

● how to apply the four rules (addition, subtraction, multiplication and division) to fractions
● how to calculate the final value after a percentage increase or decrease
● how to calculate compound interest
● how to calculate the original value after a percentage increase or decrease

What you should already know

● How to cancel down fractions to their simplest form
● How to find equivalent fractions, decimals and percentages
● How to add and subtract fractions with the same denominator
● How to work out simple percentages, such as 10%, of quantities
● How to convert a mixed number to a top-heavy fraction and vice versa

Quick check

1 Cancel down the following fractions to their simplest form.

a $\frac{8}{20}$ **b** $\frac{12}{32}$ **c** $\frac{15}{35}$

2 Complete this table of equivalences.

Fraction	Percentage	Decimal
$\frac{3}{4}$		
	40%	
		0.55

3 What is 10% of

a £230   **b** £46.00   **c** £2.30

This section will show you how to:
- find one quantity as a fraction of another

Key words

cancel

fraction

An amount often needs to be given as a **fraction** of another amount.

EXAMPLE 1

Write £5 as a fraction of £20.

As a fraction this is written $\frac{5}{20}$. This **cancels** down to $\frac{1}{4}$.

EXERCISE 2A

1 Write the first quantity as a fraction of the second.

    a 2 cm, 6 cm   **b** 4 kg, 20 kg

    c £8, £20   **d** 5 hours, 24 hours

    e 12 days, 30 days   **f** 50p, £3

    g 4 days, 2 weeks   **h** 40 minutes, 2 hours

2 In a form of 30 pupils, 18 are boys. What fraction of the form consists of boys?

3 During March, it rained on 12 days. For what fraction of the month did it rain?

4 Linda wins £120 in a competition. She keeps some to spend and puts £50 into her bank account. What fraction of her winnings does she keep to spend?

5 Frank gets a pay rise from £120 a week to £135 a weak. What fraction of his original pay was his pay rise?

6 When she was born Alice had a mass of 3 kg. After a month she had a mass of 4 kg 250 g. What fraction of her original mass had she increased by?

7 After the breeding season a bat colony increased in size from 90 bats to 108 bats. What fraction had the size of the colony increased by?

8 After dieting Bart went from 80 kg to 68 kg. What fraction did his weight decrease by?

Adding and subtracting fractions

This section will show you how to:
- add and subtract fractions with different denominators

Key words

denominator
equivalent
  fraction
lowest common
  denominator

Fractions can only be added or subtracted after we have changed them to **equivalent fractions**, both having the same **denominator**.

EXAMPLE 2

Work out $\frac{5}{6} - \frac{3}{4}$

The **lowest common denominator** of 4 and 6 is 12.

The problem becomes $\frac{5}{6} - \frac{3}{4} = \frac{5}{6} \times \frac{2}{2} - \frac{3}{4} \times \frac{3}{3} = \frac{10}{12} - \frac{9}{12} = \frac{1}{12}$

EXAMPLE 3

Work out **a** $2\frac{1}{3} + 3\frac{5}{7}$ **b** $3\frac{1}{4} - 1\frac{3}{5}$

The best way to deal with addition and subtraction of mixed numbers is to deal with the whole numbers and the fractions separately.

a $2\frac{1}{3} + 3\frac{5}{7} = 2 + 3 + \frac{1}{3} + \frac{5}{7} = 5 + \frac{7}{21} + \frac{15}{21} = 5 + \frac{22}{21} = 5 + 1\frac{1}{21} = 6\frac{1}{21}$

b $3\frac{1}{4} - 1\frac{3}{5} = 3 - 1 + \frac{1}{4} - \frac{3}{5} = 2 + \frac{5}{20} - \frac{12}{20} = 2 - \frac{7}{20} = 1\frac{13}{20}$

EXERCISE 2B

1 Evaluate the following.

a $\frac{1}{3} + \frac{1}{5}$ **b** $\frac{1}{3} + \frac{1}{4}$ **c** $\frac{1}{5} + \frac{1}{10}$ **d** $\frac{2}{3} + \frac{1}{4}$

e $\frac{1}{5} - \frac{1}{10}$ **f** $\frac{7}{8} - \frac{3}{4}$ **g** $\frac{5}{6} - \frac{3}{4}$ **h** $\frac{5}{6} - \frac{1}{2}$

2 Evaluate the following.

a $\frac{1}{3} + \frac{4}{9}$ **b** $\frac{1}{4} + \frac{3}{8}$ **c** $\frac{7}{8} - \frac{1}{2}$ **d** $\frac{3}{5} - \frac{8}{15}$

e $1\frac{7}{18} + 2\frac{3}{10}$ **f** $3\frac{1}{3} + 1\frac{9}{20}$ **g** $1\frac{1}{8} - \frac{5}{9}$ **h** $1\frac{3}{16} - \frac{7}{12}$

i $\frac{5}{6} + \frac{7}{16} + \frac{5}{8}$ **j** $\frac{7}{10} + \frac{3}{8} + \frac{5}{6}$ **k** $1\frac{1}{3} + \frac{7}{10} - \frac{4}{15}$ **l** $\frac{5}{14} + 1\frac{3}{7} - \frac{5}{12}$

D

3 In a class of children, three-quarters are Chinese, one-fifth are Malay and the rest are Indian. What fraction of the class are Indian?

4 In a class election, half of the pupils voted for Aminah, one-third voted for Janet and the rest voted for Peter. What fraction of the class voted for Peter?

5 A one-litre flask filled with milk is used to fill two glasses, one of capacity half a litre, and the other of capacity one-sixth of a litre. What fraction of a litre will remain in the flask?

6 Because of illness, $\frac{2}{5}$ of a school was absent one day. If the school had 650 pupils on the register, how many were absent that day?

7 Which is the biggest: half of 96, one-third of 141, two-fifths of 120, or three-quarters of 68?

8 To increase sales, a shop reduced the price of a car stereo radio by $\frac{2}{5}$. If the original price was £85, what was the new price?

9 At a burger-eating competition, Lionel ate 34 burgers in 20 minutes while Brian ate 26 burgers in 20 minutes. How long after the start of the competition would they have consumed a total of 30 burgers between them?

2.3 Multiplying fractions

This section will show you how to:
- multiply fractions

Key words
cancel
denominator
numerator

There are four steps to multiplying fractions.

Step 1: make any mixed numbers into top-heavy fractions.

Step 2: cancel out any common multiples on the top and bottom.

Step 3: multiply together the **numerators** to get the new numerator, and multiply the **denominators** to get the new denominator.

Step 4: if the fraction is top-heavy, make it into a mixed number.

EXAMPLE 4

Work out   **a** $\frac{4}{9} \times \frac{3}{10}$ **b** $2\frac{2}{5} \times 1\frac{7}{8}$

a 4 and 10 are both multiples of 2, and 3 and 9 are both multiples of 3. Cancel out the common multiples before multiplying.

$$\frac{\overset{2}{\cancel{4}}}{\underset{3}{\cancel{9}}} \times \frac{\overset{1}{\cancel{3}}}{\underset{5}{\cancel{10}}} = \frac{2}{15}$$

b Make the mixed numbers into top heavy fractions, then cancel if possible. Change the answer back to a mixed number.

$$2\frac{2}{5} \times 1\frac{7}{8} \qquad \frac{\overset{3}{\cancel{12}}}{\underset{1}{\cancel{5}}} \times \frac{\overset{3}{\cancel{15}}}{\underset{2}{\cancel{8}}} = \frac{9}{2} = 4\frac{1}{2}$$

EXERCISE 2C

1 Evaluate the following, leaving your answers in their simplest form.

a $\frac{1}{2} \times \frac{1}{3}$ **b** $\frac{1}{4} \times \frac{2}{5}$ **c** $\frac{3}{4} \times \frac{1}{2}$ **d** $\frac{3}{7} \times \frac{1}{2}$

e $\frac{14}{15} \times \frac{3}{8}$ **f** $\frac{8}{9} \times \frac{6}{15}$ **g** $\frac{6}{7} \times \frac{21}{30}$ **h** $\frac{9}{14} \times \frac{35}{36}$

2 Evaluate the following, leaving your answers as mixed numbers where possible.

a $1\frac{1}{4} \times \frac{1}{3}$ **b** $1\frac{2}{3} \times 1\frac{1}{4}$ **c** $2\frac{1}{2} \times 2\frac{1}{2}$ **d** $1\frac{3}{4} \times 1\frac{2}{3}$

e $3\frac{1}{4} \times 1\frac{1}{5}$ **f** $1\frac{1}{4} \times 2\frac{2}{3}$ **g** $2\frac{1}{2} \times 5$ **h** $4 \times 7\frac{1}{2}$

3 A merchant buys 28 crates, each containing three-quarters of a tonne of waste metal. What is the total weight of this order?

4 A greedy girl eats one-quarter of a cake, and then half of what is left. How much cake is left uneaten?

5 Kathleen spent three-eighths of her income on rent, and two-fifths of what was left on food. What fraction of her income was left after buying her food?

6 Which is larger, $\frac{3}{4}$ of $2\frac{1}{2}$ or $\frac{2}{5}$ of $6\frac{1}{2}$?

7 After James spent $\frac{2}{5}$ of his pocket money on magazines, and $\frac{1}{4}$ of his pocket money at a football match, he had £1.75 left. How much pocket money did he have in the beginning?

8 If £5.20 is two-thirds of three-quarters of a sum of money, what is the total amount of money?

Dividing by a fraction

This section will show you how to:
- divide by fractions

Key word
reciprocal

To divide by a fraction, we turn the fraction upside down (finding its **reciprocal**), and then multiply.

EXAMPLE 5

Work out   **a** $\frac{5}{6} \div \frac{3}{4}$ **b** $2\frac{1}{2} \div 3\frac{1}{3}$

a Rewrite as $\frac{5}{6} \times \frac{4}{3}$.

$$\frac{5}{6} \div \frac{3}{4} = \frac{5}{\cancel{6}_3} \times \frac{\cancel{4}^2}{3} = \frac{10}{9} = 1\frac{1}{9}$$

b First make the mixed numbers into top heavy fractions.

$$2\frac{1}{2} \div 3\frac{1}{3} = \frac{5}{2} \div \frac{10}{3} = \frac{\cancel{5}^1}{2} \times \frac{3}{\cancel{10}_2} = \frac{3}{4}$$

EXERCISE 2D

1 Evaluate the following, leaving your answers as mixed numbers where possible.

   a $\frac{1}{4} \div \frac{1}{3}$ **b** $\frac{2}{5} \div \frac{2}{7}$ **c** $\frac{4}{5} \div \frac{3}{4}$ **d** $\frac{3}{7} \div \frac{2}{5}$ **e** $5 \div 1\frac{1}{4}$

   f $6 \div 1\frac{1}{2}$ **g** $7\frac{1}{2} \div 1\frac{1}{2}$ **h** $3 \div 1\frac{3}{4}$ **i** $1\frac{5}{12} \div 3\frac{3}{16}$ **j** $3\frac{3}{5} \div 2\frac{1}{4}$

2 For a party, Zahar made twelve and a half litres of lemonade. His glasses could each hold five-sixteenths of a litre. How many of the glasses could he fill from the twelve and a half litres of lemonade?

3 How many strips of ribbon, each three and a half centimetres long, can I cut from a roll of ribbon that is fifty-two and a half centimetres long?

4 Joe's stride is three-quarters of a metre long. How many strides does he take to walk along a bus twelve metres long?

5 Evaluate the following, leaving your answers as mixed numbers wherever possible.

   a $2\frac{2}{9} \times 2\frac{1}{10} \times \frac{16}{35}$ **b** $3\frac{1}{5} \times 2\frac{1}{2} \times 4\frac{3}{4}$ **c** $1\frac{1}{4} \times 1\frac{2}{7} \times 1\frac{1}{6}$ **d** $\frac{18}{25} \times \frac{15}{16} \div 2\frac{2}{5}$

   e $\left(\frac{2}{5} \times \frac{2}{5}\right) \times \left(\frac{5}{6} \times \frac{5}{6}\right) \times \left(\frac{3}{4} \times \frac{3}{4}\right)$ **f** $\left(\frac{4}{5} \times \frac{4}{5}\right) \div \left(1\frac{1}{4} \times 1\frac{1}{4}\right)$

This section will show you how to:
- calculate percentage increases and decreases

Key words

multiplier

percentage decrease

percentage increase

Increase

There are two methods for **increasing** by a **percentage**.

Method 1
Find the increase and add it to the original amount.

EXAMPLE 6

Increase £6 by 5%.

Find 5% of £6: $\frac{5}{100} \times 600p = 30p$. 5% of £6 = £0.30.

Add the £0.30 to the original amount: £6 + £0.30 = £6.30.

Method 2
Using a **multiplier**. An increase of 6% is equivalent to the original 100% plus the extra 6%. This is a total of 106% ($\frac{106}{100}$) and is equivalent to the multiplier 1.06.

EXAMPLE 7

Increase £6.80 by 5%.

A 5% increase is a multiplier of 1.05.

So £6.80 increased by 5% is £6.80 × 1.05 = £7.14

EXERCISE 2E

1 What multiplier is equivalent to a percentage increase of each of the following?

    a 10%   **b** 3%   **c** 20%   **d** 7%   **e** 12%

2 Increase each of the following by the given percentage. (Use any method you like.)

    a £60 by 4%   **b** 12 kg by 8%   **c** 450 g by 5%   **d** 545 m by 10%

    e £34 by 12%   **f** £75 by 20%   **g** 340 kg by 15%   **h** 670 cm by 23%

    i 130 g by 95%   **j** £82 by 75%   **k** 640 m by 15%   **l** £28 by 8%

3 In 2000 the population of Melchester was 1 565 000. By 2005 that had increased by 8%. What was the population of Melchester in 2005?

4 A small firm made the same pay increase for all its employees: 5%.

    a Calculate the new pay of each employee listed below. Each of their salaries before the increase is given.

      Bob, caretaker, £16 500   Jean, supervisor, £19 500
      Anne, tea lady, £17 300   Brian, manager, £25 300

    b Is the actual pay increase the same for each worker?

5 An advertisement for a breakfast cereal states that a special offer packet contains 15% more cereal for the same price than a normal 500 g packet. How much breakfast cereal is in a special offer packet?

6 At a school disco there are always about 20% more girls than boys. If at one disco there were 50 boys, how many girls were there?

7 VAT is a tax that the government adds to the price of most goods in shops. At the moment, it is 17.5% on all electrical equipment.

Calculate the price of the following electrical equipment after VAT of 17.5% has been added.

Equipment	Pre-VAT price
TV set	£245
Microwave oven	£72
CD player	£115
Personal stereo	£29.50

8 A hi-fi system was priced at £420 at the start of 2004. At the start of 2005, it was 12% more expensive. At the start of 2006, it was 15% more expensive than the price at the start of 2005. What is the price of the hi-fi at the start of 2006?

9 A quick way to work out VAT is to divide the pre-VAT price by 6. For example, the VAT on an item costing £120 is approximately £120 ÷ 6 = £20. Show that this approximate method gives the VAT correct to within £5 for pre-VAT prices up to £600.

Decrease

There are two methods for **decreasing** by a **percentage**.

Method 1

Find the decrease and take it away from the original amount.

EXAMPLE 8

Decrease £8 by 4%.

Find 4% of £8: $\dfrac{4}{100} \times 800p = 32p$. 4% of £8 = £0.32.

Take the £0.32 away from the original amount: £8 − £0.32 = £7.68.

Method 2

Using a multiplier. A 7% decrease is 7% less than the original 100%, so it represents 100% − 7% = 93% of the original. This is a multiplier of 0.93.

EXAMPLE 9

Decrease £8.60 by 5%.

A decrease of 5% is a multiplier of 0.95.

So £8.60 decreased by 5% is £8.60 × 0.95 = £8.17

EXERCISE 2F

1. What multiplier is equivalent to a percentage decrease of each of the following?

    a 8% **b** 15% **c** 25% **d** 9% **e** 12%

2. Decrease each of the following by the given percentage. (Use any method you like.)

    a £10 by 6% **b** 25 kg by 8% **c** 236 g by 10%

    d 350 m by 3% **e** £5 by 2% **f** 45 m by 12%

    g 860 m by 15% **h** 96 g by 13% **i** 480 cm by 25%

3. A car valued at £6500 last year is now worth 15% less. What is its value now?

4. A large factory employed 640 people. It had to streamline its workforce and lose 30% of the workers. How big is the workforce now?

5. On the last day of the Christmas term, a school expects to have an absence rate of 6%. If the school population is 750 pupils, how many pupils will the school expect to see on the last day of the Christmas term?

6 Since the start of the National Lottery a particular charity called Young Ones said it has seen a 45% decrease in the money raised from its scratch cards. If before the Lottery the charity had an annual income of £34 500 from its scratch cards, how much does it collect now?

7 Most speedometers in cars have an error of about 5% from the true reading. When my speedometer says I am driving at 70 mph,

  a what is the slowest speed I could be doing,

  b what is the fastest speed I could be doing?

8 You are a member of a club which allows you to claim a 12% discount off any marked price in shops. What will you pay in total for the following goods?

  Sweatshirt   £19

  Tracksuit   £26

9 I read an advertisement in my local newspaper last week which stated: "By lagging your roof and hot water system you will use 18% less fuel." Since I was using an average of 640 units of gas a year, I thought I would lag my roof and my hot water system. How much gas would I expect to use now?

10 A computer system was priced at £1000 at the start of 2004. At the start of 2005, it was 10% cheaper. At the start of 2006, it was 15% cheaper than the price at the start of 2005. What is the price of the computer system at the start of 2006?

11 Show that a 10% decrease followed by a 10% increase is equivalent to a 1% decrease overall.

> **HINTS AND TIPS**
>
> Choose an amount to start with.

2.6 Expressing one quantity as a percentage of another

This section will show you how to:
● express one quantity as a percentage of another

Key words
percentage gain
percentage loss

Method 1
We express one quantity as a percentage of another by setting up the first quantity as a fraction of the second, making sure that the *units of each are the same*. Then, we convert that fraction to a percentage by simply multiplying it by 100%.

EXAMPLE 10

Express £6 as a percentage of £40.

Set up the fraction and multiply it by 100%. This gives:

$$\frac{6}{40} \times 100\% = 15\%$$

EXAMPLE 11

Express 75 cm as a percentage of 2.5 m.

First, change 2.5 m to 250 cm to get a common unit.

Hence, the problem becomes 75 cm as a percentage of 250 cm.

Set up the fraction and multiply it by 100%. This gives

$$\frac{75}{250} \times 100\% = 30\%$$

We can use this method to calculate **percentage gain** or **loss** in a financial transaction.

EXAMPLE 12

Bert buys a car for £1500 and sells it for £1800. What is Bert's percentage gain?

Bert's gain is £300, so his percentage gain is

$$\frac{300}{1500} \times 100\% = 20\%$$

Notice how the percentage gain is found by

$$\frac{\text{difference}}{\text{original}} \times 100\%$$

Method 2

This method uses a multiplier. Divide the increase by the original quantity and change the resulting decimal to a percentage.

EXAMPLE 13

Express 5 as a percentage of 40.

$$5 \div 40 = 0.125$$

$$0.125 = 12.5\%.$$

EXERCISE 2G

1 Express each of the following as a percentage. Give suitably rounded off figures where necessary.

a £5 of £20

b £4 of £6.60

c 241 kg of 520 kg

d 3 hours of 1 day

e 25 minutes of 1 hour

f 12 m of 20 m

g 125 g of 600 g

h 12 minutes of 2 hours

i 1 week of a year

j 1 month of 1 year

k 25 cm of 55 cm

l 105 g of 1 kg

2 John went to school with his pocket money of £2.50. He spent 80p at the tuck shop. What percentage of his pocket money had he spent?

3 In Greece, there are 3 654 000 acres of agricultural land. Olives are grown on 237 000 acres of this land. What percentage of agricultural land is used for olives?

4 During the wet year of 1981, it rained in Manchester on 123 days of the year. What percentage of days were wet?

5 Find, to one decimal place, the percentage profit on the following.

Item	Retail price (selling price)	Wholesale price (price the shop paid)
a CD player	£89.50	£60
b TV set	£345.50	£210
c Computer	£829.50	£750

6 Before Anton started to diet, he weighed 95 kg. He now weighs 78 kg. What percentage of his original weight has he lost?

7 In 2004 the Melchester County Council raised £14 870 000 in council tax. In 2005 it raised £15 970 000 in council tax. What was the percentage increase?

8 When Blackburn Rovers won the championship in 1995, they lost only four of their 42 league games. What percentage of games did they not lose?

9 In the year 1900 the value of Britain's imports were as follows.

British Commonwealth	£109 530 000
USA	£138 790 000
France	£53 620 000
Other countries	£221 140 000

a What percentage of the total imports came from each source?

b Add up the answers to part **a**. Explain your answer.

Compound interest and repeated percentage change

This section will show you how to:
- calculate compound interest
- solve problems involving repeated percentage change

Key words
annual rate
multiplier
principal

Compound interest is calculated where the interest earned at the end of the first year is added to the **principal** (original amount), and the new total amount then earns further interest at the same **annual rate** in the following year. (Compound interest is usually used to calculate the interest on savings accounts.) This pattern is repeated year after year while the money is in the account. Therefore, the amount in the account grows bigger by the year, as does the actual amount of interest. The best way to calculate the total interest is to use a **multiplier**.

EXAMPLE 14

A bank pays 6% compound interest per year on all amounts in a savings account. What is the final amount that Elizabeth will have in her account if she has kept £400 in her bank for three years?

The amount in the bank increases by 6% each year, so the multiplier is 1.06, and

after 1 year she will have £400 × 1.06 = £424

after 2 years she will have £424 × 1.06 = £449.44

after 3 years she will have £449.44 × 1.06 = £476.41 (rounded)

If you calculate the differences, you can see that the actual increase gets bigger and bigger.

From this example, you can see that you could have used £400 × $(1.06)^3$ to find the amount after 3 years. That is, you could have used the following formula for calculating the total amount due at any time:

total amount = P × multiplier raised to the power n = $P \times (1 + x)^n$

where P is the original amount invested, x is the rate of interest expressed as a decimal, and n is the number of years for which the money is invested.

So, in Example 14, P = £400, x = 0.06, and n = 3,

and the total amount = £400 × $(1.06)^3$

Using your calculator

You may have noticed that you can do the above calculation on your calculator without having to write down all the intermediate steps.

To add on the 6% each time just means multiplying by 1.06 each time. That is, you can do the calculation as

$$\boxed{4}\,\boxed{0}\,\boxed{0}\,\boxed{\times}\,\boxed{1}\,\boxed{.}\,\boxed{0}\,\boxed{6}\,\boxed{\times}\,\boxed{1}\,\boxed{.}\,\boxed{0}\,\boxed{6}\,\boxed{\times}\,\boxed{1}\,\boxed{.}\,\boxed{0}\,\boxed{6}\,\boxed{=}$$

Or

$$\boxed{4}\,\boxed{0}\,\boxed{0}\,\boxed{\times}\,\boxed{1}\,\boxed{.}\,\boxed{0}\,\boxed{6}\,\boxed{x^y}\,\boxed{3}\,\boxed{=}$$

Or

$$\boxed{4}\,\boxed{0}\,\boxed{0}\,\boxed{\times}\,\boxed{1}\,\boxed{0}\,\boxed{6}\,\boxed{\%}\,\boxed{x^y}\,\boxed{3}\,\boxed{=}$$

You need to find the method with which you are comfortable and which you understand.

The idea of compound interest does not only concern money. It can be about, for example, the growth in population, increases in salaries, or increases in body weight or height. Also the idea can involve regular reduction by a fixed percentage: for example, car depreciation, population losses and even water losses. Work through the next exercise and you will see the extent to which compound interest ideas are used.

EXERCISE 2H

1 A baby octopus increases its body weight by 5% each day for the first month of its life. In a safe ocean zoo, a baby octopus was born weighing 10 kg.

   a What was its weight after

     i 1 day?   **ii** 2 days?   **iii** 4 days?   **iv** 1 week?

   b After how many days will the octopus first weigh over 15 kg?

2 A certain type of conifer hedging increases in height by 17% each year for the first 20 years. When I bought some of this hedging, it was all about 50 cm tall. How long will it take to grow 3 m tall?

3 The manager of a small family business offered his staff an annual pay increase of 4% for every year they stayed with the firm.

   a Gareth started work at the business on a salary of £12 200. What salary will he be on after 4 years?

   b Julie started work at the business on a salary of £9350. How many years will it be until she is earning a salary of over £20 000?

4 Scientists have been studying the shores of Scotland and estimate that due to pollution the seal population of those shores will decline at the rate of 15% each year. In 2006 they counted around 3000 seals on those shores.

    a If nothing is done about pollution, how many seals will they expect to be there in

        i 2007?   **ii** 2008?   **iii** 2011?

    b How long will it take for the seal population to be less than 1000?

5 I am told that if I buy a new car its value will depreciate at the rate of 20% each year. I buy a car in 2006 priced at £8500. What would be the value of the car in

    a 2007?   **b** 2008?   **c** 2010?

6 At the peak of the drought during the summer of 1995, a reservoir in Derbyshire was losing water at the rate of 8% each day. On 1 August this reservoir held 2.1 million litres of water.

    a At this rate of losing water, how much would have been in the reservoir on the following days?

        i 2 August   **ii** 4 August   **iii** 8 August

    b The danger point is when the water drops below 1 million litres. When would this have been if things had continued as they were?

7 The population of a small country, Yebon, was only 46 000 in 1990, but it steadily increased by about 13% each year during the 1990s.

    a Calculate the population in

        i 1991   **ii** 1995   **iii** 1999.

    b If the population keeps growing at this rate, when will it be half a million?

8 How long will it take to accumulate one million pounds in the following situations?

    a An investment of £100 000 at a rate of 12% compound interest.

    b An investment of £50 000 at a rate of 16% compound interest.

9 An oak tree is 60 cm tall. It grows at a rate of 8% per year. A conifer is 50 cm tall. It grows at a rate of 15% per year. How many years does it take before the conifer is taller than the oak?

10 A tree increases in height by 18% per year. When it is 1 year old, it is 8 cm tall. How long will it take the tree to grow to 10 m?

11 Show that a 10% increase followed by a 10% increase is equivalent to a 21% increase overall.

Finding the original quantity (reverse percentage)

This section will show you how to:

● calculate the original amount after you know the result of a percentage increase or decrease

There are situations when we know a certain percentage and wish to get back to the **original amount**. There are two methods.

Method 1
The first method is the **unitary method**.

EXAMPLE 15

The 70 men who went on strike represented only 20% of the workforce. How large was the workforce?

Since 20% represents 70 people, then

   1% will represent 70 ÷ 20 people [don't work it out]

so 100% will represent (70 ÷ 20) × 100 = 350

Hence the workforce is 350.

Method 2
Using a **multipler**.

EXAMPLE 16

The price of a refrigerator is decreased by 12% in a sale. The new price is £220. What was the original price before the reduction?

A decrease of 12% is a multiplier of 0.88.

Simply divide the new price by the multiplier to get the original price. 220 ÷ 0.88 = 250

So the original price was £250.

EXERCISE 2I

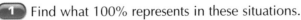

1 Find what 100% represents in these situations.

a 40% represents 320 g

b 14% represents 35 m

c 45% represents 27 cm

d 4% represents £123

e 2.5% represents £5

f 8.5% represents £34

2 On a gruelling army training session, only 28 youngsters survived the whole day. This represented 35% of the original group. How large was the original group?

3 VAT is a government tax added to goods and services. With VAT at 17.5%, what is the pre-VAT price of the following priced goods?

T shirt	£9.87	Tights	£1.41
Shorts	£6.11	Sweater	£12.62
Trainers	£29.14	Boots	£38.07

4 Howard spends £200 a month on food. This represents 24% of his monthly take-home pay. How much is his monthly take-home pay?

5 Tina's weekly pay is increased by 5% to £315. What was Tina's pay before the increase?

6 The number of workers in a factory fell by 5% to 228. How many workers were there originally?

7 In a sale a TV is reduced to a price of £325.50. This is a 7% reduction on the original price. What was the original price?

8 If 38% of plastic bottles in a production line are blue and the remaining 7750 plastic bottles are brown, how many plastic bottles are blue?

9 I received £3.85 back from the tax office, which represented the 17.5% VAT on a piece of equipment. How much did I pay for this equipment in the first place?

10 A man's salary was increased by 5% in one year and reduced by 5% in the next year. Is his final salary greater or less than the original one and by how many per cent?

11 A quick way of estimating the pre-VAT price of an item with VAT added is to divide by 6 and then multiply by 5. For example, if an item is £360 including VAT, it is approximately $(360 \div 6) \times 5 = £300$ before VAT. Show that this gives an estimate to within £5 of the pre-VAT price for items costing up to £280.

1 Mrs Senior earns £320 per week.
She is awarded a pay rise of 4%.
How much does she earn each week after the pay rise?

 2 Five boys run a 200 metre race.
Their times are shown in the table.

Name	Andy	Boris	Chris	Darren	Eric
Time (seconds)	25.0	23.4	26.1	22.8	24.2

a Write down the median time.

b The five boys run another 200 metre race.
They all reduce their times by 10%.

   i Calculate Andy's new time.

   ii Who won this race?

   iii Who improved his time by the greatest amount of time?

AQA, Question 15 Foundation, Paper 1, May 2002

3 Mr Shaw's bill for new tyres is £120 plus VAT.
VAT is charged at 17.5%. What is his total bill?

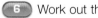 **4** Two shops sell CDs.

> **Pops Musical Shop**
> CDs £9.60 each
> By 2 CDs and get a third one FREE

> **Sounds Musical Shop**
> CD SALE
> 30% OFF normal price of £9.60 each

Jamie wants to buy 3 CDs. Which shop offers the better value? You must show all your working.

AQA, Question 21, Paper 2 Foundation, June 2002

5 Mr and Mrs Jones are buying a tumble dryer that normally costs £250. They save 12% in a sale.
How much do they pay for the tumble dryer?

 6 Work out the value of $\frac{3}{5} - \frac{3}{8}$

 7 On Monday Joe drinks $2\frac{1}{3}$ pints of milk.
On Tuesday he drinks $1\frac{3}{4}$ pints of milk.
Work out the total amount of milk that Joe drinks on Monday and Tuesday.

AQA, Question 13, Paper 1 Intermediate, June 2005

 8 Linda uses $\frac{3}{5}$ of a tin of paint to paint a fence panel.
What is the *least* number of tins she needs to paint 8 fence panels?

AQA, Question 8, Paper 2 Intermediate, November 2004

 9 For many years, people have tried to find an estimate for the value for π. Here are some of the estimates used.

Greek $\frac{22}{7}$ Hindu $\sqrt{10}$ Egyptian $\frac{256}{81}$ Roman $3\frac{1}{8}$

a Put these estimates in order of size, starting with the smallest. You *must* show all your working.

b The value of π on a calculator is 3.141592654
Which of the above estimates is closest to this value?

AQA, Question 8, Paper 2 Intermediate, November 2003

 10 These are 150 kangaroos at a wildlife park.

a There are 66 female kangaroos.
What percentage is female?

b The number of kangaroos increases by 20% each year. Calculate the number of kangaroos in the wildlife park after 2 years.

AQA, Question 18a, Paper 1 Intermediate, November 2004

 11 During 2003 the number of unemployed people in Barnsley fell from 2800 to 2576.
What was the percentage decrease?

 12 **a** A painter has 50 litres of paint.
Each litre covers 2.5 m^2.
The area to be painted is 98 m^2.
Estimate the percentage of paint used.

 13 *ABCD* is a rectangle with length 25 cm and width 10 cm.

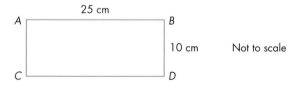

The length of the rectangle is increased by 10%.
The width of the rectangle is increased by 20%.
Find the percentage increase in the area of the rectangle.

AQA, Question 15, Paper 2 Intermediate, November 2003

 14 Zoe invests £6000 in a savings account that pays 3.5% compound interest per year.
How much does she have in the account after 6 years ?

 15 Work out $3\frac{3}{4} \div 4\frac{1}{2}$

16 A special savings account earns 10% per year compound interest.

a Jill invests £2500 in the special account. How much will she have in her account after 2 years?

b James also invests in the special account. After earning interest for one year, he has £1320 in his account. How much money did James invest?

AQA, Question 22, Paper 1 Intermediate, November 2003

 17 a Miss Evans earns £240 per week. She is awarded a pay rise of 3.5%.

Mr Dale earns £220 per week. He is awarded a pay rise of 4%.

Whose weekly pay increases by the greater amount of money? You *must* show all your working.

b In 2003 the state pension was increased by 2% to £78.03 What was the state pension before this increase?

AQA, Question 12, Paper 2 Intermediate, June 2003

WORKED EXAM QUESTION

a Kelly bought a television set. After a reduction of 15% in a sale, the one she bought cost her £319.60. What was the original price of the television set?

b A plant in a greenhouse is 10 cm high. It increases its height by 15% each day. How many days does it take to double in height?

Solution

a £376.

> A 15% reduction is a multiplier of 0.85. The original price will be the new price divided by the multiplier. $319.6 \div 0.85 = 376$

b $10 \times 1.15^3 = 15.2$

$10 \times 1.15^4 = 17.5$

$10 \times 1.15^5 = 20.1$

Therefore, it takes 5 days to double in height.

> A 15% increase is a multiplier of 1.15. After n days the plant will be 10×1.15^n high. Use trial and improvement to find the value that is over 20 cm.

Work out $\dfrac{\left(\frac{2}{3} + \frac{4}{5}\right)}{1\frac{7}{9}}$

Solution

$\dfrac{\frac{22}{15}}{1\frac{7}{9}}$

> First add the two fractions in the bracket by writing them with a common denominator, that is, $\frac{10}{15} + \frac{12}{15}$

$\dfrac{22}{15} \times \dfrac{9}{16}$

> Make the mixed number into a top heavy fraction, $\frac{16}{9}$, and turn it upside down and multiply.

$\dfrac{{}^{11}22}{{}^{5}15} \times \dfrac{{}^{}9^{3}}{16^{8}} = \dfrac{33}{40}$

> Cancel out the common factors, and multiply numerators and denominators.

Mrs Woolman is a sheep farmer in Wales. When she sends her lambs to market, she keeps a record of how many lambs she sends, and the total live weight of these lambs in kilograms.

Once they have been processed, she receives an information sheet showing the total weight of the meat from the lambs in kilograms, and the total price she has been paid for this meat.

For every week that she sends lambs to the market, she calculates the mean live weight of the lambs (to the nearest kilogram).

Copy the table below and complete the *Mean live weight in kg* column for her.

Mrs Woolman is happy with the condition of her lambs if the weight of the meat as a percentage of the live weight is over 42%.

Complete the *Meat as a % of live weight* column in your table. Indicate with a tick or a cross if she is happy with the condition of those lambs. Give percentages to one decimal place.

After Mrs Woolman has been paid for the meat, she calculates the price she is paid per kilogram of meat.

Compete the final column, *Price paid per kg of meat* in your table. Give each price to the nearest penny.

Date	Number of lambs	Total live weight in kg	Mean live weight in kg	Total weight of meat in kg	Meat as % of live weight	Total price paid for meat	Price paid per kg of meat
1st April	13	468	36	211	45.1% ✓	£812.56	£3.85
15th April	8	290		134		£451.91	
22nd April	18	672		312		£1105.31	
29th April	11	398		179		£625.04	
6th May	18	657		291		£907.89	
20th May	8	309		130		£386.15	
3rd June	10	416		171		£480.46	
17th June	4	174		72		£196.54	

At the end of the season Mrs Woolman analyses the information she has calculated.

Fill in the spaces in her notebook for her.

The mean weight per lamb has increased from _____ kg to _____ kg. This is an increase of _____%. However the price per kg of lamb has fallen from £_____ to £_____, a decrease of _____%.

The only two weeks when the condition of the lambs fell below 42% were _____ and _____.

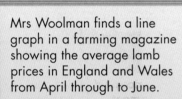

Mrs Woolman finds a line graph in a farming magazine showing the average lamb prices in England and Wales from April through to June.

Copy this graph, and complete the line showing the price per kilogram that Mrs Woolman had for her lambs.

Comment on these line graphs.

Average lamb prices, April to July

£ per kilogram of meat

Date

GRADE YOURSELF

D Able to add, subtract, multiply and divide fractions

D Able to calculate percentage increases and decreases

C Able to calculate with mixed numbers

C Able to work out compound interest problems

B Able to do reverse percentage problems

A Able to solve complex problems involving percentage increases and decreases

What you should know now

- How to calculate with fractions
- How to do percentage problems

Ratios and proportion

Chapter 3

1 Ratio

2 Speed, time and distance

3 Direct proportion problems

4 Best buys

5 Density

This chapter will show you ...

- what a ratio is
- how to divide an amount into a given ratio
- how to solve problems involving direct proportion
- how to compare prices of products
- how to calculate speed
- how to calculate density

What you should already know

- Times tables up to 10×10
- How to cancel fractions
- How to find a fraction of a quantity
- How to multiply and divide, with and without a calculator

Quick check

1 Cancel down the following fractions.

   a $\frac{6}{10}$ **b** $\frac{4}{20}$ **c** $\frac{4}{12}$ **d** $\frac{32}{50}$ **e** $\frac{36}{90}$ **f** $\frac{18}{24}$ **g** $\frac{16}{48}$

2 Find the following quantities.

   a $\frac{2}{5}$ of £30   **b** $\frac{3}{8}$ of £88   **c** $\frac{7}{10}$ of 250 litres   **d** $\frac{5}{8}$ of 24 kg

   e $\frac{2}{3}$ of 60 m   **f** $\frac{5}{6}$ of £42   **g** $\frac{9}{20}$ of 300 g   **h** $\frac{3}{10}$ of 3.5 litres

This section will show you how to:
- simplify a ratio
- express a ratio as a fraction
- divide amounts into given ratios
- complete calculations from a given ratio and partial information

A **ratio** is a way of comparing the sizes of two or more quantities.

A ratio can be expressed in a number of ways. For example, Joy is 5 years old and James is 20 years old. The ratio of their ages is Joy's age : James's age which is 5 : 20.

This simplifies to 1 : 4 (dividing both sides by 5).

A ratio can be expressed in words but it is usual to use a colon (:).

Joy's age : James's age   or   5 : 20   or   1 : 4

Common units

When working with a ratio involving different units, *always change them* to a **common unit**. A ratio can be simplified only when the units of each quantity are the *same*, because the ratio itself doesn't have any units.

For example, the ratio of 125 g to 2 kg must be changed to 125 g to 2000 g, so that we can simplify it to

	125 : 2000
Divide both sides by 25	5 : 80
Divide both sides by 5	1 : 16

Ratios as fractions

A ratio in its simplest form can be expressed as portions by changing the whole numbers in the ratio into **fractions** with the same denominator (bottom number).

EXAMPLE 1

A garden is divided into lawn and shrubs in the ratio 3 : 2.

What fraction of the garden is covered by **a** lawn, **b** shrubs?

The denominator (bottom number) of the fraction comes from *adding the numbers in the ratio* (that is, 2 + 3 = 5).

a The lawn covers $\frac{3}{5}$ of the garden.

b The shrubs cover $\frac{2}{5}$ of the garden.

EXERCISE 3A

1 A length of wood is cut into two pieces in the ratio 3 : 7. What fraction of the original length is the longer piece?

2 Jack and Thomas find a bag of marbles which they divide between them in the ratio of their ages. Jack is 10 years old and Thomas is 15. What fraction of the marbles did Jack get?

3 Dave and Sue share a pizza in the ratio of 2 : 3. They eat it all.

    a What fraction of the pizza did Dave eat?

    b What fraction of the pizza did Sue eat?

4 A camp site allocates space to caravans and tents in the ratio 7 : 3. What fraction of the total space is given to:

    a the caravans?   **b** the tents?

5 One morning a farmer notices that her hens, Gertrude, Gladys and Henrietta, have laid eggs in the ratio 2 : 3 : 4.

    a What fraction of the eggs did Gertrude lay?

    b What fraction of the eggs did Gladys lay?

    c How many more eggs did Henrietta lay than Gertrude?

6 The recipe for a pudding is 125 g of sugar, 150 g of flour, 100 g of margarine and 175 g of fruit. What fraction of the pudding is each ingredient?

Dividing amounts into given ratios

To divide an amount into portions according to a given ratio, you first change the whole numbers in the ratio into fractions with the same common denominator. Then you multiply the amount by each fraction.

EXAMPLE 2

Divide £40 between Peter and Hitan in the ratio 2 : 3.

Changing the ratio to fractions gives:

$$\text{Peter's share} = \frac{2}{(2+3)} = \frac{2}{5}$$

$$\text{Hitan's share} = \frac{3}{(2+3)} = \frac{3}{5}$$

So, Peter receives £40 × $\frac{2}{5}$ = £16 and Hitan receives £40 × $\frac{3}{5}$ = £24.

EXAMPLE 3

Divide 63 cm in the ratio 3 : 4.

An alternative method that avoids fractions is to add the parts: 3 + 4 = 7.

Divide the original amount by the total: 63 ÷ 7 = 9.

Then multiply each portion of the original ratio by the answer: 3 × 9 = 27, 4 × 9 = 36.

So 63 cm in the ratio 3 : 4 is 27 cm : 36 cm.

Note that whichever method you use, you should always check that the final values add up to the original amount: £16 + £24 = £40 and 27 cm + 36 cm = 63 cm.

EXERCISE 3B

 1 Divide the following amounts in the given ratios.

a 400 g in the ratio 2 : 3   **b** 280 kg in the ratio 2 : 5

c 500 in the ratio 3 : 7   **d** 1 km in the ratio 19 : 1

e 5 hours in the ratio 7 : 5   **f** £100 in the ratio 2 : 3 : 5

g £240 in the ratio 3 : 5 : 12   **h** 600 g in the ratio 1 : 5 : 6

 2 The ratio of female to male members of Banner Cross Church is about 5 : 3. The total number of members of the church is 256.

a How many members are female?

b What percentage of members are male?

 3 A supermarket tries to have in stock branded goods and its own goods in the ratio 2 : 5. It stocks 350 kg of breakfast cereal.

a What percentage of the cereal stock is branded?

b How much of the cereal stock is its own?

 4 The Illinois Department of Health reported that, for the years 1981 to 1992, when it tested a total of 357 horses for rabies, the ratio of horses with rabies to those without was 1 : 16.

a How many of these horses had rabies?

b What percentage of the horses did not have rabies?

 5 Being overweight increases the chances of an adult suffering from heart disease. The formulae below show a way to test whether an adult has an increased risk.

W and *H* refer to waist and hip measurements.
For women, increased risk when $W/H > 0.8$
For men, increased risk when $W/H > 1.0$

Find whether the following people have an increased risk of heart disease or not.

Miss Mott: waist 26 inches, hips: 35 inches

Mrs Wright: waist 32 inches, hips: 37 inches

Mr Brennan: waist 32 inches, hips: 34 inches

Ms Smith: waist 31 inches, hips: 40 inches

Mr Kaye: waist 34 inches, hips: 33 inches

 6 Rewrite the following scales as ratios, as simply as possible.

a 1 cm to 4 km   **b** 4 cm to 5 km   **c** 2 cm to 5 km

d 4 cm to 1 km   **e** 5 cm to 1 km   **f** 2.5 cm to 1 km

 7 A map has a scale of 1 cm to 10 km.

a Rewrite the scale as a ratio in its simplest form.

b How long is a lake that is 4.7 cm on the map?

c How long will an 8 km road be on the map?

 8 A map has a scale of 2 cm to 5 km.

a Rewrite the scale as a ratio in its simplest form.

b How long is a path that measures 0.8 cm on the map?

c How long should a 12 km road be on the map?

 9 You can simplify a ratio by changing it into the form 1 : n.

For example, 5 : 7 can be rewritten as $\dfrac{5}{5} : \dfrac{7}{5} = 1 : 1.4$

Rewrite each of the following in the form 1 : n.

a 5 : 8   **b** 4 : 13   **c** 8 : 9

d 25 : 36   **e** 5 : 27   **f** 12 : 18

g 5 hours : 1 day   **h** 4 hours : 1 week   **i** £4 : £5

Calculating a ratio when only part of the information is known

EXAMPLE 4

Two business partners, John and Ben, divided their total profit in the ratio 3 : 5. John received £2100. How much did Ben get?

John's £2100 was $\frac{3}{8}$ of the total profit. (Check you know why.)

So, $\frac{1}{8}$ of the total profit = £2100 ÷ 3 = £700

Therefore, Ben's share, which was $\frac{5}{8}$ of the total, amounted to £700 × 5 = £3500.

EXERCISE 3C

1 Derek, aged 15, and Ricki, aged 10, shared, in the same ratio as their ages, all the conkers they found in the woods. Derek had 48 conkers.

    a Simplify the ratio of their ages.

    b How many conkers did Ricki have?

    c How many conkers did they find altogether?

2 Two types of crisps, Plain and Salt'n Vinegar, were bought for a school party in the ratio 5 : 3. They bought 60 packets of Salt'n Vinegar crisps.

    a How many packets of Plain crisps did they buy?

    b How many packets of crisps did they buy altogether?

3 A blend of tea is made by mixing Lapsang with Assam in the ratio 3 : 5. I have a lot of Assam tea but only 600 g of Lapsang. How much Assam do I need to make the blend with all the Lapsang?

4 The ratio of male to female spectators at ice hockey games is 4 : 5. At the Steelers' last match, 4500 men and boys watched the match. What was the total attendance at the game?

5 "Proper tea" is made by putting milk and tea together in the ratio 2 : 9. How much "proper tea" can be made by using 1 litre of milk?

6 A "good" children's book is supposed to have pictures and text in the ratio 17 : 8. In a book I have just looked at, the pictures occupy 23 pages.

    a Approximately how many pages of text should this book have to be deemed a "good" children's book?

    b What percentage of a "good" children's book will be text?

7 Three business partners, Kevin, John and Margaret, put money into a venture in the ratio 3 : 4 : 5. They shared any profits in the same ratio. Last year, Margaret made £3400 out of the profits. How much did Kevin and John make last year?

8 Gwen is making a drink from lemonade, orange and ginger in the ratio 40 : 9 : 1. If Gwen has only 4.5 litres of orange, how much of the other two ingredients does she need to make the drink?

9 When I harvested my apples I found some had been eaten by wasps, some were just rotten and some were good ones. These were in the ratio 6 : 5 : 25. Eighteen of my apples had been eaten by wasps.

    a What percentage of my apples were just rotten?

    b How many good apples did I get?

Speed, time and distance

In this section you will learn how to:
- recognise the relationship between speed, distance and time
- calculate average speed from distance and time
- calculate distance travelled from the speed and the time
- calculate the time taken on a journey from the speed and the distance

Key words
distance
speed
time

The relationship between **speed**, **time** and **distance** can be expressed in three ways:

$$Speed = \frac{Distance}{Time} \qquad Distance = Speed \times Time \qquad Time = \frac{Distance}{Speed}$$

When we refer to speed, we usually mean *average* speed, as it is unusual to maintain one exact speed for the whole of a journey.

The relationships between distance D, time T and speed S can be recalled using this diagram.

$$D = S \times T \qquad S = \frac{D}{T} \qquad T = \frac{D}{S}$$

EXAMPLE 5

Paula drove a distance of 270 miles in 5 hours. What was her average speed?

$$\text{Paula's average speed} = \frac{\text{distance she drove}}{\text{time she took}} = \frac{270 \text{ miles}}{5 \text{ hours}} = 54 \text{ miles/h}$$

EXAMPLE 6

Edith drove from Sheffield to Peebles for $3\frac{1}{2}$ hours at an average speed of 60 miles/h. How far is it from Sheffield to Peebles?

$$Distance = Speed \times Time$$

So, distance from Sheffield to Peebles is given by

$$60 \text{ miles/h} \times 3.5 \text{ h} = 210 \text{ miles}$$

Note: We changed the time to a decimal number and used 3.5, **not** 3.30!

EXAMPLE 7

Sean is going to drive from Newcastle upon Tyne to Nottingham, a distance of 190 miles. He estimates that he will drive at an average speed of 50 miles/h. How long will it take him?

$$\text{Sean's time} = \frac{\text{distance he covers}}{\text{his average speed}} = \frac{190 \text{ miles}}{50 \text{ miles/h}} = 3.8 \text{ hours}$$

Change the 0.8 hour to minutes by multiplying by 60, to give 48 minutes.

So, the time for Sean's journey will be 3 hours 48 minutes.
(A sensible rounding off would give 4 hours or 3 hours 50 minutes.)

Remember: When you calculate a time and get a decimal answer, as in Example 7, *do not mistake* the decimal part for minutes. You must either:

- leave the time as a decimal number and give the unit as hours, or

- change the decimal part to minutes by multiplying it by 60 (1 hour = 60 minutes) and give the answer in hours and minutes.

EXERCISE 3D

1. A cyclist travels a distance of 90 miles in 5 hours. What is her average speed?

2. I drive to Bude in Cornwall from Sheffield in about 6 hours. The distance from Sheffield to Bude is 315 miles. What is my average speed?

3. The distance from Leeds to London is 210 miles. The train travels at an average speed of 90 mph. If I catch the 9:30 am train in London, at what time would you expect me to get to Leeds?

4. Complete the following table.

	Distance travelled	Time taken	Average speed
a	150 miles	2 hours	
b	260 miles		40 mph
c		5 hours	35 mph
d		3 hours	80 km/h
e	544 km	8 hours 30 minutes	
f		3 hours 15 minutes	100 km/h
g	215 km		50 km/h

> **HINTS AND TIPS**
>
> Remember to convert time to a decimal if you are using a calculator. For example, 8 hours 30 minutes is 8.5 hours.

5. A train travels at 50 km/h for 2 hours, then slows down to do the last 30 minutes of its journey at 40 km/h.

   a What is the total distance of this journey?

   b What is the average speed of the train over the whole journey?

6 Jane runs and walks to work each day. She runs the first 2 miles at a speed of 8 mph and then walks the next mile at a steady 4 mph.

    a How long does it take Jane to get to work?

    b What is her average speed?

7 Colin drives home from his son's house in 2 hours 15 minutes. He says that he drives home at an average speed of 44 mph.

    a Change the 2 hours 15 minutes to decimal time.

    b How far is it from Colin's home to his son's house?

8 The distance between Paris and Le Mans is 200 km. The express train between Paris and Le Mans travels at an average speed of 160 km/h.

    a Calculate the time taken for the journey from Paris to Le Mans, giving your answer in decimal hour notation.

    b Change your answer to part **a** to hours and minutes.

9 The distance between Sheffield and Land's End is 420 miles.

    a What is the average speed of a journey from Sheffield to Land's End if it takes 8 hours 45 minutes?

    b If I covered the distance at an average speed of 63 mph, how long would it take me?

10 Change the following speeds to metres per second.

    a 36 km/h   **b** 12 km/h   **c** 60 km/h

    d 150 km/h   **e** 75 km/h

> **HINTS AND TIPS**
>
> Remember there are 3600 seconds in an hour and 1000 metres in a kilometre.

11 Change the following speeds to kilometres per hour.

    a 25 m/s   **b** 12 m/s   **c** 4 m/s

    d 30 m/s   **e** 0.5 m/s

12 A train travels at an average speed of 18 m/s.

    a Express its average speed in km/h.

    b Find the approximate time taken to travel 500 m.

    c The train set off at 7:30 on a 40 km journey. At approximately what time will it arrive?

> **HINTS AND TIPS**
>
> To convert a decimal of an hour to minutes just multiply by 60.

This section will show you how to:
- recognise a direct proportion problem
- solve a problem involving direct proportion

Key words
direct
    proportion
unitary
    method

Suppose you buy 12 items which each cost the *same*. The total amount you spend is 12 times the cost of one item.

That is, the total cost is said to be in **direct proportion** to the number of items bought. The cost of a single item (the unit cost) is the constant factor that links the two quantities.

Direct proportion is concerned not only with costs. Any two related quantities can be in direct proportion to each other.

Finding the single unit value first is the best way to solve all problems involving direct proportion.

This method is called the **unitary method**, because it involves referring to a single *unit* value.

Remember: Before solving a direct proportion problem, think carefully about it to make sure that you know how to find the required single unit value.

EXAMPLE 8

If eight pens cost £2.64, what is the cost of five pens?

First, we need to find the cost of one pen. This is £2.64 ÷ 8 = £0.33.

So, the cost of five pens is £0.33 × 5 = £1.65.

EXAMPLE 9

Eight loaves of bread will make packed lunches for 18 people. How many packed lunches can be made from 20 loaves?

First, we need to find how many lunches *one* loaf will make.

One loaf will make 18 ÷ 8 = 2.25 lunches.

So, 20 loaves will make 2.25 × 20 = 45 lunches.

EXERCISE 3E

1. If 30 matches weigh 45 g, what would 40 matches weigh?

2. Five bars of chocolate cost £2.90. Find the cost of 9 bars.

3. Eight men can chop down 18 trees in a day. How many trees can 20 men chop down in a day?

4. Seventy maths textbooks cost £875.

   a How much will 25 maths textbooks cost?

   b How many maths textbooks can you buy for £100?

5. A lorry uses 80 litres of diesel fuel on a trip of 280 miles.

   a How much would be used on a trip of 196 miles?

   b How far would the lorry get on a full tank of 100 litres?

6. During the winter, I find that 200 kg of coal keeps my open fire burning for 12 weeks.

   a If I want an open fire all through the winter (18 weeks), how much coal will I need to get?

   b Last year I bought 150 kg of coal. For how many weeks did I have an open fire?

7. It takes a photocopier 16 seconds to produce 12 copies. How long will it take to produce 30 copies?

3.4 Best buys

This section will show you how to:	Key word
• find the cost per unit weight • find the weight per unit cost • find which product is the cheaper	best buy

When you wander around a supermarket and see all the different prices for the many different-sized packets, it is rarely obvious which are the **best buys**. However, with a calculator you can easily compare value for money by finding either:

   the cost per unit weight   *or*   the weight per unit cost

To find:

• *cost per unit weight*, divide *cost by weight*

• *weight per unit cost*, divide *weight by cost.*

The next two examples show you how to do this.

EXAMPLE 10

A 300 g tin of cocoa costs £1.20.

First change £1.20 to 120p. Then divide, using a calculator, to get:

cost per unit weight   120p ÷ 300 g = 0.4p per gram

weight per unit cost   300 g ÷ 120p = 2.5 g per penny

EXAMPLE 11

There are two different-sized packets of Whito soap powder at a supermarket. The medium size contains 800 g and costs £1.60 and the large size contains 2.5 kg and costs £4.75. Which is the better buy?

Find the weight per unit cost for both packets.

Medium: 800 g ÷ 160p = 5 g per penny

Large: 2500 g ÷ 475p = 5.26 g per penny

From these we see that there is more weight per penny with the large size, which means that the large size is the better buy.

EXERCISE 3F

1 Compare the following pairs of product and state which is the better buy, and why.

a Coffee: a medium jar which is 140 g for £1.10 or a large jar which is 300 g for £2.18

b Beans: a 125 g tin at 16p or a 600 g tin at 59p

c Flour: a 3 kg bag at 75p or a 5 kg bag at £1.20

d Toothpaste: a large tube which is 110 ml for £1.79 or a medium tube which is 75 ml for £1.15

e Frosties: a large box which is 750 g for £1.64 or a medium box which is 500 g for £1.10

f Rice Krispies: a medium box which is 440 g for £1.64 or a large box which is 600 g for £2.13

g Hair shampoo: a bottle containing 400 ml for £1.15 or a bottle containing 550 ml for £1.60

2 Julie wants to respray her car with yellow paint. In the local automart, she sees the following tins:

small tin: 350 ml at a cost of £1.79
medium tin: 500 ml at a cost of £2.40
large tin: 1.5 litres at a cost of £6.70

a Which tin is offered at the cheapest cost per litre?

b What is the cost per litre of paint in the small tin?

3 Tisco's sells bottled water in three sizes.

a Work out the cost per litre of the 'handy' size.

b Which bottle is the best value for money?

Handy size 40 cl
£0.38

Family size 2 l
£0.98

Giant size 5 l
£2.50

4 Two drivers are comparing the petrol consumption of their cars.

Ahmed says, 'I get 320 miles on a tank of 45 litres.'

Bashir says, 'I get 230 miles on a tank of 32 litres.'

Whose car is the more economical?

5 Mary and Jane are arguing about which of them is better at mathematics.

Mary scored 49 out of 80 on a test.

Jane scored 60 out of 100 on a test of the same standard.

Who is better at mathematics?

6 Paula and Kelly are comparing their running times.

Paula completed a 10-mile run in 65 minutes.

Kelly completed a 10-kilometre run in 40 minutes.

Given that 8 kilometres are equal to 5 miles, which girl has the greater average speed?

3.5 Density

This section will show you how to:	Key words
• solve problems involving density	density mass volume

Density is the mass of a substance per unit volume, usually expressed in grams per cm^3. The relationship between the three quantities is

$$Density = \frac{Mass}{Volume}$$

This is often remembered with a triangle similar to that for distance, speed and time.

$Mass \quad = Density \times Volume$

$Density = Mass \div Volume$

$Volume = Mass \div Density$

Note: Density is defined in terms of mass, which is commonly referred to as weight, although, strictly speaking, there is a difference between them. (You may already have learnt about this in science.) In this book, the two terms are assumed to have the same meaning.

EXAMPLE 12

A piece of metal weighing 30 g has a volume of 4 cm^3. What is the density of the metal?

$$Density = \frac{Mass}{Volume} = \frac{30\ g}{4\ cm^3} = 7.5\ g/cm^3$$

EXAMPLE 13

What is the weight of a piece of rock which has a volume of 34 cm^3 and a density of 2.25 g/cm^3?

$$Weight = Volume \times Density = 34\ cm^3 \times 2.25\ g/cm^3 = 76.5\ g$$

EXERCISE 3G

1. Find the density of a piece of wood weighing 6 g and having a volume of 8 cm^3.

2. Calculate the density of a metal if 12 cm^3 of it weighs 100 g.

3. Calculate the weight of a piece of plastic, 20 cm^3 in volume, if its density is 1.6 g/cm^3.

4. Calculate the volume of a piece of wood which weighs 102 g and has a density of 0.85 g/cm^3.

5. Find the weight of a marble model, 56 cm^3 in volume, if the density of marble is 2.8 g/cm^3.

6. Calculate the volume of a liquid weighing 4 kg and having a density of 1.25 g/cm^3.

7. Find the density of the material of a pebble which weighs 34 g and has a volume of 12.5 cm^3.

8. It is estimated that the statue of Queen Victoria in Endcliffe Park, Sheffield, has a volume of about 4 m^3. The density of the material used to make the statue is 9.2 g/cm^3. What is the estimated weight of the statue?

9. I bought a 50 kg bag of coal, and estimated the total volume of coal to be about 28 000 cm^3. What is the density of coal in g/cm^3?

10. A 1 kg bag of sugar has a volume of about 625 cm^3. What is the density of sugar in g/cm^3?

1 Two towns, *A* and *B*, are connected by a motorway of length 100 miles and a dual carriageway of length 80 miles as shown.

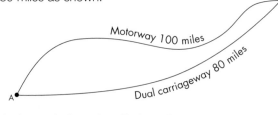

Jack travels from *A* to *B* along the motorway at an average speed of 60 mph.
Fred travels from *A* to *B* along the dual carriageway at an average speed of 50 mph.
What is the difference in time between the two journeys? Give your answers in minutes.

AQA, Question 8, Paper 2 Intermediate, June 2005

2 **a** How many 250 millilitre glasses can be filled from a 2-litre bottle of water?

b A drink is made by mixing blackcurrant juice and water in the ratio 1 : 4.
How much blackcurrant juice and how much water is needed to make 250 ml of the drink?

AQA, Question 5, Paper 1 Intermediate, May 2002

3 Share £34 800 in the ratio 1 : 5.

4 A short necklace has 32 gold beads and 8 black beads. A long necklace has 60 beads. Both necklaces have the same ratio of gold beads to black beads. How many black beads are on the long necklace?

AQA, Question 10, Paper 1 Intermediate, November 2004

5 Bill and Ben buy £10 worth of lottery tickets. Ben pays £7 and Bill pays £3. They decide to share any prize in the ratio of the money they each paid.

a They win £350. How much does Bill get?

b What percentage of the £350 does Ben get?

6 The interior angles of a triangle are in the ratio

2 : 3 : 4

Calculate the size of the smallest angle.

7 The ratio of adults to children in a pantomime audience is 3 : 16. There are 752 children in the audience. How many adults are there?

AQA, Question 15, Paper 2 Intermediate, November 2002

8 Susan completes a journey in two stages.
In stage 1 of her journey, she drives at an average speed of 80 km/h and takes 1 hour 45 minutes.

a How far does Susan travel in stage 1 of her journey?

b Altogether, Susan drives 190 km and takes a total time of 2 hours 15 minutes. What is her average speed, in km/h, in stage 2 of her journey?

WORKED EXAM QUESTION

To be on time, a train must complete a journey of 210 miles in 3 hours.
a Calculate the average speed of the train for the whole journey when it is on time.
b The train averages a speed of 56 mph over the first 98 miles of the journey. Calculate the average speed for the remainder of the journey so that the train arrives on time.

Solution

a 70 mph

Average speed = distance ÷ time = 210 ÷ 3.
Note that one question in the examination will ask you to state the units of your answer. This is often done with a speed question.

b 98 ÷ 56 = 1.75 which is 1 hour and 45 minutes.

First find out how long the train took to do the first 98 miles.

(210 − 98) ÷ (3 − 1.75) = 112 ÷ 1.25 = 89.6 mph

Now work out the distance still to be travelled (112 miles) and the time left (1 hour 15 minutes = 1.25 hours). Divide distance by time to get the average speed.

GRADE YOURSELF

D Calculate average speeds from data

D Calculate distance from speed and time

D Calculate time from speed and distance

C Solve problems using ratio in appropriate situations

B Solve problems involving density

What you should know now

- How to divide any amount into a given ratio
- The relationships between speed, time and distance
- How to do problems involving direct proportion
- How to compare the prices of products
- How to work out the density of materials

Shape

Chapter 4

① Circumference and area of a circle

② Area of a trapezium

③ Sectors

④ Volume of a prism

⑤ Cylinders

⑥ Volume of a pyramid

⑦ Cones

⑧ Spheres

This chapter will show you ...

- how to calculate the length of an arc
- how to calculate the area of a sector
- how to find the area of a trapezium
- how to calculate the surface area and volume of prisms, cylinders, pyramids, cones and spheres

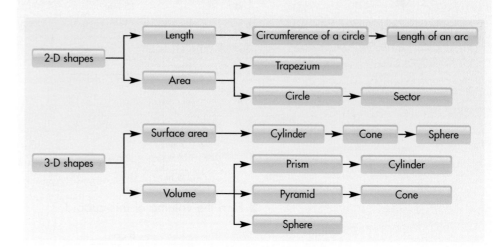

What you should already know

- The area of a rectangle is given by Area = length × width or $A = lw$
- The area of a parallelogram is given by Area = base × height or $A = bh$
- The area of a triangle is given by Area = $\frac{1}{2}$ × base × height or $A = \frac{1}{2}bh$
- The circumference of a circle is given by $C = \pi d$, where d is the diameter of the circle
- The area of a circle is given by $A = \pi r^2$, where r is the radius of the circle

continued

- The most accurate value of π that you can use is on your calculator. You should use it every time you have to work with π. Otherwise take π to be 3.142

- In problems using π, unless told otherwise, round off your answers to three significant figures

- The volume of a cuboid is given by Volume = length × width × height or $V = lwh$

- The common metric units to measure area, volume and capacity are shown in this table.

Area	Volume	Capacity
$100 \text{ mm}^2 = 1 \text{ cm}^2$	$1000 \text{ mm}^3 = 1 \text{ cm}^3$	$1000 \text{ cm}^3 = 1 \text{ litre}$
$10\,000 \text{ cm}^2 = 1 \text{ m}^2$	$1\,000\,000 \text{ cm}^3 = 1 \text{ m}^3$	$1 \text{ m}^3 = 1000 \text{ litres}$

Quick check

1 Find the areas of the following shapes.

a
15 mm
6 mm

b

8 cm
5 cm

c
7 m
6 m

2 Find the volume of this cuboid.

8 cm
5 cm
3 cm

If you need to revise circle calculations, you should work through Exercise 4A.

Circumference and area of a circle

In this section you will learn how to:

- calculate the circumference and area of a circle

Key words

π
area
circumference

EXAMPLE 1

Calculate the **circumference** of the circle. Give your answer to three significant figures.

$C = \pi d$

$\quad = \pi \times 5 \text{ cm}$

$\quad = 15.7 \text{ cm (to 3 significant figures)}$

5 cm

EXAMPLE 2

Calculate the **area** of the circle. Give your answer in terms of π.

$A = \pi r^2$

$\quad = \pi \times 6^2 \text{ m}^2$

$\quad = 36\pi \text{ m}^2$

6 m

EXERCISE 4A

1 Copy and complete the following table for each circle. Give your answers to 3 significant figures.

	Radius	Diameter	Circumference	Area
a	4 cm			
b	2.6 m			
c		12 cm		
d		3.2 m		

D

2 Find the circumference of each of the following circles. Give your answers in terms of π.

  a Diameter 5 cm   **b** Radius 4 cm   **c** Radius 9 m   **d** Diameter 12 cm

3 Find the area of each of the following circles. Give your answers in terms of π.

  a Radius 5 cm   **b** Diameter 12 cm   **c** Radius 10 cm   **d** Diameter 1 m

4 A rope is wrapped eight times round a capstan (a cylindrical post), the diameter of which is 35 cm. How long is the rope?

5 The roller used on a cricket pitch has a radius of 70 cm.

    a What is the circumference of the roller?

    b A cricket pitch has a length of 20 m. How many complete revolutions does the roller make when rolling the pitch?

6 The diameter of each of the following coins is as follows.

    1p: 2 cm,   2p: 2.6 cm,   5p: 1.7 cm,   10p: 2.4 cm

    Calculate the area of one face of each coin. Give your answers to 1 decimal place.

7 A circle has a circumference of 25 cm. What is its diameter?

8 What is the total perimeter of a semicircle of diameter 15 cm?

9 What is the total perimeter of a semicircle of radius 7 cm? Give your answer in terms of π.

10 Calculate the area of each of these shapes, giving your answers in terms of π.

    a

          12 cm

    b

          4 cm

    c

          8 cm

11 Calculate the area of the shaded part of each of these diagrams, giving your answers in terms of π.

    a

          6 m   2 m

    b

          4 cm   10 cm

    c

          4 cm   5 cm

12 Assume that the human waist is circular.

    a What are the distances around the waists of the following people?

        Sue: waist radius of 10 cm   Dave: waist radius of 12 cm

        Julie: waist radius of 11 cm   Brian: waist radius of 13 cm

    b Compare differences between pairs of waist circumferences. What connection do they have to π?

    c What would be the difference in length between a rope stretched tightly round the Earth and another rope always held 1 m above it?

Area of a trapezium

- find the area of a trapezium

Key word

trapezium

The area of a **trapezium** is calculated by finding the average of the lengths of its parallel sides and multiplying this by the perpendicular distance between them.

$$A = \tfrac{1}{2}(a + b)h$$

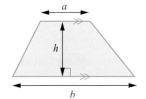

EXAMPLE 3

Find the area of the trapezium ABCD.

$$A = \tfrac{1}{2}(4 + 7) \times 3 \text{ cm}^2$$
$$= 16.5 \text{ cm}^2$$

EXERCISE 4B

1. Copy and complete the following table for each trapezium.

	Parallel side 1	Parallel side 2	Vertical height	Area
a	8 cm	4 cm	5 cm	
b	10 cm	12 cm	7 cm	
c	7 cm	5 cm	4 cm	
d	5 cm	9 cm	6 cm	
e	3 m	13 m	5 m	
f	4 cm	10 cm		42 cm²
g	7 cm	8 cm		22.5 cm²
h	6 cm		5 cm	40 cm²

2. Calculate the perimeter and the area of each of these trapeziums.

a

b

c

3 Calculate the area of each of these compound shapes.

a

b

c

4 Calculate the area of the shaded part in each of these diagrams.

a

b

c

5 A trapezium has an area of 25 cm². Its vertical height is 5 cm. Write down five different possible pairs of lengths which the two parallel sides could be.

6 What percentage of this shape has been shaded?

7 The shape of most of Egypt (see map) roughly approximates to a trapezium. The north coast is about 900 km long, the south boundary is about 1100 km long, and the distance from north to south is about 1100 km.

What is the approximate area of this part of Egypt?

Cairo ●

Sectors

In this section you will learn how to:

- calculate the length of an arc and the area of a sector

Key words

arc
sector

A **sector** is part of a circle, bounded by two radii of the circle and one of the **arcs** formed by the intersection of these radii with the circumference.

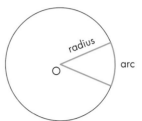

The angle subtended at the centre of the circle by the arc of a sector is known as the angle of the sector.

When a circle is divided into only two sectors, the larger one is called the major sector and the smaller one is called the minor sector.

Likewise, their arcs are called respectively the major arc and the minor arc.

Length of an arc and area of a sector

A sector is a fraction of the whole circle, the size of the fraction being determined by the size of angle of the sector. The angle is often written as θ, a Greek letter pronounced *theta*. For example, the sector shown in the diagram represents the fraction $\dfrac{\theta°}{360°}$.

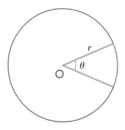

This applies to both its arc length and its area. Therefore,

$$\text{Arc length} \; = \; \frac{\theta°}{360°} \times 2\pi r \quad \text{or} \quad \frac{\theta°}{360°} \times \pi d$$

$$\text{Sector area} \; = \; \frac{\theta°}{360°} \times \pi r^2$$

EXAMPLE 4

Find the arc length and the area of the sector in the diagram.

The sector angle is 28° and the radius is 5 cm. Therefore,

$$\text{Arc length} \quad = \quad \frac{28°}{360°} \times \pi \times 2 \times 5 = 2.4 \text{ cm (1 decimal place)}$$

$$\text{Sector area} \quad = \quad \frac{28°}{360°} \times \pi \times 5^2 = 6.1 \text{ cm}^2 \text{ (1 decimal place)}$$

EXERCISE 4C

 1 For each of these sectors, calculate   **i** the arc length   **ii** the sector area

a

40°
8 cm

b
95°
5 cm

c
78°
12 cm

d
130°
7 cm

 2 Calculate the arc length and the area of a sector whose arc subtends an angle of 60° at the centre of a circle with a diameter of 12 cm. Give your answer in terms of π.

 3 Calculate the total perimeter of each of these sectors.   **a**   **b**

11 cm

22°
8.5 cm

 4 Calculate the area of each of these sectors.

a
110°
7 cm

b
50°
8 cm

c
120°
3 cm

d
250°
4 cm

 5 Calculate the area of the shaded shape giving your answer in terms of π.

12 cm
12 cm

 6 ABCD is a square of side length 8 cm. APC and AQC are arcs of the circles with centres D and B. Calculate the area of the shaded part.

A   B
P
Q
D   C

 7 A pendulum of length 72 cm swings through an angle of 15°. Through what distance does the bob swing? Give your answer in terms of π.

 8 Find **i** the perimeter and **ii** the area of this shape.

1 cm
30° 3 cm

In this section you will learn how to:
• calculate the volume of a prism

Key words
cross-section
prism

A **prism** is a 3-D shape which has the same **cross-section** running all the way through it.

Name:	Cuboid	Triangular prism	Cylinder
Cross-section:	Rectangle	Isosceles triangle	Circle

Name:	Cuboid	Hexagonal prism
Cross-section:	Square	Regular hexagon

The volume of a prism is found by multiplying the area of its cross-section by the length of the prism (or height if the prism is stood on end).

That is, Volume of prism = area of cross-section × length   **or** $V = Al$

EXAMPLE 5

Find the volume of the triangular prism.

The area of the triangular cross-section $= A = \dfrac{5 \times 7}{2} = 17.5 \text{ cm}^2$

The volume is the area of its cross-section × length $= Al$

$\quad = 17.5 \times 9 = 157.5 \text{ cm}^3$

EXERCISE 4D

1 For each prism shown

   i sketch the cross-section   **ii** calculate the area of the cross-section

   iii calculate the volume.

a

b 8 cm / 9 cm / 5 cm / 4 cm / 2 cm

6 cm / 3 cm / 7 cm

c 5 m / 6 m / 2 m / 9 m / 8 m

2 Calculate the volume of each of these prisms.

a 7 m / 4 m / 3 m / 3 m / 4 m / 6 m / 4 m

b 4 m / 6 m / 9 m / 5 m

c 15 m / 11 m / 6 m / 12 m / 3 m / 3 m

3 The uniform cross-section of a swimming pool is a trapezium with parallel sides, 1 m and 2.5 m, with a perpendicular distance of 30 m between them. The width of the pool is 10 m. How much water is in the pool when it is full? Give your answer in litres.

4 A lean-to is a prism. Calculate the volume of air inside the lean-to with the dimensions shown in the diagram. Give your answer in litres.

3 m / 1.5 m / 2 m / 1.7 m

5 Each of these prisms has a regular cross-section in the shape of a right-angled triangle.

   a Find the volume of each prism.   **b** Find the total surface area of each prism.

3.5 cm / 5 cm / 4 cm / 3 cm

7 cm / 13 cm / 5 cm / 12 cm

6 The top and bottom of the container shown here are the same size, both consisting of a rectangle, 4 cm by 9 cm, with a semicircle at each end. The depth is 3 cm. Find the volume of the container.

7 A tunnel is in the shape of a semicircle of radius 5 m, running for 500 m through a hill. Calculate the volume of soil removed when the tunnel was cut through the hill.

8 A horse trough is in the shape of a semicircular prism as shown. What volume of water will the trough hold when it is filled to the top? Give your answer in litres.

1.7 m   70 cm

9 The dimensions of the cross-section of a girder, 2 m in length, are shown on the diagram. The girder is made of iron with a density of 7.9 g/cm^3. What is the mass of the girder?

8 cm   8 cm
8 cm   12 cm   8 cm
8 cm   8 cm
30 cm

4.5 Cylinders

In this section you will learn how to:

- calculate the volume and surface area of a cylinder

Key words
cylinder
surface area
volume

Since a **cylinder** is an example of a prism, its **volume** is found by multiplying the area of one of its circular ends by the height.

That is, Volume = $\pi r^2 h$

where r is the radius of the cylinder and h is its height or length.

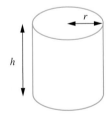

EXAMPLE 6

What is the volume of a cylinder having a radius of 5 cm and a height of 12 cm?

$$\begin{aligned} \text{Volume} &= \text{area of circular base} \times \text{height} \\ &= \pi r^2 h \\ &= \pi \times 5^2 \times 12 \text{ cm}^3 \\ &= 942 \text{ cm}^3 \text{ (3 significant figures)} \end{aligned}$$

Surface area

The total **surface area** of a cylinder is made up of the area of its curved surface plus the area of its two circular ends.

The curved surface area, when opened out, is a rectangle whose length is the circumference of the circular end.

Curved surface area = circumference of end × height of cylinder

$$= 2\pi rh \quad \textbf{or} \quad \pi dh$$

Area of one end $= \pi r^2$

Therefore, total surface area $= 2\pi rh + 2\pi r^2 \quad \textbf{or} \quad \pi dh + 2\pi r^2$

EXAMPLE 7

What is the total surface area of a cylinder with a radius of 15 cm and a height of 2.5 m?

First, you must change the dimensions to a common unit. Use centimetres in this case.

$$\begin{aligned} \text{Total surface area} &= \pi dh + 2\pi r^2 \\ &= \pi \times 30 \times 250 + 2 \times \pi \times 15^2 \text{ cm}^2 \\ &= 23\,562 + 1414 \text{ cm}^2 \\ &= 24\,976 \text{ cm}^2 \\ &= 25\,000 \text{ cm}^2 \text{ (3 significant figures)} \end{aligned}$$

EXERCISE 4E

1 Find **i** the volume and **ii** the total surface area of each of these cylinders. Give your answers to 3 significant figures.

a 3 cm, 8 cm **b** 1 cm, 19 cm **c** 9 cm, 3.5 cm **d** 6 cm, 15 cm

2 Find **i** the volume and **ii** the curved surface area of each of these cylinders. Give your answers in terms of π.

    a base radius 3 cm and height 8 cm   **b** base diameter 8 cm and height 7 cm

    c base diameter 12 cm and height 5 cm   **d** base radius of 10 m and length 6 m

3 The diameter of a marble, cylindrical column is 60 cm and its height is 4.2 m. The cost of making this column is quoted as £67.50 per cubic metre. What is the estimated total cost of making the column?

4 Find the mass of a solid iron cylinder 55 cm high with a base diameter of 60 cm. The density of iron is 7.9 g/cm³.

5 What is the radius of a cylinder, height 8 cm, with a volume of 200π cm^3?

 6 What is the radius of a cylinder, height 12 cm, with a curved surface area of 240π cm^2?

 7 What is the height of a cylinder, diameter 12 cm, with a volume of 108π cm^3?

 8 A cylindrical container is 65 cm in diameter. Water is poured into the container until it is 1 metre deep. How much water is in the container? Give your answer in litres.

 9 A cylindrical can of soup has a diameter of 7 cm and a height of 9.5 cm. It is full of soup, which weighs 625 g. What is the density of the soup?

 10 A metal bar, 1 m long, and with a diameter of 6 cm, has a mass of 22 kg. What is the density of the metal from which the bar is made?

 11 A block of wood has a hole of radius 2.5 cm drilled out as shown on the diagram. Calculate the mass of the wood if its density is 0.95 g/cm^3.

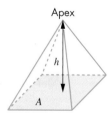

9 cm

11 cm   12 cm

4.6   Volume of a pyramid

In this section you will learn how to:
* calculate the volume of a pyramid

Key words
apex
frustum
pyramid
volume

A **pyramid** is a 3-D shape with a base from which triangular faces rise to a common vertex, called the **apex**. The base can be any polygon, but is usually a triangle, a rectangle or a square.

The **volume** of a pyramid is given by

     Volume $= \frac{1}{3} \times$ base area $\times$ vertical height

     $V = \frac{1}{3}Ah$

where A is the base area and h is the vertical height.

EXAMPLE 8

Calculate the volume of the pyramid on the right.

     Base area $= 5 \times 4 = 20$ cm^2

     Volume $= \frac{1}{3} \times 20 \times 6 = 40$ cm^3

6 cm

5 cm   4 cm

EXAMPLE 9

A pyramid, with a square base of side 8 cm, has a volume of 320 cm³. What is the vertical height of the pyramid?

Let h be the vertical height of the pyramid. Then,

$$\text{Volume} = \tfrac{1}{3} \times 64 \times h = 320 \text{ cm}^3$$

$$\frac{64h}{3} = 320 \text{ cm}^3$$

$$h = \frac{960}{64} \text{ cm}$$

$$h = 15 \text{ cm}$$

EXERCISE 4F

1 Calculate the volume of each of these pyramids, all with rectangular bases.

a

6 cm

4 cm

7 cm

b

7 cm

8 cm

9 cm

c

12 cm

13 cm

20 cm

d

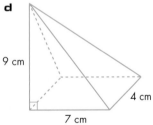

9 cm

4 cm

7 cm

e

6 cm

8 cm

10 cm

2 Calculate the volume of a pyramid having a square base of side 9 cm and a vertical height of 10 cm.

3 Calculate the volume of each of these shapes.

a

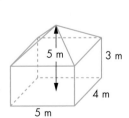

5 m

3 m

4 m

5 m

b

8 m

5 m

3 m

2.5 m

c

25 cm

20 cm

10 cm

15 cm

4 What is the mass of a solid pyramid having a square base of side 4 cm, a height of 3 cm and a density of 13 g/cm³?

5 A crystal is in the form of two square-based pyramids joined at their bases (see diagram). The crystal has a mass of 31.5 grams. What is its density?

7 cm

3 cm

6 Find the mass of each of these pyramids.

a

8 cm

4 cm

7 cm

Density 2.7 g/cm³

b

7 cm

6 cm

9 cm

Density 3.5 g/cm³

c

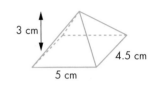

3 cm

4.5 cm

5 cm

Density 2.1 g/cm³

7 Calculate the length x in each of these rectangular-based pyramids.

a

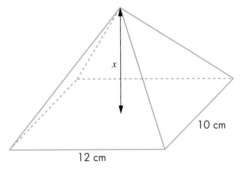

x

10 cm

12 cm

Weight 828 g
Density 2.3 g/cm³

b

5 cm

4 cm

x

Weight 180 g
Density 4.5 g/cm³

8 The pyramid in the diagram has its top 5 cm cut off as shown. The shape which is left is called a **frustum**. Calculate the volume of the frustum.

5 cm

2 cm

3 cm

10 cm

6 cm

9 cm

In this section you will learn how to:
- calculate the volume and surface area of a cone

Key words
slant height
surface area
vertical
  height
volume

A cone can be treated as a pyramid with a circular base. Therefore, the formula for the **volume** of a cone is the same as that for a pyramid.

Volume $= \frac{1}{3} \times$ base area $\times$ vertical height

$V = \frac{1}{3}\pi r^2 h$

where r is the radius of the base and h is the **vertical height** of the cone.

The curved **surface area** of a cone is given by

Curved surface area $= \pi \times$ radius $\times$ slant height

$S = \pi r l$

where l is the **slant height** of the cone.

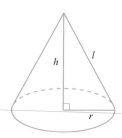

So the total surface area of a cone is given by the curved surface area plus the area of its circular base.

$A = \pi r l + \pi r^2$

EXAMPLE 10

For the cone in the diagram, calculate

i   its volume and

ii its total surface area.

Give your answers in terms of π.

i   The volume is given by $V = \frac{1}{3}\pi r^2 h$

$= \frac{1}{3} \times \pi \times 36 \times 8 = 96\pi$ cm^3

ii The total surface area is given by $A = \pi r l + \pi r^2$

$= \pi \times 6 \times 10 + \pi \times 36 = 96\pi$ cm^2

EXERCISE 4G

1 For each cone, calculate **i** its volume and **ii** its total surface area. Give your answers to 3 significant figures.

a

35.4 cm

34 cm

20 cm

b

5 cm

12 cm

13 cm

c

18 cm

12 cm

15 cm

2 A solid cone, base radius 6 cm and vertical height 8 cm, is made of metal whose density is 3.1 g/cm^3. Find the mass of the cone.

3 Find the total surface area of a cone whose base radius is 3 cm and slant height is 5 cm. Give your answer in terms of π.

4 Find the total surface area of a cone whose base radius is 5 cm and slant height is 13 cm.

5 Calculate the volume of each of these shapes. Give your answers in terms of π.

a

8 cm

10 cm

20 cm

12 cm

b

8 mm

40 mm

15 mm

6 The model shown on the right is made from aluminium. What is the mass of the model, given that the density of aluminium is 2.7 g/cm^3?

4 cm

6 cm

3 cm

7 A container in the shape of a cone, base radius 10 cm and vertical height 19 cm, is full of water. The water is poured into an empty cylinder of radius 15 cm. How high is the water in the cylinder?

Spheres

In this section you will learn how to:

- calculate the volume and surface area of a sphere

Key words

sphere
surface area
volume

The **volume** of a **sphere**, radius r, is given by

$$V = \tfrac{4}{3}\pi r^3$$

Its **surface area** is given by

$$A = 4\pi r^2$$

EXAMPLE 11

For a sphere of radius of 8 cm, calculate **i** its volume and **ii** its surface area.

i The volume is given by $\quad V = \tfrac{4}{3}\pi r^3$

$$= \tfrac{4}{3} \times \pi \times 8^3 = \tfrac{2048}{3} \times \pi = 2140 \text{ cm}^3 \text{ (3 significant figures)}$$

ii The surface area is given by $\quad A = 4\pi r^2$

$$= 4 \times \pi \times 8^2 = 256 \times \pi = 804 \text{ cm}^2 \text{ (3 significant figures)}$$

EXERCISE 4H

1 Calculate the volume of each of these spheres. Give your answers in terms of π.

    a Radius 3 cm   **b** Radius 6 cm   **c** Diameter 20 cm

2 Calculate the surface area of each of these spheres. Give your answers in terms of π.

    a Radius 3 cm   **b** Radius 5 cm   **c** Diameter 14 cm

3 Calculate the volume and the surface area of a sphere with a diameter of 50 cm.

4 A sphere fits exactly into an open cubical box of side 25 cm. Calculate the following.

    a the surface area of the sphere   **b** the volume of the sphere

5 A metal sphere of radius 15 cm is melted down and recast into a solid cylinder of radius 6 cm. Calculate the height of the cylinder.

6 Lead has a density of 11.35 g/cm^3. Calculate the maximum number of shot (spherical lead pellets) of radius 1.5 mm which can be made from 1 kg of lead.

7 Calculate, correct to one decimal place, the radius of a sphere

    a whose surface area is 150 cm^2 **b** whose volume is 150 cm^3.

A

1   The area of the trapezium is 20 m². The parallel sides a and b are different lengths. The perpendicular height h is 4 m. Find a possible pair of values for a and b.

AQA, Question 4, Paper 1 Higher, June 2001

2 A semi-circular protractor has a diameter of 9 cm.

Calculate the perimeter.

AQA, Question 2, Paper 2 Higher, November 2003

3 OAB is a minor sector of a circle of radius 6 cm. Angle AOB = 120°

a Calculate the area of the minor sector OAB. Give your answer in terms of π.

b Calculate the perimeter of the minor sector OAB. Give your answer in terms of π.

AQA, Question 14, Paper 1 Higher, June 2001

4   A solid cone has base radius 5 cm and slant height 12 cm. Calculate the *total* surface area of the cone. Give your answer in terms of π.

AQA, Question 19, Paper 1 Higher, May 2002

5 A cylinder of radius 7 cm and height 18 cm is half full of water. One litre of water is added. Will the water overflow? You must show all your working.

AQA, Question 3, Paper 2 Higher, November 2001

6 A dumbell is made from 3 cylinders of the same metal with dimensions as shown.

The mass of the dumbell is 6 kilograms. What is the density of the metal?

AQA, Question 15, Paper 2 Higher, June 2002

7 A marble paperweight consists of a cuboid and a hemisphere as shown in the diagram. The hemisphere has a radius of 4 cm.

Calculate the volume of the paperweight.

AQA, Question 15, Paper 2 Higher, June 2005

WORKED EXAM QUESTION

The diagram shows a pepper pot. The pot consists of a cylinder and a hemisphere. The cylinder has a diameter of 5 cm and a height of 7 cm.

The pepper takes up half the total volume of the pot. Find the depth of pepper in the pot marked x in the diagram.

Solution

Volume of pepper pot

$$= \pi r^2 h + \frac{2}{3}\pi r^3$$
$$= \pi \times 2.5^2 \times 7 + \frac{2}{3} \times \pi \times 2.5^3 \text{ cm}^3$$
$$= 170.2 \text{ cm}^3$$

So volume of pepper = 85.1 cm³

Therefore,

$$\pi r^2 x = 85.1 \text{ cm}^3$$

and $x = \dfrac{85.1}{\pi \times 2.5^2} = 4.3$ cm (1 decimal place)

AQA, Question 17, Paper 2 Higher, June 2000

Mr and Mrs Jones have decided to "go green". They want to install a water purifying unit and water tank in their loft to collect rain water from their roof, and use this water for the washing machine, dishwasher, shower and toilet.

Copy the table below and help them to calculate their average total daily water usage for these four items.

BATHROOM

The toilet cistern has a cross section that is a trapezium. The diagram shows the amount of water that is used in one flush of the toilet.

48cm

20cm

14cm

46cm

BATHROOM

The shower uses 2.5 gallons per minute.

An average shower takes 8 minutes.

Daily water usage			
	litres used each: flush/shower/load	frequency used	total litres per day
Toilet		12 times a day	
Shower		2 times a day	
Washing machine		3 times a week	
Dishwasher		once every 2 days	
		TOTAL:	

KITCHEN

The dishwasher uses 9 gallons per load.

KITCHEN

The washing machine uses 25 gallons per load.

1 gallon is approximately 4.55 litres.

This is a diagram showing the dimensions of their roof.

10m

15m

A gutter around the roof collects all the rainwater.

The average daily rainfall is 2 mm per square metre of roof.

On average, how much rainwater could they collect in one day?

They consider installing this cylindrical tank in their loft for the rainwater.

They know on average how much water they use and collect in one day.

If they don't start to use the tank until it is full, and assuming there is average rainfall, estimate how many days it will be before they can use the tank

1.2m

1.2m

GRADE YOURSELF

D Able to calculate the circumference and area of a circle

D Able to calculate the area of a trapezium

C Able to calculate the volume of prisms and cylinders

B Able to calculate the length of an arc and the area of a sector

B Able to calculate the surface area of cylinders, cones and spheres

B Able to calculate the volume of pyramids, cones and spheres

A Able to calculate volume and surface area of compound 3-D shapes

What you should know now

- For a sector of radius r and angle θ

$$\text{Arc length} = \frac{\theta°}{360°} \times 2\pi r \text{ or } \frac{\theta°}{360°} \times \pi d$$

$$\text{Area of a sector} = \frac{\theta°}{360°} \times \pi r^2$$

- The area of a trapezium is given by

$$A = \tfrac{1}{2}(a + b)h$$

where h is the vertical height, and a and b are the lengths of the two parallel sides

- The volume of a prism is given by $V = Al$, where A is the cross-section area and l is the length of the prism

- The volume of a cylinder is given by $V = \pi r^2 h$ where r is the radius and h is the height or length of the cylinder

- The curved surface area of a cylinder is given by $S = 2\pi rh$, where r is the radius and h is the height or length of the cylinder

- The volume of a pyramid is given by $V = \tfrac{1}{3}Ah$, where A is the area of the base and h is the vertical height of the pyramid

- The volume of a cone is given by $V = \tfrac{1}{3}\pi r^2 h$ where r is the base radius and h is the vertical height of the cone

- The curved surface area of a cone is given by $S = \pi rl$, where r is the base radius and l is the slant height of the cone

- The volume of a sphere is given by $V = \tfrac{4}{3}\pi r^3$ where r is its radius

- The surface area of a sphere is given by $A = 4\pi r^2$ where r is its radius

Algebra 1

Chapter

5

1 Basic algebra

2 Factorisation

3 Solving linear equations

4 Trial and improvement

5 Simultaneous equations

6 Rearranging formulae

This chapter will show you ...

- how to manipulate basic algebraic expressions by multiplying terms together, expanding brackets and collecting like terms
- how to factorise linear expressions
- how to solve linear equations
- how to solve simultaneous equations
- how to rearrange formulae

What you should already know

- The basic language of algebra
- How to collect together like terms
- How to multiply together terms such as $2m \times 3m$

Quick check

1 Expand the following.
  a $2(x + 6)$ **b** $4(x - 3)$ **c** $6(2x - 1)$

2 Simplify the following.
  a $4y + 2y - y$ **b** $3x + 2 + x - 5$ **c** $2(x + 1) - 3(x + 2)$

3 Simplify the following.
  a $3 \times 2x$ **b** $4y \times 2y$ **c** $c^2 \times 2c$

4 Solve the following equations
  a $2x + 4 = 6$ **b** $3x - 5 = 4$ **c** $\frac{x}{3} + 2 = 5$

  d $\frac{x}{2} = 4$ **e** $\frac{x}{3} = 8$ **f** $\frac{2x}{5} = 6$

This section will show you how to:

- substitute into, manipulate and simplify algebraic expressions

Key words
bracket
coefficient
like terms
expand
expression
substitute
simplification
variable

Substitution

EXAMPLE 1

Find the value of $3x^2 - 5$ when   **a** $x = 3$,   **b** $x = -4$.

Whenever you **substitute** a number for a **variable** in an **expression** always put the value in a bracket before working it out. This will avoid errors in calculation, especially with negative numbers.

a When $x = 3$, $3(3)^2 - 5 = 3 \times 9 - 5 = 27 - 5 = 22$

b When $x = -4$, $3(-4)^2 - 5 = 3 \times 16 - 5 = 48 - 5 = 43$

EXAMPLE 2

Find the value of $L = a^2 - 8b^2$ when $a = -6$ and $b = \frac{1}{2}$.

Substitute for the letters.

$$L = (-6)^2 - 8\left(\tfrac{1}{2}\right)^2$$

$$L = 36 - 8 \times \tfrac{1}{4} = 36 - 2 = 34$$

Note: if you do not use brackets and write -6^2, this could be wrongly evaluated as -36.

EXERCISE 5A

1 Find the value of $4b + 3$ when   **a** $b = 2.5$,   **b** $b = -1.5$,   **c** $b = \frac{1}{2}$.

2 Evaluate $\frac{x}{3}$ when   **a** $x = 6$,   **b** $x = 24$,   **c** $x = -30$.

3 Find the value of $\frac{12}{y}$ when   **a** $y = 2$,   **b** $y = 4$,   **c** $y = -6$.

4 Evaluate $3w - 4$ when   **a** $w = -1$,   **b** $w = -2$,   **c** $w = 3.5$.

5 Find the value of $\frac{24}{x}$ when   **a** $x = -5$,   **b** $x = \frac{1}{2}$,   **c** $x = \frac{3}{4}$.

D

6 Where $P = \dfrac{5w - 4y}{w + y}$, find P when

    a $w = 3$ and $y = 2$,   **b** $w = 6$ and $y = 4$,   **c** $w = 2$ and $y = 3$.

7 Where $A = b^2 + c^2$, find A when

    a $b = 2$ and $c = 3$,   **b** $b = 5$ and $c = 7$,   **c** $b = -1$ and $c = -4$.

8 Where $A = \dfrac{180(n - 2)}{n + 5}$, find A when

    a $n = 7$,   **b** $n = 3$,   **c** $n = -1$.

9 Where $Z = \dfrac{y^2 + 4}{4 + y}$, find Z when

    a $y = 4$,   **b** $y = -6$,   **c** $y = -1.5$.

Expansion

In mathematics, the term "**expand**" usually means "multiply out". For example, expressions such as $3(y + 2)$ and $4y^2(2y + 3)$ can be expanded by multiplying out.

You need to remember that there is an invisible multiplication sign between the outside number and the **bracket**. So that $3(y + 2)$ is really $3 \times (y + 2)$, and $4y^2(2y + 3)$ is really $4y^2 \times (2y + 3)$.

We expand by multiplying *everything inside* the bracket by what is outside the bracket.

So in the case of the two examples above,

$3(y + 2) = 3 \times (y + 2) = 3 \times y + 3 \times 2 = 3y + 6$

$4y^2(2y + 3) = 4y^2 \times (2y + 3) = 4y^2 \times 2y + 4y^2 \times 3 = 8y^3 + 12y^2$

Look at these next examples of expansion, which show clearly how the term outside the bracket has been multiplied with the terms inside it.

$2(m + 3) = 2m + 6$ $y(y^2 - 4x) = y^3 - 4xy$

$3(2t + 5) = 6t + 15$ $3x^2(4x + 5) = 12x^3 + 15x^2$

$m(p + 7) = mp + 7m$ $-3(2 + 3x) = -6 - 9x$

$x(x - 6) = x^2 - 6x$ $-2x(3 - 4x) = -6x + 8x^2$

$4t(t^3 + 2) = 4t^4 + 8t$ $3t(2 + 5t - p) = 6t + 15t^2 - 3pt$

Note: the signs change when a negative quantity is outside the bracket. For example,

$a(b + c) = ab + ac$ $a(b - c) = ab - ac$

$-a(b + c) = -ab - ac$ $-a(b - c) = -ab + ac$

$-(a - b) = -a + b$ $-(a + b - c) = -a - b + c$

Expand these expressions.

1 $2(3 + m)$

2 $5(2 + l)$

3 $3(4 - y)$

4 $4(5 + 2k)$

5 $3(2 - 4f)$

6 $2(5 - 3w)$

7 $5(2k + 3m)$

8 $4(3d - 2n)$

9 $t(t + 3)$

10 $k(k - 3)$

11 $4t(t - 1)$

12 $2k(4 - k)$

13 $4g(2g + 5)$

14 $5h(3h - 2)$

15 $y(y^2 + 5)$

16 $h(h^3 + 7)$

17 $k(k^2 - 5)$

18 $3t(t^2 + 4)$

19 $3d(5d^2 - d^3)$

20 $3w(2w^2 + t)$

21 $5a(3a^2 - 2b)$

22 $3p(4p^3 - 5m)$

23 $4h^2(3h + 2g)$

24 $2m^2(4m + m^2)$

Simplification

Simplification is the process whereby an expression is written down as simply as possible, any **like terms** being combined. Like terms are terms which have the same letter(s) raised to the same power and can differ only in their numerical **coefficients** (numbers in front). For example,

m, $3m$, $4m$, $-m$ and $76m$ are all like terms in m

t^2, $4t^2$, $7t^2$, $-t^2$, $-3t^2$ and $98t^2$ are all like terms in t^2

pt, $5tp$, $-2pt$, $7pt$, $-3tp$ and $103pt$ are all like terms in pt

Note also that all the terms in tp are also like terms to all the terms in pt.

In simplifying an expression, only like terms can be added or subtracted. For example,

$4m + 3m = 7m$ $3y + 4y + 3 = 7y + 3$ $4h - h = 3h$

$2t^2 + 5t^2 = 7t^2$ $2m + 6 + 3m = 5m + 6$ $7t + 8 - 2t = 5t + 8$

$3ab + 2ba = 5ab$ $5k - 2k = 3k$ $10g - 4 - 3g = 7g - 4$

Expand and simplify

When two brackets are expanded there are often like terms that can be collected together. Algebraic expressions should always be simplified as much as possible.

EXAMPLE 3

$$3(4 + m) + 2(5 + 2m) = 12 + 3m + 10 + 4m = 22 + 7m$$

EXAMPLE 4

$$3t(5t + 4) - 2t(3t - 5) = 15t^2 + 12t - 6t^2 + 10t = 9t^2 + 22t$$

EXERCISE 5C

1 Simplify these expressions.

a $4t + 3t$　　　　**b** $3d + 2d + 4d$　　**c** $5e - 2e$　　　**d** $3t - t$

e $2t^2 + 3t^2$　　　**f** $6y^2 - 2y^2$　　　**g** $3ab + 2ab$　　**h** $7a^2d - 4a^2d$

2 Expand and simplify.

a $3(4 + t) + 2(5 + t)$　　　　　　**b** $5(3 + 2k) + 3(2 + 3k)$

c $4(3 + 2f) + 2(5 - 3f)$　　　　　**d** $5(1 + 3g) + 3(3 - 4g)$

3 Expand and simplify.

a $4(3 + 2h) - 2(5 + 3h)$　　　**b** $5(3g + 4) - 3(2g + 5)$

c $5(5k + 2) - 2(4k - 3)$　　　　**d** $4(4e + 3) - 2(5e - 4)$

> **HINTS AND TIPS**
>
> Be careful with minus signs. For example $-2(5e - 4) = -10e + 8$

4 Expand and simplify.

a $m(4 + p) + p(3 + m)$　　　　**b** $k(3 + 2h) + h(4 + 3k)$

c $4r(3 + 4p) + 3p(8 - r)$　　　**d** $5k(3m + 4) - 2m(3 - 2k)$

5 Expand and simplify.

a $t(3t + 4) + 3t(3 + 2t)$　　　**b** $2y(3 + 4y) + y(5y - 1)$

c $4e(3e - 5) - 2e(e - 7)$　　　**d** $3k(2k + p) - 2k(3p - 4k)$

6 Expand and simplify.

a $4a(2b + 3c) + 3b(3a + 2c)$　　**b** $3y(4w + 2t) + 2w(3y - 4t)$

c $5m(2n - 3p) - 2n(3p - 2m)$　　**d** $2r(3r + r^2) - 3r^2(4 - 2r)$

5.2 Factorisation

This section will show you how to:
- factorise an algebraic expression

Key words
common factor
factorisation

Factorisation is the opposite of expansion. It puts an expression back into the brackets it may have come from.

In factorisation, we have to look for the **common factors** in *every* term of the expression.

EXAMPLE 5

Factorise.   **a** $6t + 9m$ **b** $6my + 4py$ **c** $5k^2 - 25k$ **d** $10a^2b - 15ab^2$

a First look at the numerical coefficients 6 and 9. These have a common factor of 3. Then look at the letters, t and m. These do not have any common factors as they do not appear in both terms. The expression can be thought of as $3 \times 2t + 3 \times 3m$, which gives the factorisation

$$6t + 9m = 3(2t + 3m)$$

Note: you can always check a factorisation by expanding the answer.

b First look at the numbers, these have a common factor of 2. m and p do not occur in both terms but y does, and is a common factor, so the factorisation is

$$6my + 4py = 2y(3m + 2p)$$

c 5 is a common factor of 5 and 25 and k is a common factor of k^2 and k.

$$5k^2 - 25k = 5k(k - 5)$$

d 5 is a common factor of 10 and 15, a is a common factor of a^2 and a, b is a common factor of b and b^2.

$$10a^2b - 15ab^2 = 5ab(2a - 3b)$$

Note: if you multiply out each answer, you will get the expressions you started with.

EXERCISE 5D

Factorise the following expressions.

1 $6m + 12t$

2 $9t + 3p$

3 $8m + 12k$

4 $4r + 8t$

5 $mn + 3m$

6 $5g^2 + 3g$

7 $4w - 6t$

8 $3y^2 + 2y$

9 $4t^2 - 3t$

10 $3m^2 - 3mp$

11 $6p^2 + 9pt$

12 $8pt + 6mp$

13 $8ab - 4bc$

14 $5b^2c - 10bc$

15 $8abc + 6bed$

16 $4a^2 + 6a + 8$

17 $6ab + 9bc + 3bd$

18 $5t^2 + 4t + at$

19 $6mt^2 - 3mt + 9m^2t$

20 $8ab^2 + 2ab - 4a^2b$

21 $10pt^2 + 15pt + 5p^2t$

22 Factorise the following expressions where possible. List those which do not factorise.

a $7m - 6t$

b $5m + 2mp$

c $t^2 - 7t$

d $8pt + 5ab$

e $4m^2 - 6mp$

f $a^2 + b$

g $4a^2 - 5ab$

h $3ab + 4cd$

i $5ab - 3b^2c$

In this section you will learn how to:
- solve equations in which the variable appears as part of the numerator of a fraction
- solve equations where you have to expand brackets first
- solve equations where the variable (the letter) appears on both sides of the equals sign
- set up equations from given information, and then solve them

Key words

brackets
do the same to both sides
equation
rearrange
solution
solve

Fractional equations

EXAMPLE 6

Solve this equation.

$$\frac{x}{3} + 1 = 5$$

First subtract 1 from both sides:

$$\frac{x}{3} = 4$$

Now multiply both sides by 3:

$$x = 12$$

EXAMPLE 7

Solve this equation.

$$\frac{x - 2}{5} = 3$$

First multiply both sides by 5:

$$x - 2 = 15$$

Now add 2 to both sides:

$$x = 17$$

EXAMPLE 8

Solve this equation.

$$\frac{3x}{4} - 3 = 1$$

First add 3 to both sides:

$$\frac{3x}{4} = 4$$

Now multiply both sides by 4:

$$3x = 16$$

Now divide both sides by 3:

$$x = \frac{16}{3} = 5\frac{1}{3}$$

EXERCISE 5E

Solve these equations.

1 $\dfrac{f}{5} + 2 = 8$

2 $\dfrac{w}{3} - 5 = 2$

3 $\dfrac{x}{8} + 3 = 12$

4 $\dfrac{5t}{4} + 3 = 18$

5 $\dfrac{3y}{2} - 1 = 8$

6 $\dfrac{2x}{3} + 5 = 12$

7 $\dfrac{t}{5} + 3 = 1$

8 $\dfrac{x + 3}{2} = 5$

9 $\dfrac{t - 5}{2} = 3$

10 $\dfrac{x + 10}{2} = 3$

11 $\dfrac{2x + 1}{3} = 5$

12 $\dfrac{5y - 2}{4} = 3$

13 $\dfrac{6y + 3}{9} = 1$

14 $\dfrac{2x - 3}{5} = 4$

15 $\dfrac{5t + 3}{4} = 1$

Brackets

When we have an equation which contains **brackets**, we first must multiply out the brackets and then solve the resulting equation.

EXAMPLE 9

Solve $5(x + 3) = 25$.

First multiply out the bracket to get:

$5x + 15 = 25$

Rearrange: $\quad\quad\quad\quad\quad 5x = 25 - 15 = 10$

Divide by 5: $\quad\quad\quad\quad \dfrac{5x}{5} = \dfrac{10}{5}$

$\quad\quad\quad\quad\quad\quad\quad\quad x = 2$

EXAMPLE 10

Solve $3(2x - 7) = 15$.

Multiply out the bracket to get:

$6x - 21 = 15$

Add 21 to both sides: $\quad\quad 6x = 36$

Divide both sides by 6: $\quad\quad x = 6$

EXERCISE 5F

Solve each of the following equations. Some of the answers may be decimals or negative numbers. Remember to check that each answer works for its original equation. Use your calculator if necessary.

1 $2(x + 5) = 16$

2 $5(x - 3) = 20$

3 $3(t + 1) = 18$

4 $4(2x + 5) = 44$

5 $2(3y - 5) = 14$

6 $5(4x + 3) = 135$

7 $4(3t - 2) = 88$

8 $6(2t + 5) = 42$

9 $2(3x + 1) = 11$

10 $4(5y - 2) = 42$

11 $6(3k + 5) = 39$

12 $5(2x + 3) = 27$

13 $9(3x - 5) = 9$

14 $2(x + 5) = 6$

15 $5(x - 4) = -25$

16 $3(t + 7) = 15$

17 $2(3x + 11) = 10$

18 $4(5t + 8) = 12$

> **HINTS AND TIPS**
>
> Once the brackets have been expanded the equations become straightforward. Remember to multiply *everything* inside the bracket with what is outside.

Equations with the variable on both sides

When a letter (or variable) appears on both sides of an equation, it is best to use the "**do the same to both sides**" method of **solution**, and collect all the terms containing the letter on the left-hand side of the equation. But when there are more of the letter on the right-hand side, it is easier to turn the equation round. When an equation contains brackets, they must be multiplied out first.

EXAMPLE 11

Solve $5x + 4 = 3x + 10$.

There are more xs on the left-hand side, so leave the equation as it is.

Subtract $3x$ from both sides: $2x + 4 = 10$

Subtract 4 from both sides: $2x = 6$

Divide both sides by 2: $x = 3$

EXAMPLE 12

Solve $2x + 3 = 6x - 5$.

There are more xs on the right-hand side, so turn round the equation.

$$6x - 5 = 2x + 3$$

Subtract $2x$ from both sides: $4x - 5 = 3$

Add 5 to both sides: $4x = 8$

Divide both sides by 4: $x = 2$

EXAMPLE 13

Solve this equation. $\qquad$ $3(2x + 5) + x = 2(2 - x) + 2$

Multiply out both brackets: $\qquad$ $6x + 15 + x = 4 - 2x + 2$

Simplify both sides: $\qquad$ $7x + 15 = 6 - 2x$

There are more xs on the left-hand side, so leave the equation as it is.

Add $2x$ to both sides: $\qquad$ $9x + 15 = 6$

Subtract 15 from both sides: $\qquad$ $9x = -9$

Divide both sides by 9: $\qquad$ $x = -1$

EXERCISE 5G

Solve each of the following equations.

1 $2x + 3 = x + 5$

2 $5y + 4 = 3y + 6$

3 $4a - 3 = 3a + 4$

4 $5t + 3 = 2t + 15$

5 $7p - 5 = 3p + 3$

6 $6k + 5 = 2k + 1$

7 $4m + 1 = m + 10$

8 $8s - 1 = 6s - 5$

9 $2(d + 3) = d + 12$

10 $5(x - 2) = 3(x + 4)$

11 $3(2y + 3) = 5(2y + 1)$

12 $3(h - 6) = 2(5 - 2h)$

13 $4(3b - 1) + 6 = 5(2b + 4)$

14 $2(5c + 2) - 2c = 3(2c + 3) + 7$

> **HINTS AND TIPS**
>
> Remember the rule "change sides, change signs".
> Show all your working on this type of question.
> **Rearrange** before you simplify. If you try to rearrange and simplify at the same time you will probably get it wrong.

Setting up linear equations

Equations are used to represent situations, so that we can solve real-life problems.

EXAMPLE 14

A milkman sets off from the dairy with eight crates of milk, each containing b bottles. He delivers 92 bottles to a large factory and finds that he has exactly 100 bottles left on his milk float. How many bottles were in each crate?

The equation is: $\qquad$ $8b - 92 = 100$

$\qquad\qquad$ $8b = 192$ $\qquad$ (Add 92 to both sides)

$\qquad\qquad$ $b = 24$ $\qquad$ (Divide both sides by 8)

Checking the answer gives: $\quad 8 \times 24 - 92 = 192 - 92 = 100$

which is correct.

EXAMPLE 15

The rectangle shown has a perimeter of 40 cm.

Find the value of x.

The perimeter of the rectangle is:

$3x + 1 + x + 3 + 3x + 1 + x + 3 = 40$

This simplifies to: $8x + 8 = 40$

Subtract 8 $8x = 32$

Divide by 8 $x = 4$

Checking the answer gives:

$3x + 1 = 3 \times 4 + 1 = 13$

$x + 3 = 4 + 3 = 7$

perimeter $= 13 + 7 + 13 + 7$

$= 40$

which is correct.

3x + 1

x + 3

EXERCISE 5H

Set up an equation to represent each situation described below. Then solve the equation. Do not forget to check each answer.

1 A man buys a daily paper from Monday to Saturday for d pence. On Sunday he buys the *Observer* for £1. His weekly paper bill is £4.30.

How much is his daily paper?

2 The diagram shows a rectangle.

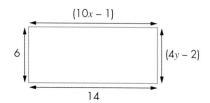

a What is the value of x?

b What is the value of y?

> **HINTS AND TIPS**
>
> Use the letter x for the variable unless you are given a letter to use. Once the equation is set up, solve it by the methods above.

3 In this rectangle, the length is 3 centimetres more than the width. The perimeter is 12 cm.

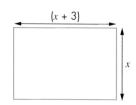

a What is the value of x?

b What is the area of the rectangle?

4 Mary has two bags of sweets, each of which contains the same number of sweets. She eats four sweets. She then finds that she has 30 sweets left. How many sweets were in each bag to start with?

5 A boy is *Y* years old. His father is 25 years older than he is. The sum of their ages is 31. How old is the boy?

6 Another boy is *X* years old. His sister is twice as old as he is. The sum of their ages is 27. How old is the boy?

7 The diagram shows a square.
Find *x* if the perimeter is 44 cm.

$(4x - 1)$

8 Max thought of a number. He then multiplied his number by 3. He added 4 to the answer. He then doubled that answer to get a final value of 38. What number did he start with?

5.4 Trial and improvement

In this section you will learn how to:

- estimate the answer to some equations that do not have exact solutions, using the method of trial and improvement

Key words

comment
decimal place
guess
trial and
  improvement

Certain equations cannot be solved exactly. However, a close enough solution to such an equation can be found by the **trial-and-improvement** method (sometimes wrongly called the trial-and-error method).

The idea is to keep trying different values in the equation which will take it closer and closer to its "true" solution. This step-by-step process is continued until a value is found which gives a solution that is close enough to the accuracy required.

The trial-and-improvement method is the way in which computers are programmed to solve equations.

EXAMPLE 16

Find a solution to the equation $x^3 + x = 105$, giving the solution to 1 **decimal place**.

The best way to do this is to set up a table to show working. There will be three columns: **guess** (the trial); the equation we are solving; and a **comment** whether the value of the guess is too high or too low.

Step 1 We must find the two consecutive whole numbers between which x lies. We do this by intelligent guessing.

    Try $x = 5$: $125 + 5 = 130$ Too high – next trial needs to be smaller

    Try $x = 4$: $64 + 4 = 68$ Too low

So we now know that a solution lies between $x = 4$ and $x = 5$.

Step 2 We must find the two consecutive one-decimal place numbers between which x lies. Try 4.5, which is halfway between 4 and 5.

    This gives $91.125 + 4.5 = 95.625$ Too small

So we attempt to improve this by trying 4.6.

    This gives $97.336 + 4.6 = 101.936$ Still too small

    Try 4.7, which gives 108.523.   This is too high, so we know the solution is between 4.6 and 4.7.

It looks as though 4.6 is closer but there is a very important final step. Never assume that the one-decimal place number that gives the closest value to a solution is the answer.

Step 3 Now try the value that is halfway between the two one-decimal place values. In this case 4.65.

    This gives 105.194 625   Too high

This means that an actual solution is between 4.60 and 4.65.

The diagram and table summarise our results.

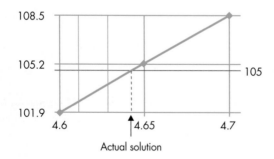

Guess	$x^3 + x$	Comment
4	68	Too low
5	130	Too high
4.5	95.625	Too low
4.6	101.936	Too low
4.7	108.523	Too high
4.65	105.194625	Too high

The approximate answer is $x = 4.6$ to 1 decimal place.

EXERCISE 5I

1 For each of the following equations, find a pair of consecutive *whole numbers*, between which a solution lies.

a $x^2 + x = 24$ **b** $x^3 + 2x = 80$ **c** $x^3 - x = 20$

2 Copy and complete the table to find an approximate solution, using trial and improvement, to this equation.

$x^3 + 2x = 50$

Guess	$x^3 + 2x$	Comment
3	33	Too low
4	72	Too high

Give your answer to 1 decimal place.

3 Copy and complete the table to find an approximate solution, using trial and improvement, to this equation.

$x^3 - 3x = 40$

Guess	$x^3 - 3x$	Comment
4	52	Too high

Give your answer to 1 decimal place.

4 Use trial and improvement to find an approximate solution to this equation.

$2x^3 + x = 35$

Give your answer to 1 decimal place.

You are given that the solution lies between 2 and 3.

> **HINTS AND TIPS**
>
> Set up a table to show your working.
> This makes it easier for you to show your method, and for the examiner to mark.

5 Use trial and improvement to find an exact solution to this equation.

$4x^2 + 2x = 12$

Do not use a calculator.

6 Find a solution to each of the following equations to 1 decimal place.

a $2x^3 + 3x = 35$ **b** $3x^3 - 4x = 52$ **c** $2x^3 + 5x = 79$

7 A rectangle has an area of 100 cm². Its length is 5 cm longer than its width.

a Show that, if x is the width then $x^2 + 5x = 100$

b Find, correct to 1 decimal place, the dimensions of the rectangle.

8 Use trial and improvement to find a solution to the equation $x^2 + x = 30$.

> I want to find a number that when you square it and add it to itself the answer is 30.

Simultaneous equations

In this section you will learn how to:

- solve simultaneous linear equations in two variables

Key words

balance
check
coefficient
eliminate
simultaneous equations
substitute
variable

A pair of **simultaneous equations** is exactly that – two equations (usually linear) for which we want the *same* solution, and which we therefore *solve together*. For example,

$x + y = 10$ has many solutions:

$x = 2, y = 8$ $x = 4, y = 6$ $x = 5, y = 5$ …

and $2x + y = 14$ has many solutions:

$x = 2, y = 10$ $x = 3, y = 8$ $x = 4, y = 6$ …

But only *one* solution, $x = 4$ and $y = 6$, satisfies *both* equations at the *same time*.

Elimination method

Here, we solve simultaneous equations by the *elimination method*. There are six steps in this method. Step 1 is to **balance** the **coefficients** of one of the **variables**. Step 2 is to **eliminate** this variable by adding or subtracting the equations. Step 3 is to solve the resulting linear equation in the other variable. Step 4 is to **substitute** the value found back into one of the previous equations. Step 5 is to solve the resulting equation. Step 6 is to **check** that the two values found satisfy the original equations.

EXAMPLE 17

Solve the equations $6x + y = 15$ and $4x + y = 11$.

The equations should be labelled so that the method can be clearly explained.

$6x + y = 15$ (1)

$4x + y = 11$ (2)

Step 1: Since the y-term in both equations has the same coefficient there is no need to balance them.

EXAMPLE 17 (contd)

Step 2: Subtract one equation from the other. (Equation (1) minus equation (2) will give positive values.)

$(1) - (2)$ $\qquad\qquad\qquad\qquad\qquad$ $2x = 4$

Step 3: Solve this equation: $\qquad\qquad\qquad$ $x = 2$

Step 4: Substitute $x = 2$ into one of the original equations. (Usually the one with smallest numbers involved.)

So substitute into: $\qquad\qquad\qquad$ $4x + y = 11$

which gives: $\qquad\qquad\qquad\qquad$ $8 + y = 11$

Step 5: Solve this equation: $\qquad\qquad\qquad$ $y = 3$

Step 6: Test our solution in the original equations. So substitute $x = 2$ and $y = 3$ into $6x + y$, which gives $12 + 3 = 15$ and into $4x + y$, which gives $8 + 3 = 11$. These are correct, so we can confidently say the solution is $x = 2$ and $y = 3$.

EXAMPLE 18

Solve these equations. $\qquad\qquad$ $5x + y = 22$ $\qquad\qquad$ (1)

$\qquad\qquad\qquad\qquad\qquad\quad$ $2x - y = 6$ $\qquad\qquad$ (2)

Step 1: Both equations have the same y-coefficient but with *different* signs so there is no need to balance them.

Step 2: As the signs are different we *add* the two equations, to eliminate the y-terms.

$(1) + (2)$ $\qquad\qquad\qquad\qquad\qquad$ $7x = 28$

Step 3: Solve this equation: $\qquad\qquad\qquad$ $x = 4$

Step 4: Substitute $x = 4$ into one of the original equations, $5x + y = 22$,

which gives: $\qquad\qquad\qquad\qquad$ $20 + y = 22$

Step 5: Solve this equation: $\qquad\qquad\qquad$ $y = 2$

Step 6: Test our solution by putting $x = 4$ and $y = 2$ into the original equations, $2x - y$, which gives $8 - 2 = 6$ and $5x + y$ which gives $20 + 2 = 22$. These are correct, so our solution is $x = 4$ and $y = 2$.

Substitution method

This is an alternative method (which is covered again on page 490). Which method you use depends very much on the coefficients of the variables and the way that the equations are written in the first place. There are five steps in the substitute method. Step 1 is to rearrange one of the equations into the form $y = \ldots$ or $x = \ldots$. Step 2 is to substitute the right hand side of this equation into the other equation in place of the variable on the left hand side. Step 3 is to expand and solve this equation. Step 4 is to substitute the value into the $y = \ldots$ or $x = \ldots$ equation. Step 5 is to check that the values work in both original equations.

EXAMPLE 19

Solve the simultaneous equations $y = 2x + 3$, $3x + 4y = 1$.

Because the first equation is in the form $y = \ldots$ it suggests that the substitution method should be used.

Equations should still be labelled to help with explaining the method

$$y = 2x + 3 \qquad\qquad (1)$$
$$3x + 4y = 1 \qquad\qquad (2)$$

Step 1: As equation (1) is in the form $y = \ldots$ there is no need to rearrange an equation.

Step 2: Substitute the right hand side of equation (1) into equation (2) for the variable y.

$$3x + 4(2x + 3) = 1$$

Step 3: Expand and solve the equation. $3x + 8x + 12 = 1$, $11x = -11$, $x = -1$

Step 4: Substitute $x = -1$ into $y = 2x + 3$: $y = -2 + 3 = 1$

Step 5: Test the values in $y = 2x + 3$ which gives $1 = -2 + 3$ and $3x + 4y = 1$, which gives $-3 + 4 = 1$. These are correct so the solution is $x = -1$ and $y = 1$.

EXERCISE 5J

In this exercise the coefficients of one of the variables in questions **1** to **9** are the same so there is no need to balance them. Subtract the equations when the identical terms have the same sign. Add the equations when the identical terms have opposite signs. In questions **10** to **12** use the substitution method.

Solve these simultaneous equations.

1 $4x + y = 17$
 $2x + y = 9$

2 $5x + 2y = 13$
 $x + 2y = 9$

3 $2x + y = 7$
 $5x - y = 14$

4 $3x + 2y = 11$
 $2x - 2y = 14$

5 $3x - 4y = 17$
 $x - 4y = 3$

6 $3x + 2y = 16$
 $x - 2y = 4$

7 $x + 3y = 9$
 $x + y = 6$

8 $2x + 5y = 16$
 $2x + 3y = 8$

9 $3x - y = 9$
 $5x + y = 11$

10 $2x + 5y = 37$
 $y = 11 - 2x$

11 $4x - 3y = 7$
 $x = 13 - 3y$

12 $4x - y = 17$
 $x = 2 + y$

You were able to solve all the pairs of equations in Exercise 5J simply by adding or subtracting the equations in each pair, or just by substituting without rearranging. This does not always happen. The next examples show you what to do when there are no identical terms to begin with, or when you need to rearrange.

EXAMPLE 20

Solve these equations. $3x + 2y = 18$ (1)

$2x - y = 5$ (2)

Step 1: Multiply equation (2) by 2. There are other ways to balance the coefficients but this is the easiest and leads to less work later. You will get used to which will be the best way to balance the coefficients.

$2 \times (2)$ $4x - 2y = 10$ (3)

Label this equation as number (3).

Be careful to multiply every term and not just the y term, it sometimes helps to write:

$2 \times (2x - y = 5) \quad \Rightarrow \quad 4x - 2y = 10$ (3)

Step 2: As the signs of the y-terms are opposite, add the equations.

$(1) + (3)$ $7x = 28$

Be careful to add the correct equations. This is why labelling them is useful.

Step 3: Solve this equation: $x = 4$

Step 4: Substitute $x = 4$ into any equation, say $2x - y = 5 \quad \Rightarrow \quad 8 - y = 5$

Step 5: Solve this equation: $y = 3$

Step 6: Check: (1), $3 \times 4 + 2 \times 3 = 18$ and (2), $2 \times 4 - 3 = 5$, which are correct so the solution is $x = 4$ and $y = 3$.

EXAMPLE 21

Solve the simultaneous equations $3x + y = 5$ and $5x - 2y = 12$ using the substitution method.

Looking at the equations there is only one that could be sensibly rearranged without involving fractions.

Step 1: Rearrange $3x + y = 5$ to get $y = 5 - 3x$ (1)

Step 2: Substitute $y = 5 - 3x$ into $5x - 2y = 12$ (2)

$5x - 2(5 - 3x) = 12$

Step 3: Expand and solve $5x - 10 + 6x = 12 \quad \Rightarrow \quad 11x = 22 \quad \Rightarrow \quad x = 2$

Step 4: Substitute into equation (1): $y = 5 - 3 \times 2 = 5 - 6 = -1$

Step 5: Check: (1), $3 \times 2 + -1 = 5$ and (2), $5 \times 2 - 2 \times -1 = 10 + 2 = 12$, which are correct so the solution is $x = 2$ and $y = -1$.

EXERCISE 5K

Solve questions **1** to **3** by the substitution method and the rest by first changing one of the equations in each pair to obtain identical terms, and then adding or subtracting the equations to eliminate those terms.

1 $5x + 2y = 4$

$4x - y = 11$

2 $4x + 3y = 37$

$2x + y = 17$

3 $x + 3y = 7$

$2x - y = 7$

4 $2x + 3y = 19$

$6x + 2y = 22$

5 $5x - 2y = 26$

$3x - y = 15$

6 $10x - y = 3$

$3x + 2y = 17$

7 $3x + 5y = 15$

$x + 3y = 7$

8 $3x + 4y = 7$

$4x + 2y = 1$

9 $5x - 2y = 24$

$3x + y = 21$

10 $5x - 2y = 4$

$3x - 6y = 6$

11 $2x + 3y = 13$

$4x + 7y = 31$

12 $3x - 2y = 3$

$5x + 6y = 12$

There are also cases where *both* equations have to be changed to obtain identical terms. The next example shows you how this is done.

Note the substitution method is not suitable for these type of equations as you end up with fractional terms.

EXAMPLE 22

Solve these equations. $4x + 3y = 27$ (1)

$5x - 2y = 5$ (2)

Both equations have to be changed to obtain identical terms in either x or y. However, we can see that if we make the y-coefficients the same, we will add the equations. This is always safer than subtraction, so this is obviously the better choice. We do this by multiplying the first equation by 2 (the y-coefficient of the other equation) and the second equation by 3 (the y-coefficient of the other equation).

Step 1:   (1) × 2 or 2 × ($4x + 3y = 27$)   ⇒ $8x + 6y = 54$ (3)

(2) × 3 or 3 × ($5x - 2y = 5$)   ⇒ $15x - 6y = 15$ (4)

Label the new equations (3) and (4).

Step 2: Eliminate one of the variables: (3) + (4) $23x = 69$

Step 3: Solve the equation: $x = 3$

Step 4: Substitute into equation (1): $12 + 3y = 27$

Step 5: Solve the equation: $y = 5$

Step 6: Check: (1), $4 \times 3 + 3 \times 5 = 12 + 15 = 27$, and (2), $5 \times 3 - 2 \times 5 = 15 - 10 = 5$, which are correct so the solution is $x = 3$ and $y = 5$.

EXERCISE 5L

Solve the following simultaneous equations.

1 $2x + 5y = 15$
$3x - 2y = 13$

2 $2x + 3y = 30$
$5x + 7y = 71$

3 $2x - 3y = 15$
$5x + 7y = 52$

4 $3x - 2y = 15$
$2x - 3y = 5$

5 $5x - 3y = 14$
$4x - 5y = 6$

6 $3x + 2y = 28$
$2x + 7y = 47$

7 $2x + y = 4$
$x - y = 5$

8 $5x + 2y = 11$
$3x + 4y = 8$

9 $x - 2y = 4$
$3x - y = -3$

10 $3x + 2y = 2$
$2x + 6y = 13$

11 $6x + 2y = 14$
$3x - 5y = 10$

12 $2x + 4y = 15$
$x + 5y = 21$

13 $3x - y = 5$
$x + 3y = -20$

14 $3x - 4y = 4.5$
$2x + 2y = 10$

15 $x - 5y = 15$
$3x - 7y = 17$

Solving problems by using simultaneous equations

We are now going to meet a type of problem which has to be expressed as a pair of simultaneous equations so that it can be solved. The next example shows you how to tackle such a problem.

EXAMPLE 23

On holiday last year, I was talking over breakfast to two families about how much it cost them to go to the theatre. They couldn't remember how much was charged for each adult or each child, but they could both remember what they had paid altogether.

The Advani family, consisting of Mr and Mrs Advani with their daughter Rupa, paid £23.

The Shaw family, consisting of Mrs Shaw with her two children, Len and Sue, paid £17.50.

How much would I have to pay for my wife, my four children and myself?

We make a pair of simultaneous equations from the situation as follows.

Let x be the cost of an adult ticket, and y be the cost of a child's ticket. Then

$2x + y = 23$ for the Advani family

and $x + 2y = 17.5$ for the Shaw family

We solve these equations just as we have done in the previous examples, to obtain

$x = £9.50$ and $y = £4$. I can now find my cost, which will be

$(2 \times £9.50) + (4 \times £4) = £35$.

EXERCISE 5M

Read each situation carefully, then make a pair of simultaneous equations in order to solve the problem.

 1 Amul and Kim have £10.70 between them. Amul has £3.70 more than Kim. Let x be the amount Amul has and y be the amount Kim has. Set up a pair of simultaneous equations. How much does each have?

 2 The two people in front of me at the Post Office were both buying stamps. One person bought 10 second-class and five first-class stamps at a total cost of £3.45. The other bought eight second-class and 10 first-class stamps at a total cost of £4.38.

   a Let x be the cost of second-class stamps and y be the cost of first-class stamps. Set up two simultaneous equations.

   b How much did I pay for 3 second-class and 4 first-class stamps?

 3 At a local tea room I couldn't help noticing that at one table, where the customers had eaten six buns and had three teas, the bill came to £4.35. At another table, the customers had eaten 11 buns and had seven teas at a total cost of £8.80.

   a Let x be the cost of a bun and y be the cost of a cup of tea. Show the situation as a pair of simultaneous equations.

   b My family and I had five buns and six teas. What did it cost us?

 4 Three chews and four bubblies cost 72p. Five chews and two bubblies cost 64p. What would three chews and five bubblies cost?

 5 On a nut-and-bolt production line, all the nuts weighed the same and all the bolts weighed the same. An order of 50 nuts and 60 bolts weighed 10.6 kg. An order of 40 nuts and 30 bolts weighed 6.5 kg. What should an order of 60 nuts and 50 bolts weigh?

 6 A taxi firm charges a fixed amount plus so much per mile. A journey of 6 miles costs £3.70. A journey of 10 miles costs £5.10. What would be the cost of a journey of 8 miles?

 7 Two members of the same church went to the same shop to buy material to make Christingles. One bought 200 oranges and 220 candles at a cost of £65.60. The other bought 210 oranges and 200 candles at a cost of £63.30. They only needed 200 of each. How much should it have cost them?

 8 When you book Bingham Hall for a conference, you pay a fixed booking fee plus a charge for each delegate at the conference. The total charge for a conference with 65 delegates was £192.50. The total charge for a conference with 40 delegates was £180. What will be the charge for a conference with 70 delegates?

 9 My mother-in-law uses this formula to cook a turkey:

$$T = a + bW$$

where T is the cooking time (minutes), W is the weight of the turkey (kg), and a and b are constants. She says it takes 4 hours 30 minutes to cook a 12 kg turkey, and 3 hours 10 minutes to cook an 8 kg turkey. How long will it take to cook a 5 kg turkey?

Rearranging formulae

In this section you will learn how to:

- rearrange formulae using the same methods as for solving equations

Key words

expression
rearrange
subject
transpose
variable

The **subject** of a formula is the **variable** (letter) in the formula which stands on its own, usually on the left-hand side of the equals sign. For example, x is the subject of each of the following equations.

$$x = 5t + 4 \qquad x = 4(2y - 7) \qquad x = \frac{1}{t}$$

If we wish to change the existing subject to a different variable, we have to **rearrange** (**transpose**) the formula to get that variable on the left-hand side. We do this by using the same rules as for solving equations. Move the terms concerned from one side of the equals sign to the other. The main difference is that when you solve an equation each step gives a numerical value. When you rearrange a formula each step gives an algebraic **expression**.

EXAMPLE 24

Make m the subject of this formula.	$T = m - 3$
Move the 3 away from the m.	$T + 3 = m$
Reverse the formula.	$m = T + 3$

EXAMPLE 25

From the formula $P = 4t$, express t in terms of P.

(This is another common way of asking you to make t the subject.)

Divide both sides by 4: $\qquad \dfrac{P}{4} = \dfrac{4t}{4}$

Reverse the formula: $\qquad t = \dfrac{P}{4}$

EXAMPLE 26

From the formula $C = 2m^2 + 3$, make m the subject.

Move the 3 away from the $2m^2$: $\qquad C - 3 = 2m^2$

Divide both sides by 2: $\qquad \dfrac{C - 3}{2} = \dfrac{2m^2}{2}$

Reverse the formula: $\qquad m^2 = \dfrac{C - 3}{2}$

Square root both sides: $\qquad m = \sqrt{\dfrac{C - 3}{2}}$

EXERCISE 5N

1 $T = 3k$ Make k the subject.

2 $X = y - 1$ Express y in terms of X.

3 $Q = \dfrac{p}{3}$ Express p in terms of Q.

4 $A = 4r + 9$ Make r the subject.

5 $W = 3n - 1$ Make n the subject.

6 $p = m + t$ **a** Make m the subject.   **b** Make t the subject.

7 $g = \dfrac{m}{v}$ Make m the subject.

8 $t = m^2$ Make m the subject.

9 $C = 2\pi r$ Make r the subject.

10 $A = bh$ Make b the subject.

11 $P = 2l + 2w$ Make l the subject.

12 $m = p^2 + 2$ Make p the subject.

13 $v = u + at$ **a** Make a the subject.   **b** Make t the subject.

14 $A = \dfrac{1}{4}\pi d^2,$ Make d the subject.

15 $W = 3n + t$ **a** Make n the subject.   **b** Express t in terms of n and W.

16 $x = 5y - w$ **a** Make y the subject.   **b** Express w in terms of x and y.

17 $k = 2p^2$ Make p the subject.

18 $v = u^2 - t$ **a** Make t the subject.   **b** Make u the subject.

19 $k = m + n^2$ **a** Make m the subject.   **b** Make n the subject.

20 $T = 5r^2$ Make r the subject.

21 $K = 5n^2 + w$ **a** Make w the subject.   **b** Make n the subject.

> **HINTS AND TIPS**
>
> Remember about inverse operations, and the rule "change sides, change signs".

1 **a** Multiply out $\qquad$ $3(4x - 5)$

  b Solve $\qquad$ $3(4x - 5) = 27$

2 Solve the equation $\qquad$ $7x - 1 = 3(x + 2)$

3 A solution of the equation $x^3 - 8x = 110$ lies between $x = 5$ and $x = 6$. Use trial and improvement to find this solution. Give your answer to one decimal place.

4 **a** Expand and simplify $\quad 3(4x - 3) + 2(x + 5)$

  b Expand $\qquad$ $2x(x^2 - 3x)$

  c Expand and simplify $\quad (x + 2)(x - 1)$

5 **a** Make t the subject of the formula $\quad s = 2 - 3t$

  b Solve the equation $\qquad \frac{1}{3}x - 4 = \frac{1}{6}x + 2$

6 Solve the equations

  a $\dfrac{17 - x}{3} = 4.5$

  b $2(y - 3) = 5 - 3y$

  c $3(2z - 1) + 4(z + 3) = 5(2z - 1) + 4(3z - 1)$

  AQA, Question 11, Paper 2 Higher, June 2005

7 Dario is using trial and improvement to find a solution to the equation

  $x + \dfrac{1}{x} = 5$

The table shows his first trial.

x	$x + \frac{1}{x}$	Comment
4	4.25	Too low

Continue the table to find a solution to the equation. Give your answer to 1 decimal place.

  AQA, Question 17, Paper 2 Intermediate, June 2004

8 **a** **i** Multiply out $\qquad s(s^2 + 6)$

  ii Multiply out and simplify $\quad 4(x - 2) + 3(x + 2)$

  iii Multiply out and simplify $\quad (n + 3)^2$

  b Factorise completely the following expressions

  i $2a^2 + a$

  ii $8x^3y^2 - 4xy^3$

  AQA, Question 5, Paper 2 Higher, June 2004

9 **a** Expand and simplify

  $4(2x - 1) + 3(x + 6)$

  b Expand

  $x^2(4 - 2x)$

  AQA, Question 16, Paper 2 Intermediate, June 2003

10 Make t the subject of the formula $\quad t^2 + s = 10$

11 Make x the subject of the formula

  $3x + 2y = 8y - 3$

  Simplify your answer as much as possible.

  AQA, Question 8, Paper 2 Higher, June 2004

12 Solve the simultaneous equations

  $4x + 3y = 14$

  $2x + \ y = \ 5$

  You *must* show your working.

  Do *not* use trial and improvement.

  AQA, Question 23, Paper 1 Intermediate, June 2004

13 Wendy does a 25 kilometre mountain race. She ran x kilometres to the top of the mountain at a speed of 9 km/h and then y kilometres to the finish at a speed of 12 km/h. She finishes the race in 2 hours and 20 minutes.

By setting up two simultaneous equations in x and y, find how long it took Wendy to reach the top of the mountain.

14 Consider the simultaneous equations

  $y = x + 1$

  $y^2 = x + 6$

  a Show why x is the solution of the equation

  $x^2 + x - 5 = 0$

  b Use trial and improvement to find a positive solution to $x^2 + x - 5 = 0$. Give your answer to 1 decimal place.

WORKED EXAM QUESTIONS

1 $4x + 3y = 6$
$3x - 2y = 13$
Solve these simultaneous equations algebraically. Show your method clearly.

$4x + 3y = 23$ (1)

$3x - 2y = 13$ (2)

> Label the equations and decide on the best way to get the coefficients of one variable the same.

(1) × 2 $8x + 6y = 46$ (3)

(2) × 3 $9x - 6y = 39$ (4)

(3) + (4) $17x = 85$

> Making the y coefficients the same will be the most efficient way as the resulting equations will be added.

$x = 5$

Substitute into (1) $20 + 3y = 23$

$y = 1$

> Solve the resulting equation and substitute into one of the original equations to find the other value.

$4 \times 5 + 3 \times 1 = 23$ ✓

$3 \times 5 - 2 \times 1 = 13$ ✓

> Check that these values work in the original equations

2 Temperatures can be measured in degrees Celsius (°C), degrees Fahrenheit (°F) or degrees Kelvin (°K). The relationships between the scales of temperature are given by

$C = \dfrac{5(F - 32)}{9}$ and

$K = C + 273$

Express F

  i in terms of C

  ii in terms of K

i $9C = 5(F - 32)$

    $9C = 5F - 160$

    $5F = 9C + 160$

    $F = \dfrac{9C + 160}{5}$

> Multiply both sides of the first equation by 9, then expand the bracket. Add 160 to both sides and change the equation round. Divide both sides by 5. Make sure you divide all of the right-hand side by 5.

ii $C = K - 273$

    $F = \dfrac{9(K - 273) + 160}{5}$

    $F = \dfrac{9K - 2457 + 160}{5}$

    $F = \dfrac{9K - 2297}{5}$

> Make C the subject of the second equation. Substitute for C in the answer to part **i**, expand the bracket and tidy up the top line of the fraction.

Riding Stables

Julia starts her new job at a riding stables, where she is responsible for six new horses. She measures the length and girth of each horse, and then uses the bodyweight calculator to work out its weight in kilograms. She then uses the feed chart and worming paste instructions to calculate how much feed and worming paste each horse needs.

Copy the stewardship table and help her to complete it for these six horses.

Summer
girth: 220 cm
length: 142 cm
work: medium

Sally
girth: 190 cm
length: 95 cm
work: hard

Skip
girth: 200 cm
length: 114 cm
work: hard

Simon
girth: 180 cm
length: 124 cm
work: medium

Body weight of horse in (kg)	Weight of feed (in kg) at different levels of work	
	Medium work	Hard work
300	2.4	3.0
350	2.8	3.5
400	3.2	4.0
450	3.6	4.5
500	4.0	5.0
Extra feed per 50 kg	300 g	400 g

Stewardship table

Horse	Weight in kg	Feed in kg	Worming paste in tubes
Summer			
Sally			
Skip			
Simon			
Barney			
Teddy			

Instructions for using the bodyweight calculator

Put a ruler from the girth line to the length line. Where the ruler crosses the weight line is the approximate weight of the horse. Give each horse's weight to the nearest 10 kg.

Bodyweight Calculator

Girth (cm)	Weight (km)	Length (cm)
111.8	115.7	71.75
112	125	75
120	150	80
130	175	85
140	200	90
	225	
150	250	95
	275	
160	300	100
	325	
	350	105
170	400	110
180	450	115
	500	
190	550	120
200	600	125
	650	
210	700	130
	750	
	800	135
220	850	
	900	140
230	950	
	1000	145
240	1045.6	150
246.4		150.5

Barney
girth: 160 cm
length: 110 cm
work: medium

Teddy
girth: 190 cm
length: 140 cm
work: hard

Worming paste instructions

Weight of horse (w) in kg	Amount of paste
w < 150	0.25 of tube
150 ≤ w < 300	0.5 of tube
300 ≤ w < 450	0.75 of tube
continue increasing dosage of paste, 0.25 of tube for every 150 kg	

During her first day, Julia sees a group of three adults and two children pay £136.50 for a 1½ hour ride. Then another group of four adults and five children pay £241.50 to go on the same ride.

Julia is hopeless at simultaneous equations. Work out for her the cost for an adult and the cost for a child to go on this ride.

GRADE YOURSELF

D Able to expand a linear bracket

D Able to substitute numbers into expressions

D Able to factorise simple linear expresions

D Able to solve simple linear equations which include the variable inside a bracket

D Able to solve linear equations where the variable occurs in the numerator of a fraction

D Able to solve linear equations where the variable appears on both sides of the equals sign.

C Able to expand and simplify expressions

C Able to solve equations using trial and improvement

C Able to rearrange simple formulae

B Able to solve two simultaneous linear equations

B Able to rearrange more complicated formulae

A Able to set up and solve two simultaneous equations from a practical problem

What you should know now

- How to manipulate and simplify algebraic expressions, including those with linear brackets
- How to factorise linear expressions
- How to solve all types of linear equations
- How to find a solution to equations by trial and improvement
- How to set up and/or solve a pair of linear simultaneous equations

Chapter
6

Pythagoras and trigonometry

This chapter will show you ...

- how to use Pythagoras' theorem in right-angled triangles
- how to solve problems using Pythagoras' theorem
- how to use trigonometric ratios in right-angled triangles
- how to use trigonometry to solve problems

What you should already know

- how to find the square and square root of a number
- how to round numbers to a suitable degree of accuracy

Quick check

Use your calculator to evaluate the following, giving your answers to one decimal place.

1 2.3^2

2 15.7^2

3 0.78^2

4 $\sqrt{8}$

5 $\sqrt{260}$

6 $\sqrt{0.5}$

In this section you will learn how to:
- calculate the length of the hypotenuse in a right-angled triangle

Key words
hypotenuse
Pythagoras' theorem

Pythagoras, who was a philosopher as well as a mathematician, was born in 580 BC, on the island of Samos in Greece. He later moved to Crotona (Italy), where he established the Pythagorean Brotherhood, which was a secret society devoted to politics, mathematics and astronomy. It is said that when he discovered his famous theorem, he was so full of joy that he showed his gratitude to the gods by sacrificing a hundred oxen.

Consider squares being drawn on each side of a right-angled triangle, with sides 3 cm, 4 cm and 5 cm.

The longest side is called the **hypotenuse** and is always opposite the right angle.

Pythagoras' theorem can then be stated as follows:

For any right-angled triangle, the area of the square drawn on the hypotenuse is equal to the sum of the areas of the squares drawn on the other two sides.

The form in which most of your parents would have learnt the theorem when they were at school – and which is still in use today – is as follows:

In any right-angled triangle, the square of the hypotenuse is equal to the sum of the squares of the other two sides.

Pythagoras' theorem is more usually written as a formula:

$$c^2 = a^2 + b^2$$

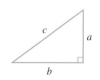

Remember that Pythagoras' theorem can only be used in right-angled triangles.

Finding the hypotenuse

EXAMPLE 1

Find the length of the hypotenuse, marked x on the diagram.

Using Pythagoras' theorem gives

$$x^2 = 8^2 + 5.2^2 \text{ cm}^2$$

$$= 64 + 27.04 \text{ cm}^2$$

$$= 91.04 \text{ cm}^2$$

So $x = \sqrt{91.04} = 9.5$ cm (1 decimal place)

EXERCISE 6A

For each of the following triangles, calculate the length of the hypotenuse, x, giving your answers to one decimal place.

1
9 cm x 5 cm

2

x 3 cm   5.1 cm

3

4.8 cm   7 cm x

4

16 cm x 13 cm

5

x 11 cm   15 cm

6

9 cm   15 cm x

7

4 cm   3 cm x

8

12 cm x 5 cm

9

8 cm x 6 cm

HINTS AND TIPS
In these examples you are finding the hypotenuse. The squares of the two short sides are added in every case.

The last three examples give whole number answers. Sets of whole numbers that obey Pythagoras' theorem are called Pythagorean triples. For example,

3, 4, 5   5, 12, 13   and   6, 8, 10.

Note that 6, 8, 10 are respectively multiples of 3, 4, 5.

Finding a shorter side

In this section you will learn how to:

- calculate the length of a shorter side in a right-angled triangle

Key word

Pythagoras' theorem

By rearranging the formula for **Pythagoras' theorem**, the length of one of the shorter sides can easily be calculated.

$$c^2 = a^2 + b^2$$

So, $a^2 = c^2 - b^2$ or $b^2 = c^2 - a^2$

EXAMPLE 2

Find the length x.

x is one of the shorter sides

So using Pythagoras' theorem gives

$x^2 = 15^2 - 11^2$ cm^2

$= 225 - 121$ cm^2

$= 104$ cm^2

So $x = \sqrt{104} = 10.2$ cm (one decimal place)

EXERCISE 6B

1 For each of the following triangles, calculate the length x, giving your answers to one decimal place.

a

17 cm

x

8 cm

b

24 cm

x

19 cm

HINTS AND TIPS

In these examples you are finding a short side. The square of the other short side is subtracted from the square of the hypotenuse in every case.

c

6.4 cm

x

9 cm

d

31 cm

25 cm

x

2 For each of the following triangles, calculate the length x, giving your answers to one decimal place.

a

17 m x

12 m

b

19 cm   11 cm

x

c

17 m

x

23 m

d

9 cm x

8.5 cm

3 For each of the following triangles, find the length marked x.

a

x

12 m

13 m

b

8 m

x

10 m

c

5 m

x

4 m

d

30 cm x

40 cm

6.3 ## Solving problems using Pythagoras' theorem

In this section you will learn how to:
- solve problems using Pythagoras' theorem

Key words
3-D
isoceles
   triangle
Pythagoras'
   theorem

Pythagoras' theorem can be used to solve certain practical problems. When a problem involves two lengths only, follow these steps.

- Draw a diagram for the problem that includes a right-angled triangle.

- Look at the diagram and decide which side has to be found: the hypotenuse or one of the shorter sides. Label the unknown side x.

- If it's the hypotenuse, then square both numbers, add the squares and take the square root of the sum.

- If it's one of the shorter sides, then square both numbers, subtract the squares and take the square root of the difference.

- Finally, round off the answer to a suitable degree of accuracy.

EXAMPLE 3

A plane leaves Manchester airport heading due east. It flies 160 km before turning due north. It then flies a further 280 km and lands. What is the distance of the return flight if the plane flies straight back to Manchester airport?

First, sketch the situation.

Using Pythagoras' theorem gives

$$x^2 = 160^2 + 280^2 \text{ km}^2$$
$$= 25\,600 + 78\,400 \text{ km}^2$$
$$= 104\,000 \text{ km}^2$$

So $x = \sqrt{104\,000} = 322$ km (3 significant figures)

Remember the following tips when solving problems.

- Always sketch the right-angled triangle you need. Sometimes, the triangle is already drawn for you but some problems involve other lines and triangles that may confuse you. So identify which right-angled triangle you need and sketch it separately.

- Label the triangle with necessary information, such as the length of its sides, taken from the question. Label the unknown side x.

- Set out your solution as in Example 3. Avoid short cuts, since they often cause errors. You gain marks in your examination for clearly showing how you are applying Pythagoras' theorem to the problem.

- Round your answer off to a suitable degree of accuracy.

EXERCISE 6C

1 A ladder, 12 metres long, leans against a wall. The ladder reaches 10 metres up the wall. How far away from the foot of the wall is the foot of the ladder?

2 A model football pitch is 2 metres long and 0.5 metre wide. How long is the diagonal?

3 How long is the diagonal of a square with a side of 8 metres?

4 A ship going from a port to a lighthouse steams 15 km east and 12 km north. How far is the lighthouse from the port?

5 Some pedestrians want to get from point X on one road to point Y on another. The two roads meet at right angles.

   a If they follow the roads, how far will they walk?

   b Instead of walking along the road, they take the shortcut, XY. Find the length of the shortcut.

   c How much distance do they save?

6 A mast on a sailboat is strengthened by a wire (called a stay), as shown on the diagram. The mast is 10 m tall and the stay is 11 m long. How far from the base of the mast does the stay reach?

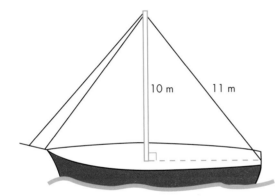

7 A ladder, 4 m long, is put up against a wall.

   a How far up the wall will it reach when the foot of the ladder is 1 m away from the wall?

   b When it reaches 3.6 m up the wall, how far is the foot of the ladder away from the wall?

8 A pole, 8 m high, is supported by metal wires, each 8.6 m long, attached to the top of the pole. How far from the foot of the pole are the wires fixed to the ground?

9 How long is the line that joins the two coordinates A(13, 6) and B(1, 1)?

10 The regulation for safe use of ladders states that: *the foot of a 5 m ladder must be placed between 1.6 m and 2.1 m from the foot of the wall.*

a What is the maximum height the ladder can safely reach up the wall?

b What is the minimum height the ladder can safely reach up the wall?

11 Is the triangle with sides 7 cm, 24 cm and 25 cm, a right-angled triangle?

Pythagoras' theorem and isosceles triangles

This section shows you how to to use Pythagoras' theorem in isosceles triangles.

Every **isosceles triangle** has a line of symmetry that divides the triangle into two congruent right-angled triangles. So when you are faced with a problem involving an isosceles triangle, be aware that you are quite likely to have to split that triangle down the middle to create a right-angled triangle which will help you to solve the problem.

EXAMPLE 4

Calculate the area of this triangle.

It is an isosceles triangle and you need to calculate its height to find its area.

First split the triangle into two right-angled triangles to find its height.

Let the height be x.

Then, using Pythagoras' theorem,

$$x^2 = 7.5^2 - 3^2 \text{ cm}^2$$
$$= 56.25 - 9 \text{ cm}^2$$
$$= 47.25 \text{ cm}^2$$

So $x = \sqrt{47.25}$ cm

$x = 6.87$ cm

Keep the accurate figure in the calculator memory.

The area of the triangle is $\frac{1}{2} \times 6 \times 6.87$ cm^2 (from the calculator memory), which is 20.6 cm^2 (1 decimal place)

EXERCISE 6D

1 Calculate the areas of these isosceles triangles.

a
9 cm   9 cm
8 cm

b
3 cm
2 cm

c
7 cm   10 cm

2 Calculate the area of an isosceles triangle whose sides are 8 cm, 8 cm and 6 cm.

3 Calculate the area of an equilateral triangle of side 6 cm.

4 An isosceles triangle has sides of 5 cm and 6 cm.

    a Sketch the two different isosceles triangles that fit this data.

    b Which of the two triangles has the greater area?

5 **a** Sketch a regular hexagon, showing all its lines of symmetry.

    b Calculate the area of the hexagon if its side is 8 cm.

6 Calculate the area of a hexagon of side 10 cm.

7 Calculate the lengths marked x in these isosceles triangles.

a
12 cm   13 cm
x

b
24 cm x
20 cm

c
10 cm
12 cm x

> **HINTS AND TIPS**
>
> Find the area first.

Pythagoras' theorem in three dimensions

This section shows you how to solve problems in **3-D** using Pythagoras' theorem.

In your GCSE examinations, there may be questions which involve applying Pythagoras' theorem in 3-D situations. Such questions are usually accompanied by clearly labelled diagrams, which will help you to identify the lengths needed for your solutions.

You deal with these 3-D problems in exactly the same way as 2-D problems.

- Identify the right-angled triangle you need.

- Redraw this triangle and label it with the given lengths and the length to be found, usually x or y.

- From your diagram, decide whether it is the hypotenuse or one of the shorter sides which has to be found.

- Solve the problem, rounding off to a suitable degree of accuracy.

EXAMPLE 5

What is the longest piece of straight wire that can be stored in this box measuring 30 cm by 15 cm by 20 cm?

The longest distance across this box is any one of the diagonals AG, DF, CE or HB.

Let us take AG.

First, identify a right-angled triangle containing AG and draw it.

This gives a triangle AFG, which contains two lengths you do not know, AG and AF. Let AG = x and AF = y.

Next identify a right-angled triangle that contains the side AF and draw it.

This gives a triangle ABF. You can now find AF.

By Pythagoras' theorem

$$y^2 = 30^2 + 20^2 \text{ cm}^2$$

$$y^2 = 1300 \text{ cm}^2 \text{ (there is no need to find } y)$$

Now find AG using triangle AFG.

By Pythagoras' theorem

$$x^2 = y^2 + 15^2 \text{ cm}^2$$

$$x^2 = 1300 + 225 = 1525 \text{ cm}^2$$

So $x = 39.1$ cm (1 decimal place)

So, the longest straight wire that can be stored in the box is 39.1 cm.

Note that in any cuboid with sides a, b and c, the length of a diagonal is given by

$$\sqrt{(a^2 + b^2 + c^2)}$$

EXERCISE 6E

1 A box measures 8 cm by 12 cm by 5 cm.

   a Calculate the lengths of the following.

      i AC   **ii** BG   **iii** BE

   b Calculate the diagonal distance BH.

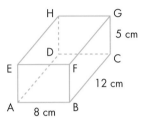

2 A garage is 5 m long, 3 m wide and 3 m high. Can a 7 m long pole be stored in it?

3 Spike, a spider, is at the corner S of the wedge shown in the diagram.
Fred, a fly, is at the corner F of the same wedge.

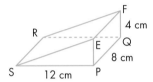

   a Calculate the two distances Spike would have to travel to get to
Fred if she used the edges of the wedge.

   b Calculate the distance Spike would have to travel across the face of the wedge to get
directly to Fred.

4 Fred is now at the top of a baked-beans can and Spike is
directly below him on the base of the can. To catch Fred by
surprise, Spike takes a diagonal route round the can.
How far does Spike travel?

HINTS AND TIPS

Imagine the can opened
out flat.

5 A corridor is 3 m wide and turns through a right angle, as in the diagram.

   a What is the longest pole that can be carried along the corridor
horizontally?

   b If the corridor is 3 m high, what is the longest pole that can be carried
along in any direction?

A*

6 The diagram shows a square-based pyramid with base length 8 cm and sloping edges 9 cm. M is the mid-point of the side AB, X is the mid-point of the base, and E is directly above X.

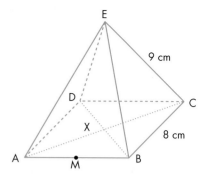

 a Calculate the length of the diagonal AC.

 b Calculate EX, the height of the pyramid.

 c Using triangle ABE, calculate the length EM.

7 The diagram shows a cuboid with sides of 40 cm, 30 cm, and 22.5 cm. M is the mid-point of the side FG. Calculate (or write down) these lengths, giving your answers to three significant figures if necessary.

 a AH   **b** AG   **c** AM   **d** HM

6.4 Trigonometric ratios

In this section you will learn how to:

- use the three trigonometric ratios

Key words

adjacent side
cosine
hypotenuse
opposite side
sine
tangent
trigonometry

Trigonometry is concerned with the calculation of sides and angles in triangles, and involves the use of three important ratios: **sine**, **cosine** and **tangent**. These ratios are defined in terms of the sides of a right-angled triangle and an angle. The angle is often written as θ.

In a right-angled triangle

- the side opposite the right angle is called the **hypotenuse** and is the longest side

- the side opposite the angle θ is called the **opposite side**

- the other side next to both the right angle and the angle θ is called the **adjacent side**.

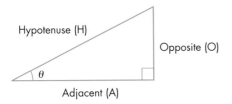

The sine, cosine and tangent ratios for θ are defined as

$$\text{sine } \theta = \frac{\text{Opposite}}{\text{Hypotenuse}} \qquad \text{cosine } \theta = \frac{\text{Adjacent}}{\text{Hypotenuse}} \qquad \text{tangent } \theta = \frac{\text{Opposite}}{\text{Adjacent}}$$

These ratios are usually abbreviated as

$$\sin \theta = \frac{O}{H} \qquad \cos \theta = \frac{A}{H} \qquad \tan \theta = \frac{O}{A}$$

These abbreviated forms are also used on calculator keys.

Memorising these formulae may be helped by a mnemonic such as

Silly **O**ld **H**itler **C**ouldn't **A**dvance **H**is **T**roops **O**ver **A**frica

in which the first letter of each word is taken in order to give

$$S = \frac{O}{H} \qquad C = \frac{A}{H} \qquad T = \frac{O}{A}$$

Using your calculator

You can use your calculator to find the sine, cosine and tangent of *any* angle.

To find the sine of an angle, press the key labelled *sin*.

To find the cosine of an angle, press the key labelled *cos*.

To find the tangent of an angle, press the key labelled *tan*.

Make sure you can find sin, cos and tan on your calculator.

Important: Make sure your calculator is working in *degrees*. Depending on the type of calculator used, you need to put it into *degree mode* before you start working on sines, cosines and tangents. This can be done either

- by using the MODE button

- or by pressing the key DRG until DEG is on display.

Try this *now* to make sure you can do it. When it is in degree mode, D or DEG appears on the calculator display.

EXAMPLE 6

Use your calculator to find the sine of 27°, written as sin 27°.

On some scientific calculators, the function is keyed in numbers first

The display should read 0.453990499. (You may have more or fewer digits depending on your calculator.) This is 0.454 to three significant figures.

If you have a graphics calculator or an 'algebraic logic' (DAL) calculator, you key in the function as it reads

You should get the same value as above. If you don't, then consult your calculator manual or your teacher.

EXAMPLE 7

Use your calculator to find the cosine of 56°, written as cos 56°.

cos 56° = 0.559 192 903 = 0.559 to 3 significant figures

Check that you agree with this, using as many digits as your calculator allows.

EXAMPLE 8

Use your calculator to work out 3 × cos 57°, written as 3 cos 57°.

Depending on your type of calculator, key in either

Check that you get an answer of 1.633 917 105 = 1.63 to 3 significant figures.

EXERCISE 6F

1 Find these values, rounding off your answers to three significant figures.

| **a** sin 43° | **b** sin 56° | **c** sin 67.2° | **d** sin 90° |
| **e** sin 45° | **f** sin 20° | **g** sin 22° | **h** sin 0° |

2 Find these values, rounding off your answers to three significant figures.

| **a** cos 43° | **b** cos 56° | **c** cos 67.2° | **d** cos 90° |
| **e** cos 45° | **f** cos 20° | **g** cos 22° | **h** cos 0° |

3 From your answers to questions **1** and **2**, what angle has the same value for sine and cosine?

4 **a** **i** What is sin 35°? **ii** What is cos 55°?

b **i** What is sin 12°? **ii** What is cos 78°?

c **i** What is cos 67°? **ii** What is sin 23°?

d What connects the values in parts **a**, **b** and **c**?

e Copy and complete these sentences.

i sin 15° is the same as cos …

ii cos 82° is the same as sin …

iii sin x is the same as cos …

5 Use your calculator to work out the values of

a tan 43° **b** tan 56° **c** tan 67.2° **d** tan 90°

e tan 45° **f** tan 20° **g** tan 22° **h** tan 0°

6 Use your calculator to work out the values of the following.

a sin 73° **b** cos 26° **c** tan 65.2° **d** sin 88°

e cos 35° **f** tan 30° **g** sin 28° **h** cos 5°

7 What is so different about tan compared with both sin and cos?

8 Use your calculator to work out the values of the following.

a 5 sin 65° **b** 6 cos 42° **c** 6 sin 90° **d** 5 sin 0°

9 Use your calculator to work out the values of the following.

a 5 tan 65° **b** 6 tan 42° **c** 6 tan 90° **d** 5 tan 0°

10 Use your calculator to work out the values of the following.

a 4 sin 63° **b** 7 tan 52° **c** 5 tan 80° **d** 9 cos 8°

11 Use your calculator to work out the values of the following.

a $\dfrac{5}{\sin 63°}$ **b** $\dfrac{6}{\cos 32°}$ **c** $\dfrac{6}{\sin 90°}$ **d** $\dfrac{5}{\sin 30°}$

12 Use your calculator to work out the values of the following.

a $\dfrac{3}{\tan 64°}$ **b** $\dfrac{7}{\tan 42°}$ **c** $\dfrac{5}{\tan 89°}$ **d** $\dfrac{6}{\tan 40°}$

13 Use your calculator to work out the values of the following.

a 8 sin 75° **b** $\dfrac{19}{\sin 23°}$ **c** 7 cos 71° **d** $\dfrac{15}{\sin 81°}$

14 Use your calculator to work out the values of the following.

a 8 tan 75°   **b** $\dfrac{19}{\tan 23°}$ **c** 7 tan 71°   **d** $\dfrac{15}{\tan 81°}$

15 Using the following triangles calculate sin x, cos x, and tan x. Leave your answers as fractions.

a

b

c
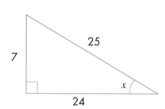

6.5 Calculating angles

In this section you will learn how to:
- use the trigonometric ratios to calculate an angle

Key word
inverse functions

The sine of 54° is 0.809 016 994 4 (to 10 decimal places).

The sine of 55° is 0.819 152 044 3 (to 10 decimal places).

What angle has a sine of 0.815?

Obviously, it is between 54° and 55°, so we could probably use a trial-and-improvement method to find it. But there is an easier way which uses the **inverse functions** on your calculator.

An inverse function can be accessed in several different ways. For example, the inverse function for sine may be any of these keys:

The inverse function printed above the sine key is usually given in either of the following ways:

sin⁻¹   arcsin
[sin]   or   [sin]

You will need to find out how your calculator deals with inverse functions.

When you do the inverse sine of 0.815, you should get 54.587 361 89°.

It is normal in trigonometry to round off angles to one decimal place. So, the angle with a sine of 0.815 is 54.6° (1 decimal place).

This can be written as $\sin^{-1} 0.815 = 54.6°$.

EXAMPLE 9

Find the angle with a cosine of 0.654.

$$\cos^{-1} 0.654 = 49.156\,131\,92° = 49.2° \text{ (1 decimal place)}$$

EXAMPLE 10

Find the angle with a sine of $(3 \div 4)$.

How you solve this will depend on your type of calculator. So key in either

| 3 | ÷ | 4 | = | INV | sin | or | INV | sin | (| 3 | ÷ | 4 |) | = |

So $\sin^{-1}\left(\frac{3}{4}\right) = 48.590\,377\,89° = 48.6°$ (1 decimal place)

EXAMPLE 11

Find the angle with a tangent of 0.75.

$$\tan^{-1} 0.75 = 36.869\,897\,65 = 36.9° \text{ (1 decimal place)}$$

EXERCISE 6G

Use your calculator to find the answers to the following. Give your answers to one decimal place.

1 What angles have the following sines?

  a 0.5   **b** 0.785   **c** 0.64   **d** 0.877   **e** 0.999   **f** 0.707

2 What angles have the following cosines?

  a 0.5   **b** 0.64   **c** 0.999   **d** 0.707   **e** 0.2   **f** 0.7

3 What angles have the following tangents?

  a 0.6   **b** 0.38   **c** 0.895   **d** 1.05   **e** 2.67   **f** 4.38

4 What angles have the following sines?

  a $4 \div 5$ **b** $2 \div 3$ **c** $7 \div 10$ **d** $5 \div 6$ **e** $1 \div 24$ **f** $5 \div 13$

5 What angles have the following cosines?

  a $4 \div 5$ **b** $2 \div 3$ **c** $7 \div 10$ **d** $5 \div 6$ **e** $1 \div 24$ **f** $5 \div 13$

6 What angles have the following tangents?

  a $3 \div 5$ **b** $7 \div 9$ **c** $2 \div 7$ **d** $9 \div 5$ **e** $11 \div 7$ **f** $6 \div 5$

7 What happens when you try to find the angle with a sine of 1.2? What is the largest value of sine you can put into your calculator without getting an error when you ask for the inverse sine? What is the smallest?

8 **a** **i** What angle has a sine of 0.3? (Keep the answer in your calculator memory.)

ii What angle has a cosine of 0.3?

iii Add the two accurate answers of parts **i** and **ii** together.

b Will you always get the same answer to the above no matter what number you start with?

6.6 Using the sine function

In this section you will learn how to:
- find lengths of sides and angles in right-angled triangles using the sine function

Key word
sine

Remember sine $\theta = \dfrac{\text{Opposite}}{\text{Hypotenuse}}$

We can use the **sine** ratio to calculate the lengths of sides and angles in right-angled triangles.

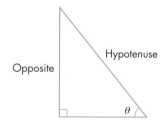

EXAMPLE 12

Find the angle θ, given that the opposite side is 7 cm and the hypotenuse is 10 cm.

Draw a diagram. (This is an essential step.)

From the information given, use sine.

$$\sin \theta = \frac{O}{H} = \frac{7}{10} = 0.7$$

What angle has a sine of 0.7? To find out, use the inverse sine function on your calculator.

$$\sin^{-1} 0.7 = 44.4° \text{ (1 decimal place)}$$

EXAMPLE 13

Find the length of the side marked a in this triangle.

Side a is the opposite side, with 12 cm as the hypotenuse, so use sine.

$$\sin \theta \;=\; \frac{O}{H}$$

$$\sin 35° = \frac{a}{12}$$

So $a = 12 \sin 35° = 6.88$ cm (3 significant figures)

EXAMPLE 14

Find the length of the hypotenuse, h, in this triangle.

Note that although the angle is in the other corner, the opposite side is again given. So use sine.

$$\sin \theta \;=\; \frac{O}{H}$$

$$\sin 52° = \frac{8}{h}$$

So $h = \dfrac{8}{\sin 52°} = 10.2$ cm (3 significant figures)

EXERCISE 6H

1 Find the angle marked x in each of these triangles.

a 10 cm 3 cm x

b 8 cm x 3 cm

c 8 cm x 15 cm

2 Find the side marked x in each of these triangles.

a 13 cm x 24°

b 8 cm 46° x

c 32° 25 cm x

3 Find the side marked x in each of these triangles.

a x 3 cm 41°

b x 61° 6 cm

c 59 cm 36° x

4 Find the side marked x in each of these triangles.

a 7 cm, x, 47° **b** x, 8 cm, 55° **c** 64°, 13 cm, x **d** 75°, x, 15 cm

5 Find the value of x in each of these triangles.

a 11 cm, 15 cm, x **b** 9 cm, x, 37° **c** 17°, x, 4 cm **d** 8 cm, x, 13 cm

6 Angle θ has a sine of $\frac{3}{5}$. Calculate the missing lengths in these triangles.

θ, 10, x; θ, x, 9; 50, x, θ

6.7 Using the cosine function

In this section you will learn how to:
- find lengths of sides and angles in right-angled triangles using the cosine function

Key word
cosine

Remember cosine $\theta = \dfrac{\text{Adjacent}}{\text{Hypotenuse}}$

We can use the **cosine** ratio to calculate the lengths of sides and angles in right-angled triangles.

EXAMPLE 15

Find the angle θ, given that the adjacent side is 5 cm and the hypotenuse is 12 cm.

Draw a diagram. (This is an essential step.)

From the information given, use cosine.

$$\cos \theta = \frac{A}{H} = \frac{5}{12}$$

What angle has a cosine of $\frac{5}{12}$? To find out, use the inverse cosine function on your calculator.

$$\cos^{-1} = 65.4° \text{ (1 decimal place)}$$

EXAMPLE 16

Find the length of the side marked a in this triangle.

Side a is the adjacent side, with 9 cm as the hypotenuse, so use cosine.

$$\cos \theta = \frac{A}{H}$$

$$\cos 47° = \frac{a}{9}$$

So $a = 9 \cos 47° = 6.14$ cm (3 significant figures)

EXAMPLE 17

Find the length of the hypotenuse, h, in this triangle.

The adjacent side is given. So use cosine.

$$\cos \theta = \frac{A}{H}$$

$$\cos 40° = \frac{20}{h}$$

So $h = \dfrac{20}{\cos 40°} = 26.1$ cm (3 significant figures)

EXERCISE 6I

B

1 Find the angle marked x in each of these triangles.

a

8 cm
5 cm
x

b

4 cm
x
1 cm

c

100 cm
160 cm
x

2 Find the side marked x in each of these triangles.

a

9 cm
44°
x

b

42 cm
39°
x

c

x
12°
140 cm

3 Find the side marked x in each of these triangles.

a

x
35°
6 cm

b

x
69°
14 cm

c

125 cm
22°
x

4 Find the side marked x in each of these triangles.

a

8 cm
48°
x

b

36°
x
12 cm

c

11 cm
24°
x

d

52° 14 cm
x

5 Find the value of x in each of these triangles.

a

10 cm
56°
x

b

16 cm
x
11 cm

c

6.5 cm
49°
x

d

13 cm
x
17 cm

6 Angle θ has a cosine of $\frac{5}{13}$. Calculate the missing lengths in these triangles.

x
θ
26

θ
15
x

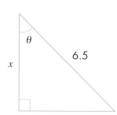
θ
6.5
x

Using the tangent function

In this section you will learn how to:

● find lengths of sides and angles in right-angled triangles using the tangent function

Key word

tangent

Remember tangent $\theta = \dfrac{\text{Opposite}}{\text{Adjacent}}$

We can use the **tangent** ratio to calculate the lengths of sides and angles in right-angled triangles.

Opposite

θ

Adjacent

EXAMPLE 18

Find the angle θ, given that the opposite side is 3 cm and the adjacent side is 4 cm.

Draw a diagram. (This is an essential step.)

From the information given, use tangent.

$$\tan \theta = \frac{O}{A} = \frac{3}{4} = 0.75$$

What angle has a tangent of 0.75? To find out, use the inverse tangent function on your calculator.

$$\tan^{-1} 0.75 = 36.9° \text{ (1 decimal place)}$$

3 cm

4 cm

θ

EXAMPLE 19

Find the length of the side marked x in this triangle.

Side x is the opposite side, with 9 cm as the adjacent side, so use tangent.

$$\tan \theta \quad = \frac{O}{A}$$

$$\tan 62° = \frac{x}{9}$$

So $x = 9 \tan 62° = 16.9$ cm (3 significant figures)

62°

9 cm

x

EXAMPLE 20

Find the length of the side marked a in this triangle.

Side a is the adjacent side and the opposite side is given.
So use tangent.

$$\tan \theta = \frac{O}{A}$$

$$\tan 35° = \frac{6}{a}$$

So $a = \dfrac{6}{\tan 35°} = 8.57$ cm (3 significant figures)

EXERCISE 6J

1 Find the angle marked x in each of these triangles.

a

b

c

2 Find the side marked x in each of these triangles.

a

b

c

3 Find the side marked x in each of these triangles.

a

b

c

4 Find the side marked x in each of these triangles.

a

b

c

d

5 Find the value x in each of these triangles.

 a

 b

 c

 d

6 Angle θ has a tangent of $\frac{4}{3}$. Calculate the missing lengths in these triangles.

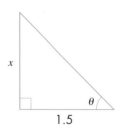

6.9 Which ratio to use

In this section you will learn how to:
- decide which trigonometric ratio to use in a right-angled triangle

Key words
sine
cosine
tangent

The difficulty with any trigonometric problem is knowing which ratio to use to solve it.

The following examples show you how to determine which ratio you need in any given situation.

EXAMPLE 21

Find the length of the side marked x in this triangle.

Step 1 Identify what information is given and what needs to be found. Namely, x is opposite the angle and 16 cm is the hypotenuse.

Step 2 Decide which ratio to use. Only one ratio uses opposite and hypotenuse: **sine**.

Step 3 Remember $\sin \theta = \dfrac{O}{H}$

Step 4 Put in the numbers and letters: $\sin 37° = \dfrac{x}{16}$

Step 5 Rearrange the equation and work out the answer: $x = 16 \sin 37° = 9.629\,040\,371$ cm

Step 6 Give the answer to an appropriate degree of accuracy: $x = 9.63$ cm (3 significant figures)

In reality, you do not write down every step as in Example 21. Step 1 can be done by marking the triangle. Steps 2 and 3 can be done in your head. Steps 4 to 6 are what you write down.

Remember that examiners will want to see evidence of working. Any reasonable attempt at identifying the sides and using a ratio will probably get you some method marks – but only if the fraction is the right way round.

The next examples are set out in a way that requires the *minimum* amount of working but gets *maximum* marks.

EXAMPLE 22

Find the length of the side marked x in this triangle.

Mark on the triangle the side you know (H) and the side you want to find (A).

Recognise it is a **cosine** problem because you have A and H.

So $\cos 50° = \dfrac{x}{7}$

$x = 7 \cos 50° = 4.50$ cm (3 significant figures)

EXAMPLE 23

Find the angle marked x in this triangle.

Mark on the triangle the sides you know.

Recognise it is a sine problem because you have O and H.

So $\sin x = \dfrac{9}{15} = 0.6$

$x = \sin^{-1} 0.6 = 36.9°$ (1 decimal place)

EXAMPLE 24

Find the angle marked x in this triangle.

Mark on the triangle the sides you know.

Recognise it is a **tangent** problem because you have O and A.

So $\tan x = \dfrac{12}{7}$

$x = \tan^{-1} \dfrac{12}{7} = 59.7°$ (1 decimal place)

EXERCISE 6K

1 Find the length marked x in each of these triangles.

a

b

c

d

e

f
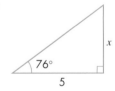

2 Find the angle marked x in each of these triangles.

a

b

c

d

e

f
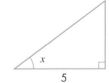

3 Find the angle or length marked *x* in each of these triangles.

a

b

c

d

e

f

g

h

i

j

4 In a maths textbook it says:

The tangent of any angle is equal to the sine of the angle divided by the cosine of the angle.

a Show clearly that this is true for an angle of 30°.

b Prove, by using the definitions of sin θ and cos θ, that the statement is true for this right-angled triangle.

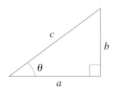

Solving problems using trigonometry

In this section you will learn how to:
- solve practical problems using trigonometry
- solve problems using an angle of elevation or an angle of depression
- solve bearing problems using trigonometry
- using trigonometry to solve problems involving isosceles triangles

Key words
angle of depression
angle of elevation
bearing
isosceles triangle
three-figure bearing
trigonometry

Most **trigonometry** problems in GCSE examination papers do not come as straightforward triangles. Usually, solving a triangle is part of solving a practical problem. You should follow these steps when solving a practical problem using trigonometry.

- Draw the triangle required.

- Put on the information given (angles and sides).

- Put on x for the unknown angle or side.

- Mark on two of O, A or H as appropriate.

- Choose which ratio to use.

- Write out the equation with the numbers in.

- Rearrange the equation if necessary, then work out the answer.

- Give your answer to a sensible degree of accuracy. Answers given to three significant figures or to the nearest degree are acceptable in exams.

EXAMPLE 25

A window cleaner has a ladder which is 7 m long. The window cleaner leans it against a wall so that the foot of the ladder is 3 m from the wall. What angle does the ladder make with the wall?

Draw the situation as a right-angled triangle.

Then mark the sides and angle.

Recognise it is a sine problem because you have O and H.

So $\sin x = \dfrac{3}{7}$

$x = \sin^{-1} \dfrac{3}{7} = 25°$ (to the nearest degree)

EXERCISE 6L

In these questions, give answers involving angles to the nearest degree.

1 A ladder, 6 m long, rests against a wall. The foot of the ladder is 2.5 m from the base of the wall. What angle does the ladder make with the ground?

2 The ladder in question **1** has a "safe angle" with the ground of between 60° and 70°. What are the safe limits for the distance of the foot of the ladder from the wall?

3 Another ladder, of length 10 m, is placed so that it reaches 7 m up the wall. What angle does it make with the ground?

4 Yet another ladder is placed so that it makes an angle of 76° with the ground. When the foot of the ladder is 1.7 m from the foot of the wall, how high up the wall does the ladder reach?

5 Calculate the angle that the diagonal makes with the long side of a rectangle which measures 10 cm by 6 cm.

6 This diagram shows a frame for a bookcase.

   a What angle does the diagonal strut make with the long side?

   b Use Pythagoras' theorem to calculate the length of the strut.

0.9 m

1.9 m

7 This diagram shows a roof truss.

   a What angle will the roof make with the horizontal?

   b Use Pythagoras' theorem to calculate the length of the sloping strut.

1.6 m

4.5 m

8 Alicia paces out 100 m from the base of a church. She then measures the angle to the top of the spire as 23°. How high is the church spire?

23°

100 m

9 A girl is flying a kite on a string 32 m long. The string, which is being held at 1 m above the ground, makes an angle of 39° with the horizontal. How high is the kite above the ground?

32 m

39°

1 m

10 Angle θ has a sine of $\frac{3}{5}$.

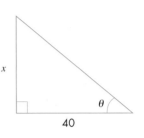

a Use Pythagoras' theorem to calculate the missing side of this triangle.

b Write down the cosine and the tangent of θ.

c Calculate the missing lengths marked x in these triangles.

i   **ii**   **iii**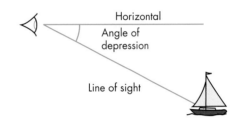

Angles of elevation and depression

When you look *up* at an aircraft in the sky, the angle through which your line of sight turns from looking straight ahead (the horizontal) is called the **angle of elevation**.

When you are standing on a high point and look *down* at a boat, the angle through which your line of sight turns from looking straight ahead (the horizontal) is called the **angle of depression**.

EXAMPLE 26

From the top of a vertical cliff, 100 m high, Andrew sees a boat out at sea. The angle of depression from Andrew to the boat is 42°. How far from the base of the cliff is the boat?

The diagram of the situation is shown in figure **i**.

From this, you get the triangle shown in figure **ii**.

From figure **ii**, you see that this is a tangent problem.

So $\tan 42° = \dfrac{100}{x}$

$x = \dfrac{100}{\tan 42°} = 111$ m (3 significant figures)

EXERCISE 6M

In these questions, give any answers involving angles to the nearest degree.

1 Eric sees an aircraft in the sky. The aircraft is at a horizontal distance of 25 km from Eric. The angle of elevation is 22°. How high is the aircraft?

2 A passenger in an aircraft hears the pilot say that they are flying at an altitude of 4000 m and are 10 km from the airport. If the passenger can see the airport, what is the angle of depression?

3 A man standing 200 m from the base of a television transmitter looks at the top of it and notices that the angle of elevation of the top is 65°. How high is the tower?

4 From the top of a vertical cliff, 200 m high, a boat has an angle of depression of 52°. How far from the base of the cliff is the boat?

5 From a boat, the angle of elevation of the foot of a lighthouse on the edge of a cliff is 34°.

   a If the cliff is 150 m high, how far from the base of the cliff is the boat?

   b If the lighthouse is 50 m high, what would be the angle of elevation of the top of the lighthouse from the boat?

6 A bird flies from the top of a 12 m tall tree, at an angle of depression of 34°, to catch a worm on the ground.

   a How far does the bird actually fly?   **b** How far was the worm from the base of the tree?

7 Sunil stands about 50 m away from a building. The angle of elevation from Sunil to the top of the building is about 15°. How tall is the building?

8 The top of a ski run is 100 m above the finishing line. The run is 300 m long. What is the angle of depression of the ski run?

Trigonometry and bearings

A **bearing** is the direction to one place from another. The usual way of giving a bearing is as an angle measured from north in a clockwise direction. This is how a navigational compass and a surveyor's compass measure bearings.

A bearing is always written as a three-digit number, known as a **three-figure bearing**.

The diagram shows how this works, using the main compass points as examples.

When working with bearings, follow these three rules.

- Always start from *north*.

- Always measure *clockwise*.

- Always give a bearing in degrees and as a *three-figure bearing*.

The difficulty with trigonometric problems involving bearings is dealing with those angles greater than 90° whose trigonometric ratios have negative values. To avoid this, we have to find a right-angled triangle that we can readily use. Example 27 shows you how to deal with such a situation.

EXAMPLE 27

A ship sails on a bearing of 120° for 50 km. How far east has it travelled?

The diagram of the situation is shown in figure **i**. From this, you can get the acute-angled triangle shown in figure **ii**.

From figure **ii**, you see that this is a cosine problem.

So $\cos 30° = \dfrac{x}{50}$

$x = 50 \cos 30° = 43.301 = 43.3$ km (3 significant figures)

EXERCISE 6N

1 A ship sails for 75 km on a bearing of 078°.

    a How far east has it travelled?   **b** How far north has it travelled?

2 Lopham is 17 miles from Wath on a bearing of 210°.

    a How far south of Wath is Lopham?   **b** How far east of Lopham is Wath?

3 A plane sets off from an airport and flies due east for 120 km, then turns to fly due south for 70 km before landing at Seddeth. What is the bearing of Seddeth from the airport?

4 A helicopter leaves an army base and flies 60 km on a bearing of 278°.

    a How far west has the helicopter flown?   **b** How far north has the helicopter flown?

5 A ship sails from a port on a bearing of 117° for 35 km before heading due north for 40 km and docking at Angle Bay.

    a How far south had the ship sailed before turning?

    b How far north had the ship sailed from the port to Angle Bay?

    c How far east is Angle Bay from the port?

    d What is the bearing from the port to Angle Bay?

6 Mountain A is due west of a walker. Mountain B is due north of the walker. The guidebook says that mountain B is 4.3 km from mountain A, on a bearing of 058°. How far is the walker from mountain B?

7 The diagram shows the relative distances and bearings of three ships A, B and C.

   a How far north of A is B? (Distance x on diagram.)

   b How far north of B is C? (Distance y on diagram.)

   c How far west of A is C? (Distance z on diagram.)

   d What is the bearing of A from C? (Angle $w°$ on diagram.)

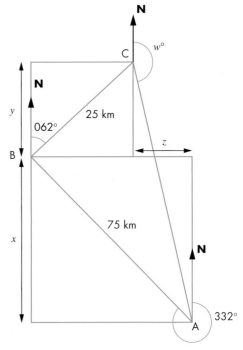

8 A ship sails from port A for 42 km on a bearing of 130° to point B. It then changes course and sails for 24 km on a bearing of 040° to point C, where it breaks down and anchors. What distance and on what bearing will a helicopter have to fly from port A to go directly to the ship at C?

Trigonometry and isosceles triangles

Isosceles triangles often feature in trigonometry problems because such a triangle can be split into two right-angled triangles that are congruent.

EXAMPLE 28

   a Find the length x in this isosceles triangle.

   b Calculate the area of the triangle.

Draw a perpendicular from the apex of the triangle to its base, splitting the triangle into two congruent, right-angled triangles.

   a To find the length y, which is $\frac{1}{2}$ of x, use cosine.

      So, $\cos 53° = \dfrac{y}{7}$

      $y = 7\cos 53° = 4.2127051$ cm

      So the length $x = 2y = 8.43$ cm (3 significant figures).

b To calculate the area of the original triangle, you first need to find its vertical height, *h*.

You have two choices, both of which involve the right-angled triangle of part a. We can use either Pythagoras' theorem ($h^2 + y^2 = 7^2$) or trigonometry. It is safer to use trigonometry again, since we are then still using known information.

This is a sine problem.

So, $\sin 53° = \dfrac{h}{7}$

$h = 7 \sin 53° = 5.590\,448\,6$ cm (Keep the accurate figure in the calculator.)

The area of the triangle $= \frac{1}{2} \times$ base $\times$ height. (We should use the most accurate figures we have for this calculation.)

$A = \frac{1}{2} \times 8.425\,410\,3 \times 5.590\,448\,6 = 23.6$ cm^2 (3 significant figures)

You are not expected to write down these eight-figure numbers, just to use them.

Note: If you use rounded-off values to calculate the area, the answer would be 23.5 cm^2, which is different from the one calculated using the most accurate data. So never use rounded-off data when you can use accurate data – unless you are just estimating.

EXERCISE 6P

In questions 1–4, find the side or angle marked *x*.

5 This diagram below shows a roof truss. How wide is the roof?

6 Calculate the area of each of these triangles.

a

b

c

d

1 A rectangular field ABCD is shown.
The length of the field, AB = 160 m.
The width of the field, BC = 75 m.

Calculate the length of the diagonal BD.

Give your answer to a suitable degree of accuracy.

AQA, Question 1, Paper 2 Higher, November 2004

2 A support for a flagpole is attached at a height of 3 m and is fixed to the ground at a distance of 1.2 m from the base.

Calculate the length of the support (marked x on the diagram).

AQA, Question 1, Paper 2 Higher, June 2003

3 **a** The diagram shows a right-angled triangle ABC.
AB = 10 cm and AC = 15 cm

Calculate the length of BC.

b Triangle PQR is similar to triangle ABC.
angle CAB = angle RPQ
PQ = 25 cm

Work out the length of PR.

AQA, Question 9a, Paper 1 Higher, June 2004

4 A ladder leans against the side of a house. The ladder is 4.5 m in length.

a The ladder makes an angle of 74° with the ground. How high up the wall will it reach? (marked x in the diagram) Give your answer to an appropriate degree of accuracy.

b The same ladder is now placed 0.9 m away from the side of the house. What angle does the ladder now make with the ground? (marked y in the diagram)

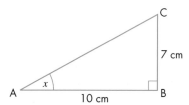

AQA, Question 10, Paper 2 Higher, June 2001

5 **a** ABC is a right angled triangle. AB = 10 cm, BC = 7 cm. Find the size of angle CAB (marked x in the diagram).

b PQR is a right-angled triangle. PQ = 12 cm, angle QPR = 48°. Find the length of PR (marked y in the diagram). Give your answer to an appropriate degree of accuracy.

AQA, Question 3, Paper 2 Higher, November 2002

6 The diagram shows the side view of a wheelchair ramp. The ramp makes an angle of 4° with the horizontal. Calculate the length, marked x, of the ramp. Give your answer in metres to a sensible degree of accuracy.

AQA, Question 5, Paper 2 Higher, November 2001

7 The diagram shows two right-angled triangles. AD = 15 cm. CD = 6 cm.

a Given that $\cos x° = \dfrac{2}{3}$, calculate the length BD.

b Find the value of $\sin y°$.

AQA, Question 9, Paper 1 Higher, November 2003

WORKED EXAM QUESTION

a ABC is a right-angled triangle. AC = 19 cm and AB = 9 cm.

Calculate the length of BC.

b PQR is a right-angled triangle. PQ = 11 cm and QR = 24 cm.

Calculate the size of angle PRQ.

c ABC and ACD are right-angled triangles. AD is parallel to BC. AB = 12 cm, BC = 5 cm and AD = 33.8 cm.

Calculate the size of angle ADC.

AQA, Question 10, Paper 2 Higher, June 2005

Solution

a Let BC = x
By Pythagoras' theorem
$$x^2 = 19^2 - 9^2 \text{ cm}^2$$
$$= 280 \text{ cm}^2$$
So $x = \sqrt{280} = 16.7$ cm (3 sf)

b Let $\angle PRQ = \theta$
So $\tan \theta = \dfrac{11}{24}$

$\theta = \tan^{-1} \dfrac{11}{24} = 24.6°$ (1 dp)

c In triangle ABC, let AC = y
By Pythagoras' theorem
$$y^2 = 5^2 + 12^2 \text{ cm}^2$$
$$= 169 \text{ cm}^2$$
$$y = \sqrt{169} = 13 \text{ cm}$$
In triangle ACD, let $\angle ADC = z$
So, $\sin z = \dfrac{13}{33.8} = 0.3846$
$z = \sin^{-1} 0.3846 = 22.6°$ (1 dp)

GRADE YOURSELF

C Able to use Pythagoras' theorem in right-angled triangles

C Able to solve problems in 2-D using Pythagoras' theorem

B Able to solve problems in 3-D using Pythagoras' theorem

B Able to use trigonometry to find lengths of sides and angles in right-angled triangles

B Able to use trigonometry to solve problems

What you should know now

- How to use Pythagoras' theorem
- How to solve problems using Pythagoras' theorem
- How to use the trigonometric ratios for sine, cosine and tangent in right-angled triangles
- How to solve problems using trigonometry
- How to solve problems using angles of elevation, angles of depression and bearings

Geometry

1 Special triangles and quadrilaterals

2 Angles in polygons

3 Circle theorems

4 Cyclic quadrilaterals

5 Tangents and chords

6 Alternate segment theorem

This chapter will show you ...

- how to find angles in triangles and quadrilaterals
- how to find interior and exterior angles in polygons
- how to find angles using circle theorems

What you should already know

- Vertically opposite angles are equal. The angles labelled a and b are vertically opposite angles.

- The angles on a straight line add up to 180°, so $a + b = 180°$. This is true for any number of angles on a line. For example, $c + d + e + f = 180°$

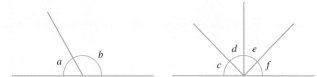

- The sum of the angles around a point is 360°. For example, $a + b + c + d + e = 360°$

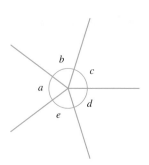

continued

- The three interior angles of a triangle add up to 180°. So, $a + b + c = 180°$

- The four interior angles of a quadrilateral add up to 360°.

  So, $a + b + c + d = 360°$

- A line which cuts parallel lines is called a transversal. The equal angles so formed are called alternate angles.

corresponding angles

Because of their positions, the angles shown above are called corresponding angles.

Two angles positioned like a and b, which add up to 180°, are called allied angles.

- A polygon is a 2-D shape with straight sides.

- Circle terms

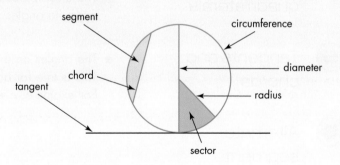

Quick check

Find the marked angles in these diagrams.

1

2

3

Special triangles and quadrilaterals

In this section you will learn how to:
- find angles in triangles and quadrilaterals

Key words

equilateral
   triangle
isosceles
   triangle
kite
parallelogram
rhombus
trapezium

Special triangles

An **equilateral triangle** is a triangle with all its sides equal.

Therefore, all three interior angles are 60°.

An **isosceles triangle** is a triangle with two equal sides, and therefore with two equal angles.

Notice how we mark the equal sides and equal angles.

EXAMPLE 1

Find the angle marked a in the triangle.

The triangle is isosceles, so both base angles are 70°.

So $a = 180° - 70° - 70° = 40°$

Special quadrilaterals

A **trapezium** has two parallel sides.

The sum of the interior angles at the ends of each non-parallel side is 180°: that is, ∠A + ∠D = 180° and ∠B + ∠C = 180°.

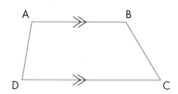

A **parallelogram** has opposite sides parallel.

Its opposite sides are equal. Its diagonals bisect each other. Its opposite angles are equal: that is, ∠A = ∠C and ∠B = ∠D.

A **rhombus** is a parallelogram with all its sides equal.

Its diagonals bisect each other at right angles. Its diagonals also bisect the angles at the vertices.

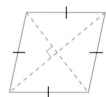

A **kite** is a quadrilateral with two pairs of equal adjacent sides.

Its longer diagonal bisects its shorter diagonal at right angles.
The opposite angles between the sides of different lengths are equal.

EXAMPLE 2

Find the angles marked x and y in this parallelogram.

$x = 55°$ (opposite angles are equal) and $y = 125°$ ($x + y = 180°$)

EXERCISE 7A

1 Calculate the lettered angles in each triangle.

2 An isosceles triangle has an angle of 50°. Sketch the two different possible triangles that match this description, showing what each angle is.

3 Find the missing angles in these quadrilaterals.

a

b

c

d

e

f

4 The three angles of an isosceles triangle are $2x$, $x - 10$ and $x - 10$. What is the actual size of each angle?

5 Calculate the lettered angles in these diagrams.

6 Calculate the values of x and y in each of these quadrilaterals.

a

b

c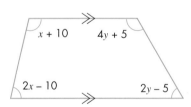

7 Find the value of x in each of these quadrilaterals and hence state the type of quadrilateral it is.

a a quadrilateral with angles $x + 10$, $x + 20$, $2x + 20$, $2x + 10$

b a quadrilateral with angles $x - 10$, $2x + 10$, $x - 10$, $2x + 10$

c a quadrilateral with angles $x - 10$, $2x$, $5x - 10$, $5x - 10$

d a quadrilateral with angles $4x + 10$, $5x - 10$, $3x + 30$, $2x + 50$

In this section you will learn how to:

- find interior angles and exterior angles in a polygon

Key words

exterior angle
heptagon
hexagon
interior angle
octagon
pentagon
polygon
regular
    polygon

A **polygon** has two kinds of angle.

- **Interior angles** are angles made by adjacent sides of the polygon and lying inside the polygon.

- **Exterior angles** are angles lying on the outside of the polygon, so that the interior angle + the exterior angle = 180°.

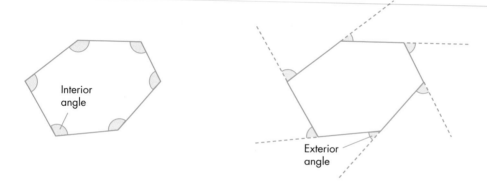

The *exterior* angles of *any* polygon add up to 360°.

Interior angles

You can find the sum of the interior angles of any polygon by splitting it into triangles.

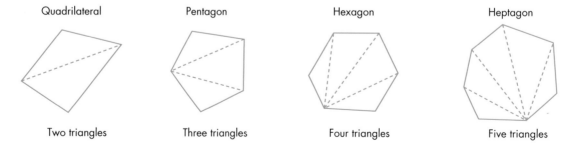

Quadrilateral   Pentagon   Hexagon   Heptagon

Two triangles   Three triangles   Four triangles   Five triangles

Since we already know that the angles in a triangle add up to 180°, the sum of the interior angles in a polygon is found by multiplying the number of triangles in the polygon by 180°, as shown in this table.

Shape	Name	Sum of interior angles
4-sided	Quadrilateral	$2 \times 180° = 360°$
5-sided	Pentagon	$3 \times 180° = 540°$
6-sided	Hexagon	$4 \times 180° = 720°$
7-sided	Heptagon	$5 \times 180° = 900°$
8-sided	Octagon	$6 \times 180° = 1080°$

As you can see from the table, for an n-sided polygon, the sum of the interior angles, S, is given by the formula

$$S = 180(n - 2)°$$

Exterior angles

As you see from the diagram, the sum of an exterior angle and its adjacent interior angle is 180°.

Interior angle

Exterior angle

Regular polygons

A polygon is regular if all its interior angles are equal and all its sides have the same length. This means that all the exterior angles are also equal.

Here are two simple formulae for calculating the interior and the exterior angles of **regular polygons**.

The exterior angle, E, of a regular n-sided polygon is $E = \dfrac{360°}{n}$

The interior angle, I, of a regular n-sided polygon is $I = 180° - E = 180° - \dfrac{360°}{n}$

EXAMPLE 3

Find the exterior angle, x, and the interior angle, y, for this regular octagon.

$x = \dfrac{360°}{8} = 45°$ and $y = 180° - 45° = 135°$

EXERCISE 7B

1 Calculate the sum of the interior angles of polygons with these numbers of sides.

a 10 sides **b** 15 sides **c** 100 sides **d** 45 sides

2 Calculate the size of the interior angle of regular polygons with these numbers of sides.

a 12 sides **b** 20 sides **c** 9 sides **d** 60 sides

3 Find the number of sides of polygons with these interior angle sums.

a 1260° **b** 2340° **c** 18 000° **d** 8640°

4 Find the number of sides of regular polygons with these exterior angles.

a 24° **b** 10° **c** 15° **d** 5°

5 Find the number of sides of regular polygons with these interior angles.

a 150° **b** 140° **c** 162° **d** 171°

6 Calculate the size of the unknown angle in each of these polygons.

a

b

c
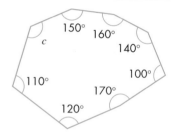

7 Find the value of x in each of these polygons.

a

b

c

8 What is the name of the regular polygon whose interior angles are twice its exterior angles?

9 Wesley measured all the interior angles in a polygon. He added them up to make 991°, but he had missed out one angle.

a What type of polygon did Wesley measure?

b What is the size of the missing angle?

10 **a** In the triangle ABC, angle A is 42°, angle B is 67°.

    i Calculate the value of angle C.

    ii What is the value of the exterior angle at C.

    iii What connects the exterior angle at C with the sum of the angles at A and B?

  b Prove that any exterior angle of a triangle is equal to the sum of the two opposite interior angles.

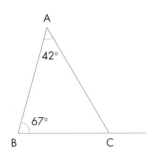

7.3 Circle theorems

In this section you will learn how to:

- find angles in circles

Key words

arc
circle
circumference
diameter
segment
semicircle
subtended

Here are three **circle** theorems you need to know.

- **Circle theorem 1**

The angle at the centre of a circle is twice the angle at the **circumference subtended** by the same **arc**.

$$\angle AOB = 2 \times \angle ACB$$

- **Circle theorem 2**

Every angle at the circumference of a **semicircle** that is subtended by the **diameter** of the semicircle is a right angle.

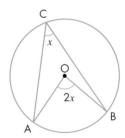

- **Circle theorem 3**

Angles at the circumference in the same **segment** of a circle are equal.

Points C_1, C_2, C_3 and C_4 on the circumference are subtended by the same arc AB.

So $\angle AC_1B = \angle AC_2B = \angle AC_3B = \angle AC_4B$

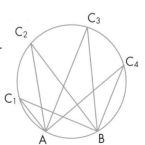

Follow through Examples 4–6 to see how these theorems are applied.

EXAMPLE 4

O is the centre of each circle. Find the angles marked *a* and *b* in each circle.

i

ii

i   *a* = 35° (angles in same segment)

   b = 2 × 35° (angle at centre = twice angle at circumference)

   = 70°

ii With OP = OQ, triangle OPQ is isosceles and the sum of the angles in this triangle = 180°

   So   *a* + (2 × 25°) = 180°

      a = 180° − (2 × 25°)

         = 130°

      b = 130° ÷ 2 (angle at centre = twice angle at circumference)

         = 65°

EXAMPLE 5

O is the centre of the circle. PQR is a straight line.

Find the angle labelled *a*.

   ∠PQT = 180° − 72° = 108° (angles on straight line)

The reflex angle ∠POT = 2 × 108° (angle at centre = twice angle at circumference)

      = 216°

   a + 216° = 360° (sum of angles around a point)

      a = 360° − 216°

      a = 144°

EXAMPLE 6

O is the centre of the circle. POQ is parallel to TR.

Find the angles labelled *a* and *b*.

$a = 64° ÷ 2$ (angle at centre = twice angle at circumference)

$a = 32°$

$∠TQP = a$ (alternate angles)

$= 32°$

$∠PTQ = 90°$ (angle in a semicircle)

$b + 90° + 32° = 180°$ (sum of angles in △PQT)

$b = 180° - 122°$

$b = 58°$

EXERCISE 7C

1 Find the angle marked *x* in each of these circles with centre O.

a

b

c

d

e

f

g

h

2 Find the angle marked *x* in each of these circles with centre O.

a

b

c

d

e

f

g

h

3 In the diagram, O is the centre of the circle. Find these angles.

a ∠ADB

b ∠DBA

c ∠CAD

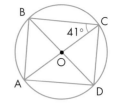

4 In the diagram, O is the centre of the circle. Find these angles.

a ∠EDF

b ∠DEG

c ∠EGF

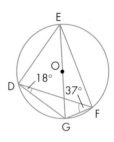

5 Find the angles marked x and y in each of these circles. O is the centre where shown.

a

b

c

d

e

f

  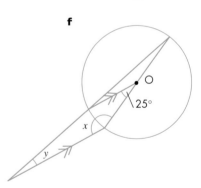

6 In the diagram, O is the centre and AD a diameter of the circle. Find x.

 7 A, B, C and D are points on the circumference of a circle with centre O. Angle ABO is $x°$ and angle CBO is $y°$.

a State the value of angle BAO.

b State the value of angle AOD

c Prove that the angle subtended by the chord AC at the centre of a circle is twice the angle subtended at the circumference.

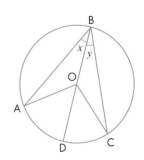

Cyclic quadrilaterals

In this section you will learn how to:
- find angles in cyclic quadrilaterals

Key word

cyclic quadrilateral

A quadrilateral whose four vertices lie on the circumference of a circle is called a **cyclic quadrilateral**.

- **Circle theorem 4**

The sum of the opposite angles of a cyclic quadrilateral is 180°.

$a + c = 180°$ and $b + d = 180°$

EXAMPLE 7

Find the angles marked x and y in the diagram.

$x + 85° = 180°$ (angles in a cyclic quadrilateral)

So $x = 95°$

$y + 108° = 180°$ (angles in a cyclic quadrilateral)

So $y = 72°$

EXERCISE 7D

1 Find the sizes of the lettered angles in each of these circles.

a

85°
130°
a b

b
x c
88° x

c
d e
f 70°

d
81°
g
h 105°

e
l
89°
j k

f
120°
140°
m
n

g
p
O ·)136°
q

h
34°
x
50° y

2 Find the values of *x* and *y* in each of these circles. Where shown, O marks the centre of the circle.

a

b

c

d

e

f

g

h

3 Find the values of *x* and *y* in each of these circles. Where shown, O marks the centre of the circle.

a

b

c

d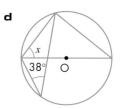

4 Find the values of *x* and *y* in each of these circles.

a **b** **c** **d**

5 Find the values of *x* and *y* in each of these circles with centre O.

a **b** **c** **d**

6 The cyclic quadrilateral PQRT has ∠ROQ equal to 38° where O is the centre of the circle. POT is a diameter and parallel to QR. Calculate these angles.

a ∠ROT

b ∠QRT

c ∠QPT

ABCD is a cyclic quadrilateral within a circle centre O and ∠AOC is 2x°.

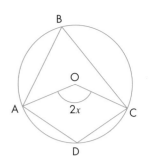

    a Write down the value of ∠ABC.

    b Write down the value of the reflex angle AOC.

    c Prove that the sum of a pair of opposite angles of a cyclic quadrilateral is 180°.

7.5 Tangents and chords

In this section you will learn how to:

- find angles in circles when tangents or chords are used

Key words

chord
point of contact
radius
tangent

A **tangent** is a straight line that touches a circle at one point only. This point is called the **point of contact**. A **chord** is a line that joins two points on the circumference.

- **Circle theorem 5**

    A tangent to a circle is perpendicular to the **radius** drawn to the point of contact.

    The radius OX is perpendicular to the tangent AB.

- **Circle theorem 6**

    Tangents to a circle from an external point to the points of contact are equal in length.

    AX = AY

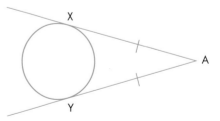

- **Circle theorem 7**

    The line joining an external point to the centre of the circle bisects the angle between the tangents.

    ∠OAX = ∠OAY

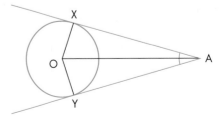

163

- **Circle theorem 8**

  A radius bisects a chord at 90°.

  If O is the centre of the circle

  ∠BMO = 90° and BM = CM.

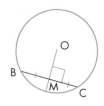

EXAMPLE 8

OA is the radius of the circle and AB is a tangent.

OA = 5 cm and AB = 12 cm.

Calculate the length OB.

∠OAB = 90° (radius is perpendicular to a tangent)

Let OB = x

By Pythagoras' theorem

$x^2 = 5^2 + 12^2$ cm^2

$x^2 = 169$ cm^2

So $x = \sqrt{169} = 13$ cm

EXERCISE 7E

1 In each diagram, TP and TQ are tangents to a circle with centre O. Find each value of x.

a   b   c   d

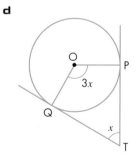

2 Each diagram shows tangents to a circle with centre O. Find each value of y.

a   b   c   d

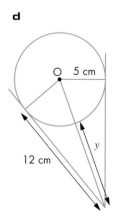

3 Each diagram shows a tangent to a circle with centre O. Find x and y in each case.

a

$78°$ x
y
O

b
y
x $40°$
O

c

$31°$
O x
y

d
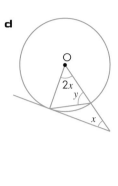
O
$2x$
y
x

4 In each of the diagrams, TP and TQ are tangents to the circle with centre O. Find each value of x.

a
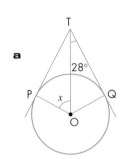
T
$28°$
P x Q
O

b
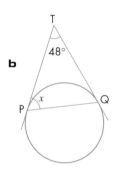
T
$48°$
P x Q
O

c
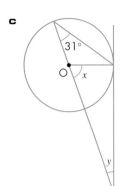
T
x
P $71°$ Q
O

d

P
x
$4x$ T
Q

5 Two circles with the same centre have radii of 7 cm and 12 cm respectively. A tangent to the inner circle cuts the outer circle at A and B. Find the length of AB.

6 AB and CB are tangents from B to the circle with centre O.
OA and OC are radii.

a Prove that angles AOB and COB are equal.

b Prove that OB bisects the angle ABC.

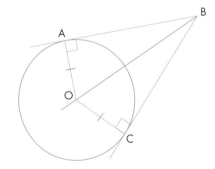
B
A
O
C

In this section you will learn how to:

- find angles in circles using the alternate segment theorem

Key words

alternate
    segment
chord
tangent

PTQ is the **tangent** to a circle at T. The segment containing ∠TBA is known as the **alternate segment** of ∠PTA, because it is on the other side of the **chord** AT from ∠PTA.

- **Circle theorem 9**

  The angle between a tangent and a chord through the point of contact is equal to the angle in the alternate segment.

  ∠PTA = ∠TBA

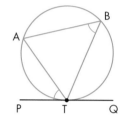

EXAMPLE 9

In the diagram, find **a** ∠ATS and **b** ∠TSR.

a ∠ATS = 80° (angle in alternate segment)

b ∠TSR = 70° (angle in alternate segment)

EXERCISE 7F

1   Find the size of each lettered angle.

a

b

c

d

2 In each diagram, find the size of each lettered angle.

a

b

c

d

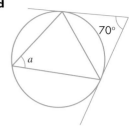

3 In each diagram, find the value of x.

a

b

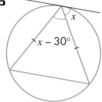

4 ATB is a tangent to each circle with centre O. Find the size of each lettered angle.

a

b

c

d

5 PT is a tangent to a circle with centre O.
AB are points on the circumference. Angle PBA is $x°$.

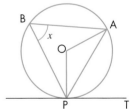

a Write down the value of angle AOP.

b Calculate the angle OPA in terms of x.

c Prove that the angle APT is equal to the angle PBA.

1 The diagram shows a regular octagon.

Calculate the size of the exterior angle of the regular octagon, marked y on the diagram.

AQA, Question 7, Paper 1 Intermediate, November 2004

2 The diagram shows part of a regular polygon. Each interior angle is 162°.

Calculate the number of sides of the polygon.

AQA, Question 1, Paper 1 Higher, June 2003

3 In the diagram, AOB is a diameter of the circle, centre O. TS is a tangent to the circle at C. Angle ABC = 57°.

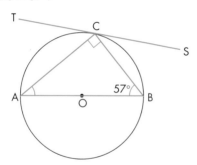

Calculate
a Angle CAB
b Angle ACS

AQA, Question 17, Paper 1 Higher, May 2002

4 A, B and C are points on the circumference of a circle with centre O. BD and CD are tangents. Angle BDC = 40°

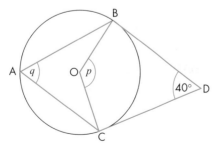

a i Work out the value of p.
   ii Hence write down the value of q.

b The tangent DB is extended to T. The line AO is added to the diagram from part **a**.
Angle TBA = 62°.

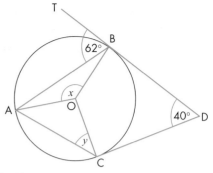

i Work out the value of x.
ii Work out the value of y.

AQA, Question 12, Paper 1 Higher, June 2005

5 a i The diagram shows a circle with centre O.

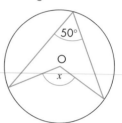

Work out the size of the angle marked x.

ii The diagram shows a different circle with centre O.

Work out the size of the angle marked y.

b The diagram shows a cyclic quadrilateral ABCD. The straight lines BA and CD are extended and meet at E.
EA = AC.
Angle ABC = $3x°$.
Angle ADC = $9x°$.
Angle DAC = $2x°$.

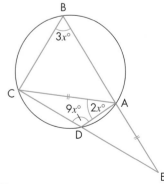

i Show that $x = 15$.
ii Calculate the size of angle EAD.

AQA, Question 15, Paper 1 Higher, November 2003

6 A, B, C are three points on a circle. ABE is a straight line and DCE is a tangent to the circle at C.
ABC is an isosceles triangle such that AB = AC.
ACE is an isosceles triangle such that AC = CE.

Find the angle BEC (marked x in the diagram).

AQA, Question 20, Paper 2 Higher, November 2002

WORKED EXAM QUESTION

a

   i Write down the value of x.

   ii Calculate the value of y.

b A and C are points on the circumference of a circle centre B.
AD and CD are tangents. Angle ADB = 40°.

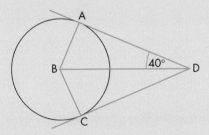

Explain why angle ABC is 100°.

c ABCD is a cyclic quadrilateral.
PAQ is a tangent to the circle at A.
BC = CD.
AD is parallel to BC.
Angle BAQ = 32°.

Find the size of angle BAD.
You must show all your working.

AQA, Question 14, Paper 2 Higher, November 2002

Solution

a i x = 40° (angle in same segment)

  ii y = 140° (opposite angles in cyclic
               quadrilateral = 180°)

b ∠BAD = 90° (radius is perpendicular to tangent)
   ∠ABD = 50° (angles in a triangle)

Similarly:

   ∠BCD = 90° (radius is perpendicular to tangent)
   ∠CBD = 50° (angles in a triangle)

So ∠ABC = 100°

c ∠ADB = 32° (alternate segment theorem)
   ∠DBC = 32° (alternate angles in parallel lines)
   ∠BDC = 32° (isosceles triangle)
   ∠DCB = 116° (angles in a triangle)

So ∠BAD = 64° (opposite angles in cyclic
                   quadrilateral = 180°)

GRADE YOURSELF

D Able to find angles in triangles and quadrilaterals

C Able to find interior angles and exterior angles in polygons

B Able to find angles in circles

A Able to find angles in circles using the alternate segment theorem

A* Can use circle theorems to prove geometrical results

What you should know now

- How to find angles in any triangle or in any quadrilateral
- How to calculate interior and exterior angles in polygons
- How to use circle theorems to find angles

Transformation geometry

1. Congruent triangles

2. Translations

3. Reflections

4. Rotations

5. Enlargements

6. Combined transformations

This chapter will show you ...
- how to show that two triangles are congruent
- what is meant by a transformation
- how to translate, reflect, rotate and enlarge 2-D shapes

What you should already know
- How to find the lines of symmetry of a 2-D shape
- How to find the order of rotational symmetry of a 2-D shape
- How to recognise congruent shapes
- How to draw the lines with equations $y = x$ and $y = -x$, and lines with equations like $x = 2$ and $y = 3$

Quick check

Which of these shapes is not congruent to the others?

a   b   c   d

In this section you will learn how to:
- show that two triangles are congruent

Key word

congruent

Two shapes are **congruent** if they are exactly the same size and shape.

For example, these triangles are all congruent.

Notice that the triangles can be differently orientated (reflected or rotated).

Conditions for congruent triangles

Any one of the following four conditions is sufficient for two triangles to be congruent.

- **Condition 1**

All three sides of one triangle are equal to the corresponding sides of the other triangle.

This condition is known as SSS (side, side, side).

- **Condition 2**

Two sides and the angle between them of one triangle are equal to the corresponding sides and angle of the other triangle.

This condition is known as SAS (side, angle, side).

- **Condition 3**

Two angles and a side of one triangle are equal to the corresponding angles and side of the other triangle.

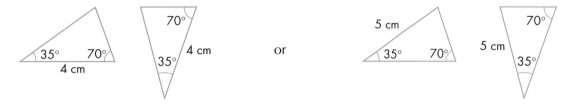

or

This condition is known as ASA (angle, side, angle) or AAS (angle, angle, side).

- **Condition 4**

Both triangles have a right angle, an equal hypotenuse and another equal side.

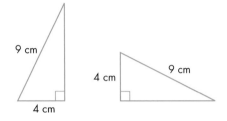

This condition is known as RHS (right angle, hypotenuse, side).

Notation

Once you have shown that triangle ABC is congruent to triangle PQR by one of the above conditions, it means that

$\angle A = \angle P$ AB = PQ

$\angle B = \angle Q$ BC = QR

$\angle C = \angle R$ AC = PR

In other words, the points ABC correspond exactly to the points PQR in that order. Triangle ABC is congruent to triangle PQR can be written as $\triangle ABC \equiv \triangle PQR$.

EXAMPLE 1

ABCD is a kite. Show that triangle ABC is congruent to triangle ADC.

AB = AD

BC = CD

AC is common

So $\triangle ABC \equiv \triangle ADC$ (SSS)

EXERCISE 8A

1 State whether each pair of triangles in **a** to **h** is congruent. If a pair is congruent, give the condition which shows that the triangles are congruent.

a

b

c

d

e

f

g

h

2 State whether each pair of triangles given below is congruent or not. If the triangles are congruent, give the reason and state which points correspond to which.

a ABC where AB = 8 cm, BC = 9 cm, AC = 7.4 cm
PQR where PQ = 9 cm, QR = 7.4 cm, PR = 8 cm

b ABC where AB = 7.5 cm, AC = 8 cm, angle A = 50°
PQR where PQ = 8 cm, QR = 75 mm, angle R = 50°

c ABC where AB = 5 cm, BC = 6 cm, angle B = 35°
PQR where PQ = 6 cm, QR = 50 mm, angle Q = 35°

d ABC where AB = 6 cm, angle B = 35°, angle C = 115°
PQR where PQ = 6 cm, angle Q = 115°, angle R = 35°

3 Triangle ABC is congruent to triangle PQR, ∠A = 60°, ∠B = 80° and AB = 5 cm. Find these.

i ∠P   **ii** ∠Q   **iii** ∠R   **iv** PQ

4 ABCD is congruent to PQRS, ∠A= 110°, ∠B = 55°, ∠C = 85° and RS = 4 cm. Find these.

i ∠P   **ii** ∠Q   **iii** ∠R   **iv** ∠S   **v** CD

5 Draw a rectangle EFGH. Draw in the diagonal EG. Prove that triangle EFG is congruent to triangle EHG.

6 Draw an isosceles triangle ABC where AB = AC. Draw the line from A to X, the mid-point of BC. Prove that triangle ABX is congruent to triangle ACX.

In this section you will learn how to:

● translate a 2-D shape

Key words
transformation
translation
vector

A **transformation** changes the position or the size of a shape.

There are four basic ways of changing the position and size of 2-D shapes: a translation, a reflection, a rotation or an enlargement. All of these transformations, except enlargement, keep shapes congruent.

A **translation** is the "movement" of a shape from one place to another without reflecting it or rotating it. It is sometimes called a glide, since the shape appears to glide from one place to another. Every point in the shape moves in the same direction and through the same distance.

We describe translations by using **vectors**. A vector is represented by the combination of a horizontal shift and a vertical shift.

EXAMPLE 2

Use vectors to describe the translations of the following triangles.

a A to B

b B to C

c C to D

d D to A

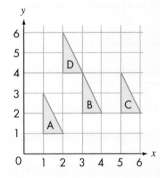

a The vector describing the translation from A to B is $\begin{pmatrix} 2 \\ 1 \end{pmatrix}$.

b The vector describing the translation from B to C is $\begin{pmatrix} 2 \\ 0 \end{pmatrix}$.

c The vector describing the translation from C to D is $\begin{pmatrix} -3 \\ 2 \end{pmatrix}$.

d The vector describing the translation from D to A is $\begin{pmatrix} -1 \\ -3 \end{pmatrix}$.

Note:

● The top number in the vector describes the horizontal movement. To the right +, to the left −.

● The bottom number in the vector describes the vertical movement. Upwards +, downwards −.

EXERCISE 8B

1 Use vectors to describe the following translations.

a i A to B   **ii** A to C   **iii** A to D   **iv** A to E   **v** A to F   **vi** A to G

b i B to A   **ii** B to C   **iii** B to D   **iv** B to E   **v** B to F   **vi** B to G

c i C to A   **ii** C to B   **iii** C to D   **iv** C to E   **v** C to F   **vi** C to G

d i D to E   **ii** E to B   **iii** F to C   **iv** G to D   **v** F to G   **vi** G to E

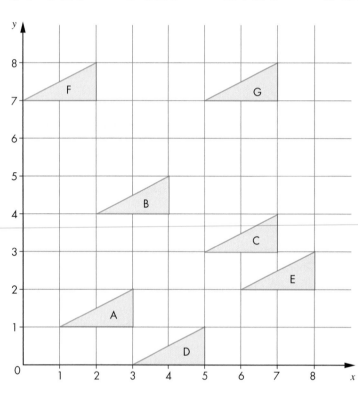

2 **a** Draw the triangle with coordinates A(1,1), B(2,1) and C(1,3).

b Draw the image of ABC after a translation with vector $\begin{pmatrix} 2 \\ 3 \end{pmatrix}$. Label this triangle P.

c Draw the image of ABC after a translation with vector $\begin{pmatrix} -1 \\ 2 \end{pmatrix}$. Label this triangle Q.

d Draw the image of ABC after a translation with vector $\begin{pmatrix} 3 \\ -2 \end{pmatrix}$. Label this triangle R.

e Draw the image of ABC after a translation with vector $\begin{pmatrix} -2 \\ -4 \end{pmatrix}$. Label this triangle S.

3 Using your diagram from question **2**, use vectors to describe the translation that will move

a P to Q   **b** Q to R   **c** R to S   **d** S to P

e R to P   **f** S to Q   **g** R to Q   **e** P to S

 4 Take a 10 × 10 grid and the triangle A(0, 0), B(1, 0) and C(0, 1). How many different translations are there that use integer values only and will move the triangle ABC to somewhere in the grid?

Reflections

In this section you will learn how to:
- reflect a 2-D shape in a mirror line

Key words

image
mirror line
object
reflection

A **reflection** transforms a shape so that it becomes a mirror image of itself.

EXAMPLE 3

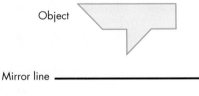

Object

Mirror line

Image

Notice the reflection of each point in the original shape, called the **object**, is perpendicular to the **mirror line**. So if you "fold" the whole diagram along the mirror line, the object will coincide with its reflection, called its **image**.

EXERCISE 8C

1 Copy the diagram below and draw the reflection of the given triangle in the following lines.

a $x = 2$ **b** $x = -1$ **c** $x = 3$ **d** $y = 2$ **e** $y = -1$ **f** y-axis

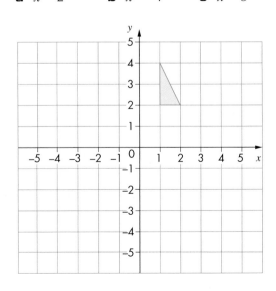

D

2 **a** Draw a pair of axes, x-axis from –5 to 5, y-axis from –5 to 5.

b Draw the triangle with coordinates A(1, 1), B(3, 1), C(4, 5).

c Reflect the triangle ABC in the x-axis. Label the image P.

d Reflect triangle P in the y-axis. Label the image Q.

e Reflect triangle Q in the x-axis. Label the image R.

f Describe the reflection that will move triangle ABC to triangle R.

3 **a** Draw a pair of axes, x-axis from –5 to +5 and y-axis from –5 to +5.

b Reflect the points A(2, 1), B(5, 0), C(–3, 3), D(3, –2) in the x-axis.

c What do you notice about the values of the coordinates of the reflected points?

d What would the coordinates of the reflected point be if the point (a, b) were reflected in the x-axis?

4 **a** Draw a pair of axes, x-axis from –5 to +5 and y-axis from –5 to +5.

b Reflect the points A(2, 1), B(0, 5), C(3, –2), D(–4, –3) in the y-axis.

c What do you notice about the values of the coordinates of the reflected points?

d What would the coordinates of the reflected point be if the point (a, b) were reflected in the y-axis?

5 Draw each of these triangles on squared paper, leaving plenty of space on the opposite side of the given mirror line. Then draw the reflection of each triangle.

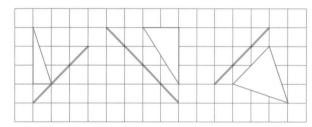

HINTS AND TIPS

Turn the page so that the mirror line is horizontal or vertical.

6 **a** Draw a pair of axes and the lines y = x and y = –x, as shown.

b Draw the triangle with coordinates A(2, 1), B(5, 1), C(5, 3).

c Draw the reflection of triangle ABC in the x-axis and label the image P.

d Draw the reflection of triangle P in the line y = –x and label the image Q.

e Draw the reflection of triangle Q in the y-axis and label the image R.

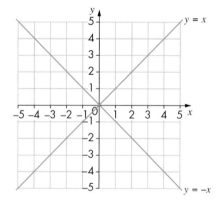

f Draw the reflection of triangle R in the line y = x and label the image S.

g Draw the reflection of triangle S in the x-axis and label the image T.

h Draw the reflection of triangle T in the line y = –x and label the image U.

i Draw the reflection of triangle U in the y-axis and label the image W.

j What single reflection will move triangle W to triangle ABC?

7 Copy the diagram and reflect the triangle in these lines.

a $y = x$

b $x = 1$

c $y = -x$

d $y = -1$

8 a Draw a pair of axes, x-axis from –5 to +5 and y-axis from –5 to +5.

b Draw the line $y = x$.

c Reflect the points A(2, 1), B(5, 0), C(–3, 2), D(–2, –4) in the line $y = x$.

d What do you notice about the values of the coordinates of the reflected points?

e What would the coordinates of the reflected point be if the point (a, b) were reflected in the line $y = x$?

9 a Draw a pair of axes, x-axis from –5 to +5 and y-axis from –5 to +5.

b Draw the line $y = -x$.

c Reflect the points A(2, 1), B(0, 5), C(3, –2), D(–4, –3) in the line $y = -x$.

d What do you notice about the values of the coordinates of the reflected points?

e What would the coordinates of the reflected point be if the point (a, b) were reflected in the line $y = -x$?

8.4 Rotations

In this section you will learn how to:
● rotate a 2-D shape about a point

Key words

angle of rotation
anticlockwise
centre of rotation
clockwise
rotation

A **rotation** transforms a shape to a new position by turning it about a fixed point called the **centre of rotation**.

EXAMPLE 4

Rotation of 90° clockwise   Rotation of 180°

Note:

- The direction of turn or the **angle of rotation** is expressed as **clockwise** or **anticlockwise**.
- The position of the centre of rotation is always specified.
- The rotations 180° clockwise and 180° anticlockwise are the same.

The rotations which most often appear in examination questions are 90° and 180°.

EXERCISE 8D

1 On squared paper, draw each of these shapes and its centre of rotation, leaving plenty of space all round the shape.

a Rotate each shape about its centre of rotation

   i first by 90° clockwise (call the image A)   **ii** then by 90° anticlockwise (call the image B).

b Describe, in each case, the rotation that would take

   i A back to its original position   **ii** A to B.

2 Copy the diagram and rotate the given triangle by the following.

a 90° clockwise about (0, 0)

b 180° about (3, 3)

c 90° anticlockwise about (0, 2)

d 180° about (−1, 0)

e 90° clockwise about (−1, −1)

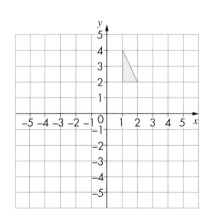

C

3 What other rotations are equivalent to these rotations?

a 270° clockwise   **b** 90° clockwise   **c** 60° anticlockwise   **d** 100° anticlockwise

4 **a** Draw a pair of axes where both the x and y values are from –5 to 5.

b Draw the triangle ABC, where A = (1, 2), B = (2, 4) and C = (4, 1).

c **i** Rotate triangle ABC 90° clockwise about the origin (0, 0) and label the image A′, B′, C′, where A′ is the image of A, etc.

ii Write down the coordinates of A′, B′, C′.

iii What connection is there between A, B, C and A′, B′, C′?

iv Will this connection always be so for a 90° clockwise to rotation about the origin?

5 Repeat question **4**, but rotate triangle ABC through 180°.

6 Repeat question **4**, but rotate triangle ABC 90° anticlockwise.

7 Show that a reflection in the x-axis followed by a reflection in the y-axis is equivalent to a rotation of 180° about the origin.

8 Show that a reflection in the line $y = x$ followed by a reflection in the line $y = -x$ is equivalent to a rotation of 180° about the origin.

9 **a** Draw a regular hexagon ABCDEF with centre O.

b Using O as the centre of rotation, describe a transformation that will result in the following movements.

i triangle AOB to triangle BOC   **ii** triangle AOB to triangle COD

iii triangle AOB to triangle DOE   **iv** triangle AOB to triangle EOF

c Describe the transformations that will move the rhombus ABCO to these positions.

i rhombus BCDO   **ii** rhombus DEFO

In this section you will learn how to:
● enlarge a 2-D shape by a scale factor

Key words
centre of
    enlargement
enlargement
scale factor

An **enlargement** changes the size of a shape to give a similar image. It always has a **centre of enlargement** and a **scale factor**. Every length of the enlarged shape will be

Original length × Scale factor

The distance of each image point on the enlargement from the centre of enlargement will be

Distance of original point from centre of enlargement × Scale factor

EXAMPLE 5

The diagram shows the enlargement of triangle ABC by scale factor 3 about the centre of enlargement X.

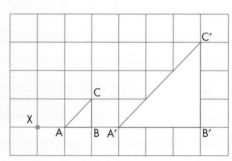

Note:

● Each length on the enlargement A′B′C′ is three times the corresponding length on the original shape.

This means that the corresponding sides are in the same ratio:

AB:A′B′ = AC:A′C′ = BC:B′C′ = 1:3

● The distance of any point on the enlargement from the centre of enlargement is three times longer than the distance from the corresponding point on the original shape to the centre of enlargement.

There are two distinct ways to enlarge a shape: the ray method and the coordinate method.

Ray method

This is the *only* way to construct an enlargement when the diagram is not on a grid.

EXAMPLE 6

Enlarge triangle ABC by scale factor 3 about the centre of enlargement X.

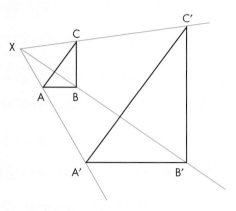

Notice that the rays have been drawn from the centre of enlargement to each vertex and beyond.

The distance from X to each vertex on triangle ABC is measured and multiplied by 3 to give the distance from X to each vertex A', B' and C' for the enlarged triangle A'B'C'.

Once each image vertex has been found, the whole enlarged shape can then be drawn.

Check the measurements and see for yourself how the calculations have been done.

Notice again that the length of each side on the enlarged triangle is three times longer than the length of the corresponding side on the original triangle.

Counting squares method

EXAMPLE 7

Enlarge the triangle ABC by scale factor 3 from the centre of enlargement (1, 2).

To find the coordinates of each image vertex, first work out the horizontal and vertical distances from each original vertex to the centre of enlargement.

Then multiply each of these distances by 3 to find the position of each image vertex.

For example, to find the coordinates of C' work out the distance from the centre of enlargement (1, 2) to the point C(3, 5).

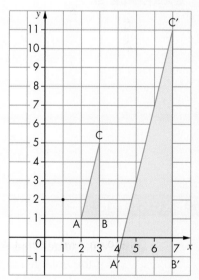

horizontal distance = 2

vertical distance = 3

Make these 3 times longer to give

new horizontal distance = 6

new vertical distance = 9

So the coordinates of C' are

(1 + 6, 2 + 9) = (7, 11)

Notice again that the length of each side is three times longer in the enlargement.

Negative enlargement

A negative enlargement produces an image shape on the opposite side of the centre of enlargement to the original shape.

EXAMPLE 8

Triangle ABC has been enlarged by scale factor –2, with the centre of enlargement at (1, 0).

You can enlarge triangle ABC to give triangle A'B'C' by either the ray method or the coordinate method. You calculate the new lengths on the opposite side of the centre of enlargement to the original shape.

Notice how a negative scale factor also inverts the original shape.

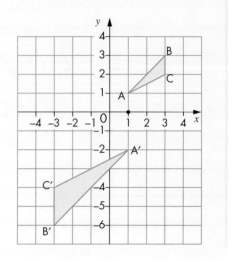

Fractional enlargement

Strange but true … you can have an enlargement in mathematics that is actually smaller than the original shape!

EXAMPLE 9

Triangle ABC has been enlarged by a scale factor of $\frac{1}{2}$ about the centre of enlargement O to give triangle A'B'C'.

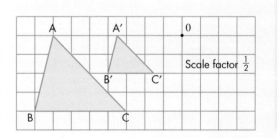

Scale factor $\frac{1}{2}$

EXERCISE 8E

1 Make larger copies of each of these figures with its centre of enlargement, leaving plenty of space for the enlargement. Then enlarge it by the given scale factor, using the ray method.

Scale factor 2

Scale factor 3

Scale factor 2

Scale factor –3

C

2 a Draw a triangle ABC on squared paper.

b Mark four different centres of enlargement on your diagram as follows.

one above your triangle   one to the left of your triangle

one below your triangle   one to the right of your triangle

c Enlarge the triangle by a scale factor of 2 from each centre.

d What do you notice about each enlarged shape?

3 Enlarge each of these shapes by a scale factor of $\frac{1}{2}$ about the given centre of enlargement.

4 Copy this diagram onto squared paper.

a Enlarge the rectangle A by scale factor $\frac{1}{3}$ about the origin. Label the image B.

b Write down the ratio of the lengths of the sides of rectangle A to the lengths of the sides of rectangle B.

c Work out the ratio of the perimeter of rectangle A to the perimeter of rectangle B.

d Work out the ratio of the area of rectangle A to the area of rectangle B.

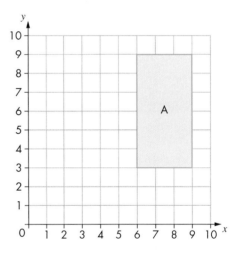

5 Copy the diagram onto squared paper.

a Enlarge A by a scale factor of 3 about a centre (4, 5).

b Enlarge B by a scale factor $\frac{1}{2}$ about a centre (−1, −3).

c Enlarge B by scale factor $-\frac{1}{2}$ about a centre (−3, −1).

d What is the centre of enlargement and scale factor which maps B onto A?

e What is the centre of enlargement and scale factor which maps A onto B?

f What is the centre of enlargement and scale factor which maps the answer to part **b** to the answer to part **c**?

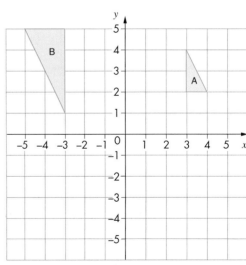

g What is the centre of enlargement and scale factor which maps the answer to part **c** to the answer to part **b**?

h What is the connection between the scale factors and the centres of enlargement in parts **d** and **e**, and in parts **f** and **g**?

Combined transformations

In this section you will learn how to:

● combine transformations

Key words
enlargement
reflection
rotation
transformation
translation

Examination questions often require you to use more than one transformation in a question. This exercise will revise the transformations you have met in this chapter.

EXERCISE 8F

1 Describe fully the transformations that will map the shaded triangle onto each of the triangles A–F.

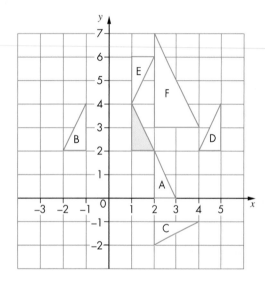

2 Describe fully the transformations that will result in the following movements.

a T_1 to T_2

b T_1 to T_6

c T_2 to T_3

d T_6 to T_2

e T_6 to T_5

f T_5 to T_4

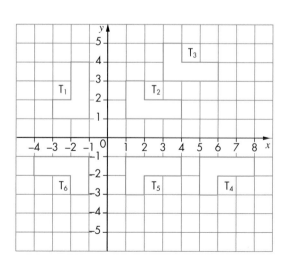

C

3 **a** Plot a triangle T with vertices (1,1), (2,1), (1,3).

   b Reflect triangle T in the y-axis and label the image T_b.

   c Rotate triangle T_b 90° anticlockwise about the origin and label the image T_c.

   d Reflect triangle T_c in the y-axis and label the image T_d.

   e Describe fully the transformation that will move triangle T_d back to triangle T.

4 The point P(3, 4) is reflected in the x-axis, then rotated by 90° clockwise about the origin. What are the coordinates of the image of P?

5 A point Q(5, 2) is rotated by 180°, then reflected in the x-axis.

   a What are the coordinates of the image point of Q?

   b What single transformation would have taken point Q directly to the image point?

6 Find the coordinates of the image of the point (3, 5) after a clockwise rotation of 90° about the point (1, 3).

7 Describe fully at least three different transformations that could move the square labelled S to the square labelled T.

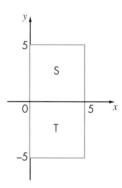

8 The point A(4, 4) has been transformed to the point A'(4, –4). Describe as many different transformations as you can that could transform point A to point A'.

9 Describe the single transformation equivalent to a reflection in the y-axis followed by a reflection in the x-axis.

1 Triangle T and triangles A, B, C, D and E are not drawn accurately.

Which two of triangles A, B, C, D and E are congruent to triangle T?

AQA, Question 3, Paper 1 Higher, June 2003

2 **a** Copy the grid below.

i Reflect the shaded triangle in the line $y = x$. Label it A.

ii Rotate the shaded triangle 90° anticlockwise about (1, 1). Label it B.

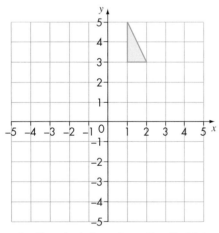

b Describe the *single* transformation that takes triangle A to triangle B.

AQA, Question 5, Paper 2 Higher, June 2002

3 Copy the doagram below and enlarge the shaded triangle by a scale factor of 3. Use P as the centre of enlargement.

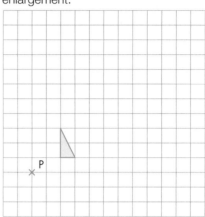

AQA, Question 12, Paper 2 Intermediate, November 2002

4 On the grid below there are two shapes, A and B.

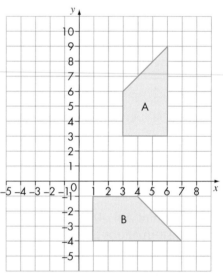

a Describe fully the *single* transformation that takes shape A to shape B.

b Copy the grid and draw the enlargement of shape A with scale factor $\frac{1}{3}$ and centre of enlargement (0, 0).

AQA, Question 9, Paper 1 Higher, November 2004

5 Triangle P is an enlargement of the shaded triangle.

a What is the scale factor of the enlargement?

b What is the centre of enlargement?

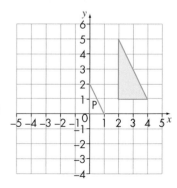

AQA, Question 9, Paper 2 Higher, June 2003

6 The grid shows two congruent shapes, A and B

a Describe the single transformation of shape A to shape B.

b On a copy of the grid, draw the enlargement of shape A by scale factor –2, centre of enlargement (2, 1).

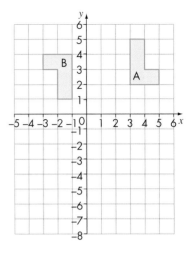

AQA, Question 3, Paper 1 Higher, November 2002

WORKED EXAM QUESTION

Triangle ABC has vertices A(6, 0), B(6, 9), C(9, 3).

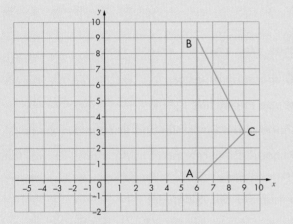

a Rotate triangle ABC through 180° about the point (2, 4). Label the image triangle R.

b Enlarge triangle ABC by scale factor $\frac{1}{3}$ from the centre of enlargement (3, 0). Label the image triangle E.

c Describe fully the single transformation which maps triangle E to triangle R.

c

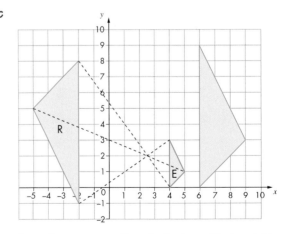

Solution

a Join each vertex to (2, 4) and rotate each line through 180°.

b Use the ray method or the counting squares method. Remember a fractional scale factor, makes the image smaller.

An enlargement of scale factor –3 about the point $(2\frac{1}{2}, 2)$. Draw in the ray lines to find the centre of enlargement.

AQA, Question 7, Paper 1 Higher, June 2001

GRADE YOURSELF

D Able to reflect a 2-D shape in a line $x = a$ or $y = b$

D Able to rotate a 2-D shape about the origin

D Able to enlarge a 2-D shape by a whole number scale factor

C Able to translate a 2-D shape by a vector

C Able to reflect a 2-D shape in the line $y = x$ or $y = -x$

C Able to rotate a 2-D shape about any point

C Able to enlarge a 2-D shape by a fractional scale factor

C Able to enlarge a 2-D shape about any point

B Know the conditions to show two triangles are congruent

B Able to enlarge a 2-D shape by a negative scale factor

A Able to prove two triangles are congruent

What you should know now

- How to translate a 2-D shape by a vector
- How to reflect a 2-D shape in any line
- How to rotate a 2-D shape about any point and through any angle
- How to enlarge a 2-D shape about any point using a positive, fractional or negative scale factor
- How to show that two triangles are congruent

Constructions

1 Bisectors

2 Other angle constructions

3 Defining a locus

4 Loci problems

This chapter will show you ...

- how to bisect a line and an angle
- how to construct perpendiculars
- how to define a locus
- how to solve locus problems

What you should already know

- How to construct triangles using a protractor and a pair of compasses
- How to use scale drawings

Quick check

Construct these triangles using a ruler, protractor and a pair of compasses.

1
4 cm
52°
6 cm

2
65° 75°
4 cm

3

5 cm 4 cm
6 cm

Bisectors

In this section you will learn how to:

- bisect a line and an angle

Key words

angle bisector
bisector
line bisector
perpendicular
    bisector

To bisect means to divide in half. So a **bisector** divides something into two equal parts.

- A **line bisector** divides a straight line into two equal lengths.

- An **angle bisector** is the straight line which divides an angle into two equal angles.

EXAMPLE 1

To construct a line bisector

It is usually more accurate to construct a line bisector than to measure its position (the midpoint of the line).

Bisect the line AB.

- Open your compasses to a radius of about three quarters of the length of the line. Using A and B as centres, draw two intersecting arcs without changing the radius of your compasses.

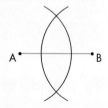

- Join the two points at which the arcs intersect to meet AB at X. This line is known as the **perpendicular bisector** of AB.

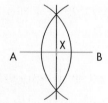   X is the midpoint of AB.

EXAMPLE 2

To construct an angle bisector

It is much more accurate to construct an angle bisector than to measure with a protractor.

Bisect ∠BAC.

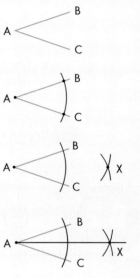

- Open your compasses to any reasonable radius. If in doubt, go for about 3 cm. With centre at A, draw an arc through both lines of the angle.

- With centres at the two points at which this arc intersects the lines, draw two more arcs so that they intersect at X. (The radius of the compasses may have to be increased to do this.)

- Join AX.

  This line is the **angle bisector** of ∠BAC.

  So ∠BAX = ∠CAX.

EXERCISE 9A

In this exercise, it is important to leave in all your construction lines.

1 Draw a line 7 cm long. Bisect it using a pair of compasses and a ruler only. Check your accuracy by measuring to see if each half is 3.5 cm.

2 **a** Draw any triangle whose sides are between 5 cm and 10 cm.

b On each side construct the perpendicular bisector as on the diagram. All your perpendicular bisectors should intersect at the same point.

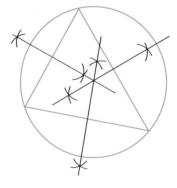

c Use this point as the centre of a circle that touches each vertex of the triangle. Draw this circle. This circle is known as the *circumscribed circle* of the triangle.

3 Repeat question **2** with a different triangle and check that you get a similar result.

4 **a** Draw a quadrilateral whose opposite angles add up to 180°.

b On each side construct the perpendicular bisectors. They all should intersect at the same point.

c Use this point as the centre of a circle that touches the quadrilateral at each vertex. Draw this circle.

5 **a** Draw an angle of 50°.

b Construct the angle bisector.

c Use a protractor to check how accurate you have been. Each angle should be 25°.

6 **a** Draw any triangle whose sides are between 5 cm and 10 cm.

b At each angle construct the angle bisector as on the diagram. All three bisectors should intersect at the same point.

c Use this point as the centre of a circle that touches each side of the triangle once. Draw this circle. This circle is known as the *inscribed circle* of the triangle.

7 Repeat question **6** with a different triangle and check that you get a similar result.

 Other angle constructions

In this section you will learn how to:
- construct perpendiculars from a point
- construct an angle of 60°

Key words

construct
perpendicular

EXAMPLE 3

To construct a perpendicular from a point on a line

This construction will produce a perpendicular from a point A on a line.

- Open your compasses to about 2 or 3 cm. With point A as centre, draw two short arcs to intersect the line at each side of the point.

- Now extend the radius of your compasses to about 4 cm. With centres at the two points at which the arcs intersect the line, draw two arcs to intersect at X above the line.

- Join AX.

  AX is perpendicular to the line.

  Note: If you needed to construct a 90° angle at the end of a line, you would first have to extend the line.

  You could be even more accurate by also drawing two arcs underneath the line, which would give three points in line.

EXAMPLE 4

To construct a perpendicular from a point to a line

This construction will produce a perpendicular from a point A to a line.

- With point A as centre, draw an arc which intersects the line at two points.

- With centres at these two points of intersection, draw two arcs to intersect each other both above and below the line.

- Join the two points at which the arcs intersect. The resulting line passes through point A and is perpendicular to the line.

Examination note: When a question says *construct*, you must only use compasses – no protractor. When it says *draw*, you may use whatever you can to produce an accurate diagram. But also note, when constructing you may use your protractor to check your accuracy.

EXAMPLE 5

To construct an angle of 60°

This construction will produce an angle of 60° from a point A on a line.

- Open your compasses to about 3 cm. With point A as centre, draw an arc from above to intersect the line at point B.

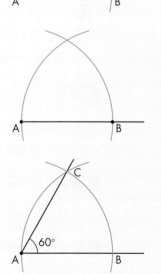

- With point B as centre, draw a second arc which passes through point A to intersect the first arc at point C.

- Join AC.

    ∠CAB = 60°

EXERCISE 9B

In this exercise, it is important to leave in all your construction lines.

1 Construct these triangles accurately without using a protractor.

2 a Without using a protractor, construct a square of side 6 cm.

b See how accurate you have been by constructing an angle bisector on any of the right angles and seeing whether this also cuts through the opposite right angle.

3 a Construct an angle of 90°.

b Bisect this angle to construct an angle of 45°.

4 a Construct these angles.   **i** 30°   **ii** 15°   **iii** 22.5°   **iv** 75°

b Check your accuracy by measuring with a protractor. (The allowable error is ±1°.)

5 With ruler and compasses only, construct these triangles.

6 Construct an isosceles triangle ABC, where AB = AC = 7 cm and ∠CAB = 120°.

7 Construct a trapezium whose parallel sides are 8 cm and 6 cm, and having an angle of 60° at each end of the longer side.

8 a Construct the triangle ABC, where AB = 7 cm, ∠BAC = 60° and ∠ABC = 45°.

b Measure the lengths of AC and BC.

9 a Construct the triangle PQR, where PQ = 8 cm, ∠RPQ = 30° and ∠PQR = 45°.

b Measure the lengths of PR and RQ.

10 Construct a parallelogram which has sides of 6 cm and 8 cm and with an angle of 105°.

11 Draw a straight line and mark a point above the line. Construct the perpendicular which passes through that point to the line.

Defining a locus

In this section you will learn how to:
- draw a locus for a given rule

Key words
loci
locus

A **locus** (plural **loci**) is the movement of a point according to a given rule.

EXAMPLE 6

A point P that moves so that it is always at a distance of 5 cm from a fixed point A will have a locus that is a circle of radius 5 cm.

You can express this mathematically by saying

the locus of the point P is such that AP = 5 cm.

EXAMPLE 7

A point P that moves so that it is always the same distance from two fixed points A and B will have a locus that is the perpendicular bisector of the line joining A and B.

You can express this mathematically by saying

the locus of the point P is such that AP = BP.

.A

P

.B

EXAMPLE 8

A point that moves so that it is always 5 cm from a line AB will have a locus that is a racetrack shape around the line.

This is difficult to express mathematically.

In your GCSE examination, you will usually get practical situations rather than abstract mathematical ones.

EXAMPLE 9

A point that is always 5 m from a long, straight wall will have a locus that is a line parallel to the wall and 5 m from it.

EXAMPLE 10

Imagine a grassy, flat field in which a horse is tethered to a stake by a rope that is 10 m long. What is the shape of the area that the horse can graze?

In reality, the horse may not be able to reach the full 10 m if the rope is tied round its neck but ignore fine details like that. You "model" the situation by saying that the horse can move around in a 10 m circle and graze all the grass within that circle.

In this example, the locus is the whole of the area inside the circle.

You can express this mathematically as

the locus of the point P is such that AP ⩽ 10 m.

EXERCISE 9C

1 A is a fixed point. Sketch the locus of the point P in each of these situations.

   a AP = 2 cm   **b** AP = 4 cm   **c** AP = 5 cm

2 A and B are two fixed points 5 cm apart. Sketch the locus of the point P for each of these situations.

   a AP = BP

   b AP = 4 cm and BP = 4 cm

   c P is always within 2 cm of the line AB

3 A horse is tethered in a field on a rope 4 m long. Describe or sketch the area that the horse can graze.

4 The horse is still tethered by the same rope but there is now a long, straight fence running 2 m from the stake. Sketch the area that the horse can now graze.

5 ABCD is a square of side 4 cm. In each of the following loci, the point P moves only inside the square. Sketch the locus in each case.

   a AP = BP   **b** AP < BP   **c** AP = CP

   d CP < 4 cm   **e** CP > 2 cm   **f** CP > 5 cm

A   B
4 cm
D   C

6 One of the following diagrams is the locus of a point on the rim of a bicycle wheel as it moves along a flat road. Which is it?

7 Draw the locus of the centre of the wheel for the bicycle in question 6.

Loci problems

In this section you will learn how to:
- solve practical problems using loci

Key words
loci
scale

Most of the **loci** problems in your GCSE examination will be of a practical nature, as in the next example.

EXAMPLE 11

Imagine that a radio company wants to find a site for a transmitter. The transmitter must be the same distance from Doncaster and Leeds and within 20 miles of Sheffield.

In mathematical terms, this means they are concerned with the perpendicular bisector between Leeds and Doncaster and the area within a circle of radius 20 miles from Sheffield.

The map, drawn to a **scale** of 1 cm = 10 miles, illustrates the situation and shows that the transmitter can be built anywhere along the thick part of the blue line.

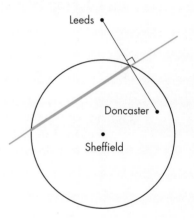

EXERCISE 9D

For questions **1** to **7**, you should start by sketching the picture given in each question on a 6 × 6 grid, each square of which is 1 cm by 1 cm. The scale for each question is given.

1 A goat is tethered by a rope, 7 m long, in a corner of a field with a fence at each side. What is the locus of the area that the goat can graze? Use a scale of 1 cm ≡ 2 m.

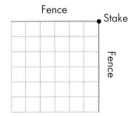

2 In a field a horse is tethered to a stake by a rope 6 m long. What is the locus of the area that the horse can graze? Use a scale of 1 cm ≡ 2 m.

3 A cow is tethered to a rail at the top of a fence 6 m long. The rope is 3 m long. Sketch the area that the cow can graze. Use a scale of 1 cm ≡ 2 m.

4 A horse is tethered to a stake near a corner of a fenced field, at a point 4 m from each fence. The rope is 6 m long. Sketch the area that the horse can graze. Use a scale of 1 cm ≡ 2 m.

5 A horse is tethered to a corner of a shed, 2 m by 1 m. The rope is 2 m long. Sketch the area that the horse can graze. Use a scale of 1 cm ≡ 1 m.

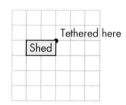

6 A goat is tethered by a 4 m rope to a stake at one corner of a pen, 4 m by 3 m. Sketch the area of the pen on which the goat cannot graze. Use a scale of 1 cm ≡ 1 m.

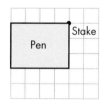

7 A puppy is tethered to a stake by a rope, 1.5 m long, on a flat lawn on which are two raised brick flower beds. The stake is situated at one corner of a bed, as shown. Sketch the area that the puppy is free to roam in. Use a scale of 1 cm ≡ 1 m.

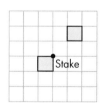

For questions **8** to **15**, you should use a copy of the map opposite. For each question, trace the map and mark on those points that are relevant to that question.

8 A radio station broadcasts from London on a frequency of 1000 kHz with a range of 300 km. Another radio station broadcasts from Glasgow on the same frequency with a range of 200 km.

   a Sketch the area to which each station can broadcast.

   b Will they interfere with each other?

   c If the Glasgow station increases its range to 400 km, will they then interfere with each other?

9 The radar at Leeds airport has a range of 200 km. The radar at Exeter airport has a range of 200 km.

   a Will a plane flying over Birmingham be detected by the Leeds radar?

   b Sketch the area where a plane can be picked up by both radars at the same time.

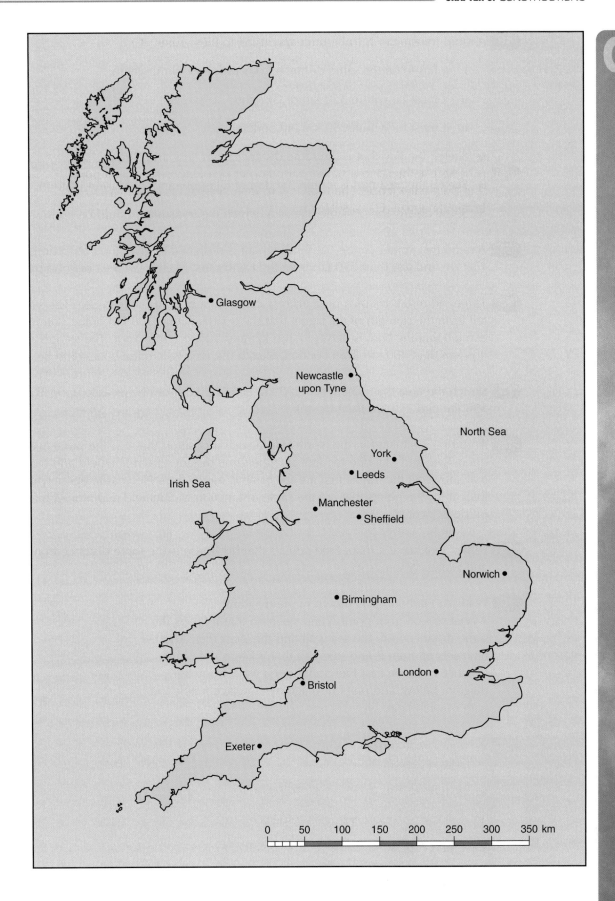

10 A radio transmitter is to be built according to these rules.

    i It has to be the same distance from York and Birmingham.

    ii It must be within 350 km of Glasgow.

    iii It must be within 250 km of London.

  a Sketch the line that is the same distance from York and Birmingham.

  b Sketch the area that is within 350 km of Glasgow and 250 km of London.

  c Show clearly the possible places at which the transmitter could be built.

11 A radio transmitter centred at Birmingham is designed to give good reception in an area greater than 150 km and less than 250 km from the transmitter. Sketch the area of good reception.

12 Three radio stations pick up a distress call from a boat in the Irish Sea. The station at Glasgow can tell from the strength of the signal that the boat is within 300 km of the station. The station at York can tell that the boat is between 200 km and 300 km from York. The station at London can tell that it is less than 400 km from London. Sketch the area where the boat could be.

13 Sketch the area that is between 200 km and 300 km from Newcastle upon Tyne, and between 150 km and 250 km from Bristol.

14 An oil rig is situated in the North Sea in such a position that it is the same distance from Newcastle upon Tyne and Manchester. It is also the same distance from Sheffield and Norwich. Draw the line that shows all the points that are the same distance from Newcastle upon Tyne and Manchester. Repeat for the points that are the same distance from Sheffield and Norwich and find out where the oil rig is located.

15 Whilst looking at a map, Fred notices that his house is the same distance from Glasgow, Norwich and Exeter. Where is it?

16 Wathsea Harbour is as shown in the diagram.
A boat sets off from point A and steers so that it keeps the same distance from the sea wall and the West Pier. Another boat sets off from B and steers so that it keeps the same distance from the East Pier and the sea wall. Copy the diagram below, and on your diagram show accurately the path of each boat.

1 Make an accurate drawing of this triangle.

2 Construct an accurate drawing of this triangle.

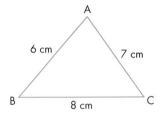

3 **a** Construct an accurate drawing of this triangle

   b Measure the length BC.

4 The map shows a small island with two towns A and B. Town B is north west of town A. The map is drawn to a scale of 1 square to 10 km.

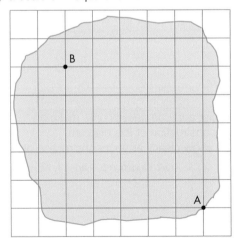

   a What bearing is the direction north west?

   b A mobile phone mast is to be built. It has to be within 40 km of both towns. Copy the map and shade the area in which the mast could be built.

5 **a** Construct an angle of 60°.

   b Copy the line AB and then construct the perpendicular bisector of the points A and B.

6 In this question, you should use a ruler and compasses.

The diagram shows an equilateral triangle of side 10 cm.

Copy the diagram and show all the points inside the triangle that are more than 5 cm from each vertex of the triangle.

You *must* show clearly all your constructions arcs.

AQA, Question 6, Paper 2 Higher, November 2004

7 This is a map of an island with two television transmitters at A and B. There is one town on the island which is shown shaded. The map is drawn to a scale of 1 cm represents 20 km. The transmitters at A and B both have a range of 40 km.

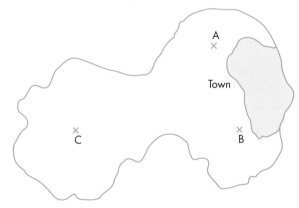

   a Trace the map and show clearly that, between them, the two transmitters at A and B can send a signal to all parts of the town.

   b A further transmitter is to be built at C so that the whole island can receive a signal. What minimum range should the transmitter at C have to ensure that all parts of the island can receive a signal?

AQA, Question 6, Paper 2 Higher, November 2002

8 The scale diagram below shows a plan of a room. The dimensions of the room are 9 m and 7 m.

 Two plug sockets are fitted along the walls.
One is at the point marked A. The other is at the point marked B. A third plug socket is to be fitted along a wall. It must be equidistant from A and B.

Using ruler and compasses, find the position of the new socket. Label it C.

Scale: 1 cm represents 1 m.

AQA, Question 5, Paper 1 Higher, June 2000

 9 The diagram shows an L shape.

Copy the diagram and draw the locus of all points 2 cm from the L shape.

AQA, Question 5, Paper 1 Higher, June 2005

 10 The map shows a field that is 100 m by 100 m.

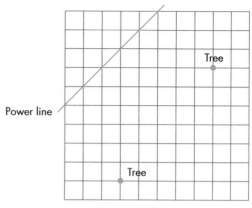

There are two large trees in the field and a power line runs across it.

a Make an accurate scale drawing of the field, using a scale of 1 cm ≡ 10 m.

b Bernice wants to fly a kite.

She cannot fly the kite within 50 m of the power line.

She cannot fly the kite within 30 m of a tree.

Show the area where she can fly the kite.

AQA, Question 5, Paper 1 Higher, November 2005

 11 ABC is a triangle.
ACD is a straight line.

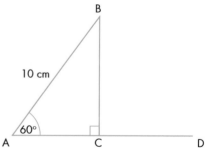

Using a ruler and compasses only, make an accurate construction of this diagram.
You *must* show clearly all your construction arcs.

AQA, Question 5, Paper 1, November 2003

WORKED EXAM QUESTION

The map below shows three boats, A, B and C, on a lake. Along one edge of the lake there is a straight path.

Treasure lies at the bottom of the lake.

The treasure is:

    between 150 m and 250 m from B,

    nearer to A than C,

    more than 100 m from the path.

Path

A

B

C

Scale: 1 cm represents 50 m

Using a ruler and compasses only, shade the region in which the treasure lies.
You must show clearly all your constructions arcs.

AQA, Question 6, Paper 1 Higher, June 2003

Solution

Draw two circles with centre at B with radii 3 cm and 5 cm.

Draw the perpendicular bisector of AC.

Draw a parallel line 2 cm from the path.

The region required is shaded on the diagram.

A

B

C

Scale: 1 cm represents 50 m

Bill the builder builds a street of 100 bungalows, 50 on each side of the street.

He builds them in blocks of 5.

The bungalows at the end of the blocks are called end-terraced, and the other bungalows are called mid-terraced.

3.2m

Key:
■ gate
▬ door
▬ window
— fence
☐ garden shed

Here is the plan of one block of five.

A tree is to be planted in the back garden of each mid-terraced house. The tree must be at least 2 m from the back of the house, at least 1 m from the back fence of the garden, and at least 3.5 m from each of the bottom corners of the garden. It must also be at least 1.5 m from the garden shed.

Draw an accurate scale drawing, using a scale of 1 cm ≡ 1 m, of a mid-terraced house and garden. Shade the region in which Bill can plant the tree.

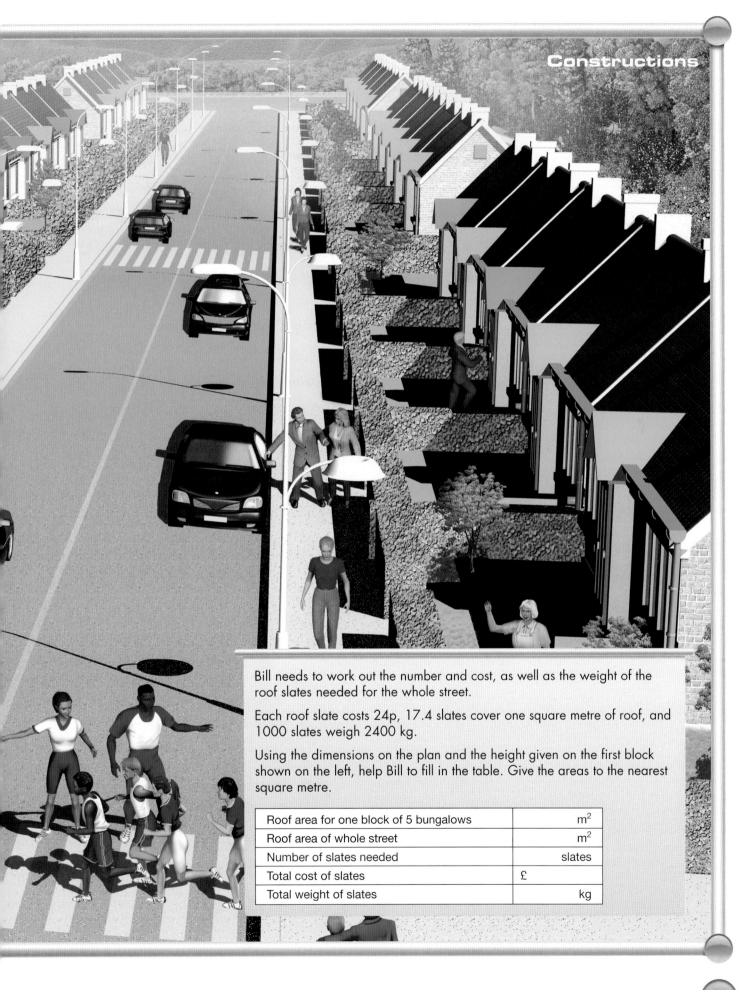

Bill needs to work out the number and cost, as well as the weight of the roof slates needed for the whole street.

Each roof slate costs 24p, 17.4 slates cover one square metre of roof, and 1000 slates weigh 2400 kg.

Using the dimensions on the plan and the height given on the first block shown on the left, help Bill to fill in the table. Give the areas to the nearest square metre.

Roof area for one block of 5 bungalows		m²
Roof area of whole street		m²
Number of slates needed		slates
Total cost of slates	£	
Total weight of slates		kg

GRADE YOURSELF

C Able to construct line and angle bisectors

C Able to draw and describe the locus of a point from a given rule

C Able to solve problems using loci

B Able to construct a perpendicular from a point on a line

B Able to construct a perpendicular from a point to a line

B Able to construct an angle of 60°

What you should know now

- How to construct line and angle bisectors
- How to construct perpendiculars
- How to construct angles without a protractor
- Understand what is meant by a locus
- How to solve problems using loci

Powers, standard form and surds

Chapter 10

1 Indices

2 Standard form

3 Reciprocals and rational numbers

4 Surds

This chapter will show you ...

- how to calculate with indices
- how to write numbers in standard form and how to calculate with standard form
- how to convert fractions to terminating and recurring decimals, and vice versa
- how to work out a reciprocal
- how to calculate with surds

Visual overview

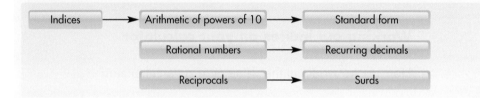

What you should already know

- How to convert a fraction to a decimal
- How to convert a decimal to a fraction
- How to find the lowest common denominator of two fractions
- The meaning of square root and cube root

Quick check

1 Convert the following fractions to decimals.

  a $\frac{6}{10}$ **b** $\frac{11}{25}$ **c** $\frac{3}{8}$

2 Convert the following decimals to fractions.

  a 0.17   **b** 0.64   **c** 0.858

3 Work these out.   **a** $\frac{2}{3} + \frac{1}{5}$ **b** $\frac{5}{8} - \frac{2}{5}$

4 Write down the values.   **a** $\sqrt{25}$ **b** $\sqrt[3]{64}$

Indices

This section will show you how to:
- use indices (also known as powers)

index
(pl: indices)
powers
reciprocal

The **index** is the number of times a number is multiplied by itself. For example,

$$4^6 = 4 \times 4 \times 4 \times 4 \times 4 \times 4,\ 6^4 = 6 \times 6 \times 6 \times 6,\ 7^3 = 7 \times 7 \times 7,\ 12^2 = 12 \times 12$$

Here, 4 has an index of 6, 6 has an index of 4, 7 has an index of 3 and 12 has an index of 2.

Indices (or **powers**) can also be used to simplify the writing of repetitive multiplications, For example,

$$3 \times 3 \times 3 \times 3 \times 3 \times 3 \times 3 \times 3 = 3^8,\ 13 \times 13 \times 13 \times 13 \times 13 = 13^5,\ 7 \times 7 \times 7 \times 7 = 7^4$$

A commonly used power is "2", which has the special name "squared". The only other power with a special name is "3", which is called "cubed".

The value of "7 squared" is $7^2 = 7 \times 7 = 49$ and the value of "5 cubed" is $5^3 = 5 \times 5 \times 5 = 125$.

Working out indices on your calculator

How do we work out the value of 5^7 on a calculator?

We could do the calculation as $5 \times 5 \times 5 \times 5 \times 5 \times 5 \times 5 =$. But if we tried to key this in, we would probably end up missing a "× 5" or pressing a wrong key. Instead, we use the power key x^y (or, on some calculators, y^x). So

$$5^7 = \boxed{5}\ \boxed{x^y}\ \boxed{7}\ \boxed{=}\ = 78\,125$$

Make sure you know where to find the power key on your calculator. It may be an INV or SHIFT function.

Two special powers

Choose any number, say 5, and use your calculator to raise it to the power 1. You will find that $5^1 = 5$. That is, a number raised to the power 1 stays the same number. This is true for *any* number, so we do not normally write down the power 1.

Choose any number, say 9, and use your calculator to raise it to the power 0. You will find that $9^0 = 1$. This is true for *any* number raised to the power 0. The answer is *always* 1.

EXERCISE 10A

1 Write these expressions using power notation. Do not work them out yet.

a $2 \times 2 \times 2 \times 2$

b $3 \times 3 \times 3 \times 3 \times 3$

c 7×7

d $5 \times 5 \times 5$

e $10 \times 10 \times 10 \times 10 \times 10 \times 10 \times 10$

f $6 \times 6 \times 6 \times 6$

g 4

h $1 \times 1 \times 1 \times 1 \times 1 \times 1 \times 1$

i $0.5 \times 0.5 \times 0.5 \times 0.5$

j $100 \times 100 \times 100$

2 Write these power terms out in full. Do not work them out yet.

a 3^4

b 9^3

c 6^2

d 10^5

e 2^{10}

f 8^1

g 0.1^3

h 2.5^2

i 0.7^3

j 1000^2

3 Using the power key on your calculator (or another method), work out the values of the power terms in question **1**.

4 Using the power key on your calculator (or another method), work out the values of the power terms in question **2**.

5 Without using a calculator, work out the values of these power terms.

a 2^0

b 4^1

c 5^0

d 1^9

e 1^{235}

6 The answers to question **5**, parts **d** and **e**, should tell you something special about powers of 1. What is it?

7 Write the answer to question **1**, part **j** as a power of 10.

8 Write the answer to question **2**, part **j** as a power of 10.

9 Using your calculator, or otherwise, work out the values of these power terms.

a $(-1)^0$

b $(-1)^1$

c $(-1)^2$

d $(-1)^4$

e $(-1)^5$

10 Using your answers to question **9**, write down the answers to these power terms.

a $(-1)^8$

b $(-1)^{11}$

c $(-1)^{99}$

d $(-1)^{80}$

e $(-1)^{126}$

Negative indices

A negative index is a convenient way of writing the **reciprocal** of a number or term. (That is, one divided by that number or term.) For example,

$$x^{-a} = \frac{1}{x^a}$$

Here are some other examples:

$$5^{-2} = \frac{1}{5^2} \qquad 3^{-1} = \frac{1}{3} \qquad 5x^{-2} = \frac{5}{x^2}$$

EXAMPLE 1

Rewrite the following in the form 2^n.

a 8 　　　　　　**b** $\frac{1}{4}$ 　　　　　　**c** -32 　　　　　　**d** $-\frac{1}{64}$

a $8 = 2 \times 2 \times 2 = 2^3$ 　　　　　　　**b** $\frac{1}{4} = \frac{1}{2^2} = 2^{-2}$

c $-32 = -2^5$ 　　　　　　　　　　　　**d** $-\frac{1}{64} = -\frac{1}{2^6} = -2^{-6}$

EXERCISE 10B

1 Write down each of these in fraction form.

a 5^{-3} 　　**b** 6^{-1} 　　**c** 10^{-5} 　　**d** 3^{-2} 　　**e** 8^{-2}

f 9^{-1} 　　**g** w^{-2} 　　**h** t^{-1} 　　**i** x^{-m} 　　**j** $4m^{-3}$

2 Write down each of these in negative index form.

a $\frac{1}{3^2}$ 　　**b** $\frac{1}{5}$ 　　**c** $\frac{1}{10^3}$ 　　**d** $\frac{1}{m}$ 　　**e** $\frac{1}{t^n}$

3 Change each of the following expressions into an index form of the type shown.

a all of the form 2^n

　i 16 　　　　**ii** $\frac{1}{2}$ 　　　　**iii** $\frac{1}{16}$ 　　　　**iv** -8

b all of the form 10^n

　i 1000 　　　**ii** $\frac{1}{10}$ 　　　**iii** $\frac{1}{100}$ 　　　**iv** 1 million

c all of the form 5^n

　i 125 　　　**ii** $\frac{1}{5}$ 　　　　**iii** $\frac{1}{25}$ 　　　**iv** $\frac{1}{625}$

d all of the form 3^n

　i 9 　　　　**ii** $\frac{1}{27}$ 　　　**iii** $\frac{1}{81}$ 　　　**iv** -243

4 Rewrite each of the following expressions in fraction form.

a $5x^{-3}$ 　　**b** $6t^{-1}$ 　　**c** $7m^{-2}$ 　　**d** $4q^{-4}$ 　　**e** $10y^{-5}$

f $\frac{1}{2}x^{-3}$ 　　**g** $\frac{1}{2}m^{-1}$ 　　**h** $\frac{3}{4}t^{-4}$ 　　**i** $\frac{4}{5}y^{-3}$ 　　**j** $\frac{7}{8}x^{-5}$

5 Change each fraction to index form.

a $\dfrac{7}{x^3}$ **b** $\dfrac{10}{p}$ **c** $\dfrac{5}{t^2}$ **d** $\dfrac{8}{m^5}$ **e** $\dfrac{3}{y}$

6 Find the value of each of the following, where the letters have the given values.

 a Where $x = 5$

  i x^2 **ii** x^{-3} **iii** $4x^{-1}$

 b Where $t = 4$

  i t^3 **ii** t^{-2} **iii** $5t^{-4}$

 c Where $m = 2$

  i m^3 **ii** m^{-5} **iii** $9m^{-1}$

 d Where $w = 10$

  i w^6 **ii** w^{-3} **iii** $25w^{-2}$

Rules for multiplying and dividing numbers in index form

When we *multiply* together powers of the same number or variable, we *add* the indices. For example,

$$3^4 \times 3^5 = 3^{(4+5)} = 3^9$$

$$2^3 \times 2^4 \times 2^5 = 2^{12}$$

$$10^4 \times 10^{-2} = 10^2$$

$$10^{-3} \times 10^{-1} = 10^{-4}$$

$$a^x \times a^y = a^{(x+y)}$$

When we *divide* powers of the same number or variable, we *subtract* the indices. For example,

$$a^4 \div a^3 = a^{(4-3)} = a^1 = a$$

$$b^4 \div b^7 = b^{-3}$$

$$10^4 \div 10^{-2} = 10^6$$

$$10^{-2} \div 10^{-4} = 10^2$$

$$a^x \div a^y = a^{(x-y)}$$

When we *raise* a power term to a further power, we *multiply* the indices. For example,

$$(a^2)^3 = a^{2 \times 3} = a^6$$

$$(a^{-2})^4 = a^{-8}$$

$$(a^2)^6 = a^{12}$$

$$(a^x)^y = a^{xy}$$

Here are some examples of different kinds of power expressions.

$$2a^2 \times 3a^4 = (2 \times 3) \times (a^2 \times a^4) = 6 \times a^6 = 6a^6$$

$$4a^2b^3 \times 2ab^2 = (4 \times 2) \times (a^2 \times a) \times (b^3 \times b^2) = 8a^3b^5$$

$$12a^5 \div 3a^2 = (12 \div 3) \times (a^5 \div a^2) = 4a^3$$

$$(2a^2)^3 = (2)^3 \times (a^2)^3 = 8 \times a^6 = 8a^6$$

EXERCISE 10C

1 Write these as single powers of 5.

   a $5^2 \times 5^2$ **b** 5×5^2 **c** $5^{-2} \times 5^4$ **d** $5^6 \times 5^{-3}$ **e** $5^{-2} \times 5^{-3}$

2 Write these as single powers of 6.

   a $6^5 \div 6^2$ **b** $6^4 \div 6^4$ **c** $6^4 \div 6^{-2}$ **d** $6^{-3} \div 6^4$ **e** $6^{-3} \div 6^{-5}$

3 Simplify these and write them as single powers of a.

   a $a^2 \times a$ **b** $a^3 \times a^2$ **c** $a^4 \times a^3$

   d $a^6 \div a^2$ **e** $a^3 \div a$ **f** $a^5 \div a^4$

4 Write these as single powers of 4.

   a $(4^2)^3$ **b** $(4^3)^5$ **c** $(4^1)^6$

   d $(4^3)^{-2}$ **e** $(4^{-2})^{-3}$ **f** $(4^7)^0$

5 Simplify these expressions.

   a $2a^2 \times 3a^3$ **b** $3a^4 \times 3a^{-2}$ **c** $(2a^2)^3$

   d $-2a^2 \times 3a^2$ **e** $-4a^3 \times -2a^5$ **f** $-2a^4 \times 5a^{-7}$

> **HINTS AND TIPS**
>
> Deal with numbers and indices separately and do not confuse the rules. For example $12a^5 \div 4a^2 = (12 \div 4) \times (a^5 \div a^2)$

6 Simplify these expressions.

   a $6a^3 \div 2a^2$ **b** $12a^5 \div 3a^2$ **c** $15a^5 \div 5a$

   d $18a^{-2} \div 3a^{-1}$ **e** $24a^5 \div 6a^{-2}$ **f** $30a \div 6a^5$

7 Simplify these expressions.

   a $2a^2b^3 \times 4a^3b$ **b** $5a^2b^4 \times 2ab^{-3}$ **c** $6a^2b^3 \times 5a^{-4}b^{-5}$

   d $12a^2b^4 \div 6ab$ **e** $24a^{-3}b^4 \div 3a^2b^{-3}$

8 Simplify these expressions.

   a $\dfrac{6a^4b^3}{2ab}$ **b** $\dfrac{2a^2bc^2 \times 6abc^3}{4ab^2c}$ **c** $\dfrac{3abc \times 4a^3b^2c \times 6c^2}{9a^2bc}$

9 Use the general rule for dividing powers of the same number, $\dfrac{a^x}{a^y} = a^{x-y}$, to prove that any number raised to the power zero is 1.

Indices of the form $\frac{1}{n}$

Consider the problem $7^x \times 7^x = 7$. This can be written as:

$$7^{(x+x)} = 7$$

$$7^{2x} = 7^1 \implies 2x = 1 \implies x = \tfrac{1}{2}$$

If we now substitute $x = \tfrac{1}{2}$ back into the original equation, we see that:

$$7^{\frac{1}{2}} \times 7^{\frac{1}{2}} = 7$$

This makes $7^{\frac{1}{2}}$ the same as $\sqrt{7}$.

You can similarly show that $7^{\frac{1}{3}}$ is the same as $\sqrt[3]{7}$. And that, generally,

$$x^{\frac{1}{n}} = \sqrt[n]{x} \text{ (}n\text{th root of } x\text{)}$$

For example,

$$49^{\frac{1}{2}} = \sqrt{49} = 7 \qquad 8^{\frac{1}{3}} = \sqrt[3]{8} = 2 \qquad 10\,000^{\frac{1}{4}} = \sqrt[4]{10\,000} = 10 \qquad 36^{-\frac{1}{2}} = \frac{1}{\sqrt{36}} = \frac{1}{6}$$

EXERCISE 10D

Evaluate the following.

1 $25^{\frac{1}{2}}$ **2** $100^{\frac{1}{2}}$ **3** $64^{\frac{1}{2}}$ **4** $81^{\frac{1}{2}}$ **5** $625^{\frac{1}{2}}$

6 $27^{\frac{1}{3}}$ **7** $64^{\frac{1}{3}}$ **8** $1000^{\frac{1}{3}}$ **9** $125^{\frac{1}{3}}$ **10** $512^{\frac{1}{3}}$

11 $144^{\frac{1}{2}}$ **12** $400^{\frac{1}{2}}$ **13** $625^{\frac{1}{4}}$ **14** $81^{\frac{1}{4}}$ **15** $100\,000^{\frac{1}{5}}$

16 $729^{\frac{1}{6}}$ **17** $32^{\frac{1}{5}}$ **18** $1024^{\frac{1}{10}}$ **19** $1296^{\frac{1}{4}}$ **20** $216^{\frac{1}{3}}$

21 $16^{-\frac{1}{2}}$ **22** $8^{-\frac{1}{3}}$ **23** $81^{-\frac{1}{4}}$ **24** $3125^{-\frac{1}{5}}$ **25** $1\,000\,000^{-\frac{1}{6}}$

26 $\left(\dfrac{25}{36}\right)^{\frac{1}{2}}$ **27** $\left(\dfrac{100}{36}\right)^{\frac{1}{2}}$ **28** $\left(\dfrac{64}{81}\right)^{\frac{1}{2}}$ **29** $\left(\dfrac{81}{25}\right)^{\frac{1}{2}}$ **30** $\left(\dfrac{25}{64}\right)^{\frac{1}{2}}$

31 $\left(\dfrac{27}{125}\right)^{\frac{1}{3}}$ **32** $\left(\dfrac{8}{512}\right)^{\frac{1}{3}}$ **33** $\left(\dfrac{1000}{64}\right)^{\frac{1}{3}}$ **34** $\left(\dfrac{64}{125}\right)^{\frac{1}{3}}$ **35** $\left(\dfrac{512}{343}\right)^{\frac{1}{3}}$

 36 Use the general rule for raising a power to another power to prove that $x^{\frac{1}{n}}$ is equivalent to $\sqrt[n]{x}$

Indices of the form $\frac{a}{b}$

Here are two examples of this form.

$$t^{\frac{2}{3}} = t^{\frac{1}{3}} \times t^{\frac{1}{3}} = (\sqrt[3]{t})^2 \qquad 81^{\frac{3}{4}} = (\sqrt[4]{81})^3 = 3^3 = 27$$

EXAMPLE 2

Evaluate the following.   **a** $16^{-\frac{1}{4}}$ **b** $32^{-\frac{4}{5}}$

When dealing with negative indices do not make the mistake of thinking that the answer will be negative. Do problems like these in three steps.

Step 1: take the root of the base number given by the denominator of the fraction.

Step 2: raise the result to the power given by the numerator of the fraction.

Step 3: take the reciprocal (divide into 1) of the answer, which is what the negative power tells you to do.

a Step 1: $\sqrt[4]{16} = 2$.   Step 2: $2^1 = 2$.   Step 3: reciprocal of 2 is $\frac{1}{2}$

b Step 1: $\sqrt[5]{32} = 2$.   Step 2: $2^4 = 16$.   Step 3: reciprocal of 16 is $\frac{1}{16}$

EXERCISE 10E

1 Evaluate the following.

a $32^{\frac{4}{5}}$ **b** $125^{\frac{2}{3}}$ **c** $1296^{\frac{3}{4}}$ **d** $243^{\frac{4}{5}}$

2 Rewrite the following in index form.

a $\sqrt[3]{t^2}$ **b** $\sqrt[4]{m^3}$ **c** $\sqrt[5]{k^2}$ **d** $\sqrt{x^3}$

3 Evaluate the following.

a $8^{\frac{2}{3}}$ **b** $27^{\frac{2}{3}}$ **c** $16^{\frac{3}{2}}$ **d** $625^{\frac{5}{4}}$

4 Evaluate the following.

a $25^{-\frac{1}{2}}$ **b** $36^{-\frac{1}{2}}$ **c** $16^{-\frac{1}{4}}$ **d** $81^{-\frac{1}{4}}$

e $16^{-\frac{1}{2}}$ **f** $8^{-\frac{1}{3}}$ **g** $32^{-\frac{1}{5}}$ **h** $27^{-\frac{1}{3}}$

5 Evaluate the following.

a $25^{-\frac{3}{2}}$ **b** $36^{-\frac{3}{2}}$ **c** $16^{-\frac{3}{4}}$ **d** $81^{-\frac{3}{4}}$

e $64^{-\frac{4}{3}}$ **f** $8^{-\frac{2}{3}}$ **g** $32^{-\frac{2}{5}}$ **h** $27^{-\frac{2}{3}}$

6 Evaluate the following.

a $100^{-\frac{5}{2}}$ **b** $144^{-\frac{1}{2}}$ **c** $125^{-\frac{2}{3}}$ **d** $9^{-\frac{3}{2}}$

e $4^{-\frac{5}{2}}$ **f** $64^{-\frac{5}{6}}$ **g** $27^{-\frac{4}{3}}$ **h** $169^{-\frac{1}{2}}$

Standard form

This section will introduce you to:

- standard form and show you how to calculate with standard form

Key words

powers
standard
form

Arithmetic of powers of 10

Multiplying

You have already done some arithmetic with multiples of 10 in Chapter 1. We will now look at **powers** of 10.

How many zeros does a million have? What is a million as a power of 10? This table shows some of the pattern of the powers of 10.

Number	0.001	0.01	0.1	1	10	100	1000	10 000	100 000
Powers	10^{-3}	10^{-2}	10^{-1}	10^0	10^1	10^2	10^3	10^4	10^5

What pattern is there in the top row? What pattern is there to the powers in the bottom row?

To multiply by any power of 10, we simply move the digits according to these two rules.

- When the index is *positive*, move the digits to the *left* by the same number of places as the value of the index.

- When the index is *negative*, move the digits to the *right* by the same number of places as the value of the index.

For example,

$12.356 \times 10^2 = 1235.6$ $3.45 \times 10^1 = 34.5$

$753.4 \times 10^{-2} = 7.534$ $6789 \times 10^{-1} = 678.9$

In certain cases, we have to insert the "hidden" zeros. For example,

$75 \times 10^4 = 750\,000$ $2.04 \times 10^5 = 204\,000$

$6.78 \times 10^{-3} = 0.006\,78$ $0.897 \times 10^{-4} = 0.000\,0897$

Dividing

To divide by any power of 10, we simply move the digits according to these two rules.

- When the index is *positive*, move the digits to the *right* by the same number of places as the value of the index.

- When the index is *negative*, move the digits to the *left* by the same number of places as the value of the index.

For example,

$$712.35 \div 10^2 = 7.1235 \qquad\qquad 38.45 \div 10^1 = 3.845$$

$$3.463 \div 10^{-2} = 346.3 \qquad\qquad 6.789 \div 10^{-1} = 67.89$$

In certain cases, we have to insert the "hidden" zeros. For example,

$$75 \div 10^4 = 0.0075 \qquad\qquad 2.04 \div 10^5 = 0.000\,0204$$

$$6.78 \div 10^{-3} = 6780 \qquad\qquad 0.08 \div 10^{-4} = 800$$

When doing the next exercise, remember:

$$
\begin{aligned}
10\,000 &= 10 \times 10 \times 10 \times 10 &= 10^4 \\
1000 &= 10 \times 10 \times 10 &= 10^3 \\
100 &= 10 \times 10 &= 10^2 \\
10 &= 10 &= 10^1
\end{aligned}
\qquad\qquad
\begin{aligned}
1 & &= 10^0 \\
0.1 &= 1 \div 10 &= 10^{-1} \\
0.01 &= 1 \div 100 &= 10^{-2} \\
0.001 &= 1 \div 1000 &= 10^{-3}
\end{aligned}
$$

EXERCISE 10F

1 Write down the value of each of the following.

    a 3.1×10 **b** 3.1×100 **c** 3.1×1000 **d** $3.1 \times 10\,000$

2 Write down the value of each of the following.

    a 6.5×10 **b** 6.5×10^2 **c** 6.5×10^3 **d** 6.5×10^4

3 Write down the value of each of the following.

    a $3.1 \div 10$ **b** $3.1 \div 100$ **c** $3.1 \div 1000$ **d** $3.1 \div 10\,000$

4 Write down the value of each of the following.

    a $6.5 \div 10$ **b** $6.5 \div 10^2$ **c** $6.5 \div 10^3$ **d** $6.5 \div 10^4$

5 Evaluate the following.

    a 2.5×100 **b** 3.45×10 **c** 4.67×1000 **d** 34.6×10

    e 20.789×10 **f** 56.78×1000 **g** 2.46×10^2 **h** 0.076×10

    i 0.999×10^6 **j** 234.56×10^2 **k** 98.7654×10^3 **l** 43.23×10^6

    m $0.003\,4578 \times 10^5$ **n** 0.0006×10^7 **o** $0.005\,67 \times 10^4$ **p** 56.0045×10^4

6 Evaluate the following.

    a $2.5 \div 100$ **b** $3.45 \div 10$ **c** $4.67 \div 1000$ **d** $34.6 \div 10$

    e $20.789 \div 100$ **f** $56.78 \div 1000$ **g** $2.46 \div 10^2$ **h** $0.076 \div 10$

    i $0.999 \div 10^6$ **j** $234.56 \div 10^2$ **k** $98.7654 \div 10^3$ **l** $43.23 \div 10^6$

    m $0.003\,4578 \div 10^5$ **n** $0.0006 \div 10^7$ **o** $0.005\,67 \div 10^4$ **p** $56.0045 \div 10^4$

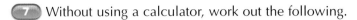
7 Without using a calculator, work out the following.

a 2.3×10^2 **b** 5.789×10^5 **c** 4.79×10^3 **d** 5.7×10^7

e 2.16×10^2 **f** 1.05×10^4 **g** 3.2×10^{-4} **h** 9.87×10^3

8 Which of these statements is true about the numbers in question **7**?

a The first part is always a number between 1 and 10.

b There is always a multiplication sign in the middle of the expression.

c There is always a power of 10 at the end.

d Calculator displays sometimes show numbers in this form.

Standard form

Standard form is also known as standard index form or SI form. On calculators, it is usually called scientific notation.

Standard form is a way of writing very large and very small numbers using powers of 10. In this form, a number is given a value between 1 and 10 multiplied by a power of 10. That is,

$a \times 10^n$ where $1 \leqslant a < 10$, and n is a whole number

Follow through these examples to see how numbers are written in standard form.

$52 = 5.2 \times 10 = \mathbf{5.2 \times 10^1}$

$73 = 7.3 \times 10 = \mathbf{7.3 \times 10^1}$

$625 = 6.25 \times 100 = \mathbf{6.25 \times 10^2}$ The numbers in bold are in standard form.

$389 = 3.89 \times 100 = \mathbf{3.89 \times 10^2}$

$3147 = 3.147 \times 1000 = \mathbf{3.147 \times 10^3}$

When writing a number in this way, two rules must always be followed.

- The first part must be a number between 1 and 10 (1 is allowed but 10 isn't).

- The second part must be a whole number (negative or positive) power of 10. Note that we would *not normally* write the power 1.

Standard form on a calculator

A number such as 123 000 000 000 is obviously difficult to key into a calculator. Instead, you enter it in standard form (assuming you are using a scientific calculator):

$123\,000\,000\,000 = 1.23 \times 10^{11}$

The key strokes to enter this into your calculator will be

1 **•** **2** **3** **EXP** **1** **1**   (On some calculators EXP is EE.)

Your calculator display should now show

1.23 $^{\boxed{11}}$ or   1.23 $\boxed{11}$

Be careful when you get an answer like this on your calculator. It needs to be written properly in standard form with × 10, not copied exactly as shown on the calculator display.

Standard form of numbers less than 1

These numbers are written in standard form. Make sure that you understand how they are formed.

a $0.4 = 4 \times 10^{-1}$

b $0.05 = 5 \times 10^{-2}$

c $0.007 = 7 \times 10^{-3}$

d $0.123 = 1.23 \times 10^{-1}$

e $0.007\,65 = 7.65 \times 10^{-3}$

f $0.9804 = 9.804 \times 10^{-1}$

g $0.0098 = 9.8 \times 10^{-3}$

h $0.000\,0078 = 7.8 \times 10^{-6}$

On a calculator you would enter 1.23×10^{-6}, for example, as

1 **•** **2** **3** **EXP** **+/−** **6**

or **1** **•** **2** **3** **EXP** **6** **+/−**

How you enter such numbers will depend on your type of calculator. Try some of the numbers **a** to **h** (above) to see what happens.

EXERCISE 10G

1 Write down the value of each of the following.

a 3.1×0.1 **b** 3.1×0.01 **c** 3.1×0.001 **d** 3.1×0.0001

2 Write down the value of each of the following.

a 6.5×10^{-1} **b** 6.5×10^{-2} **c** 6.5×10^{-3} **d** 6.5×10^{-4}

3 **a** What is the largest number you can enter into your calculator?

b What is the smallest number you can enter into your calculator?

4 Work out the value of each of the following.

a $3.1 \div 0.1$ **b** $3.1 \div 0.01$ **c** $3.1 \div 0.001$ **d** $3.1 \div 0.0001$

5 Work out the value of each of the following.

a $6.5 \div 10^{-1}$ **b** $6.5 \div 10^{-2}$ **c** $6.5 \div 10^{-3}$ **d** $6.5 \div 10^{-4}$

6 Write these numbers out in full.

  a 2.5×10^2 **b** 3.45×10 **c** 4.67×10^{-3} **d** 3.46×10

  e 2.0789×10^{-2} **f** 5.678×10^3 **g** 2.46×10^2 **h** 7.6×10^3

  i 8.97×10^5 **j** 8.65×10^{-3} **k** 6×10^7 **l** 5.67×10^{-4}

7 Write these numbers in standard form.

  a 250   **b** 0.345   **c** 46 700

  d 3 400 000 000   **e** 20 780 000 000   **f** 0.000 5678

  g 2460   **h** 0.076   **i** 0.000 76

  j 0.999   **k** 234.56   **l** 98.7654

  m 0.0006   **n** 0.005 67   **o** 56.0045

In questions **8** to **10**, write the numbers given in each question in standard form.

8 One year, 27 797 runners completed the New York marathon.

9 The largest number of dominoes ever toppled by one person is 281 581, although 30 people set up and toppled 1 382 101.

10 The asteroid Phaethon comes within 12 980 000 miles of the sun, whilst the asteroid Pholus, at its furthest point, is a distance of 2997 million miles from the earth. The closest an asteroid ever came to Earth was 93 000 miles from the planet.

Calculating with standard form

Calculations involving very large or very small numbers can be done more easily using standard form. In these examples, we work out the area of a pixel on a computer screen, and how long it takes light to reach the Earth from a distant star.

EXAMPLE 3

A pixel on a computer screen is 2×10^{-2} cm long by 7×10^{-3} cm wide.

What is the area of the pixel?

The area is given by length times width:

  Area $= 2 \times 10^{-2}$ cm $\times 7 \times 10^{-3}$ cm

   $= (2 \times 7) \times (10^{-2} \times 10^{-3})$ cm$^2 = 14 \times 10^{-5}$ cm^2

Note that you multiply the numbers and add the powers of 10. (You should not need to use a calculator to do this calculation.) The answer is not in standard form as the first part is not between 1 and 10, so we have to change it to standard form.

  Area $= 14 \times 10^{-5}$ cm$^2 = 1.4 \times 10^{-4}$ cm^2

EXAMPLE 4

The star Betelgeuse is 1.8×10^{15} miles from Earth. Light travels at 1.86×10^5 miles per second.

a How many seconds does it take light to travel from Betelgeuse to Earth? Give your answer in standard form.

b How many years does it take light to travel from Betelgeuse to Earth?

a Time = distance ÷ speed = 1.8×10^{15} miles ÷ 1.86×10^5 miles per second

$$= (1.8 \div 1.86) \times (10^{15} \div 10^5) \text{ seconds}$$

$$= 0.967\ 741\ 935 \times 10^{10} \text{ seconds}$$

Note that you divide the numbers and subtract the powers of 10. To change the answer to standard form, first round it off, which gives

$$0.97 \times 10^{10} = 9.7 \times 10^9 \text{ seconds}$$

b To convert from seconds to years, you have to divide first by 3600 to get to hours, then by 24 to get to days, and finally by 365 to get to years.

$$9.7 \times 10^9 \div (3600 \times 24 \times 365) = 307.6 \text{ years}$$

EXERCISE 10H

1 These numbers are not in standard form. Write them in standard form.

a 56.7×10^2	**b** 0.06×10^4	**c** 34.6×10^{-2}
d 0.07×10^{-2}	**e** 56×10	**f** $2 \times 3 \times 10^5$
g $2 \times 10^2 \times 35$	**h** 160×10^{-2}	**i** 23 million
j 0.0003×10^{-2}	**k** 25.6×10^5	**l** $16 \times 10^2 \times 3 \times 10^{-1}$
m $2 \times 10^4 \times 56 \times 10^{-4}$	**n** $18 \times 10^2 \div 3 \times 10^3$	**o** $56 \times 10^3 \div 2 \times 10^{-2}$

2 Work out the following. Give your answers in standard form.

a $2 \times 10^4 \times 5.4 \times 10^3$	**b** $1.6 \times 10^2 \times 3 \times 10^4$	**c** $2 \times 10^4 \times 6 \times 10^4$
d $2 \times 10^{-4} \times 5.4 \times 10^3$	**e** $1.6 \times 10^{-2} \times 4 \times 10^4$	**f** $2 \times 10^4 \times 6 \times 10^{-4}$
g $7.2 \times 10^{-3} \times 4 \times 10^2$	**h** $(5 \times 10^3)^2$	**i** $(2 \times 10^{-2})^3$

3 Work out the following. Give your answers in standard form, rounding off to an appropriate degree of accuracy where necessary.

a $2.1 \times 10^4 \times 5.4 \times 10^3$	**b** $1.6 \times 10^3 \times 3.8 \times 10^3$	**c** $2.4 \times 10^4 \times 6.6 \times 10^4$
d $7.3 \times 10^{-6} \times 5.4 \times 10^3$	**e** $(3.1 \times 10^4)^2$	**f** $(6.8 \times 10^{-4})^2$
g $5.7 \times 10 \times 3.7 \times 10$	**h** $1.9 \times 10^{-2} \times 1.9 \times 10^9$	**i** $5.9 \times 10^3 \times 2.5 \times 10^{-2}$
j $5.2 \times 10^3 \times 2.2 \times 10^2 \times 3.1 \times 10^3$		**k** $1.8 \times 10^2 \times 3.6 \times 10^3 \times 2.4 \times 10^{-2}$

4 Work out the following. Give your answers in standard form.

a $5.4 \times 10^4 \div 2 \times 10^3$	**b** $4.8 \times 10^2 \div 3 \times 10^4$	**c** $1.2 \times 10^4 \div 6 \times 10^4$
d $2 \times 10^{-4} \div 5 \times 10^3$	**e** $1.8 \times 10^4 \div 9 \times 10^{-2}$	**f** $\sqrt{(36 \times 10^{-4})}$
g $5.4 \times 10^{-3} \div 2.7 \times 10^2$	**h** $1.8 \times 10^6 \div 3.6 \times 10^3$	**i** $5.6 \times 10^3 \div 2.8 \times 10^2$

5 Work out the following. Give your answers in standard form, rounding off to an appropriate degree of accuracy where necessary.

    a $2.7 \times 10^4 \div 5 \times 10^2$ **b** $2.3 \times 10^4 \div 8 \times 10^6$ **c** $3.2 \times 10^{-1} \div 2.8 \times 10^{-1}$

    d $2.6 \times 10^{-6} \div 4.1 \times 10^3$ **e** $\sqrt{(8 \times 10^4)}$ **f** $\sqrt{(30 \times 10^{-4})}$

    g $5.3 \times 10^3 \times 2.3 \times 10^2 \div 2.5 \times 10^3$ **h** $1.8 \times 10^2 \times 3.1 \times 10^3 \div 6.5 \times 10^{-2}$

6 A typical adult has about 20 000 000 000 000 red corpuscles. Each red corpuscle weighs about 0.000 000 000 1 gram. Write both of these numbers in standard form and work out the total mass of red corpuscles in a typical adult.

7 If a man puts 1 grain of rice on the first square of a chess board, 2 on the second square, 4 on the third, 8 on the fourth and so on,

    a how many grains of rice will he put on the 64th square of the board?

    b how many grains of rice will there be altogether?

Give your answers in standard form.

8 The surface area of the Earth is approximately 2×10^8 square miles. The surface area of the earth covered by water is approximately 1.4×10^8 square miles.

    a Calculate the surface area of the Earth not covered by water. Give your answer in standard form.

    b What percentage of the Earth's surface is not covered by water?

9 The moon is a sphere with a radius of 1.080×10^3 miles. The formula for working out the surface area of a sphere is

    Surface area = $4\pi r^2$

Calculate the surface area of the moon.

10 Evaluate $\dfrac{E}{M}$ when $E = 1.5 \times 10^3$ and $M = 3 \times 10^{-2}$, giving your answer in standard form.

11 Work out the value of $\dfrac{3.2 \times 10^7}{1.4 \times 10^2}$ giving your answer in standard form, correct to two significant figures.

12 In 2005, British Airways carried 23 million passengers. Of these, 70% passed through Heathrow Airport. On average, each passenger carried 19.7 kg of luggage. Calculate the total weight of the luggage carried by these passengers.

13 Many people withdraw money from their banks by using hole-in-the-wall machines. Each day there are eight million withdrawals from 32 000 machines. What is the average number of withdrawals per machine?

14 The mass of Saturn is 5.686×10^{26} tonnes. The mass of the Earth is 6.04×10^{21} tonnes. How many times heavier is Saturn than the Earth? Give your answer in standard form to a suitable degree of accuracy.

This section will explain about:

* reciprocals, and terminating and recurring decimals

Key words

rational
  number
reciprocal
recurring
  decimal
terminating
  decimal

Rational decimal numbers

A fraction, also known as a **rational number**, can be expressed as a decimal which is either a **terminating decimal** or a **recurring decimal**.

A terminating decimal contains a finite number of digits (decimal places). For example, changing $\frac{3}{16}$ into a decimal gives 0.1875 exactly.

A recurring decimal contains a digit or a block of digits that repeats. For example, changing $\frac{5}{9}$ into a decimal gives 0.5555 …, while changing $\frac{14}{27}$ into a decimal gives 0.518 518 5 … with the recurring block 518.

Recurring decimals are indicated by a dot placed over the first and last digits in the recurring block. For example, 0.5555 … becomes $0.\dot{5}$, 0.518 518 5 … becomes $0.\dot{5}1\dot{8}$, and 0.583 33 becomes $0.58\dot{3}$.

Converting decimals into fractions

Terminating decimals
When converting a terminating decimal, the numerator of the fraction is formed from the decimal, and its denominator is given by 10, 100 or 1000, depending on the number of decimal places. Because the terminating decimal ends at a specific decimal place, we know the place value at which the numerator ends. For example,

$$0.7 = \frac{7}{10}$$

$$2.34 = 2\frac{34}{100} = 2\frac{17}{50}$$

$$0.045 = \frac{45}{1000} = \frac{9}{200}$$

$$0.625 = \frac{625}{1000} = \frac{5}{8}$$

Recurring decimals
If a fraction does not give a terminating decimal, it will give a recurring decimal. You already know that $\frac{1}{3} = 0.333 … = 0.\dot{3}$. This means that the 3s go on forever and the decimal never ends. To check whether a fraction is a recurring decimal, you usually have to use a calculator to divide the numerator by the denominator. Use a calculator to check the following recurring decimals. (Note that calculators round off the last digit so it may not always be a true recurring decimal in the display.)

$$\frac{2}{11} = 0.181818 \ldots = 0.\dot{1}\dot{8}$$

$$\frac{4}{15} = 0.2666\ldots = 0.2\dot{6}$$

$$\frac{8}{13} = 0.6153846153846 \ldots = 0.\dot{6}1538\dot{4}$$

To convert a recurring decimal to a fraction, you have to multiply the decimal by a suitable power of 10, and then perform a subtraction. These examples demonstrate the method.

EXAMPLE 5

Convert $0.\dot{7}$ to a fraction.

Let x be the fraction. Then

$$x = 0.777\ 777\ 777 \ldots \quad (1)$$

Multiply (1) by 10 $\qquad 10x = 7.777\ 777\ 777 \ldots \quad (2)$

Subtract (2) − (1) $\qquad 9x = 7$

$$\Rightarrow x = \frac{7}{9}$$

EXAMPLE 6

Convert $0.\dot{5}6\dot{4}$ to a fraction.

Let x be the fraction. Then

$$x = 0.564\ 564\ 564 \ldots \quad (1)$$

Multiply (1) by 1000 $\qquad 1000x = 564.564\ 564\ 564 \ldots \quad (2)$

Subtract (2) − (1) $\qquad 999x = 564$

$$\Rightarrow \quad x = \frac{564}{999} = \frac{188}{333}$$

As a general rule multiply by 10 if one digit recurs, multiply by 100 if two digits recur, multiply by 1000 if three digits recur, and so on.

Reciprocals

The **reciprocal** of a number is the number divided into 1. So the reciprocal of 2 is $1 \div 2 = \frac{1}{2}$ or 0.5.

Reciprocals of fractions are quite easy to find as you just have to turn the fraction upside down.
For example, the reciprocal of $\frac{2}{3}$ is $\frac{3}{2}$.

C

1 Work out each of these fractions as a decimal. Give them as terminating decimals or recurring decimals as appropriate.

   a $\frac{1}{2}$ **b** $\frac{1}{3}$ **c** $\frac{1}{4}$ **d** $\frac{1}{5}$ **e** $\frac{1}{6}$

   f $\frac{1}{7}$ **g** $\frac{1}{8}$ **h** $\frac{1}{9}$ **i** $\frac{1}{10}$ **j** $\frac{1}{13}$

2 There are several patterns to be found in recurring decimals. For example,

$\frac{1}{7}$ = 0.142 857 142 857 142 857 142 857…

$\frac{2}{7}$ = 0.285 714 285 714 285 714 285 714…

$\frac{3}{7}$ = 0.428 571 428 571 428 571 428 571…

and so on.

   a Write down the decimals for $\frac{4}{7}, \frac{5}{7}, \frac{6}{7}$ to 24 decimal places.

   b What do you notice?

3 Work out the ninths as recurring decimals, that is $\frac{1}{9}, \frac{2}{9}, \frac{3}{9}$ and so on, up to $\frac{8}{9}$.

Describe any patterns that you notice.

4 Work out the elevenths as recurring decimals, that is $\frac{1}{11}, \frac{2}{11}, \frac{3}{11}$ and so on, up to $\frac{10}{11}$.

Describe any patterns that you notice.

5 Write each of these fractions as a decimal. Use this to write the list in order of size, smallest first.

   $\frac{4}{9}$ $\frac{5}{11}$ $\frac{3}{7}$ $\frac{9}{22}$ $\frac{16}{37}$ $\frac{6}{13}$

6 Write each of the following as a fraction with a denominator of 120. Use this to put them in order of size, smallest first.

   $\frac{19}{60}$ $\frac{7}{24}$ $\frac{3}{10}$ $\frac{2}{5}$ $\frac{5}{12}$

7 Convert each of these terminating decimals to a fraction.

   a 0.125   **b** 0.34   **c** 0.725   **d** 0.3125

   e 0.89   **f** 0.05   **g** 2.35   **h** 0.218 75

8 Use a calculator to work out the reciprocals of the following values.

   a 12   **b** 16   **c** 20   **d** 25   **e** 50

9 Write down the reciprocals of the following fractions.

   a $\frac{3}{4}$ **b** $\frac{5}{6}$ **c** $\frac{2}{5}$ **d** $\frac{7}{10}$

   e $\frac{11}{20}$ **f** $\frac{4}{15}$

10 **a** Work out the fractions and their reciprocals from question **9** as decimals. Write them as terminating decimals or recurring decimals as appropriate.

b Is it always true that a fraction that gives a terminating decimal has a reciprocal that gives a recurring decimal?

11 Multiply together the fractions and their reciprocals from question **9**. What results do you get every time?

12 $x = 0.242\ 424 \ldots$

a What is $100x$?

b By subtracting the original value from your answer to part **a**, work out the value of $99x$.

c What is x as a fraction?

13 Convert each of these recurring decimals to a fraction.

a $0.\dot{8}$	**b** $0.\dot{3}\dot{4}$	**c** $0.4\dot{5}$	**d** $0.5\dot{6}\dot{7}$
e $0.\dot{4}$	**f** $0.0\dot{4}$	**g** $0.1\dot{4}$	**h** $0.04\dot{5}$
i $2.\dot{7}$	**j** $7.\dot{6}\dot{3}$	**k** $3.\dot{3}$	**l** $2.0\dot{6}$

14 **a** $\frac{1}{7}$ is a recurring decimal. $\left(\frac{1}{7}\right)^2 = \frac{1}{49}$ is also a recurring decimal.

Is it true that when you square any fraction that is a recurring decimal, you get another fraction that is also a recurring decimal? Try this with at least four numerical examples before you make a decision.

b $\frac{1}{4}$ is a terminating decimal. $\left(\frac{1}{4}\right)^2 = \frac{1}{16}$ is also a terminating decimal.

Is it true that when you square any fraction that is a terminating decimal, you get another fraction that is also a terminating decimal? Try this with at least four numerical examples before you make a decision.

c What type of fraction do you get when you multiply a fraction that gives a recurring decimal by another fraction that gives a terminating decimal? Try this with at least four numerical examples before you make a decision.

15 **a** Convert the recurring decimal $0.\dot{9}$ to a fraction.

b Prove that $0.4\dot{9}$ is equal to 0.5.

Surds

In this section you will learn how to:
- calculate and manipulate surds

Key words
rationalise
surds

It is useful at higher levels of mathematics to be able to work with **surds**, which are roots of numbers written as, for example,

$\sqrt{2}$ $\sqrt{5}$ $\sqrt{15}$ $\sqrt{9}$ $\sqrt{3}$ $\sqrt{10}$

Four general rules governing surds (which you can verify yourself by taking numerical examples) are:

$$\sqrt{a} \times \sqrt{b} = \sqrt{ab} \qquad C\sqrt{a} \times D\sqrt{b} = CD\sqrt{ab}$$

$$\sqrt{a} \div \sqrt{b} = \sqrt{\frac{a}{b}} \qquad C\sqrt{a} \div D\sqrt{b} = \frac{C}{D}\sqrt{\frac{a}{b}}$$

For example,

$\sqrt{2} \times \sqrt{2} = \sqrt{4} = 2$ $\sqrt{2} \times \sqrt{10} = \sqrt{20} = \sqrt{(4 \times 5)} = \sqrt{4} \times \sqrt{5} = 2\sqrt{5}$

$\sqrt{2} \times \sqrt{3} = \sqrt{6}$ $\sqrt{6} \times \sqrt{15} = \sqrt{90} = \sqrt{9} \times \sqrt{10} = 3\sqrt{10}$

$\sqrt{2} \times \sqrt{8} = \sqrt{16} = 4$ $3\sqrt{5} \times 4\sqrt{3} = 12\sqrt{15}$

EXERCISE 10J

A

1 Simplify each of the following. Leave your answers in surd form.

a $\sqrt{2} \times \sqrt{3}$ b $\sqrt{5} \times \sqrt{3}$ c $\sqrt{2} \times \sqrt{2}$ d $\sqrt{2} \times \sqrt{8}$

e $\sqrt{5} \times \sqrt{8}$ f $\sqrt{3} \times \sqrt{3}$ g $\sqrt{6} \times \sqrt{2}$ h $\sqrt{7} \times \sqrt{3}$

i $\sqrt{2} \times \sqrt{7}$ j $\sqrt{2} \times \sqrt{18}$ k $\sqrt{6} \times \sqrt{6}$ l $\sqrt{5} \times \sqrt{6}$

2 Simplify each of the following. Leave your answers in surd form.

a $\sqrt{12} \div \sqrt{3}$ b $\sqrt{15} \div \sqrt{3}$ c $\sqrt{12} \div \sqrt{2}$ d $\sqrt{24} \div \sqrt{8}$

e $\sqrt{40} \div \sqrt{8}$ f $\sqrt{3} \div \sqrt{3}$ g $\sqrt{6} \div \sqrt{2}$ h $\sqrt{21} \div \sqrt{3}$

i $\sqrt{28} \div \sqrt{7}$ j $\sqrt{48} \div \sqrt{8}$ k $\sqrt{6} \div \sqrt{6}$ l $\sqrt{54} \div \sqrt{6}$

3 Simplify each of the following. Leave your answers in surd form.

a $\sqrt{2} \times \sqrt{3} \times \sqrt{2}$ b $\sqrt{5} \times \sqrt{3} \times \sqrt{15}$ c $\sqrt{2} \times \sqrt{2} \times \sqrt{8}$ d $\sqrt{2} \times \sqrt{8} \times \sqrt{3}$

e $\sqrt{5} \times \sqrt{8} \times \sqrt{8}$ f $\sqrt{3} \times \sqrt{3} \times \sqrt{3}$ g $\sqrt{6} \times \sqrt{2} \times \sqrt{48}$ h $\sqrt{7} \times \sqrt{3} \times \sqrt{3}$

i $\sqrt{2} \times \sqrt{7} \times \sqrt{2}$ j $\sqrt{2} \times \sqrt{18} \times \sqrt{5}$ k $\sqrt{6} \times \sqrt{6} \times \sqrt{3}$ l $\sqrt{5} \times \sqrt{6} \times \sqrt{30}$

A

4 Simplify each of the following. Leave your answers in surd form.

a $\sqrt{2} \times \sqrt{3} \div \sqrt{2}$

b $\sqrt{5} \times \sqrt{3} \div \sqrt{15}$

c $\sqrt{32} \times \sqrt{2} \div \sqrt{8}$

d $\sqrt{2} \times \sqrt{8} \div \sqrt{8}$

e $\sqrt{5} \times \sqrt{8} \div \sqrt{8}$

f $\sqrt{3} \times \sqrt{3} \div \sqrt{3}$

g $\sqrt{8} \times \sqrt{12} \div \sqrt{48}$

h $\sqrt{7} \times \sqrt{3} \div \sqrt{3}$

i $\sqrt{2} \times \sqrt{7} \div \sqrt{2}$

j $\sqrt{2} \times \sqrt{18} \div \sqrt{3}$

k $\sqrt{6} \times \sqrt{6} \div \sqrt{3}$

l $\sqrt{5} \times \sqrt{6} \div \sqrt{30}$

5 Simplify each of these expressions.

a $\sqrt{a} \times \sqrt{a}$

b $\sqrt{a} \div \sqrt{a}$

c $\sqrt{a} \times \sqrt{a} \div \sqrt{a}$

6 Simplify each of the following surds into the form $a\sqrt{b}$.

a $\sqrt{18}$

b $\sqrt{24}$

c $\sqrt{12}$

d $\sqrt{50}$

e $\sqrt{8}$

f $\sqrt{27}$

g $\sqrt{48}$

h $\sqrt{75}$

i $\sqrt{45}$

j $\sqrt{63}$

k $\sqrt{32}$

l $\sqrt{200}$

m $\sqrt{1000}$

n $\sqrt{250}$

o $\sqrt{98}$

p $\sqrt{243}$

7 Simplify each of these.

a $2\sqrt{18} \times 3\sqrt{2}$

b $4\sqrt{24} \times 2\sqrt{5}$

c $3\sqrt{12} \times 3\sqrt{3}$

d $2\sqrt{8} \times 2\sqrt{8}$

e $2\sqrt{27} \times 4\sqrt{8}$

f $2\sqrt{48} \times 3\sqrt{8}$

g $2\sqrt{45} \times 3\sqrt{3}$

h $2\sqrt{63} \times 2\sqrt{7}$

i $2\sqrt{32} \times 4\sqrt{2}$

j $\sqrt{1000} \times \sqrt{10}$

k $\sqrt{250} \times \sqrt{10}$

l $2\sqrt{98} \times 2\sqrt{2}$

8 Simplify each of these.

a $4\sqrt{2} \times 5\sqrt{3}$

b $2\sqrt{5} \times 3\sqrt{3}$

c $4\sqrt{2} \times 3\sqrt{2}$

d $2\sqrt{2} \times 2\sqrt{8}$

e $2\sqrt{5} \times 3\sqrt{8}$

f $3\sqrt{3} \times 2\sqrt{3}$

g $2\sqrt{6} \times 5\sqrt{2}$

h $5\sqrt{7} \times 2\sqrt{3}$

i $2\sqrt{2} \times 3\sqrt{7}$

j $2\sqrt{2} \times 3\sqrt{18}$

k $2\sqrt{6} \times 2\sqrt{6}$

l $4\sqrt{5} \times 3\sqrt{6}$

9 Simplify each of these.

a $6\sqrt{12} \div 2\sqrt{3}$

b $3\sqrt{15} \div \sqrt{3}$

c $6\sqrt{12} \div \sqrt{2}$

d $4\sqrt{24} \div 2\sqrt{8}$

e $12\sqrt{40} \div 3\sqrt{8}$

f $5\sqrt{3} \div \sqrt{3}$

g $14\sqrt{6} \div 2\sqrt{2}$

h $4\sqrt{21} \div 2\sqrt{3}$

i $9\sqrt{28} \div 3\sqrt{7}$

j $12\sqrt{56} \div 6\sqrt{8}$

k $25\sqrt{6} \div 5\sqrt{6}$

l $32\sqrt{54} \div 4\sqrt{6}$

10 Simplify each of these.

a $4\sqrt{2} \times \sqrt{3} \div 2\sqrt{2}$

b $4\sqrt{5} \times \sqrt{3} \div \sqrt{15}$

c $2\sqrt{32} \times 3\sqrt{2} \div 2\sqrt{8}$

d $6\sqrt{2} \times 2\sqrt{8} \div 3\sqrt{8}$

e $3\sqrt{5} \times 4\sqrt{8} \div 2\sqrt{8}$

f $12\sqrt{3} \times 4\sqrt{3} \div 2\sqrt{3}$

g $3\sqrt{8} \times 3\sqrt{12} \div 3\sqrt{48}$

h $4\sqrt{7} \times 2\sqrt{3} \div 8\sqrt{3}$

i $15\sqrt{2} \times 2\sqrt{7} \div 3\sqrt{2}$

j $8\sqrt{2} \times 2\sqrt{18} \div 4\sqrt{3}$

k $5\sqrt{6} \times 5\sqrt{6} \div 5\sqrt{3}$

l $2\sqrt{5} \times 3\sqrt{6} \div \sqrt{30}$

11 Simplify each of these expressions.

a $a\sqrt{b} \times c\sqrt{b}$

b $a\sqrt{b} \div c\sqrt{b}$

c $a\sqrt{b} \times c\sqrt{b} \div a\sqrt{b}$

12 Find the value of *a* that makes each of these surds true.

a $\sqrt{5} \times \sqrt{a} = 10$ **b** $\sqrt{6} \times \sqrt{a} = 12$ **c** $\sqrt{10} \times 2\sqrt{a} = 20$

d $2\sqrt{6} \times 3\sqrt{a} = 72$ **e** $2\sqrt{a} \times \sqrt{a} = 6$ **f** $3\sqrt{a} \times 3\sqrt{a} = 54$

13 Simplify the following.

a $\left(\dfrac{\sqrt{3}}{2}\right)^2$ **b** $\left(\dfrac{5}{\sqrt{3}}\right)^2$ **c** $\left(\dfrac{\sqrt{5}}{4}\right)^2$

d $\left(\dfrac{6}{\sqrt{3}}\right)^2$ **e** $\left(\dfrac{\sqrt{8}}{2}\right)^2$

14 The following rules are *not* true. Try some numerical examples to show this.

a $\sqrt{(a + b)} = \sqrt{a} + \sqrt{b}$ **b** $\sqrt{(a - b)} = \sqrt{a} - \sqrt{b}$

Calculating with surds

The following two examples show how surds can be used in solving problems.

EXAMPLE 7

In the right-angled triangle ABC, the side BC is $\sqrt{6}$ cm and the side AC is $\sqrt{18}$ cm.

Calculate the length of AB. Leave your answer in surd form.

Using Pythagoras' theorem

$$AC^2 + BC^2 = AB^2$$
$$(\sqrt{18})^2 + (\sqrt{6})^2 = 18 + 6 = 24$$
$$\Rightarrow AB = \sqrt{24} \text{ cm}$$
$$= 2\sqrt{6} \text{ cm}$$

EXAMPLE 8

Calculate the area of a square with a side of $2 + \sqrt{3}$ cm. Give your answer in the form $a + b\sqrt{3}$.

Area $= (2 + \sqrt{3})^2$ cm^2

$= (2 + \sqrt{3})(2 + \sqrt{3})$ cm^2

$= 4 + 2\sqrt{3} + 2\sqrt{3} + 3$ cm^2

$= 7 + 4\sqrt{3}$ cm^2

Rationalising the denominator

It is not good mathematical practice to leave a surd on the bottom of an expression. To get rid of it, we make the denominator into a whole number, which we do by multiplying by the appropriate square root. This means that we must also multiply the top of the expression by the same root. The following example shows you what to do.

EXAMPLE 9

Rationalise the denominator of   **a** $\dfrac{1}{\sqrt{3}}$ and   **b** $\dfrac{2\sqrt{3}}{\sqrt{8}}$.

a   Multiply the top and the bottom by $\sqrt{3}$:

$$\frac{1 \times \sqrt{3}}{\sqrt{3} \times \sqrt{3}} = \frac{\sqrt{3}}{3}$$

b   Multiply the top and the bottom by $\sqrt{8}$:

$$\frac{2\sqrt{3} \times \sqrt{8}}{\sqrt{8} \times \sqrt{8}} = \frac{2\sqrt{24}}{8} = \frac{4\sqrt{6}}{8} = \frac{\sqrt{6}}{2}$$

EXERCISE 10K

1   Show that:

    a $(2 + \sqrt{3})(1 + \sqrt{3}) = 5 + 3\sqrt{3}$

    b $(1 + \sqrt{2})(2 + \sqrt{3}) = 2 + 2\sqrt{2} + \sqrt{3} + \sqrt{6}$

    c $(4 - \sqrt{3})(4 + \sqrt{3}) = 13$

2   Expand and simplify where possible.

    a $\sqrt{3}(2 - \sqrt{3})$ **b** $\sqrt{2}(3 - 4\sqrt{2})$ **c** $\sqrt{5}(2\sqrt{5} + 4)$

    d $3\sqrt{7}(4 - 2\sqrt{7})$ **e** $3\sqrt{2}(5 - 2\sqrt{8})$ **f** $\sqrt{3}(\sqrt{27} - 1)$

3   Expand and simplify where possible.

    a $(1 + \sqrt{3})(3 - \sqrt{3})$ **b** $(2 + \sqrt{5})(3 - \sqrt{5})$ **c** $(1 - \sqrt{2})(3 + 2\sqrt{2})$

    d $(3 - 2\sqrt{7})(4 + 3\sqrt{7})$ **e** $(2 - 3\sqrt{5})(2 + 3\sqrt{5})$ **f** $(\sqrt{3} + \sqrt{2})(\sqrt{3} + \sqrt{8})$

    g $(2 + \sqrt{5})^2$ **h** $(1 - \sqrt{2})^2$ **i** $(3 + \sqrt{2})^2$

4   Work out the missing lengths in each of these triangles, giving the answer in as simple a form as possible.

    a

    b

    c

5 Calculate the area of each of these rectangles, simplifying your answers where possible.

a

$1 + \sqrt{3}$ cm

$2 - \sqrt{3}$ cm

b

$2 + \sqrt{10}$ cm

$\sqrt{5}$ cm

c

$2\sqrt{3}$ cm

$1 + \sqrt{27}$ cm

6 Rationalise the denominators of these expressions.

a $\dfrac{1}{\sqrt{3}}$ **b** $\dfrac{1}{\sqrt{2}}$ **c** $\dfrac{1}{\sqrt{5}}$ **d** $\dfrac{1}{2\sqrt{3}}$

e $\dfrac{3}{\sqrt{3}}$ **f** $\dfrac{5}{\sqrt{2}}$ **g** $\dfrac{3\sqrt{2}}{\sqrt{8}}$ **h** $\dfrac{5\sqrt{3}}{\sqrt{6}}$

i $\dfrac{\sqrt{7}}{\sqrt{3}}$ **j** $\dfrac{1 + \sqrt{2}}{\sqrt{2}}$ **k** $\dfrac{2 - \sqrt{3}}{\sqrt{3}}$ **l** $\dfrac{5 + 2\sqrt{3}}{\sqrt{3}}$

7 **a** Expand and simplify the following.

i $(2 + \sqrt{3})(2 - \sqrt{3})$ **ii** $(1 - \sqrt{5})(1 + \sqrt{5})$ **iii** $(\sqrt{3} - 1)(\sqrt{3} + 1)$

iv $(3\sqrt{2} + 1)(3\sqrt{2} - 1)$ **v** $(2 - 4\sqrt{3})(2 + 4\sqrt{3})$

b What happens in the answers to part **a**? Why?

c Rationalise the denominators of the following.

i $\dfrac{5}{1 - \sqrt{5}}$ **ii** $\dfrac{2 + \sqrt{3}}{\sqrt{3} - 1}$

1 **a** Simplify

    i $d^3 \times d^2$ **ii** $\dfrac{e}{e^8}$ **iii** $(2g^2h^4) \times (3g^2h)$

AQA, Question 8c, Paper 1 Higher, November 2004

2 Astronomers measure distances in the solar system in astronomical units (AU).
One AU is 150 000 000 kilometres.
The distance from the Sun to Pluto is 39.5 AU.
How many kilometres is the Sun from Pluto?
Give your answer in standard form to a sensible degree of accuracy.

AQA, Question 9, Paper 2 Higher, June 2005

3 Here are six numbers written in standard form.

    2.6×10^5 1.75×10^6 5.84×10^0
    8.2×10^{-3} 3.5×10^{-1} 4.9×10^{-2}

  a Write down the largest number.
  b Write down the smallest number.
  c Write 4.9×10^{-2} as an ordinary number.
  d Work out $2.6 \times 10^5 \div 0.1$
     Give your answer in standard form.

AQA, Question 5, Paper 1 Higher, June 2004

4 Simplify   **a** $\dfrac{6a^2b \times 4ab^3}{8a^2b^2}$ **b** $(3x^3y^2)^4$

5 Express the recurring decimal 0.5333333… as a fraction. Give your answer in its simplest form.

6 Find values of a and b such that
    $(2 + \sqrt{3})(4 - \sqrt{3}) = a + b\sqrt{3}$

AQA, Question 15, Paper 2 Higher, November 2004

7 The area of this rectangle is 40 cm^2
Find the value of x. Give your answer in the form $a\sqrt{b}$ where a and b are integers

8 **a** Prove that $0.\dot{7}\dot{2} = \dfrac{8}{11}$

  b Hence, or otherwise, express $0.3\dot{7}\dot{2}$ as a fraction.

9 **a** **i** Show that $\sqrt{32} = 4\sqrt{2}$

    ii Expand and simplify $(\sqrt{2} + \sqrt{12})^2$

  b Show clearly that this triangle is right angled

10 Rationalise the denominator of $\dfrac{2 + \sqrt{3}}{\sqrt{3}}$

Simplify your answer fully.

AQA, Question 16, Paper 2 Higher, June 2004

WORKED EXAM QUESTION

a Expand and simplify as far as possible $(\sqrt{2} + 3)(\sqrt{2} - 1)$.

b Show clearly that $\dfrac{3}{\sqrt{6}} + \dfrac{\sqrt{6}}{3} = \dfrac{5}{\sqrt{6}}$

Solution

a $\sqrt{2} \times \sqrt{2} + \sqrt{2} \times -1 + 3 \times \sqrt{2} + 3 \times -1$

   $2 - \sqrt{2} + 3\sqrt{2} - 3 = -1 + 2\sqrt{2}$

> Expand the brackets to get four terms.

> Simplify the terms and collect together like terms.

b $\dfrac{3 \times 3 + \sqrt{6} \times \sqrt{6}}{\sqrt{6} \times 3}$

   $\dfrac{9 + 6}{\sqrt{6} \times 3} = \dfrac{15}{3\sqrt{6}} = \dfrac{5}{\sqrt{6}}$

> Combine the fractions together with the same common denominator.

> Simplify the terms and collect together and cancel the common multiple of 3.

A scientist is doing some research on the production and consumption of oil in the world. She looks at 10 oil producing countries and, for each country, finds the most recent figures on the country's population, and its oil production and consumption, measured in barrels per day.

GREENLAND

CANADA

U. S. A.

NORTH
AMERICA

NORTH
ATLANTIC
OCEAN

USA
Population: 295 734 134
Oil production: 7.8×10^6
Oil consumption: 19.65×10^6

With these figures she calculates for each country the oil produced per person *per year*, and the oil consumed per person *per year*, then finds the difference (all to 1 decimal place).

She then ranks the countries from 1 to 10 (highest difference to lowest difference), to see which countries are using less than they produce, and which countries are using more than they produce.

She also calculates each country's consumption as a percentage of its production (to the nearest 1%).

Help her complete the table and write a short paragraph on the results of the calculations.

PACIFIC
OCEAN

MEXICO

CUBA
DOMINICAN REPUBLIC

GUATEMALA BELIZE
EL SALVADOR HONDURAS
NICARAGUA

COSTA RICA VENEZUELA
PANAMA GUYANA
SURINAME
COLUMBIA FRENCH GUIANA

ECUADOR

PERU BRAZIL

SOUTH
AMERICA

BOLIVIA

PARAGUAY

CHILE ARGENTINA URUGUAY

Venezuela
Population: 25 375 281
Oil production: 2.6×10^6
Oil consumption: 500 000

Chile
Population: 15 980 912
Oil production: 18,500
Oil consumption: 240 000

Country	Oil produced, barrels per person per year	Oil consumed, barrels per person per year	Difference (produced – consumed)	Rank order	Consumption as a % of production
Algeria	13.5	2.3	11.2	3	17%
Australia					
Chile					
Indonesia					
Japan					
Nigeria					
Saudi Arabia					
UK					
USA					
Venezuela					

UK
Population: 60 441 457
Oil production: 1.957×10^6
Oil consumption: 1.692×10^6

Japan
Population: 127 417 244
Oil production: 17 330
Oil consumption: 5.29×10^6

Indonesia
Population: 241 973 879
Oil production: 971 000
Oil consumption: 1.183×10^6

Australia
Population: 20 090 437
Oil production: 537 500
Oil consumption: 796 500

Saudi Arabia
Population: 26 417 599
Oil production: 9.021×10^6
Oil consumption: 1.55×10^6

Nigeria
Population: 128 771 988
Oil production: 2.356×10^6
Oil consumption: 275 000

Algeria
Population: 32 531 853
Oil production: 1.2×10^6
Oil consumption: 209 000

The scientist also compares the total world oil production with the total world population. Help her calculate the barrels produced per person *per year* to 1 decimal place, and comment on these figures. Compare them with the results for the individual countries.

Year	World population	World oil production, barrels per day	World oil production, barrels per person per year
1984	4.77×10^9	5.45×10^7	4.2
1989	5.19×10^9	5.99×10^7	
1994	5.61×10^9	6.10×10^7	
1999	6.01×10^9	6.58×10^7	
2004	6.38×10^9	7.25×10^7	

GRADE YOURSELF

D Able to write and calculate numbers written in index form

C Able to multiply and divide numbers written in index form

B Able to write numbers in standard form and use these in various problems

A Know how to use the rules of indices for negative and fractional values

A Able to convert recurring decimals to fractions

A Able to simplify surds

A* Able to manipulate expressions containing surds and rationalise denominators

A* Able to solve problems using surds

What you should know now

- How to write numbers in standard form
- How to solve problems using numbers in standard form
- How to manipulate indices, both integer (positive and negative) and fractional
- How to compare fractions by converting them to decimals
- How to convert decimals into fractions
- What surds are and how to manipulate them

Statistics 1

This chapter will show you ...

- how to calculate and use the mode, median, mean and range from frequency tables of discrete data
- how to decide which is the best average for different types of data
- how to recognise the modal class and calculate an estimate of the mean from frequency tables of grouped data
- how to draw frequency polygons and histograms
- how to calculate and use a moving average
- how to design questions for questionnaires and surveys

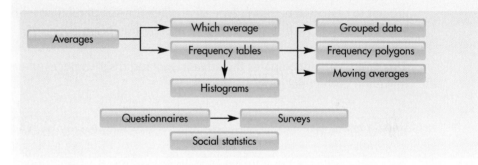

What you should already know

- How to work out the mean, mode, median and range of small sets of discrete data
- How to extract information from tables and diagrams

Quick check

1 The marks for 15 students in a maths test are

2, 3, 4, 5, 5, 6, 6, 6, 7, 7, 7, 7, 7, 8, 10

a What is the modal mark?

b What is the median mark?

c What is the range of the marks?

d What is the mean mark?

In this section you will learn how to:
- use averages
- solve more complex problems using averages
- identify the advantages and disadvantages of each type of average and learn which one to use in different situations

Key words
mean
measure of location
median
mode

Average is a term we often use when describing or comparing sets of data. The average is also known as a **measure of location**. For example, we refer to the average rainfall in Britain, the average score of a batsman, an average weekly wage, the average mark in an examination. In each of these examples, we are representing the whole set of many values by just one single, typical value, which we call the average.

The idea of an average is extremely useful, because it enables us to compare one set of data with another set by comparing just two values – their averages.

There are several ways of expressing an average, but the most commonly used averages are the **mode**, the **median** and the **mean**.

An average must be truly representative of a set of data. So, when you have to find an average, it is crucial to choose the *correct type of average* for this particular set of data. If you use the wrong average, your results will be distorted and give misleading information.

This table, which compares the advantages and disadvantages of each type of average, will help you to make the correct decision.

	Mode	Median	Mean
Advantages	Very easy to find Not affected by extreme values Can be used for non-numerical data	Easy to find for ungrouped data Not affected by extreme values	Easy to find Uses all the values The total for a given number of values can be calculated from it
Disadvantages	Doesn't use all the values May not exist	Doesn't use all the values Often not understood	Extreme values can distort it Has to be calculated
Used for	Non-numerical data For finding the most likely value	Data with extreme values	Data whose values are spread in a balanced way

EXAMPLE 1

The ages of 20 people attending a conference are

23, 25, 26, 28, 28, 34, 34, 34, 37, 45, 47, 48, 52, 53, 56, 63, 67, 70, 73, 77

a Find **i** the mode, **ii** the median, **iii** the mean of the data.

b Which average best represents the age of the people at the conference.

a **i** The mode is 34, **ii** the median is 46, **iii** the mean is $920 \div 20 = 46$

b The mean is distorted because of the few very old people at the conference. The median is also distorted by the larger values, so in this case the mode would be the most representative average.

EXERCISE 11A

1 Shopkeepers always want to keep the most popular items in stock. Which average do you think is often known as the shopkeeper's average?

2 A list contains seven even numbers. The largest number is 24. The smallest number is half the largest. The mode is 14 and the median is 16. Two of the numbers add up to 42. What are the seven numbers?

3 The marks of 25 students in an English examination are as follows.

55, 63, 24, 47, 60, 45, 50, 89, 39, 47, 38, 42, 69, 73, 38, 47, 53, 64, 58, 71, 41, 48, 68, 64, 75

Find the median.

4 Decide which average you would use for each of the following. Give a reason for your answer.

a The average mark in an examination.

b The average pocket money for a group of 16-year-old students.

c The average shoe size for all the girls in Year 10.

d The average height for all the artistes on tour with a circus.

e The average hair colour for pupils in your school.

f The average weight of all newborn babies in a hospital's maternity ward.

5 A pack of matches consisted of 12 boxes. The contents of each box are as follows.

34   31   29   35   33   30   31   28   29   35   32   31

On the box it states that the average contents is 32 matches. Is this correct?

6 This table shows the annual salaries for a firm's employees.

Chairman	£43 000
Managing director	£37 000
Floor manager	£25 000
Skilled worker 1	£24 000
Skilled worker 2	£24 000
Machinist	£18 000
Computer engineer	£18 000
Secretary	£18 000
Office junior	£7 000

a What is **i** the modal salary, **ii** the median salary, and **iii** the mean salary?

b The management has suggested a pay rise for all of 6%. The shopfloor workers want a pay rise for all of £1500. What difference to the mean salary would each suggestion make?

7 Mr Brennan, a caring maths teacher, told each pupil their individual test mark and only gave the test statistics to the whole class. He gave the class the modal mark, the median mark and the mean mark.

a Which average would tell a pupil whether he/she were in the top half or the bottom half of the class?

b Which average tells the pupils nothing really?

c Which average allows a pupil really to gauge how well he/she has done compared with everyone else?

8 A list of 9 numbers has a mean of 7.6. What number must be added to the list to give a new mean of 8?

9 A dance group of 17 teenagers had a mean weight of 44.5 kg. To enter a competition there needs to be 18 people in the group with an average weight of 44.4 kg or less. What is the maximum weight that the eighteenth person could be?

10 The mean age of a group of eight walkers is 42. Joanne joins the group and the mean age changes to 40. How old is Joanne?

11.2 Frequency tables

In this section you will learn how to:
- calculate the mode and median from a frequency table
- calculate the mean from a frequency table

Key word
frequency
table

When a lot of information has been gathered, it is often convenient to put it together in a **frequency table**. From this table, you can then find the values of the mode, median, mean and range of the data.

EXAMPLE 2

A survey was done on the number of people in each car leaving the Meadowhall Shopping Centre, in Sheffield. The results are summarised in the table.

Calculate **a** the mode, **b** the median, **c** the mean number of people in a car.

Number of people in each car	1	2	3	4	5	6
Frequency	45	198	121	76	52	13

a The modal number of people in a car is easy to spot. It is the number with the largest frequency (198). Hence, the modal number of people in a car is 2.

b The median number of people in a car is found by working out where the middle of the set of numbers is located. First, add up frequencies to get the total number of cars surveyed, which comes to 505. Next, calculate the middle position

$$(505 + 1) \div 2 = 253$$

You now need to add the frequencies across the table to find which group contains the 253rd item. The 243rd item is the end of the group with 2 in a car. Therefore, the 253rd item must be in the group with 3 in a car. Hence, the median number of people in a car is 3.

c The mean number of people in a car is found by calculating the total number of people, and then dividing this total by the number of cars surveyed.

Number in car	Frequency	Number in these cars
1	45	$1 \times 45 = 45$
2	198	$2 \times 198 = 396$
3	121	$3 \times 121 = 363$
4	76	$4 \times 76 = 304$
5	52	$5 \times 52 = 260$
6	13	$6 \times 13 = 78$
Totals	505	1446

Hence, the mean number of people in a car is $1446 \div 505 = 2.9$ (2 significant figures).

Using your calculator

The previous example can also be done by using the statistical mode which is available on some calculators. However, not all calculators are the same, so you will have to either read your instruction manual or experiment with the statistical keys on your calculator.

You may find one labelled

DATA or M+ or Σ+ or $\bar{x}$ where $\bar{x}$ is printed in blue.

Try the following key strokes.

EXERCISE 11B

1 Find **i** the mode, **ii** the median and **iii** the mean from each frequency table below.

a A survey of the shoe sizes of all the Y10 boys in a school gave these results.

Shoe size	4	5	6	7	8	9	10
Number of pupils	12	30	34	35	23	8	3

b This is a record of the number of babies born each week over one year in a small maternity unit.

Number of babies	0	1	2	3	4	5	6	7	8	9	10	11	12	13	14
Frequency	1	1	1	2	2	2	3	5	9	8	6	4	5	2	1

2 A survey of the number of children in each family of a school's intake gave these results.

Number of children	1	2	3	4	5
Frequency	214	328	97	26	3

a Assuming each child at the school is shown in the data, how many children are at the school?

b Calculate the mean number of children in a family.

c How many families have this mean number of children?

d How many families would consider themselves average from this survey?

3 A dentist kept records of how many teeth he extracted from his patients.

In 1970 he extracted 598 teeth from 271 patients.

In 1980 he extracted 332 teeth from 196 patients.

In 1990 he extracted 374 teeth from 288 patients.

a Calculate the average number of teeth taken from each patient in each year.

b Explain why you think the average number of teeth extracted falls each year.

4 The teachers in a school were asked to indicate the average number of hours they spent each day marking. The table summarises their replies.

Number of hours spent marking	1	2	3	4	5	6
Number of teachers	10	13	12	8	6	1

a How many teachers are at the school?

b What is the modal number of hours spent marking?

c What is the mean number of hours spent marking?

5 Two friends often played golf together. They recorded their scores for each hole over five games to determine who was more consistent and who was the better player. The results are summarised in the table.

No. of shots to hole ball	1	2	3	4	5	6	7	8	9
Roger	0	0	0	14	37	27	12	0	0
Brian	5	12	15	18	14	8	8	8	2

a What is the modal score for each player?

b What is the range of scores for each player?

c What is the median score for each player?

d What is the mean score for each player?

e Which player is the more consistent and explain why?

f Who would you say is the better player and state why?

6 The number of league goals scored by a football team over a season is given in the table.

Number of goals scored	0	1	2	3	4	5	6	7
Number of matches	3	8	10	11	4	2	1	1

a How many games were played that season?

b What is the range of goals scored?

c What is the modal number of goals scored?

d What is the median number of goals scored?

e What is the mean number of goals scored?

f Which average do you think the team's supporters would say is the average number of goals scored by the team that season?

g If the team also scored 20 goals in ten cup matches that season, what was the mean number of goals the team scored throughout the whole season?

7 The table shows the number of passengers in each of 100 taxis leaving London Airport one day.

No. of passengers in a taxi	1	2	3	4
No. of taxis	x	40	y	26

a Find the value of $x + y$.

b If the mean number of passengers per taxi is 2.66, show that $x + 3y = 82$.

c Find the values of x and y by solving appropriate equations.

d State the median of the number of passengers per taxi.

Grouped data

In this section you will learn how to:
- identify the modal group
- calculate and estimate the mean from a grouped table

Key words

continuous data
discrete data
estimated mean
groups
modal group

Sometimes the information we are given is grouped in some way, as in the table in Example 3, which shows the range of weekly pocket money given to Y10 students in a particular class.

EXAMPLE 3

From the data in the table

a write down the **modal group**

b calculate an estimate of the mean weekly pocket money.

Pocket money, p, (£)	$0 < p \leqslant 1$	$1 < p \leqslant 2$	$2 < p \leqslant 3$	$3 < p \leqslant 4$	$4 < p \leqslant 5$
No. of students	2	5	5	9	15

a The modal group is still easy to pick out, since it is simply the one with the largest frequency. Here the modal group is £4 to £5.

b The mean can only be estimated, since you do not have all the information. To estimate the mean, you simply assume that each person in each group has the midway amount, then you can proceed to build up the table as before.

Note how you find the midway value. The two end values are added together and then divided by two.

Pocket money, p, (£)	Frequency (f)	Midway (m)	$f \times m$
$0 < p \leqslant 1$	2	0.50	1.00
$1 < p \leqslant 2$	5	1.50	7.50
$2 < p \leqslant 3$	5	2.50	12.50
$3 < p \leqslant 4$	9	3.50	31.50
$4 < p \leqslant 5$	15	4.50	67.50
Totals	36		120

The **estimated mean** will be £120 ÷ 36 = £3.33 (rounded off).

Note the notation used for the groups.

$0 < p \leqslant 1$ means any amount above 0p up to and including £1.

$1 < p \leqslant 2$ means any amount above £1 up to and including £2.

If you had written 0.01 – 1.00, 1.01 – 2.00, etc. for the **groups**, then the midway values would have been 0.505, 1.505, etc. Although technically correct, this makes the calculation of the mean harder and does not have a significant effect on the final answer, which is an estimate anyway.

This issue only arises because money is **discrete data**, which is data that consists of separate numbers, such as goals scored, marks in a test, number of children and shoe sizes. Normally grouped tables use **continuous data** which is data which can have an infinite number of different values, such as height, weight, time, area and capacity. It is always rounded-off information.

Whatever the type of data, remember to find the midway value by adding the two end values of the group and dividing by 2.

EXERCISE 11C

1 For each table of values, find the following.

    i   the modal group   **ii**   an estimate for the mean

a

x	$0 < x \leqslant 10$	$10 < x \leqslant 20$	$20 < x \leqslant 30$	$30 < x \leqslant 40$	$40 < x \leqslant 50$
Frequency	4	6	11	17	9

b

y	$0 < y \leqslant 100$	$100 < y \leqslant 200$	$200 < y \leqslant 300$	$300 < y \leqslant 400$	$400 < y \leqslant 500$	$500 < y \leqslant 600$
Frequency	95	56	32	21	9	3

c

z	$0 < z \leqslant 5$	$5 < z \leqslant 10$	$10 < z \leqslant 15$	$15 < z \leqslant 20$
Frequency	16	27	19	13

> **HINTS AND TIPS**
>
> When you copy the tables, draw them vertically as in Example 3.

c

Weeks	1–3	4–6	7–9	10–12	13–15
Frequency	5	8	14	10	7

2 Jason brought 100 pebbles back from the beach and weighed them all to the nearest gram. His results are summarised in this table.

Weight, w (grams)	$40 < w \leqslant 60$	$60 < w \leqslant 80$	$80 < w \leqslant 100$	$100 < w \leqslant 120$	$120 < w \leqslant 140$	$140 < w \leqslant 160$
Frequency	5	9	22	27	26	11

Find the following.

    a   the modal weight of the pebbles

    b   an estimate of the total weight of all the pebbles

    c   an estimate of the mean weight of the pebbles

One hundred light bulbs were tested by their manufacturer to see whether the average life span of the manufacturer's bulbs was over 200 hours. The table summarises the results.

Life span, h (hours)	$150 < h \leqslant 175$	$175 < h \leqslant 200$	$200 < h \leqslant 225$	$225 < h \leqslant 250$	$250 < h \leqslant 275$
Frequency	24	45	18	10	3

a What is the modal length of time a bulb lasts?

b What percentage of bulbs last longer than 200 hours?

c Estimate the mean life span of the light bulbs.

d Do you think the test shows that the average life span is over 200 hours? Fully explain your answer.

  The table shows the distances run by an athlete who is training for a marathon.

Distance, d, miles	$0 < d \leqslant 5$	$5 < d \leqslant 10$	$10 < d \leqslant 15$	$15 < d \leqslant 20$	$20 < d \leqslant 25$
Frequency	3	8	13	5	2

a It is recommended that an athlete's daily average mileage should be at least one third of the distance of the race being trained for. A marathon is 26.2 miles. Is this athlete doing enough training?

b The athlete records the times of some runs and calculates that her average pace for all runs is $6\frac{1}{2}$ minutes to a mile. Explain why she is wrong to expect a finishing time of $26.2 \times 6\frac{1}{2}$ minutes $\approx$ 170 minutes for the marathon.

c The athlete claims that the difference between her shortest and longest run is 21 miles. Could this be correct? Explain your answer.

 The owners of a boutique did a survey to find the average age of people using the boutique. The table summarises the results.

Age (years)	14–18	19–20	21–26	27–35	36–50
Frequency	26	24	19	16	11

What do you think is the average age of the people using the boutique?

 Three supermarkets each claimed to have the lowest average price increase over the year. The table summarises their average price increases.

Price increase (p)	1–5	6–10	11–15	16–20	21–25	26–30	31–35
Soundbuy	4	10	14	23	19	8	2
Springfields	5	11	12	19	25	9	6
Setco	3	8	15	31	21	7	3

Using their average price increases, make a comparison of the supermarkets and write a report on which supermarket, in your opinion, has the lowest price increases over the year. Don't forget to justify your answers.

Frequency diagrams

In this section you will learn how to:
- draw frequency polygons for discrete and continuous data
- draw histograms for continuous data with equal intervals

Key words

continuous
    data
discrete
    data
frequency
    polygon
histogram

Frequency polygons

To help people understand it, statistical information is often presented in pictorial or diagrammatic form. For example, you should have seen pie charts, bar charts and stem-and-leaf diagrams. Another method of showing data is by **frequency polygons**.

Frequency polygons can be used to represent both ungrouped data and grouped data, as shown in Example 4 and Example 5 respectively. They are useful to show the shapes of distributions, and can be used to compare distributions.

EXAMPLE 4

No. of children	0	1	2	3	4	5
Frequency	12	23	36	28	16	11

This is the frequency polygon for the *ungrouped* data in the table.

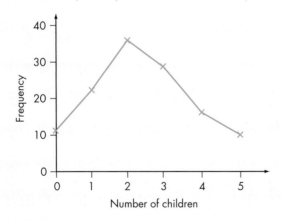

- You simply plot the coordinates from each ordered pair in the table.
- You complete the polygon by joining up the plotted points with straight lines.

EXAMPLE 5

Weight, w (kilograms)	$0 < w \leqslant 5$	$5 < w \leqslant 10$	$10 < w \leqslant 15$	$15 < w \leqslant 20$	$20 < w \leqslant 25$	$25 < w \leqslant 30$
Frequency	4	13	25	32	17	9

This is the frequency polygon for the *grouped data* in the table.

- You use the midway value of each group, just as in estimating the mean.
- You plot the ordered pairs of midway values with frequency, namely,

(2.5, 4), (7.5, 13), (12.5, 25), (17.5, 32), (22.5, 17), (27.5, 9)

- You do not know what happens above and below the groups in the table, so do not draw lines before (2.5, 4) or after (27.5, 9). The diagram shows the shape of the distribution.

Bar charts and histograms

You should already be familiar with the bar chart in which the vertical axis represents frequency, and the horizontal axis represents the type of data. (Sometimes it is more convenient to have the axes the other way.)

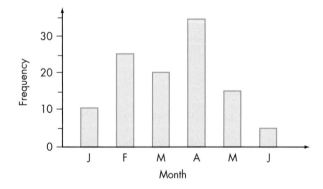

A **histogram** looks similar to a bar chart, but there are four fundamental differences.

- There are no gaps between the bars.

- The horizontal axis has a continuous scale since it represents **continuous** data, such as time, weight or length.

- The area of each bar represents the class or group frequency of the bar.

- The vertical axis is labelled "Frequency density", where

$$\text{Frequency density } = \frac{\text{Frequency of class interval}}{\text{Width of class interval}}$$

When the data is not continuous, a simple bar chart is used. For example, you would use a bar chart to represent the runs scored in a test match or the goals scored by a hockey team.

Look at the histogram below, which has been drawn from this table of times taken by people to walk to work.

Time, t (min)	$0 < t \le 4$	$4 < t \le 8$	$8 < t \le 12$	$12 < t \le 16$
Frequency	8	12	10	7
Frequency density	2	3	2.5	1.75

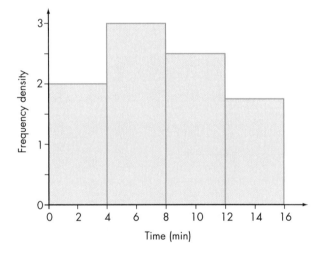

Notice that each histogram bar starts at the *least possible* time and finishes at the *greatest possible* time for its group.

Using your calculator

Histograms can also be drawn on graphics calculators or by using computer software packages. If you have access to either of these, try to use them.

EXERCISE 11D

D

1 The table shows how many students were absent from one particular class throughout the year.

Students absent	1	2	3	4	5
Frequency	48	32	12	3	1

a Draw a frequency polygon to illustrate the data.

b Calculate the mean number of absences each lesson.

2 The table shows the number of goals scored by a hockey team in one season.

Goals	1	2	3	4	5
Frequency	3	9	7	5	2

a Draw the frequency polygon for this data.

b Calculate the mean number of goals scored per game in the season.

C

3 The frequency polygon shows the amount of money spent in a corner shop by the first 40 customers on one day.

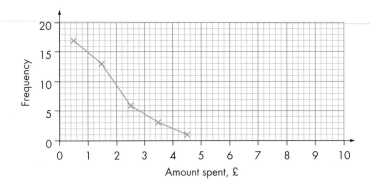

a i Use the frequency polygon to complete the table for the amounts spent by the first 40 customers

Amount spent, m, £	$0 < m \leq 1$	$1 < m \leq 2$	$2 < m \leq 3$	$3 < m \leq 4$	$4 < m \leq 5$
Frequency					

ii Work out the mean amount of money spent by these 40 customers.

b Mid morning the shopkeeper records the amount spent by another 40 customers. The table below shows the data.

Amount spent, m, £	$0 < m \leq 2$	$2 < m \leq 4$	$4 < m \leq 6$	$6 < m \leq 8$	$8 < m \leq 10$
Frequency	3	5	18	10	4

i On a copy of the graph above, draw the frequency polygon to show this data?

ii Calculate the mean amount spent by the 40 mid-morning customers..

c Comment on the differences between the frequency polygons and the average amounts spent by the different sets of customers.

4 The table shows the range of heights of the girls in Y11 at a London school.

Height, h (cm)	$120 < h \leqslant 130$	$130 < h \leqslant 140$	$140 < h \leqslant 150$	$150 < h \leqslant 160$	$160 < h \leqslant 170$
Frequency	15	37	25	13	5

   a Draw a frequency polygon for this data.   **b** Draw a histogram for this data

   c Estimate the mean height of the girls.

5 A doctor was concerned at the length of time her patients had to wait to see her when they came to the morning surgery. The survey she did gave her these results.

Time, m (minutes)	$0 < m \leqslant 10$	$10 < m \leqslant 20$	$20 < m \leqslant 30$	$30 < m \leqslant 40$	$40 < m \leqslant 50$	$50 < m \leqslant 60$
Monday	5	8	17	9	7	4
Tuesday	9	8	16	3	2	1
Wednesday	7	6	18	2	1	1

   a Draw a frequency polygon for each day on the same pair of axes.

   b What is the average amount of time spent waiting each day?

   c Why might the average time for each day be different?

11.5 Histograms with bars of unequal width

In this section you will learn how to:

- draw and read histograms where the bars are of unequal width
- find the median, quartiles and interquartile range from a histogram

Key words

class interval
interquartile
  range
lower quartile
median
upper
  quartile

Sometimes the data in a frequency distribution are grouped into classes whose intervals are different. In this case, the resulting histogram has bars of unequal width.

The key fact that you should always remember is that the *area* of a bar in a histogram represents the class *frequency* of the bar. So, in the case of an unequal-width histogram, the height to draw each bar is found by dividing its class frequency by its class interval width (bar width), which is the difference between the lower and upper bounds for each interval. Conversely, given a histogram, any of its class frequencies can be found by multiplying the height of the corresponding bar by its width.

It is for this reason that the scale on the vertical axes of histograms is nearly always labelled "Frequency density", where

$$\text{Frequency density} = \frac{\text{Frequency of class interval}}{\text{Width of class interval}}$$

EXAMPLE 6

The heights of a group of girls were measured. The results were classified as shown in the table.

Height, h (cm)	$151 \leqslant h < 153$	$153 \leqslant h < 154$	$154 \leqslant h < 155$	$155 \leqslant h < 159$	$159 \leqslant h < 160$
Frequency	64	43	47	96	12

It is convenient to write the table vertically and add two columns, class width and frequency density.

The class width is found by subtracting the lower class boundary from the upper class boundary. The frequency density is found by dividing the frequency by the class width.

Height, h (cm)	Frequency	Class width	Frequency density
$151 \leqslant h < 153$	64	2	32
$153 \leqslant h < 154$	43	1	43
$154 \leqslant h < 155$	47	1	47
$155 \leqslant h < 159$	96	4	24
$159 \leqslant h < 160$	12	1	12

The histogram can now be drawn. The horizontal scale should be marked off as normal from a value below the lowest value in the table to a value above the largest value in the table. In this case, mark the scale from 150 cm to 160 cm. The vertical scale is always frequency density and is marked up to at least the largest frequency density in the table. In this case, 50 is a sensible value.

Each bar is drawn between the lower **class interval** and the upper class interval horizontally, and up to the frequency density vertically.

EXAMPLE 7

This histogram shows the distribution of heights of daffodils in a greenhouse.

a Complete a frequency table for the heights of the daffodils, and show the cumulative frequency.

b Find the **median** height.

c Find the **interquartile range** of the heights.

d Estimate the mean of the distribution.

a The frequency table will have groups of $24 \leqslant h < 26$, $26 \leqslant h < 27$, etc. These are read from the height axis. The frequencies will be found by multiplying the width of each bar by the frequency density. Remember that the value on the vertical axis is not the frequency.

Height, h (cm)	$24 \leqslant h < 26$	$26 \leqslant h < 27$	$27 \leqslant h < 28$	$28 \leqslant h < 31$	$31 \leqslant h < 37$
Frequency	50	50	60	120	120
Cumulative frequency	50	100	160	280	400

b There are 400 values so the median will be the 200th value. Counting up the frequencies from the beginning we get the third row of the table above.

The median occurs in the $28 \leqslant h < 31$ group. There are 160 values before this group and 120 in it. To get to the 200th value we need to go 40 more values into this group. 40 out of 120 is one-third. One third of the way through this group is the value 29 cm. Hence the median is 29 cm.

c The interquartile range is the difference between the **upper quartile** and the **lower quartile**, the quarter and three-quarter values respectively. In this case, the lower quartile is the 100th value (found by dividing 400, the total number of values, by 4) and the upper quartile is the 300th value. So, in the same way that you found the median, you can find the lower (100th value) and upper (300th value) quartiles. The 100th value is at 27 cm and the 300th value is at 32 cm. The interquartile range is 32 cm – 27 cm = 5 cm.

d To estimate the mean, use the table to get the midway values of the groups and multiply these by the frequencies. The sum of these divided by 400 will give the estimated mean. So, the mean is

$(25 \times 50 + 26.5 \times 50 + 27.5 \times 60 + 29.5 \times 120 + 34 \times 120) \div 400$
$= 11\,845 \div 400 = 29.6$ cm (3 significant figures)

1 Draw histograms for these grouped frequency distributions.

a

Temperature, t (°C)	$8 \leq t < 10$	$10 \leq t < 12$	$12 \leq t < 15$	$15 \leq t < 17$	$17 \leq t < 20$	$20 \leq t < 24$
Frequency	5	13	18	4	3	6

b

Wage, w (£1000)	$6 \leq w < 10$	$10 \leq w < 12$	$12 \leq w < 16$	$16 \leq w < 24$
Frequency	16	54	60	24

c

Age, a (nearest year)	$11 \leq a < 14$	$14 \leq a < 16$	$16 \leq a < 17$	$17 \leq a < 20$
Frequency	51	36	12	20

d

Pressure, p (mm)	$745 \leq p < 755$	$755 \leq p < 760$	$760 \leq p < 765$	$765 \leq p < 775$
Frequency	4	6	14	10

e

Time, t (min)	$0 \leq t < 8$	$8 \leq t < 12$	$12 \leq t < 16$	$16 \leq t < 20$
Frequency	72	84	54	36

2 The following information was gathered about the weekly pocket money given to 14 year olds.

Pocket money, p (£)	$0 \leq p < 2$	$2 \leq p < 4$	$4 \leq p < 5$	$5 \leq p < 8$	$8 \leq p < 10$
Girls	8	15	22	12	4
Boys	6	11	25	15	6

a Represent the information about the boys on a histogram.

b Represent both sets of data with a frequency polygon, using the same pair of axes.

c What is the mean amount of pocket money given to each sex? Comment on your answer.

3 The sales of the Star newspaper over 65 years are recorded in this table.

Years	1930–50	1951–70	1971–80	1981–90	1991–95	1995–2000
Copies	62 000	68 000	71 000	75 000	63 000	52 000

Illustrate this information on a histogram. Take the class boundaries as 1930, 1950, 1970, 1980, 1990, 1995, 2000.

4 The London trains were always late, so one month a survey was undertaken to find how many trains were late, and by how many minutes (to the nearest minute). The results are illustrated by this histogram.

a How many trains were in the survey?

b How many trains were delayed for longer than 15 minutes?

5 For each of the frequency distributions illustrated in the histograms

i write down the grouped frequency table,

ii state the modal group,

iii estimate the median,

iv find the lower and upper quartiles and the interquartile range,

v estimate the mean of the distribution.

a

b

c

6 All the patients in a hospital were asked how long it was since they last saw a doctor. The results are shown in the table.

Hours, h	$0 \leqslant h < 2$	$2 \leqslant h < 4$	$4 \leqslant h < 6$	$6 \leqslant h < 10$	$10 \leqslant h < 16$	$16 \leqslant h < 24$
Frequency	8	12	20	30	20	10

a Find the median time since a patient last saw a doctor.

b Estimate the mean time since a patient last saw a doctor.

c Find the interquartile range of the times.

7 One summer, Albert monitored the weight of the tomatoes grown on each of his plants. His results are summarised in this table.

Weight, w (kg)	$6 \leqslant w < 10$	$10 \leqslant w < 12$	$12 \leqslant w < 16$	$16 \leqslant w < 20$	$20 \leqslant w < 25$
Frequency	8	15	28	16	10

a Draw a histogram for this distribution.

b Estimate the median weight of tomatoes the plants produced.

c Estimate the mean weight of tomatoes the plants produced.

d How many plants produced more than 15 kg?

8 A survey was carried out to find the speeds of cars passing a particular point on the M1. The histogram illustrates the results of the survey.

a Copy and complete this table.

Speed, v (mph)	$0 < v \leqslant 40$	$40 < v \leqslant 50$	$50 < v \leqslant 60$	$60 < v \leqslant 70$	$70 < v \leqslant 80$	$80 < v \leqslant 100$
Frequency		10	40	110		

b Find the number of cars included in the survey.

c Work out an estimate of the median speed of the cars on this part of the M1.

d Work out an estimate of the mean speed of the cars on this part of the M1.

11.6 Moving averages

In this section you will learn how to:
- calculate a moving average and use it to predict future trends

Key words

moving average
seasonal
trend
trend line

A **moving average** gives a clear indication of the trend of a set of data. It smoothes out, for example, **seasonal trends** such as monthly variations or daily differences.

EXAMPLE 8

A van rental firm has a record of how many vans were hired in each month of a year. This data is shown in the table. Using a four-point moving average, predict the number of vans the firm will rent out during the following January.

Months	Jan	Feb	Mar	Apr	May	Jun	Jul	Aug	Sep	Oct	Nov	Dec
Vans	9	22	37	14	18	24	42	17	20	27	48	20

First, plot the raw data. The resulting line graph shows a normal variation of business for the hire firm, but does not reveal the general trend of business. Is the firm's business improving, declining or remaining the same?

You can show the general trend by first calculating the mean for each four-month span, month on month. This is the four-point moving average.

Mean for Jan, Feb, Mar and April
$(9 + 22 + 37 + 14) \div 4 = 20.5$

Mean for Feb, Mar, Apr and May
$(22 + 37 + 14 + 18) \div 4 = 22.75$

Mean for Mar, Apr, May and Jun $(37 + 14 + 18 + 24) \div 4 = 23.25$

And so on, giving 24.5, 25.25, 25.75, 26.5, 28, 28.75 as the remaining averages.

Then plot, on the first graph, each mean value at the midpoint of the corresponding four-month span. This produces a much smoother graph, which, in this case, shows a slight upward trend. In other words, business is improving.

Draw a line of best fit (the **trend line**) through the data and read off the predicted value of the next four-point moving average. This is about 30.

Let the value for the next January be x, then $(27 + 48 + 20 + x) \div 4 = 30$

$\Rightarrow 95 + x = 120$

$\Rightarrow \quad x = 25$

So we can predict that the firm will rent out 25 vans the following January.

In Example 8, we used an interval of four months to construct a moving average but there is nothing special about this interval. It could well have been five or six months, except that you would then have needed data for more months to give sufficient mean values to show a trend. The number of months, weeks or even years used for moving averages depends on the likely variations of the data. You would not expect to use less than three or more than 12 items of data at a time.

EXERCISE 11F

1 The table shows the daily sales of milk at a local corner shop for a month.

Sun	Mon	Tue	Wed	Thu	Fri	Sat
12	8	6	9	4	11	15
11	7	7	6	3	15	14
14	9	7	7	5	12	15
11	12	8	7	4	14	19

Make a table showing the moving average using a seven-day span, and draw a graph to show the trend of milk sales over the month.

2 The table shows the amounts collected for a charity by the students at Pope Pius School in the ten weeks leading up to Christmas.

Week	1	2	3	4	5	6	7	8	9	10
Amount (£)	42	45	44	47	33	40	45	51	42	45

a Plot a line graph of the amounts collected and a four-week moving average.

b Comment on the trend shown.

3 The table shows the quarterly electricity bill over a four-year period.

	2002	2003	2004	2005
First quarter	£123.39	£119.95	£127.39	£132.59
Second quarter	£108.56	£113.16	£117.76	£119.76
Third quarter	£87.98	£77.98	£102.58	£114.08
Fourth quarter	£112.47	£127.07	£126.27	£130.87

a Plot the line graph of the electricity bills shown in the table, and on the same axes plot a four-quarter moving average.

b Comment on the price of electricity over the four years.

c Use the trend line of the moving averages to predict the bill for the first quarter of 2006.

4 The table shows the telephone bills for a family over four years.

	2002	2003	2004	2005
First quarter	£82	£87	£98	£88
Second quarter	£87	£88	£95	£91
Third quarter	£67	£72	£87	£78
Fourth quarter	£84	£81	£97	£87

a Plot a line graph showing the amounts paid each month.

b Plot a four-quarter moving average.

c Comment on the trend shown and give a possible reason for it.

d Use the trend line of the moving averages to predict the bill for the first quarter of 2006.

A factory making computer components has the following sales figures (in hundreds) for electric fans.

	Jan	Feb	Mar	Apr	May	Jun	Jul	Aug	Sep	Oct	Nov	Dec
2004	12	13	12	14	13	3	15	12	14	13	14	12
2005	13	14	12	14	13	14	13	13	15	15	15	14

a Plot a line graph of the sales, and a three-month moving average.

b Comment on the trend in the sales.

c Use the trend line of the moving averages to predict the number of electric fan sales in January 2006.

 The table shows the total sales of video recorders and DVD players from 1999 to 2005 from an electrical store in the USA.

	1999	2000	2001	2002	2003	2004	2005
Video (thousands)	3.4	3.8	3.9	3.2	2.8	2.5	2.3
DVD (thousands)	0.2	0.8	0.9	1.5	1.9	2.8	3.7

a Plot a line graph showing the sales for each product over these years.

b On the same diagram, plot the three-year moving average of each product.

c Comment on the trends seen in the sales of video recorders and DVDs.

d Use the trend line of the moving averages to predict the number of video recorders and DVD players sold in 2006.

11.7 Surveys

In this section you will learn how to:
- conduct surveys
- ask good questions in order to collect reliable and valid data

Key words
data collection sheet
hypothesis
leading question
survey

A **survey** is an organised way of asking a lot of people a few, well-constructed questions, or of making a lot of observations in an experiment, in order to reach a conclusion about something.

Surveys are used to test out people's opinions or to test a **hypothesis**.

Simple data collection sheet

If you just need to collect some data to analyse, you will have to design a simple **data collection sheet**. This section will show you how to design a clear, easy-to-fill-in data collection sheet.

For example, if you want to find out Y10 students' preferences for the end-of-term trip from four options you could ask:

> *Where do you want to go for the Y10 trip at the end of term – Blackpool, Alton Towers, The Great Western Show or London?*

You would put this question, on the same day, to a lot of Y10 students, and enter their answers straight onto a data collection sheet, as below.

Place	Tally	Frequency
Blackpool	ЖЖ ЖЖ ЖЖ ЖЖ III	23
Alton Towers	ЖЖ ЖЖ ЖЖ ЖЖ ЖЖ ЖЖ ЖЖ ЖЖ ЖЖ I	46
The Great Western Show	ЖЖ ЖЖ IIII	14
London	ЖЖ ЖЖ ЖЖ ЖЖ II	22

Notice how plenty of space is available for the tally marks, and how the tallies are gated in groups of five to make counting easier when the survey is complete.

This is a good, simple data collection sheet because:

- only one question (*Where do you want to go?*) has to be asked

- all the four possible venues are listed

- the answer from each interviewee can be easily and quickly tallied, then on to the next interviewee.

Notice, too, that since the question listed specific places, they must appear on the data collection sheet. You would lose many marks in an examination if you just asked the open question: *Where do you want to go?*

Data sometimes needs to be collected to obtain responses for two different categories. The data collection sheet is then in the form of a two-way table.

EXAMPLE 9

The head of a school carries out a survey to find out how much time students in different year groups spend on their homework during a particular week. He asks a sample of 60 students and fills in a two-way table with headings as follows.

	0–5 hours	0–10 hours	10–20 hours	More than 20 hours
Year 7				

This is not a good table as the headings overlap. A student who does 10 hours work a week could tick either of two columns. Response sections should not overlap, so that there is only one possible place to put a tick.

A better table would be:

	0 up to 5 hours	More than 5 and up to 10 hours	More than 10 and up to 15 hours	More than 15 hours
Year 7	ЖН II	ЖН		
Year 8	ЖН	ЖН II		
Year 9	III	ЖН II	II	
Year 10	III	ЖН	III	I
Year 11	II	IIII	IIII	II

This gives a clearer picture of the amount of homework done in each year group.

Using your computer

Once the data has been collected for your survey, it can be put into a computer database. This allows the data to be stored and amended or updated at a later date if necessary.

From the database, suitable statistical diagrams can easily be drawn using software, and averages calculated. The results can then be published in, for example, the school magazine.

EXERCISE 11G

1 "People like the supermarket to open on Sundays."

   a To see whether this statement is true, design a data collection sheet which will allow you to capture data while standing outside a supermarket.

   b Does it matter on which day you collect data outside the supermarket?

2 The school tuck shop wants to know which types of chocolate it should get in to sell – plain, milk, fruit and nut, wholenut or white chocolate.

   a Design a data collection sheet which you could use to ask pupils in your school which of these chocolate types are their favourite.

HINTS AND TIPS

Include space for tallies.

   b Invent the first 30 entries on the chart.

3 When you throw two dice together, what number are you most likely to get?

   a Design a data collection sheet on which you can record the data from an experiment in which two dice are thrown together and note the sum of the two numbers shown on the dice.

   b Carry out this experiment for at least 100 throws.

   c Which sums are most likely to occur?

   d Illustrate your results on a frequency polygon.

4 Who uses the buses the most in the mornings? Is it pensioners, mums, schoolchildren, the unemployed or some other group? Design a data collection sheet to be used in a survey of bus passengers.

5 Design two-way tables to show

HINTS AND TIPS

Make sure all possible responses are covered.

   a how students in different year groups travel to school in the morning

   b the type of programme which different age groups prefer to watch on TV

   c the favourite sport of boys and girls

   d how much time students in different year groups spend on the computer in the evening.

   Invent about 40 entries for each one.

Questionnaires

This section will show you how to put together a clear, easy-to-use questionnaire.

When you are putting together a questionnaire, you must think very carefully about the sorts of question you are going to ask. Here are five rules that you should *always* follow.

- Never ask a **leading question** designed to get a particular response.

- Never ask a personal, irrelevant question.

- Keep each question as simple as possible.

- Include questions that will get a response from whomever is asked.

- Make sure the responses do not overlap and keep the number of choices to a reasonable number (six at the most).

The following questions are badly constructed and should *never* appear in any questionnaire.

What is your age? This is personal. Many people will not want to answer. It is always better to give a range of ages.

☐ Under 15   ☐ 16–20   ☐ 21–30   ☐ 31–40   ☐ Over 40

Slaughtering animals for food is cruel to the poor defenceless animals. Don't you agree? This is a **leading question**, designed to get a "yes" response. It is better to ask an impersonal question.

Are you a vegetarian?   ☐ Yes   ☐ No

Do you go to discos when abroad? This can be answered only by people who have been abroad. It is better to ask a starter question, with a follow-up question.

Have you been abroad for a holiday?   ☐ Yes   ☐ No

If yes, did you go to a disco whilst you were away?   ☐ Yes   ☐ No

When you first get up in a morning and decide to have some sort of breakfast that might be made by somebody else, do you feel obliged to eat it all or not? This is a too-complicated question. It is better to ask a series of shorter questions.

What time do you get up for school?   ☐ Before 7   ☐ Between 7 and 8   ☐ After 8

Do you have breakfast every day?   ☐ Yes   ☐ No

If No, on how many school days do you have breakfast?   ☐ 0   ☐ 1   ☐ 2   ☐ 3   ☐ 4   ☐ 5

A questionnaire is usually put together to test a hypothesis or a statement. For example, a questionnaire might be constructed to test this statement.

People buy cheaper milk from the supermarket as they don't mind not getting it on their doorstep. They'd rather go out to buy it.

A questionnaire designed to test whether this statement is true or not should include these questions:

Do you have milk delivered to your doorstep?

Do you buy cheaper milk from the supermarket?

Would you buy your milk only from the supermarket?

Once these questions have been answered, the responses can be looked at to see whether the majority of people hold views that agree with the statement.

1 These are questions from a questionnaire on healthy eating.

a
| Fast food is bad for you. Don't you agree? |
| ☐ Strongly agree ☐ Agree ☐ Don't know |

Give two criticisms of the question.

b
| Do you eat fast food? ☐ Yes ☐ No |
| If yes, how many times on average do you eat fast food a week? |
| ☐ Once or less ☐ 2 or 3 times ☐ 4 or 5 times ☐ More than 5 times |

Give two reasons why these are good questions.

2 This is a question from a survey on pocket money.

| How much pocket money do you get each week? |
| ☐ £0–£2 ☐ £0–£5 ☐ £5–£10 ☐ £10 or more |

a Give a reason why this is not a good question.

b Rewrite the question to make it good question.

3 Design a questionnaire to test this statement.

People under 16 do not know what is meant by all the jargon used in the business news on TV, but the over-twenties do.

4 Design a questionnaire to test this statement.

The under-twenties feel quite at ease with computers, while the over-forties would rather not bother with them. The 20–40s are all able to use computers effectively.

5 Design a questionnaire to test this hypothesis.

The older you get, the less sleep you need.

6 A head teacher wants to find out if her pupils think they have too much, too little or just the right amount of homework. She also wants to know the parents' views about homework.

Design a questionnaire that could be used to find the data that the head teacher needs to look at.

In this section you will learn about:
- learn about social statistics
- be introduced to some of the more common social statistics in daily use

Key words

margin of error
national census
polls
Retail Price Index
social statistics
time series

Many situations occur in daily life where statistical techniques are used to produce data. The results of surveys appear in newspapers every day. There are many on-line **polls** and phone-ins to vote in reality TV shows, for example.

Results for these polls are usually given as a percentage with a **margin of error**, which is a measure of how accurate the information is.

Here are some common social statistics in daily use.

General Index of Retail Prices

This is also know as the **Retail Price Index** (RPI). It measures how much the daily cost of living increases (or decreases). One year is chosen as the base year and given an index number, usually 100. The costs of subsequent years are compared to this and given a number proportional to the base year, say 103, etc.

Note the numbers do not represent actual values but just compare current prices to the base year.

Time series

Like the RPI, a **time series** measures changes in a quantity over time. Unlike the RPI the actual values of the quantity are used. This might measure how the exchange rate between the pound and the dollar changes over time.

National Census

A **national census** is a survey of all people and households in a country. Data about age, gender, religion, employment status, etc. is collected to enable governments to plan where to allocate resources in the future. In Britain, a national census is taken every 10 years. The last census was in 2001.

EXERCISE 11I

1 In 2000, the cost of a litre of petrol was 68p. Using 2000 as a base year, the price index of petrol for the next 5 years is shown in this table.

Year	2000	2001	2002	2003	2004	2005
Index	100	103	108	109	112	120
Price	78p					

Work out the price of petrol in each subsequent year. Give your answers to 1 decimal place.

2 The graph shows the exchange rate for the dollar against the pound for each month in 2005.

a What was the exchange rate in January?

b Between which two months did the exchange rate fall the most ?

c Explain why you could not use the graph to predict the exchange rate in January 2006.

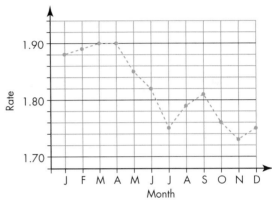
Exchange rate of the dollar against the pound, 2005

3 The following is taken from the UK government statistics website.

> In mid-2004 the UK was home to 59.8 million people, of which 50.1 million lived in England. The average age was 38.6 years, an increase on 1971 when it was 34.1 years. In mid-2004 approximately one in five people in the UK were aged under 16 and one in six people were aged 65 or over.

Use this extract to answer these questions.

a How many of the population of the UK *do not* live in England?

b By how much has the average age increased since 1971?

c Approximately how many of the population are under 16?

d Approximately how many of the population are over 65?

4 The General Index of Retail Prices started in January 1987 when it was given a base number of 100. In January 2006 the index number was 194.1.

If the "standard weekly shopping basket" cost £38.50 in January 1987, how much would it be in January 2006?

5 This time series shows car production in Britain from November 2004 to November 2005.

a Why was there a sharp drop in production in July?

b The average production over the first three months shown was 172 thousand cars.

i Work out an approximate number for the average production over the last three months shown.

ii The base month for the index is January 2000 when the index was 100. What was the approximate production in January 2000?

Car production in Britain, November 2004 to November 2005

11.9 Sampling

In this section you will learn how to:
- understand different methods of sampling
- collect unbiased reliable data

Key words
population
random
sample
stratified
unbiased

Statisticians often have to carry out surveys to collect information and test hypotheses about the **population** of a wide variety of things. (In statistics, population does not only mean a group of people, it also means a group of objects or events.)

It is seldom possible to survey a whole population, mainly because such a survey would cost too much and take a long time. Also there are populations for which it would be physically impossible to survey every member. For example, if you wanted to find the average length of eels in the North Sea, it would be impossible to find and measure every eel. So a statistician chooses a small part of the population to survey and assumes that the results for this **sample** are representative of the whole population.

Therefore, to ensure the accuracy of a survey, two questions have to be considered.

- Will the sample be representative of the whole population and thereby eliminate bias?

- How large should the sample be to give results which are valid for the whole population?

You will use many of these ideas in your Handling Data coursework.

Sampling methods

There are two main types of sample: **random** and **stratified**.

In a random sample, every member of the population has an equal chance of being chosen. For example, it may be the first 100 people met in a survey, or 100 names picked from a hat, or 100 names taken at random from the electoral register or a telephone directory.

In a stratified sample, the population is first divided into categories and the number of members in each category determined. The sample is then made up of members from these categories in the same proportions as they are in the population. The required sample in each category is chosen by random sampling.

EXAMPLE 10

A school's pupil numbers are given in the table. The head teacher wants to take a stratified sample of 100 pupils for a survey.

a Calculate the number of boys and girls in each year that should be interviewed.

b Explain how the pupils could then be chosen to give a random sample.

School year	Boys	Girls	Total
7	52	68	120
8	46	51	97
9	62	59	121
10	47	61	108
11	39	55	94
Total number in school			540

a To get the correct number in each category, say, boys in year 7, the calculation is done as follows.

$$\frac{52}{540} \times 100 = 9.6 \text{ (1 decimal place)}$$

After all calculations are done, you should get the values in this table.

School Year	Boys	Girls
7	9.6	12.6
8	8.5	9.4
9	11.5	10.9
10	8.7	11.3
11	7.2	10.2

Obviously you cannot have a decimal point of a pupil, so round off all values and make sure that the total is 100. This gives the final table.

School year	Boys	Girls	Total
7	10	13	23
8	8	9	17
9	12	11	23
10	9	11	20
11	7	10	17

b Within each category, choose pupils to survey at random. For example, all the year 7 girls could have their names put into a hat and 13 names drawn out or they could be listed alphabetically and a random number generator used to pick out 13 names from 68.

Sample size

Before the sampling of a population can begin, it is necessary to determine how much data needs to be collected to ensure that the sample is representative of the population. This is called the sample size.

Two factors determine sample size:

● the desired precision with which the sample represents the population

● the amount of money available to meet the cost of collecting the sample data.

The greater the precision desired, the larger the sample size needs to be. But the larger the sample size, the higher the cost will be. Therefore, the benefit of achieving high accuracy in a sample will always have to be set against the cost of achieving it.

There are statistical procedures for determining the most suitable sample size, but these are beyond the scope of the GCSE syllabus.

The next example addresses some of the problems associated with obtaining an **unbiased** sample.

EXAMPLE 11

You are going to conduct a survey among an audience of 30 000 people at a rock concert. How would you choose the sample?

1 You would not want to question all of them, so you might settle for a sample size of 2%, which is 600 people.

2 Assuming that there will be as many men at the concert as women, you would need the sample to contain the same proportion of each, namely, 300 men and 300 women.

3 Assuming that about 20% of the audience will be aged under 20, you would also need the sample to contain 120 people aged under 20 (20% of 600) and 480 people aged 20 and over (600 − 120 or 80% of 600).

4 You would also need to select people from different parts of the auditorium in equal proportions so as to get a balanced view. Say this breaks down into three equal groups of people, taken respectively from the front, the back and the middle of the auditorium. So, you would further need the sample to consist of 200 people at the front, 200 at the back and 200 in the middle.

5 If you now assume that one researcher can survey 40 concert-goers, you would arrive at this sampling strategy

   600 ÷ 40 = 15 researchers to conduct the survey

   15 ÷ 3 = 5 researchers in each part of the auditorium

Each researcher would need to question four men aged under 20, 16 men aged 20 and over, four women aged under 20 and 16 women aged 20 and over.

EXERCISE 11J

1 Comment on the reliability of the following ways of finding a sample.

    a Find out about smoking by asking 50 people in a non-smoking part of a restaurant.

    b Find out how many homes have video recorders by asking 100 people outside a video hire shop.

    c Find the most popular make of car by counting 100 cars in a city car park.

    d Find a year representative on a school's council by picking a name out of a hat.

    e Decide whether the potatoes have cooked properly by testing one with a fork.

2 Comment on the way the following samples have been taken. For those that are not satisfactory, suggest a better way to find a more reliable sample.

    a Joseph had a discussion with his dad about pocket money. To get some information, he asked 15 of his friends how much pocket money they each received.

    b Douglas wanted to find out what proportion of his school went abroad for holidays, so he asked the first 20 people he came across in the school yard.

    c A teacher wanted to know which lesson his pupils enjoyed most. So he asked them all.

    d It has been suggested that more females go to church than males. So Ruth did a survey in her church that Sunday and counted the number of females there.

    e A group of local people asked for a crossing on a busy road. The council conducted a survey by asking a randomly selected 100 people in the neighbourhood.

3 For a school project you have been asked to do a presentation of the social activities of the pupils in your school. You decide to interview a sample of pupils. Explain how you will choose the pupils you wish to interview if you want your results to be

    a reliable,   **b** unbiased,   **c** representative,   **d** random.

4 A fast-food pizza chain attempted to estimate the number of people who eat pizzas in a certain town. One evening they telephoned 50 people living in the town and asked: "Have you eaten a pizza in the last month?" Eleven people said "Yes". The pizza chain stated that 22% of the town's population eat pizzas. Give three criticisms of this method of estimation.

5 **a** Adam is writing a questionnaire for a survey about the Meadowhall shopping centre in Sheffield. He is told that fewer local people visit Meadowhall than people from further away. He is also told that the local people spend less money per visit. Write two questions which would help him to test these ideas. Each question should include at least three options for a response. People are asked to choose one of these options.

    b For another survey, Adam investigates how much is spent at the chocolate machines by students at his school. The number of students in each year group is shown in the table. Explain, with calculations, how Adam should obtain a stratified random sample of 100 students for his survey.

Year group	7	8	9	10	11
Numbers of students	143	132	156	131	108

6 Claire made a survey of pupils in her school. She wanted to find out their opinions on the eating facilities in the school. The size of each year group in the school is shown in the table.

Year group	Boys	Girls	Total
8	96	78	174
9	84	86	170
10	84	91	175
11	82	85	167
6th form	83	117	200
			886

Claire took a sample of 90 pupils.

a Explain why she should not have sampled equal numbers of boys and girls in the sixth form.

b Calculate the number of pupils she should have sampled in the sixth form.

Using the Internet

Through the Internet you have access to a vast amount of data on many topics, which you can use to carry out statistical investigations. This data will enable you to draw statistical diagrams, answer a variety of questions and test all manner of hypotheses.

Here are some examples of hypotheses you can test.

Football teams are most likely to win when they are playing at home.

Boys do better than girls at GCSE mathematics.

The number 3 gets drawn more often than the number 49 in the National Lottery.

The literacy rate in a country is linked to that country's average income.

People in the north of England have larger families than people who live in the south.

The following websites are a useful source of data for some of the above.

www.statistics.gov.uk

www.lufc.co.uk

www.national-lottery.co.uk

www.cia.gov/cia/publications/factbook/

1 The number of matches in 20 matchboxes is shown in the table.

No. of matches (*m*)	Frequency
42	2
43	5
44	11
45	1
46	1

Calculate the mean number of matches in the 20 boxes.

2 50 people were asked how long they had to wait for a bus. The table shows the results.

a Which class interval contains the median time?

Time taken, *t* (min)	Frequency
$0 < t \leqslant 5$	16
$5 < t \leqslant 10$	21
$10 < t \leqslant 15$	10
$15 < t \leqslant 20$	3

b Draw a frequency diagram to represent the data.

AQA, Question 8, Paper 1 Higher, May 2005

3 In year 9 there are 30 students who study both French and Spanish. Their National Curriculum levels in these subjects are shown in the two-way table.

		Level in Spanish					
		1	2	3	4	5	6
Level in French	1	0	0	0	0	0	0
	2	1	0	0	0	0	0
	3	2	1	1	0	0	0
	4	0	3	4	1	0	0
	5	0	1	2	3	2	0
	6	0	0	3	3	2	1

a What is the modal level for French?

b What is the median level for French? Show clearly how you obtained your answer.

c What is the mean level for Spanish? Show clearly how you obtained your answer.

d The teacher claims that the students are better at French than at Spanish. How can you tell from the table that this is true?

AQA, Question 3, Paper 2 Higher, November 2004

4 The table shows the times taken for a train journey for 20 days.

Time taken, *t* (min)	Frequency
$18 < t \leqslant 20$	4
$20 < t \leqslant 22$	6
$22 < t \leqslant 24$	5
$24 < t \leqslant 26$	3
$26 < t \leqslant 28$	2

Calculate an estimate of the mean journey time

5 Susan completes a journey in two stages.
In stage 1 of her journey, she drives at an average speed of 80 km/h and takes 1 hour 45 minutes.

a How far does Susan travel in stage 1 of her journey?

b Altogether, Susan drives 190 km and takes a total time of 2 hours 15 minutes. What is her average speed, in km/h, in stage 2 of her journey?

AQA, Question 4, Paper 1 Higher, November 2003

6 Jack and Jill are doing a survey on fast food.

a This is one of Jack's questions.

> Burgers are bad for you and make you fat.
> Yes ☐   No ☐

Give two reasons why this is not a good question.

b This is one of Jill's questions.

> How many times, on average, do you visit a fast food outlet in a week
> Never ☐   1 or 2 times ☐
> 3 or 4 times ☐   More than 4 times ☐

Give two reasons why this is good question.

7 The table shows the cost of the gas at the end of every three months and some four-point moving averages.

The graph shows the actual cost of the gas and some of the moving averages.

Year	2002				2003				2004			
Quarter	1st	2nd	3rd	4th	1st	2nd	3rd	4th	1st	2nd	3rd	4th
Cost (£)	86	90	93	99	94	94	97	103	94	98	101	
Four-point moving average		92	94	95	96	97	97	98	99			

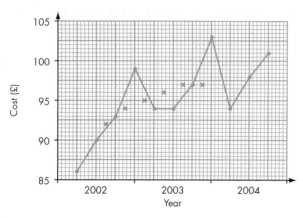

Cost (£) / Year

Key: • Actual cost
        ✕ Moving average

a Copy the graph and plot the last two four-point moving averages.

b Use the trend of the moving averages to predict the cost of the gas at the end of the 4th quarter of 2004.

Question 8, Paper 2 Higher, June 2005

8 An inspector visits a large company to check their vehicles. The company has 4 large-load vehicles, 136 light vans and 21 cars. The inspector decides to sample 10% of the vehicles. Each type of vehicle is to be represented in the sample.

a What is this kind of sampling procedure called?

b How many of each type of vehicle should be inspected?

AQA, Question 10, Paper 2 Higher, June 2005

9 The masses of 50 marrows are measured.

Mass, m, (grams)	Frequency
$500 < m \leq 600$	4
$600 < m \leq 800$	8
$800 < m \leq 850$	11
$850 < m \leq 1000$	12
$1000 < m \leq 1250$	15

a Draw a histogram to show this information

b Use, your histogram, or otherwise, to estimate the median mass of the marrows.

10 The histogram shows the test scores of 320 children in a school.

Frequency density / Score

a Find the median score.

b Find the interquartile range of the scores.

AQA, Question 17, Paper 2 Higher, June 2005

11 **a** This histogram shows the test scores of 100 female students.

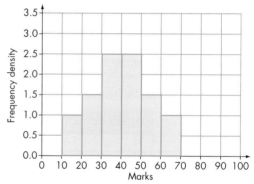

Frequency density / Marks

i What is the median score?

ii What is the interquartile range?

b This histogram is incomplete. It shows some of the test scores for 100 male students. The median test score for males is the same as for females. The upper quartile for the males is 50.

Frequency density / Marks

i What is the lower quartile for the male students?

ii Complete a possible histogram.

AQA, Question 24, Paper 2 Higher, November 2004

WORKED EXAM QUESTION

The distances travelled by 100 cars using 10 litres of petrol is shown in the histogram and table.

a Complete the histogram and the table.

b Estimate the number of cars that travel between 155 km and 185 km using 10 litres of petrol.

Distance (km)	80–110	110–130	130–140	140–150	150–160	160–200
Frequency	9	22	20			

Solution

a Set up the table with columns for class width and frequency density and fill in the given information, reading frequency densities from the graph (be careful with scales).

Now fill in the rest of the information

using f.d. = $\dfrac{\text{frequency}}{\text{class width}}$ and

frequency = f.d. × class width.

These values are shown in red.

Complete the graph.

Distance (km)	Frequency	Class width	Frequency density
80–110	9	30	0.3
110–130	22	20	1.1
130–140	20	10	2
140–150	17	10	1.7
150–160	14	10	1.4
160–200	18	40	0.45

b Draw lines at 155 and 185. The number of cars is represented by the area between these lines. In the 150–160 bar the area is $\frac{1}{2}$ of the total. In the 160–200 bar the area is $\frac{5}{8}$ of the total.

Number of cars = $\frac{1}{2} \times 14 + \frac{5}{8} \times 18 = 18.25 \approx 18$ cars

Mr Davies is a dairy farmer. Every month he records the thousands of litres of milk produced by his cows.

For his business plan he compares the amount of milk he produces in 2004 with 2005.

Monthly milk production in thousands of litres		
Month	2004	2005
Jan	51	62
Feb	53	65
Mar	55	62
Apr	56	67
May	64	72
Jun	72	83
Jul	70	81
Aug	75	86
Sep	64	75
Oct	64	73
Nov	62	70
Dec	58	68

Mr Davies calculates three-month moving averages for 2004 and 2005. He plots line graphs showing the moving averages for these two years.

Help him to complete the moving averages table, and the line graphs. Comment on the trends shown.

3-month moving average for milk production in thousands of litres												
	Jan	Feb	Mar	Apr	May	Jun	Jul	Aug	Sep	Oct	Nov	Dec
2004		53	54.7									
2005	61.7	63										

For his business plan Mr Davies compares the amount of milk he produces in 2005, with the graphs showing the hours of sunshine and amount of rain that year.

Monthly rainfall in millimetres in 2005

Months of the year

Monthly sunshine in hours in 2005

Months of the year

Draw two scatter graphs; one showing his monthly milk production and monthly rainfall, the other showing his monthly milk production and the monthly sunshine.

Comment on the correlation shown by these graphs.

GRADE YOURSELF

D Able to find the mean from a frequency table of discrete data

D Able to draw a frequency polygon for discrete data

C Able to find an estimate of the mean from a grouped table of continuous data

C Able to draw a frequency polygon for continuous data

C Able to design questionnaires and surveys

B Able to use a moving average to predict future values

A Able to draw histograms from frequency tables with unequal class intervals

A Able to calculate the numbers to be surveyed for a stratified sample

A* Able to find the median, quartiles and the interquartile range from a histogram

What you should know now

- Which average to use in different situations
- How to find the modal class and an estimated mean for continuous data
- How to draw frequency polygons and histograms for discrete and continuous data
- How to design questionnaires and surveys

Algebra 2

This chapter will show you ...

- how to expand two linear brackets to obtain a quadratic expression
- how to factorise a quadratic expression
- how to solve quadratic equations by factorisation, the quadratic formula and completing the square

What you should already know

- The basic language of algebra
- How to collect together like terms
- How to multiply together two algebraic expressions
- How to solve simple linear equations

Quick check

1 Simplify the following.

   a $-2x - x$ **b** $3x - x$ **c** $-5x + 2x$

   d $2m \times 3m$ **e** $3x \times -2x$ **f** $-4p \times 3p$

2 Solve these equations.

   a $x + 6 = 0$ **b** $2x + 1 = 0$ **c** $3x - 2 = 0$

Expanding brackets

This section will show you how to:
- expand two linear brackets to obtain a quadratic expression

Key words
coefficient
linear
quadratic
    expression

Quadratic expansion

A **quadratic expression** is one in which the highest power of the variables is 2. For example,

$$y^2 \qquad 3t^2 + 5t \qquad 5m^2 + 3m + 8$$

An expression such as $(3y + 2)(4y - 5)$ can be expanded to give a quadratic expression.

This multiplying out of such pairs of brackets is usually called **quadratic expansion**.

The rule for expanding expressions such as $(t + 5)(3t - 4)$ is similar to that for expanding single brackets: multiply everything in one bracket by everything in the other bracket.

There are several methods for doing this. Examples 1 to 3 show the three main methods, "expansion", "FOIL" and "the box method".

EXAMPLE 1

In the expansion method split up the first bracket and make each of its terms multiply the second bracket. We then simplify the outcome.

Expand $(x + 3)(x + 4)$.

$$(x + 3)(x + 4) = x(x + 4) + 3(x + 4)$$
$$= x^2 + 4x + 3x + 12$$
$$= x^2 + 7x + 12$$

EXAMPLE 2

FOIL stands for First, Outer, Inner and Last. This is the order of multiplying the terms from each bracket.

Expand $(t + 5)(t - 2)$.

First terms give: $t \times t = t^2$. Outer terms give: $t \times -2 = -2t$.

Inner terms give: $5 \times t = 5t$. Last terms give: $+5 \times -2 = -10$.

$$(t + 5)(t - 2) = t^2 - 2t + 5t - 10$$
$$= t^2 + 3t - 10$$

EXAMPLE 3

The box method is similar to that used to do long multiplication.

Expand $(k-3)(k-2)$.

$$(k-3)(k-2) = k^2 - 2k - 3k + 6$$
$$= k^2 - 5k + 6$$

×	k	−3
k	k^2	−3k
−2	−2k	+6

Warning: Be careful with the signs. This is the main place where marks are lost in examination questions involving the expansion of brackets.

EXERCISE 12A

Expand the following expressions.

1 $(x + 3)(x + 2)$ **2** $(t + 4)(t + 3)$ **3** $(w + 1)(w + 3)$

4 $(m + 5)(m + 1)$ **5** $(k + 3)(k + 5)$ **6** $(a + 4)(a + 1)$

7 $(x + 4)(x - 2)$ **8** $(t + 5)(t - 3)$ **9** $(w + 3)(w - 1)$

10 $(f + 2)(f - 3)$ **11** $(g + 1)(g - 4)$ **12** $(y + 4)(y - 3)$

13 $(x - 3)(x + 4)$ **14** $(p - 2)(p + 1)$ **15** $(k - 4)(k + 2)$

16 $(y - 2)(y + 5)$ **17** $(a - 1)(a + 3)$ **18** $(t - 3)(t + 4)$

> **HINTS AND TIPS**
>
> Use whichever method you prefer. There is no fixed method in GCSE examinations. Examiners give credit for all methods.

> **HINTS AND TIPS**
>
> A common error is to get minus signs wrong.
> $-2x - 3x = -5x$ and
> $-2 \times -3 = +6$

The expansions of the expressions below follow a pattern. Work out the first few and try to spot the pattern that will allow you immediately to write down the answers to the rest.

19 $(x + 3)(x - 3)$ **20** $(t + 5)(t - 5)$ **21** $(m + 4)(m - 4)$

22 $(t + 2)(t - 2)$ **23** $(y + 8)(y - 8)$ **24** $(p + 1)(p - 1)$

25 $(5 + x)(5 - x)$ **26** $(7 + g)(7 - g)$ **27** $(x - 6)(x + 6)$

All the algebraic terms in x^2 in Exercise 12A have a **coefficient** of 1 or −1. The next two examples show you what to do if you have to expand brackets containing terms in x^2 whose coefficients are not 1 or −1.

EXAMPLE 4

Expand $(2t + 3)(3t + 1)$.

$$(2t + 3)(3t + 1) = 6t^2 + 2t + 9t + 3$$
$$= 6t^2 + 11t + 3$$

×	2t	+3
3t	$6t^2$	+9t
+1	+2t	+3

EXAMPLE 5

Expand $(4x - 1)(3x - 5)$.

$(4x - 1)(3x - 5) = 4x(3x - 5) - (3x - 5)$ [**Note:** $(3x - 5)$ is the same as $1(3x - 5)$.]

$\qquad\qquad\qquad\quad = 12x^2 - 20x - 3x + 5$

$\qquad\qquad\qquad\quad = 12x^2 - 23x + 5$

EXERCISE 12B

Expand the following expressions.

1 $(2x + 3)(3x + 1)$

2 $(3y + 2)(4y + 3)$

3 $(3t + 1)(2t + 5)$

4 $(4t + 3)(2t - 1)$

5 $(5m + 2)(2m - 3)$

6 $(4k + 3)(3k - 5)$

7 $(3p - 2)(2p + 5)$

8 $(5w + 2)(2w + 3)$

9 $(2a - 3)(3a + 1)$

10 $(4r - 3)(2r - 1)$

11 $(3g - 2)(5g - 2)$

12 $(4d - 1)(3d + 2)$

13 $(5 + 2p)(3 + 4p)$

14 $(2 + 3t)(1 + 2t)$

15 $(4 + 3p)(2p + 1)$

16 $(6 + 5t)(1 - 2t)$

17 $(4 + 3n)(3 - 2n)$

18 $(2 + 3f)(2f - 3)$

19 $(3 - 2q)(4 + 5q)$

20 $(1 - 3p)(3 + 2p)$

21 $(4 - 2t)(3t + 1)$

> **HINTS AND TIPS**
>
> Always give answers in the form $\pm ax^2 \pm bx \pm c$ even if the quadratic coefficient is negative.

EXERCISE 12C

Try to spot the pattern in each of the following expressions so that you can immediately write down the expansion.

1 $(2x + 1)(2x - 1)$

2 $(3t + 2)(3t - 2)$

3 $(5y + 3)(5y - 3)$

4 $(4m + 3)(4m - 3)$

5 $(2k - 3)(2k + 3)$

6 $(4h - 1)(4h + 1)$

7 $(2 + 3x)(2 - 3x)$

8 $(5 + 2t)(5 - 2t)$

9 $(6 - 5y)(6 + 5y)$

10 $(a + b)(a - b)$

11 $(3t + k)(3t - k)$

12 $(2m - 3p)(2m + 3p)$

13 $(5k + g)(5k - g)$

14 $(ab + cd)(ab - cd)$

15 $(a^2 + b^2)(a^2 - b^2)$

Expanding squares

Whenever you see a **linear** bracket squared you must write the bracket down twice and then use whichever method you prefer to expand the brackets.

EXAMPLE 6

Expand $(x + 3)^2$.

$(x + 3)^2 = (x + 3)(x + 3)$

$\quad = x(x + 3) + 3(x + 3)$

$\quad = x^2 + 3x + 3x + 9$

$\quad = x^2 + 6x + 9$

EXAMPLE 7

Expand $(3x - 2)^2$.

$(3x - 2)^2 = (3x - 2)(3x - 2)$

$\quad = 9x^2 - 6x - 6x + 4$

$\quad = 9x^2 - 12x + 4$

EXERCISE 12D

Expand the following squares.

HINTS AND TIPS

Remember *always* write down the bracket twice. Do not try to take any short cuts.

1. $(x + 5)^2$
2. $(m + 4)^2$
3. $(6 + t)^2$

4. $(3 + p)^2$
5. $(m - 3)^2$
6. $(t - 5)^2$

7. $(4 - m)^2$
8. $(7 - k)^2$

9. $(3x + 1)^2$
10. $(4t + 3)^2$
11. $(2 + 5y)^2$
12. $(3 + 2m)^2$

13. $(4t - 3)^2$
14. $(3x - 2)^2$
15. $(2 - 5t)^2$
16. $(6 - 5r)^2$

17. $(x + y)^2$
18. $(m - n)^2$
19. $(2t + y)^2$
20. $(m - 3n)^2$

21. $(x + 2)^2 - 4$
22. $(x - 5)^2 - 25$
23. $(x + 6)^2 - 36$
24. $(x - 2)^2 - 4$

Factorisation involves putting a **quadratic expression** back into its **brackets** (if possible). We start with the factorisation of quadratic expressions of the type

$$x^2 + ax + b$$

where a and b are integers.

Sometimes it is easy to put a quadratic expression back into its brackets, other times it seems hard. However, there are some simple rules that will help you to factorise.

- Each bracket will start with an x, and the signs in the quadratic expression show which signs to put after the xs.

- When the *second* sign in the expression is a *plus*, both bracket signs are the *same* as the *first* sign.

  $x^2 + ax + b = (x + ?)(x + ?)$ Since everything is positive.

  $x^2 - ax + b = (x - ?)(x - ?)$ Since $-$ve $\times$ $-$ve $=$ $+$ve.

- When the *second* sign is a *minus*, the bracket signs are *different*.

  $x^2 + ax - b = (x + ?)(x - ?)$ Since $+$ve $\times$ $-$ve $=$ $-$ve.

  $x^2 - ax - b = (x + ?)(x - ?)$

- Next, look at the *last* number, b, in the expression. When multiplied together, the two numbers in the brackets must give b.

- Finally, look at the *coefficient of x* number, a. The *sum* of the two numbers in the brackets will give a.

EXAMPLE 8

Factorise $x^2 - x - 6$.

Because of the signs we know the brackets must be $(x + ?)(x - ?)$.

Two numbers that have a product of -6 and a sum of -1 are -3 and $+2$.

So, $x^2 - x - 6 = (x + 2)(x - 3)$

EXAMPLE 9

> Factorise $x^2 - 9x + 20$.
>
> Because of the signs we know the brackets must be $(x - ?)(x - ?)$.
>
> Two numbers that have a product of $+ 20$ and a sum of $- 9$ are $- 4$ and $- 5$.
>
> So, $x^2 - 9x + 20 = (x - 4)(x - 5)$

EXERCISE 12E

Factorise the following.

1 $x^2 + 5x + 6$ **2** $t^2 + 5t + 4$ **3** $m^2 + 7m + 10$ **4** $k^2 + 10k + 24$

5 $p^2 + 14p + 24$ **6** $r^2 + 9r + 18$ **7** $w^2 + 11w + 18$ **8** $x^2 + 7x + 12$

9 $a^2 + 8a + 12$ **10** $k^2 + 10k + 21$ **11** $f^2 + 22f + 21$ **12** $b^2 + 20b + 96$

13 $t^2 - 5t + 6$ **14** $d^2 - 5d + 4$ **15** $g^2 - 7g + 10$ **16** $x^2 - 15x + 36$

17 $c^2 - 18c + 32$ **18** $t^2 - 13t + 36$ **19** $y^2 - 16y + 48$ **20** $j^2 - 14j + 48$

21 $p^2 - 8p + 15$ **22** $y^2 + 5y - 6$ **23** $t^2 + 2t - 8$

24 $x^2 + 3x - 10$ **25** $m^2 - 4m - 12$ **26** $r^2 - 6r - 7$

27 $n^2 - 3n - 18$ **28** $m^2 - 7m - 44$ **29** $w^2 - 2w - 24$

30 $t^2 - t - 90$ **31** $h^2 - h - 72$ **32** $t^2 - 2t - 63$

33 $d^2 + 2d + 1$ **34** $y^2 + 20y + 100$ **35** $t^2 - 8t + 16$ **36** $m^2 - 18m + 81$

37 $x^2 - 24x + 144$ **38** $d^2 - d - 12$ **39** $t^2 - t - 20$ **40** $q^2 - q - 56$

> **HINTS AND TIPS**
>
> First decide on the signs in the brackets, then look at the numbers.

Difference of two squares

In Exercise 12C, you multiplied out, for example, $(a + b)(a - b)$ and obtained $a^2 - b^2$. This type of quadratic expression with only two terms, both of which are perfect squares separated by a minus sign, is called the **difference of two squares**. You should have found that all the expansions in Exercise 12C are the differences of two squares.

The exercise illustrates a system of factorisation that will *always* work for the difference of two squares such as these.

     $x^2 - 9$ $x^2 - 25$ $x^2 - 4$ $x^2 - 100$

- Recognise the pattern of the expression as x^2 minus a square number n^2.

- Its factors are $(x + n)(x - n)$.

EXAMPLE 10

Factorise $x^2 - 36$.

- Recognise the difference of two squares x^2 and 6^2.

- So it factorises to $(x + 6)(x - 6)$.

Expanding the brackets shows that they do come from the original expression.

EXAMPLE 11

$9x^2 - 169$

- Recognise the difference of two squares $(3x)^2$ and 13^2.

- So it factorises to $(3x + 13)(3x - 13)$.

EXERCISE 12F

Each of these is the difference of two squares. Factorise them.

HINTS AND TIPS

Learn how to spot the difference of two squares as it occurs a lot in GCSE examinations.

1 $x^2 - 9$

2 $t^2 - 25$

3 $m^2 - 16$

4 $9 - x^2$

5 $49 - t^2$

6 $k^2 - 100$

7 $4 - y^2$

8 $x^2 - 64$

9 $t^2 - 81$

10 $x^2 - y^2$

11 $x^2 - 4y^2$

12 $x^2 - 9y^2$

13 $9x^2 - 1$

14 $16x^2 - 9$

15 $25x^2 - 64$

16 $4x^2 - 9y^2$

17 $9t^2 - 4w^2$

18 $16y^2 - 25x^2$

Factorising $ax^2 + bx + c$

We can adapt the method for factorising $x^2 + ax + b$ to take into account the factors of the **coefficient** of x^2.

EXAMPLE 12

Factorise $3x^2 + 8x + 4$.

- First we note that both signs are positive. So both bracket signs must be $(?x + ?)(?x + ?)$
- As 3 has only 3×1 as factors, the brackets must be $(3x + ?)(x + ?)$
- Next, we note that the factors of 4 are 4×1 and 2×2.
- We now have to find which pair of factors of 4 combine with 3×1 to give 8.

$$\begin{array}{c|cc} ③ & 4 & ② \\ ① & 1 & ② \end{array}$$

We see that the combination 3×2 and 1×2 adds up to 8.

- So, the complete factorisation becomes $(3x + 2)(x + 2)$.

EXAMPLE 13

Factorise $6x^2 - 7x - 10$.

- First we note that both signs are negative. So both bracket signs must be $(?x + ?)(?x - ?)$
- As 6 has 6×1 and 3×2 as factors, the brackets could be $(6x \pm ?)(x \pm ?)$ or $(3x \pm ?)(2x \pm ?)$
- Next, we note that the factors of 10 are 5×2 and 1×10.
- We now have to find which pair of factors of 10 combine with the factors of 6 to give -7.

$$\begin{array}{cc|cc} 3 & ⑥ & \pm 1 & ⑵\pm2 \\ 2 & ① & \pm 10 & ⑤\pm5 \end{array}$$

We see that the combination 6×-2 and 1×5 adds up to -7.

- So, the complete factorisation becomes $(6x + 5)(x - 2)$.

Although this seems to be very complicated, it becomes quite easy with practice and experience.

EXERCISE 12G

Factorise the following expressions.

1 $2x^2 + 5x + 2$

2 $7x^2 + 8x + 1$

3 $4x^2 + 3x - 7$

4 $24t^2 + 19t + 2$

5 $15t^2 + 2t - 1$

6 $16x^2 - 8x + 1$

7 $6y^2 + 33y - 63$

8 $4y^2 + 8y - 96$

9 $8x^2 + 10x - 3$

10 $6t^2 + 13t + 5$

11 $3x^2 - 16x - 12$

12 $7x^2 - 37x + 10$

This section will show you how to:
- solve a quadratic equation by factorisation

Key words
factors
solve

Solving the quadratic equation $x^2 + ax + b = 0$

To **solve** a quadratic equation such as $x^2 - 2x - 3 = 0$, you first have to be able to factorise it. Follow through Examples 14 to 16 below to see how this is done.

EXAMPLE 14

Solve $x^2 + 6x + 5 = 0$.

This factorises into $(x + 5)(x + 1) = 0$.

The only way this expression can ever equal 0 is if the value of one of the brackets is 0. Hence either $(x + 5) = 0$ or $(x + 1) = 0$

$\Rightarrow$ $x + 5 = 0$ or $x + 1 = 0$

$\Rightarrow$ $x = -5$ or $x = -1$

So the solution is $x = -5$ or $x = -1$.

EXAMPLE 15

Solve $x^2 + 3x - 10 = 0$.

This factorises into $(x + 5)(x - 2) = 0$.

Hence $x + 5 = 0$ or $x - 2 = 0$

$\Rightarrow$ $x = -5$ or $x = 2$

So the solution is $x = -5$ or $x = 2$.

EXAMPLE 16

Solve $x^2 - 6x + 9 = 0$.

This factorises into $(x - 3)(x - 3) = 0$.

The equation has repeated roots. That is $(x - 3)^2 = 0$.

Hence, there is only one solution, $x = 3$.

EXERCISE 12H

Solve these equations.

1 $(x + 2)(x + 5) = 0$

2 $(t + 3)(t + 1) = 0$

3 $(a + 6)(a + 4) = 0$

4 $(x + 3)(x - 2) = 0$

5 $(x + 1)(x - 3) = 0$

6 $(t + 4)(t - 5) = 0$

7 $(x - 1)(x + 2) = 0$

8 $(x - 2)(x + 5) = 0$

9 $(a - 7)(a + 4) = 0$

10 $(x - 3)(x - 2) = 0$

11 $(x - 1)(x - 5) = 0$

12 $(a - 4)(a - 3) = 0$

First factorise, then solve these equations.

13 $x^2 + 5x + 4 = 0$

14 $x^2 + 11x + 18 = 0$

15 $x^2 - 6x + 8 = 0$

16 $x^2 - 8x + 15 = 0$

17 $x^2 - 3x - 10 = 0$

18 $x^2 - 2x - 15 = 0$

19 $t^2 + 4t - 12 = 0$

20 $t^2 + 3t - 18 = 0$

21 $x^2 - x - 2 = 0$

22 $x^2 + 4x + 4 = 0$

23 $m^2 + 10m + 25 = 0$

24 $t^2 - 8t + 16 = 0$

25 $t^2 + 8t + 12 = 0$

26 $k^2 - 2k - 15 = 0$

27 $a^2 - 14a + 49 = 0$

First rearrange these equations, then solve them.

28 $x^2 + 10x = -24$

29 $x^2 - 18x = -32$

30 $x^2 + 2x = 24$

31 $x^2 + 3x = 54$

32 $t^2 + 7t = 30$

33 $x^2 - 7x = 44$

34 $t^2 - t = 72$

35 $x^2 = 17x - 72$

36 $x^2 + 1 = 2x$

> **HINTS AND TIPS**
>
> You cannot solve a quadratic equation unless it is in the form
> $x^2 + ax + b = 0$

Solving the general quadratic equation by factorisation

The general quadratic equation is of the form $ax^2 + bx + c = 0$ where a, b and c are positive or negative whole numbers. (It is easier to make sure that a is always positive). Before any quadratic equation can be solved it must be rearranged to this form.

The method is similar to that used to solve equations of the form $x^2 + ax + b = 0$. That is, we have to find two **factors** of $ax^2 + bx + c$ whose product is 0.

EXAMPLE 17

Solve these quadratic equations.   **a** $12x^2 - 28x = -15$ **b** $30x^2 - 5x - 5 = 0$

a First, rearrange the equation to the general form.

$$12x^2 - 28x + 15 = 0$$

This factorises into $(2x - 3)(6x - 5) = 0$.

The only way this product can equal 0 is if the value of one of the brackets is 0. Hence,

$$\text{either } 2x - 3 = 0 \quad \text{or} \quad 6x - 5 = 0$$
$$\Rightarrow \quad 2x = 3 \quad \text{or} \quad 6x = 5$$
$$\Rightarrow \quad x = \tfrac{3}{2} \quad \text{or} \quad x = \tfrac{5}{6}$$

So the solution is $x = 1\tfrac{1}{2}$ or $x = \tfrac{5}{6}$.

Note: It is almost always the case that if a solution is a fraction which is then changed into a rounded-off decimal number, the original equation cannot be evaluated exactly using that decimal number. So it is preferable to leave the solution in its fraction form. This is called the rational form (see page 224).

b This equation is already in the general form and it will factorise to $(15x + 5)(2x - 1) = 0$ or $(3x + 1)(10x - 5) = 0$.

Look again at the equation. There is a common factor of 5 which can be factorised out to give

$$5(6x^2 - x - 1 = 0).$$

This is much easier to factorise to $5(3x + 1)(2x - 1) = 0$, which can be solved to give $x = -\tfrac{1}{3}$ or $x = \tfrac{1}{2}$.

Sometimes the values of b and c are zero. (Note that if a is zero the equation is no longer a quadratic equation but a linear equation. These were covered in Chapter 5.)

EXAMPLE 18

Solve these quadratic equations.   **a** $3x^2 - 4 = 0$ **b** $4x^2 - 25 = 0$ **c** $6x^2 - x = 0$

a Rearrange to get $3x^2 = 4$.

Divide both sides by 3: $x^2 = \tfrac{4}{3}$

Square root both sides: $x = \pm\sqrt{\tfrac{4}{3}} = \pm\dfrac{2}{\sqrt{3}}$

Note: A square root can be positive or negative. The answer is in surd form (see Chapter 10).

b You can use the method of part **a** or you should recognise this as the difference of two squares (page 285). This can be factorised to $(2x - 5)(2x + 5) = 0$

Each bracket can be put equal to zero.

$$2x - 5 = 0 \quad \Rightarrow \quad x = +\tfrac{5}{2}$$
$$2x + 5 = 0 \quad \Rightarrow \quad x = -\tfrac{5}{2} \qquad \text{So the solution is } x = \pm\tfrac{5}{2}.$$

c There is a common factor of x, so factorise as $x(6x - 1) = 0$

There is only one bracket this time but each factor can be equal to zero, so $x = 0$ or $6x - 1 = 0$

Hence $x = 0$ or $\tfrac{1}{6}$.

EXERCISE 12I

Give your answers either in rational form or as mixed numbers.

1 Solve the following equations.

HINTS AND TIPS

Look out for the special cases where b or c is zero.

a $3x^2 + 8x - 3 = 0$

b $6x^2 - 5x - 4 = 0$

c $5x^2 - 9x - 2 = 0$

d $4t^2 - 4t - 35 = 0$

e $18t^2 + 9t + 1 = 0$

f $3t^2 - 14t + 8 = 0$

g $6x^2 + 15x - 9 = 0$

h $12x^2 - 16x - 35 = 0$

i $15t^2 + 4t - 35 = 0$

j $28x^2 - 85x + 63 = 0$

k $24x^2 - 19x + 2 = 0$

l $16t^2 - 1 = 0$

m $4x^2 + 9x = 0$

n $25t^2 - 49 = 0$

p $9m^2 - 24m - 9 = 0$

2 Rearrange into the general form then solve the following equations.

a $x^2 - x = 42$

b $8x(x + 1) = 30$

c $(x + 1)(x - 2) = 40$

d $13x^2 = 11 - 2x$

e $(x + 1)(x - 2) = 4$

f $10x^2 - x = 2$

g $8x^2 + 6x + 3 = 2x^2 + x + 2$

h $25x^2 = 10 - 45x$

i $8x - 16 - x^2 = 0$

j $(2x + 1)(5x + 2) = (2x - 2)(x - 2)$

k $5x + 5 = 30x^2 + 15x + 5$

l $2m^2 = 50$

m $6x^2 + 30 = 5 - 3x^2 - 30x$

n $4x^2 + 4x - 49 = 4x$

p $2t^2 - t = 15$

12.4 # Solving a quadratic equation by the quadratic formula

This section will show you how to:

- solve a quadratic equation by using the quadratic formula

Key words

quadratic formula
soluble
solve

Many quadratic equations cannot be solved by factorisation because they do not have simple factors. Try to factorise, for example, $x^2 - 4x - 3 = 0$ or $3x^2 - 6x + 2 = 0$. You will find it is impossible.

One way to **solve** this type of equation is to use the **quadratic formula**. This formula can be used to solve *any* quadratic equation that is **soluble**. (Some are not, which the quadratic formula would immediately show. See section 12.6.)

The solution of the equation $ax^2 + bx + c = 0$ is given by:

$$x = \frac{-b \pm \sqrt{b^2 - 4ac}}{2a}$$

This is the quadratic formula. It is given on the formula sheet of GCSE exams but it is best to learn it.

The symbol ± states that the square root has a positive and a negative value, *both* of which must be used in solving for *x*.

EXAMPLE 19

Solve $5x^2 - 11x - 4 = 0$, correct to two decimal places.

Take the quadratic formula:

$$x = \frac{-b \pm \sqrt{b^2 - 4ac}}{2a}$$

and put $a = 5$, $b = -11$ and $c = -4$, which gives:

$$x = \frac{-(-11) \pm \sqrt{(-11)^2 - 4(5)(-4)}}{2(5)}$$

Note that the values for *a*, *b* and *c* have been put into the formula in brackets. This is to avoid mistakes in calculation. It is a very common mistake to get the sign of *b* wrong or to think that -11^2 is -121. Using brackets will help you do the calculation correctly.

$$x = \frac{11 \pm \sqrt{121 + 80}}{10} = \frac{11 \pm \sqrt{201}}{10}$$

$$\Rightarrow \quad x = 2.52 \text{ or } -0.32$$

Note: The calculation has been done in stages. With a calculator it is possible just to work out the answer, but make sure you can use your calculator properly. If not, break the calculation down. Remember the rule "if you try to do two things at once, you will probably get one of them wrong".

Examination tip: If you are asked to solve a quadratic equation to one or two decimal places, you can be sure that it can be solved *only* by the quadratic formula.

EXERCISE 12J

Solve the following equations using the quadratic formula.
Give your answers to 2 decimal places.

> **HINTS AND TIPS**
>
> Use brackets when substituting and do not try to work two things out at the same time.

1 $2x^2 + x - 8 = 0$

2 $3x^2 + 5x + 1 = 0$

3 $x^2 - x - 10 = 0$

4 $5x^2 + 2x - 1 = 0$

5 $7x^2 + 12x + 2 = 0$

6 $3x^2 + 11x + 9 = 0$

7 $4x^2 + 9x + 3 = 0$

8 $6x^2 + 22x + 19 = 0$

9 $x^2 + 3x - 6 = 0$

10 $3x^2 - 7x + 1 = 0$

11 $2x^2 + 11x + 4 = 0$

12 $4x^2 + 5x - 3 = 0$

13 $4x^2 - 9x + 4 = 0$

14 $7x^2 + 3x - 2 = 0$

15 $5x^2 - 10x + 1 = 0$

Solving a quadratic equation by completing the square

This section will show you how to:

- solve a quadratic equation by completing the square

Key words

completing the
square
square root
surd

Another method for solving quadratic equations is **completing the square**. This method can be used to give answers to a specified number of decimal places or to leave answers in **surd** form.

You will remember that:

$$(x + a)^2 = x^2 + 2ax + a^2$$

which gives:

$$x^2 + 2ax = (x + a)^2 - a^2$$

This is the basic principle behind completing the square.

EXAMPLE 20

Rewrite $x^2 + 4x - 7$ in the form $(x + a)^2 - b$. Hence solve the equation $x^2 + 4x - 7 = 0$, giving your answers to 2 decimal places.

We note that:

$$x^2 + 4x = (x + 2)^2 - 4$$

So, we have:

$$x^2 + 4x - 7 = (x + 2)^2 - 4 - 7 = (x + 2)^2 - 11$$

When $x^2 + 4x - 7 = 0$, we can rewrite the equations using completing the square, as $(x + 2)^2 - 11 = 0$.

Rearranging gives $(x + 2)^2 = 11$

Taking the **square root** of both sides gives

$$x + 2 = \pm\sqrt{11}$$
$$\Rightarrow x = -2 \pm \sqrt{11}$$

This answer is in surd form and could be left like this, but we are asked to evaluate it to $x = 1.32$ or -5.32 (to 2 decimal places)

EXAMPLE 21

Solve $x^2 - 6x - 1 = 0$ by completing the square. Leave your answer in the form $a \pm \sqrt{b}$.

$x^2 - 6x = (x - 3)^2 - 9$

So $x^2 - 6x - 1 = (x - 3)^2 - 9 - 1 = (x - 3)^2 - 10$

When $x^2 - 6x - 1 = 0$, then $(x - 3)^2 - 10 = 0$

$\Rightarrow (x - 3)^2 = 10$

Taking the square root of both sides gives:

$x - 3 = \pm\sqrt{10}$

$\Rightarrow x = 3 \pm \sqrt{10}$

EXERCISE 12K

1 Write an equivalent expression in the form $(x \pm a)^2 - b$.

a $x^2 + 4x$ **b** $x^2 + 14x$ **c** $x^2 - 6x$ **d** $x^2 + 6x$

e $x^2 - 4x$ **f** $x^2 + 3x$ **g** $x^2 - 5x$ **h** $x^2 + x$

i $x^2 + 10x$ **j** $x^2 + 7x$ **k** $x^2 - 2x$ **l** $x^2 + 2x$

2 Write an equivalent expression in the form $(x \pm a)^2 - b$.

Question **1** will help with **a** to **h**.

a $x^2 + 4x - 1$ **b** $x^2 + 14x - 5$ **c** $x^2 - 6x + 3$ **d** $x^2 + 6x + 7$

e $x^2 - 4x - 1$ **f** $x^2 + 3x + 3$ **g** $x^2 - 5x - 5$ **h** $x^2 + x - 1$

i $x^2 + 8x - 6$ **j** $x^2 + 2x - 1$ **k** $x^2 - 2x - 7$ **l** $x^2 + 2x - 9$

3 Solve the following equations by completing the square. Leave your answers in surd form where appropriate. The answers to question **2** will help.

a $x^2 + 4x - 1 = 0$ **b** $x^2 + 14x - 5 = 0$ **c** $x^2 - 6x + 3 = 0$

d $x^2 + 6x + 7 = 0$ **e** $x^2 - 4x - 1 = 0$ **f** $x^2 + 3x + 3 = 0$

g $x^2 - 5x - 5 = 0$ **h** $x^2 + x - 1 = 0$ **i** $x^2 + 8x - 6 = 0$

j $x^2 + 2x - 1 = 0$ **k** $x^2 - 2x - 7 = 0$ **l** $x^2 + 2x - 9 = 0$

> **HINTS AND TIPS**
>
> When the coefficient of x is an odd number you will get fractional values.

4 Solve by completing the square. Give your answers to two decimal places.

a $x^2 + 2x - 5 = 0$ **b** $x^2 - 4x - 7 = 0$ **c** $x^2 + 2x - 9 = 0$

5 Prove that the solutions to the equation $x^2 + bx + c = 0$ are

$$-\frac{b}{2} \pm \sqrt{\left(\frac{b^2}{4} - c\right)}$$

This section will show you why:

- some quadratic equations do not factorise and explain how to solve practical problems using quadratic equations

Key word

discriminant

Quadratic equations with no solution

The quantity $(b^2 - 4ac)$ in the quadratic formula is known as the **discriminant**.

When $b^2 > 4ac$, $(b^2 - 4ac)$ is positive. This has been the case in almost all of the quadratics you have solved so far and it means there are two solutions.

When $b^2 = 4ac$, $(b^2 - 4ac)$ is zero. This has been the case in some of the quadratics you have solved so far. It means there is only one solution (the repeated root).

When $b^2 < 4ac$, $(b^2 - 4ac)$ is negative. So its square root is that of a negative number.

Such a square root cannot be found (at GCSE level) and therefore there are no solutions. You will not be asked about this in examinations but if it happens then you will have made a mistake and should check your working.

EXAMPLE 22

Find the discriminant $b^2 - 4ac$ of the equation $x^2 + 3x + 5 = 0$ and explain what the result tells you.

$b^2 - 4ac = (3)^2 - 4(1)(5) = 9 - 20 = -11.$

This means there are no solutions for x.

EXERCISE 12L

Work out the discriminant $b^2 - 4ac$ of the following equations. In each case say how many solutions the equation has.

1. $3x^2 + 2x - 4 = 0$

2. $2x^2 - 7x - 2 = 0$

3. $5x^2 - 8x + 2 = 0$

4. $3x^2 + x - 7 = 0$

5. $16x^2 - 23x + 6 = 0$

6. $x^2 - 2x - 16 = 0$

7. $5x^2 + 5x + 3 = 0$

8. $4x^2 + 3x + 2 = 0$

9. $5x^2 - x - 2 = 0$

10. $x^2 + 6x - 1 = 0$

11. $17x^2 - x + 2 = 0$

12. $x^2 + 5x - 3 = 0$

A*

Using the quadratic formula without a calculator

In the non-calculator paper, you could be asked to solve a quadratic equation that does not factorise. The clue would be that you would be asked to leave your answer in root or surd form. You could use completing the square but this gets very messy if the coefficient of x^2 is not 1 and/or the coefficient of x is not an even number. In these cases the quadratic formula is easier to use.

EXAMPLE 23

Solve the equation $x^2 - 5x - 5 = 0$. Give your answer in the form $a \pm \sqrt{b}$.

Using the quadratic formula gives:

$$x = \frac{-(-5) \pm \sqrt{(-5)^2 - 4(1)(-5)}}{2(1)}$$

$$x = \frac{5 \pm \sqrt{45}}{2} = \frac{5}{2} \pm \frac{3\sqrt{5}}{2}$$

EXAMPLE 24

Solve the equation $2x^2 + 6x - 5 = 0$. Give your answer in surd form.

Using the quadratic formula gives:

$$x = \frac{-(6) \pm \sqrt{(6)^2 - 4(2)(-5)}}{2(2)}$$

$$x = \frac{-6 \pm \sqrt{76}}{4} = \frac{-6 \pm 2\sqrt{19}}{4} = \frac{-3 \pm \sqrt{19}}{2}$$

EXERCISE 12M

 Solve the following equations by the quadratic formula.

Give your answers in the form $a \pm \sqrt{b}$.

a $x^2 - 2x - 4 = 0$	**b** $x^2 + 2x - 7 = 0$
c $x^2 + 4x - 44 = 0$	**d** $x^2 + 2x - 6 = 0$
e $x^2 - 8x + 2 = 0$	**f** $x^2 - 4x + 2 = 0$

> **HINTS AND TIPS**
>
> The form $a \pm \sqrt{b}$ and surd form are basically the same thing.
> You should try to simplify surds if possible.

2 Solve the following equations by the quadratic formula. Give your answers in surd form.

a $2x^2 + 4x - 5 = 0$	**b** $2x^2 + 4x - 7 = 0$	**c** $2x^2 + 6x - 5 = 0$
d $2x^2 - 5x - 8 = 0$	**e** $5x^2 + x - 3 = 0$	**f** $2x^2 + 3x - 3 = 0$

Problems solved by quadratic equations

You are likely to have to solve a problem which involves generating a quadratic equation and finding its solution.

EXAMPLE 25

Find the sides of the right-angled triangle shown in the diagram.

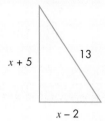

Applying the theorem of Pythagoras gives:

$$(x + 5)^2 + (x - 2)^2 = 13^2$$
$$(x^2 + 10x + 25) + (x^2 - 4x + 4) = 169$$
$$2x^2 + 6x + 29 = 169$$
$$2x^2 + 6x - 140 = 0$$

Divide by a factor of 2: $\quad x^2 + 3x - 70 = 0$

This factorises to $\quad\quad (x + 10)(x - 7) = 0$

Giving $x = -10$ or 7. We reject the negative value as it would give negative lengths.

Hence the sides of the triangle are 5, 12 and 13.

Note: You may know the Pythagorean triple 5, 12, 13 and guessed the answer but you would be expected to show working. Most "real-life" problems will end up with a quadratic that factorises as the questions are complicated enough without expecting you to use the quadratic formula or completing the square.

EXAMPLE 26

Solve this equation. $\qquad\qquad\qquad 2x - \dfrac{3}{x} = 5$

Multiply through by x to give: $\qquad\quad 2x^2 - 3 = 5x$

Rearrange into the general form: $\quad\;\; 2x^2 - 5x - 3 = 0$

This factorises to: $\qquad\qquad\qquad (2x + 1)(x - 3) = 0$

So $x = -\dfrac{1}{2}$ or $x = 3$.

EXAMPLE 27

A coach driver undertook a journey of 300 km. Her actual average speed turned out to be 10 km/h slower than expected. Therefore, she took 1 hour longer over the journey than expected. Find her actual average speed.

Let the driver's actual average speed be x km/h. So the estimated speed would have been $(x + 10)$ km/h.

Time taken $= \dfrac{\text{Distance travelled}}{\text{Speed}}$ $\qquad$ At x km/h, she did the journey in $\dfrac{300}{x}$ hours.

At $(x + 10)$ km/h, she would have done the journey in $\dfrac{300}{x + 10}$ hours.

Since the journey took 1 hour longer than expected, then

$$\text{time taken} = \frac{300}{x + 10} + 1 = \frac{300 + x + 10}{x + 10} = \frac{310 + x}{x + 10}$$

So $\qquad \dfrac{300}{x} = \dfrac{310 + x}{x + 10} \Rightarrow 300(x + 10) = x(310 + x) \Rightarrow 300x + 3000 = 310x + x^2$

Rearranging into the general form gives: $\quad x^2 + 10x - 3000 = 0$

This factorises into: $\qquad\qquad\qquad\qquad (x + 60)(x - 50) = 0 \Rightarrow x = -60$ or 50

The coach's average speed could not be -60 km/h, so it has to be 50 km/h.

EXERCISE 12N

1 The sides of a right-angled triangle are x, $(x + 2)$ and $(2x - 2)$. The hypotenuse is length $(2x - 2)$. Find the actual dimensions of the triangle.

2 The length of a rectangle is 5 m more than its width. Its area is 300 m². Find the actual dimensions of the rectangle.

3 The average weight of a group of people is 45.2 kg. A newcomer to the group weighs 51 kg, which increases the average weight by 0.2 kg. How many people are now in the group?

4 Solve the equation $x + \dfrac{3}{x} = 7$. Give your answers correct to 2 decimal places.

5 Solve the equation $2x + \dfrac{5}{x} = 11$.

6 A tennis court has an area of 224 m². If the length were decreased by 1 m and the width increased by 1 m, the area would be increased by 1 m². Find the dimensions of the court.

7 On a journey of 400 km, the driver of a train calculates that if he were to increase his average speed by 2 km/h, he would take 20 minutes less. Find his average speed.

8 The difference of the squares of two positive numbers, whose difference is 2, is 184. Find these two numbers.

9 The length of a carpet is 1 m more than its width. Its area is 9 m². Find the dimensions of the carpet to 2 decimal places.

10 The two shorter sides of a right-angled triangle differ by 2 cm. The area is 24 cm². Find the shortest side of the triangle.

11 Helen worked out that she could save 30 minutes on a 45 km journey if she travelled at an average speed which was 15 km/h faster than that at which she had planned to travel. Find the speed at which Helen had originally planned to travel.

12 Claire intended to spend £3.20 on balloons for her party. But each balloon cost her 2p more than she expected, so she had to buy 8 fewer balloons. Find the cost of each balloon.

13 The sum of a number and its reciprocal is 2.05. What are the two numbers?

14 A woman buys goods for £60x and sells them for £$(600 - 6x)$ at a loss of x%. Find x.

15 A train has a scheduled time for its journey. If the train averages 50 km/h, it arrives 12 minutes early. If the train averages 45 km/h, it arrives 20 minutes late. Find how long the train should take for the journey.

16 A rectangular garden measures 15 m by 11 m and is surrounded by a path of uniform width whose area is 41.25 m². Find the width of the path.

1 a Factorise $8p - 6$ b Factorise $r^2 + 6r$
  c Simplify $s^2 \times s^4$

2 Find, using trial and improvement, an exact solution of
$3x^2 - 2x = 96$

x	$3x^2 - 2x$	Comment
1	1	Too small

AQA, Spec B, Question 12, Module 5, Paper 1 Intermediate, June 2005

3 a Factorise $x^5 - 4x^2$
  b i Factorise $x^2 - 3x - 10$
    ii Hence solve the equation $x^2 - 3x - 10 = 0$

4 Multiply and simplify $(2p - 5q)(3p - q)$

AQA, Spec B, Question 15, Module 5, Paper 1 Intermediate, November 2004

5 a Expand and simplify $(a + b)(a - b)$
  b i Factorise $x^2 - 20x + 36$
    ii Hence solve the equation $x^2 - 20x + 36 = 0$

6 The perimeter of a rectangle is 25 cm.
The length of the rectangle is x cm
  a Write down an expression for the width of the rectangle in terms of x.
  b The area of the rectangle is 38 cm². Show that $2x^2 - 25x + 76 = 0$.
  c Solve the equation given in part b to find the value of x. Give your answer to 2 decimal places.

AQA, Spec B, Question 12, Module 5, Paper 2 Higher, June 2005

7 a Find the values of a and b such that
$x^2 + 10x + 40 = (x + a)^2 + b$
  b Hence, or otherwise, write down the minimum value of $x^2 + 10x + 40$

AQA, Spec B, Question 14, Module 5, Paper 1 Higher, June 2005

8 Factorise fully $3x^2 - 12y^2$

9 a Factorise $2n^2 + 5n + 3$
  b Hence, or otherwise, write 253 as the product of two prime factors.

AQA, Question 16, Paper 1 Higher, June 2004

10 Solve the equation $x^2 + 4x - 10 = 0$
Give your answers to 2 decimal places.
Your *must* show your working.

AQA, Spec B, Question 10, Module 5, Paper 2 Intermediate, June 2003

11 a Find the values of a and b such that
$x^2 + 6x - 3 = (x + a)^2 + b$
  b Hence, or otherwise, solve the equation
$x^2 + 6x - 3 = 0$
giving your answers in surd form.

AQA, Question 20, Paper 1 Higher, June 2004

12 a Factorise $x^2 - 8x + 12$
  b Hence, or otherwise, solve the equation
$(y + 1)^2 - 8(y + 1) + 12 = 0$

AQA, Question 18a, Paper 1 Higher, June 2004

WORKED EXAM QUESTION

a You are given that
$(2x + b)^2 + c = ax^2 - 4x - 5$
Calculate the values a, b and c

b You are given $q = a(p + 3)^{-3}$. When $p = 7$, $q = 2$.
Find p when $q = \frac{1}{4}$.

Solution

a $4x^2 + 4bx + b^2 + c = ax^2 - 4x - 5$
$4x^2 = ax^2 \Rightarrow a = 4$
$4bx = -4x \Rightarrow b = -1$
$b^2 + c = -5 \Rightarrow c = -6$

> Expand and simplify the left-hand side.

> Equate the terms in x^2, x and the constant term. Solve the resulting equations.

b $2 = a(7 + 3)^{-3} \Rightarrow 2 = \dfrac{a}{1000} \Rightarrow a = 2000$

$\dfrac{1}{4} = 2000(p + 3)^{-3} \qquad \dfrac{1}{4} = \dfrac{2000}{(p + 3)^3}$

$(p + 3)^3 = 8000 \quad p + 3 = 20 \quad p = 17$

> Substitute the given values into the equation and solve to get the value of a.

> Substitute these values into the equation and solve to get p.

A garden designer sketches the following design for a client.

This is his notepad with the details of each area.

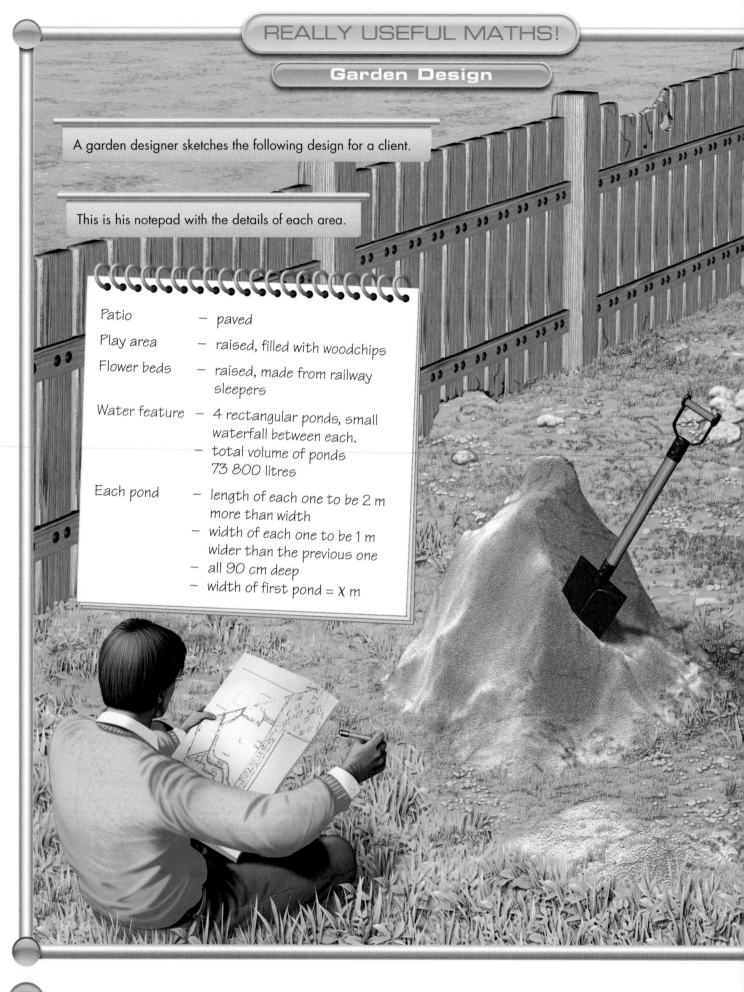

Patio — paved

Play area — raised, filled with woodchips

Flower beds — raised, made from railway sleepers

Water feature — 4 rectangular ponds, small waterfall between each.
— total volume of ponds 73 800 litres

Each pond — length of each one to be 2 m more than width
— width of each one to be 1 m wider than the previous one
— all 90 cm deep
— width of first pond = x m

Flower bed

Lawn

40m

Play area

18m

8m

Water
feature

Patio

18m

30m

3m

5m

Help the designer to calculate:

Perimeter of patio			Area of patio	
Perimeter of play area			Area of play area	
Perimeter of one flower bed			Area of one flower bed	
Dimensions of top pond	length =	width =	Area of top pond	
Dimensions of second pond	length =	width =	Area of second pond	
Dimensions of third pond	length =	width =	Area of third pond	
Dimensions of bottom pond	length =	width =	Area of bottom pond	
			Area of lawn	

C Able to expand a pair of linear brackets to get a quadratic expression

B Able to factorise a quadratic expression of the form $x^2 + ax + b$

B Able to solve a quadratic equation of the form $x^2 + ax + b = 0$

A Able to factorise a quadratic expression of the form $ax^2 + bx + c$

A Able to solve a quadratic equation of the form $ax^2 + bx + c = 0$ by factorisation

A Able to solve a quadratic equation of the form $ax^2 + bx + c = 0$ by the quadratic formula

A* Able to solve a quadratic equation using completing the square

A* Able to solve real-life problems that lead to a quadratic equation

What you should know now

- How to expand linear brackets
- How to solve quadratic equations by factorisation, the quadratic formula and completing the square
- How to set up practical problems using algebra to obtain a quadratic equation which can then be solved

Real-life graphs

1 Straight-line distance–time graphs

2 Straight-line velocity–time graphs

3 Other types of graphs

This chapter will show you ...

- how to interpret distance–time and velocity–time graphs
- how to interpret other types of graph associated with real-life situations

Visual overview

What you should already know

- How to plot coordinate points
- How to read scales

Quick check

1 Give the coordinates of points A, B and C.

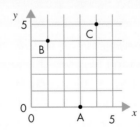

2 What are the values shown on the following scales?

This section you will learn how to:
● interpret distance–time graphs

Key words
distance
gradient
speed
time

Units of speed

Sometimes when using **distance–time** graphs, you will need to change the given units of **speed**.

EXAMPLE 1

Change 15 metres per second to kilometres per hour.

15 m/s = 15 × 60 × 60 metres per hour = 54 000 m/h

54 000 m/h = 54 000 ÷ 1000 km/h = 54 km/h

EXAMPLE 2

Change 24 kilometres per hour to metres per minute.

24 km/h = 24 × 1000 m/h = 24 000 m/h

24 000 m/h = 24 000 ÷ 60 m/min = 400 m/min

EXERCISE 13A

1 Paul was travelling in his car to a meeting. He set off from home at 7:00 am, and stopped on the way for a break. This distance–time graph illustrates his journey.

a At what time did he:

  i stop for his break?

  ii set off after his break?

  iii get to his meeting place?

b At what average speed was he travelling:

  i over the first hour?

  ii over the second hour?

  iii for the last part of his journey?

2 James was travelling to Cornwall on his holidays. This distance–time graph illustrates his journey.

a His fastest speed was on the motorway.

    i How much motorway did he use?

    ii What was his average speed on the motorway?

b **i** When did he travel the slowest?

    ii What was his slowest average speed?

3 Richard and Paul had a 5000 m race. The distance covered is illustrated below.

a Paul ran a steady race. What is his average speed in:

    i metres per minute?

    ii km/h?

b Richard ran in spurts. What was his quickest average speed?

c Who won the race and by how much?

4 Three friends, Patrick, Araf and Sean, ran a 1000 metres race. The race is illustrated on the distance–time graph below.

a Describe the race of each friend.

b **i** What is the average speed of Araf in m/s?

    ii What is this speed in km/h?

Gradient of straight-line distance–time graphs

The **gradient** of a straight line is a measure of its slope.

The gradient of this line can be found by constructing a right-angled triangle whose hypotenuse (sloping side) is on the line. Then:

$$\text{Gradient} = \frac{\text{Distance measured vertically}}{\text{Distance measured horizontally}} = \frac{6}{4} = 1.5$$

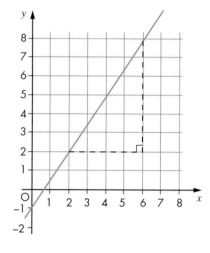

Look at the following examples of straight lines and their gradients.

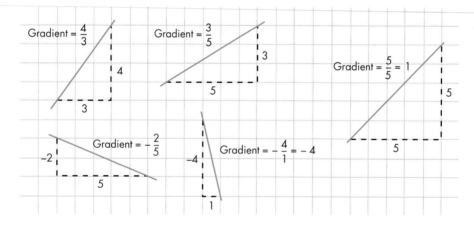

Note: Lines which slope downwards from left to right have *negative gradients*.

In the case of a straight-line graph between two quantities, its gradient is found using the *scales* on its axes, *not* the actual number of grid squares. The gradient usually represents a third quantity whose value we want to know. For example, look at the next graph.

The gradient on this distance–time graph represents average speed.

$$\text{Gradient} = \frac{500 \text{ km}}{2 \text{ h}} = 250 \text{ km/h}$$

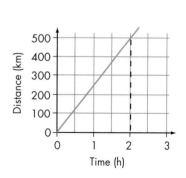

EXERCISE 13B

1 Calculate the gradient of each line, using the scales on the axes.

 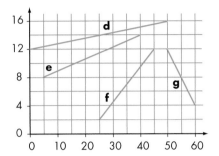

2 Calculate the average speed of the journey represented by each line in the following diagrams.

a **b** **c**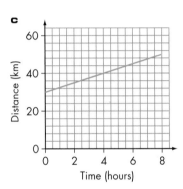

3 From each diagram below, calculate the speed between each stage of each journey.

a **b**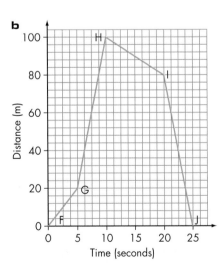

In this section you will learn how to:
- interpret velocity–time graphs

Key words
acceleration
gradient
time
velocity

Velocity

In our calculations of speed, we have ignored the sign of the **gradient**. The sign of the gradient of a distance–time graph gives the *direction of travel*. Once we introduce the direction of travel into our calculations, then we must use the term **velocity** instead of speed.

Velocity at time t is the gradient of the distance–time graph at t, *including its sign*.

When the velocity of a moving object is plotted against time, the gradient of the **velocity–time** graph at any time t is equal to the **acceleration** of the object at that time.

Acceleration is rate of change of velocity, so when the gradient becomes negative, the object is slowing down. Negative acceleration is called *deceleration*.

The units of acceleration and deceleration are m/s² or m s^{-2}, and km/h² or km h^{-2}.

EXAMPLE 3

Below is the velocity–time graph of a particle over a 6-second period, drawn from measurements made during a scientific experiment. Describe what is happening at each stage of the 6 seconds.

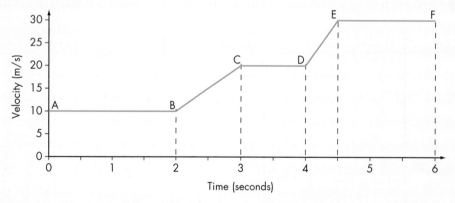

The graph shows a constant particle velocity of 10 m/s for the first 2 seconds (AB). Then the velocity increases uniformly from 10 m/s to 20 m/s over 1 second (BC). Then follows another period of constant velocity (20 m/s) over 1 second (CD), after which the velocity increases uniformly from 20 m/s to 30 m/s in 0.5 seconds (DE). During the final 1.5 seconds the velocity is constant at 30 m/s.

There are two periods of acceleration: BC and DE.

$$\text{Acceleration over BC} = \text{gradient of BC} = \frac{10 \text{ m/s}}{1 \text{ s}} = 10 \text{ m/s}^2$$

$$\text{Acceleration over DE} = \text{gradient of DE} = \frac{10 \text{ m/s}}{0.5 \text{ s}} = 20 \text{ m/s}^2$$

1 The diagram shows the velocity of a model car over 6 seconds.

Calculate the acceleration:

a over the first second

b after 5 seconds.

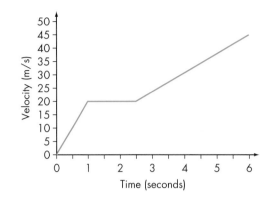

2 The diagram shows the velocity–time graph for a short tram journey between stops.

Find:

a the acceleration over the first 10 seconds

b the deceleration over the last 10 seconds.

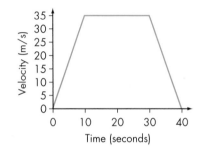

3 The diagram shows the velocity of a boat over an 18-hour period.

Calculate:

a the times at which the boat was travelling at a constant velocity

b the acceleration during each part of the journey.

4 An aircraft flying at a constant height of 300 m dropped a load fitted to a parachute. During the times stated, the velocity of the parachute was as follows:

0–2 seconds	The load accelerated uniformly up to 20 m/s.
2–6 seconds	The parachute opened, which brought the velocity down uniformly to 2 m/s.
After 6 seconds	The load fell with a constant speed of 2 m/s.

Draw a velocity–time graph for the first 8 seconds.

5 Starting from rest (zero velocity), a particle travels as indicated below.

- Accelerates at a constant rate over 5 seconds to reach 15 m/s.
- Keeps this velocity for 10 seconds.
- Accelerates over the next 5 seconds to reach 25 m/s.
- Steadily slows down to reach rest (zero velocity) over the next 10 seconds.

a Draw the velocity–time graph.

b Calculate the acceleration over the first 5 seconds.

In this section you will learn how to:

● identify and draw some of the more unusual types of real-life graphs

Some situations can lead to unusual graphs. For example, this graph represents the cost of postage of a first-class letter against its weight.

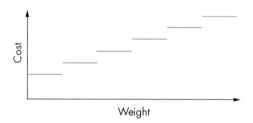

This next graph shows the change in the depth of water in a flat-bottomed flask, as it is filled from a tap delivering water at a steady rate. The graph shows that at first the depth of water increases quickly then slows down as the flask gets wider. As the flask gets narrower, the depth increases at a faster rate. Finally, when the water reaches the neck, which has a constant cross-section, the depth increases at a constant rate to the top of the neck.

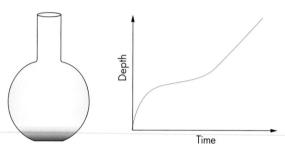

The application of graphs to describe the rate of change of depth as a container is filled with water is also covered in question **1** (Exercise 13D).

Two other examples of the use of graphs are set-out in Exercise 13D. They are the calculation of personal income tax (question **2**) and the calculation of mortgage repayments (question **3**).

Further practical applications of graphs, with special reference to finding the formulae or rules governing them, are featured on pages 375.

EXERCISE 13D

1 Draw a graph of the depth of water in each of these containers as it is filled steadily.

a

b

c

d

e

f

2 The following is a simplified model of how income tax is calculated for an individual.

The first £4000 earned is tax free. Any income over £4000 up to £30 000 is taxed at 25%. For example, a person who earns £10 000 per year would pay 25% of £6000 = £1500. Any income over £30 000 is taxed at 40%.

a Draw a graph to show the amount of tax paid by people who earn up to £40 000 per year.

(Take the horizontal axis as "Income" from £0 to £40 000. Take the vertical axis as "Tax paid" from £0 to £11 000.)

b For people who earn up to £40 000 per year, draw a graph of the percentage of income paid as tax against income.

(Take the horizontal axis as "Income" from £0 to £40 000. Take the vertical axis as "Percentage of income paid as tax" from 0% to 30%.)

3 In a repayment mortgage, a fixed amount is paid per month for a long period (usually 15 to 25 years). At first, most of the money is used to pay off the interest and only a small amount is paid off the sum borrowed. Over time, the amount due to interest reduces and more money is used to pay off the sum borrowed. The following is a simple model for a loan of £50 000 (the capital) borrowed over 15 years at a fixed annual rate of interest of 5%. The monthly amount to be paid is £400.

a Copy and complete the following calculations to show that it takes approximately 15 years to pay off the money borrowed plus interest.

Amount owing at end of year 1	=	50 000 + 5%	=	52 500
Repayments over year 1	=	12 × 400	=	4 800
Total owed at end of year 1			=	47 700
Amount owing at end of year 2	=	47 700 + 5%	=	50 085
Repayments over year 2	=	12 × 400	=	4 800
Total owed at end of year 2			=	45 285
Amount owing at end of year 3	=	45 285 + 5%	=	....
Repayments over year 3	=	12 × 400	=	4 800
Total owed at end of year 3			=	....

and so on

b Draw a graph of "Amount owing (£)" against "Time (years)".

(Take the horizontal axis as "Time" from 0 to 15 years. Take the vertical axis as "Amount owing" from £0 to £50 000.)

Plot the first point as (0, 50 000), The second as (1, 47 700), and so on.

> **HINTS AND TIPS**
>
> This repeat calculation can easily be set up on a scientific calculator or a graphics calculator.

1 Mr Smith leaves home at 10 am to go to the shopping mall. He walks to the station where he catches a train. He gets off at the mall. The travel graph shows his journey.

After shopping Mr Smith goes home by taxi. The taxi leaves the mall at 1 pm and arrives at his home at 1:45 pm.

a Complete the travel graph.

b Calculate the average speed of the taxi.

AQA, Question 1, Paper 2 (2-tier trial), June 2005

2 Wayne cycles from Newcastle to Ashington, a distance of 20 miles. The diagram shows the distance–time graph of his journey.

a Describe what is happening between 12:00 and 13:00.

b How far does Wayne travel in the first 2 hours of his journey?

c What is Wayne's average speed over the first 2 hours of his journey?

d Darren travels from Ashington to Newcastle by bus. He leaves Ashington at 10:00 and arrives in Newcastle at 11:00. Copy the diagram and draw a possible distance–time graph of Darren's journey on it.

AQA, Question 5, Paper 2 Intermediate, June 2003

3 A train travels from Glasgow to London in $4\frac{3}{4}$ hours. The distance travelled is 323 miles. Find the average speed of the train in miles per hour.

4 A motorbike drives from Sheffield to Plymouth. The journey is 468 kilometres in total. 372 kilometres are on motorway and 96 kilometres on normal roads. On normal roads the bike does 15 kilometres to a litre of petrol. In total the bike uses 25 litres of petrol on the journey. How many kilometres per litre does the bike do on average on motorways?

5 **a** Liquid is poured at a steady rate into the bottle shown in the diagram.

As the bottle is filled, the height, h, of the liquid in the bottle changes.

Which of the five graphs below shows this change? Give a reason for your choice.

b Liquid is poured at a steady rate into another container. The graph shows how the height, h, of the liquid in this container changes. Sketch a picture of this container.

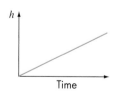

AQA, Question 5, Paper 2 Higher, November 2003

6 A swimming pool takes 6 hours to fill. For the first 2 hours the pool is filled at 80 000 litres per hour. For the next two hours the pool is filled at 100 000 litres per hour. For the last 2 hours the pool is filled at 70 000 litres per hour.

a Show this information on a graph with a horizontal axis showing time from 0 to 6 hours and a vertical axis showing litres from 0 to 800 000.

b The pool takes 10 hours to empty at a steady rate. What is the rate of flow when the pool is emptying?

AQA, Question 4, Paper 2 Higher, November 2003

 7 A cyclist sets off on a ride over the moors at 9 am. The climb up to the highest point is 25 km. It takes the cyclist 1 hour 30 minutes to do this. She rests at the highest point for 15 minutes then sets off back. She arrives home at 11:45 am.

a Show this information on a travel graph with a horizontal axis showing time from 9 am to 12 pm and a vertical axis showing distance from home from 0 to 40 km.

b Calculate the average speed of the return journey in km per hour.

AQA, Question 8, Paper 2 Higher, June 2005

WORKED EXAM QUESTION

Jane cycles from A to B and then from B to C. Details of each stage of her journey are given below.

> A to B   Distance 55 km
>
>   Average speed 22 km per hour
>
> B to C   Time taken 1 hour 30 minutes
>
>   Average speed 30 km per hour

Calculate Jane's average speed over the whole of her journey from A to C.

Time = Distance ÷ Speed = 55 ÷ 22 = 2.5 hours

                            = 2 hours 30 minutes

> Calculate the time taken for the journey from A to B. Remember to convert the decimal to hours and minutes.

Distance = Speed × Time = 30 × 1.5 = 45 km

> Now calculate the distance of the journey from A to B. Remember to change the time from hours and minutes to a decimal.

Average speed = Total distance ÷ Total time

                  = (55 + 45) ÷ (1.5 + 2.5) = 100 ÷ 4

                  = 25 km/h

> Now calculate the total distance and total time. Remember to change the time from hours and minutes to a decimal.

GRADE YOURSELF

D Able to draw and read information from a distance–time graph

C Able to calculate the gradient of a straight line and use this to find speed from a distance–time graph

B Able to interpret real-life graphs

A Able to interpret and draw more complex real-life graphs

What you should know now

- How to find the speed from a distance–time graph
- How to interpret real-life graphs

Chapter

14

Similarity

1 Similar triangles

2 Areas and volumes of similar shapes

This chapter will show you ...

- what similar triangles are
- how to work out the scale factor between similar figures
- how to use the scale factor to work out lengths in similar figures
- how to use the scale factor to work out areas and volumes of similar shapes

What you should already know

- The meaning of congruency
- How to calculate a ratio and cancel it down
- The square and cubes of integers
- How to solve equations of the form $\frac{x}{9} = \frac{2}{3}$

Quick check

1 Which of the following triangles is congruent to this triangle.

2 Solve the equations.

a $\frac{x}{12} = \frac{7}{3}$

b $\frac{x}{10} = \frac{21}{15}$

14.1 Similar triangles

In this section you will learn how to:
- show two triangles are similar
- work out the scale factor between similar triangles

Key word
similar

Triangles are **similar** if their corresponding angles are equal. Their corresponding sides are then in the same ratio.

EXAMPLE 1

The triangles ABC and PQR are similar. Find the length of the side PR.

 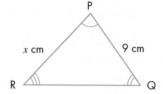

Take two pairs of corresponding sides, one pair of which must contain the unknown side. Form each pair into a fraction, so that x is on top. Since these fractions must be equal

$$\frac{PR}{AC} = \frac{PQ}{AB}$$

$$\frac{x}{8} = \frac{9}{6}$$

To find x.

$$x = \frac{9 \times 8}{6} \text{ cm} \quad \Rightarrow \quad x = \frac{72}{6} = 12 \text{ cm}$$

EXERCISE 14A

1 These diagrams are drawn to scale. What is the scale factor of the enlargement in each case?

 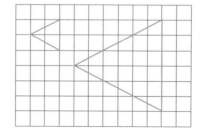

HINTS AND TIPS

If you need to revise scale of enlargement, look back at Section 8.5.

2 Are these pairs of shapes similar? If so, give the scale factor. If not, give a reason.

a

5 cm
3 cm

20 cm
12 cm

b

12 cm
5 cm

22 cm
15 cm

3 **a** Explain why these shapes are similar.

b Give the ratio of the sides.

c Which angle corresponds to angle C?

d Which side corresponds to side QP?

A
5 cm / 70° \ 6 cm
B   C

P
15 cm / 70° \ 18 cm
Q   R

4 **a** Explain why these shapes are similar.

b Which angle corresponds to angle A?

c Which side corresponds to side AC?

B
6 cm
A   5 cm   C

Q
9 cm
P   7.5 cm   R

5 **a** Explain why triangle ABC is similar to triangle AQR.

b Which angle corresponds to the angle at B?

c Which side of triangle AQR corresponds to side AC of triangle ABC?
Your answers to question **4** may help you.

Q
B
9 cm
6 cm
A   5 cm   C   2.5 cm   R

6 In the diagrams **a** to **f**, each pair of shapes are similar but not drawn to scale. Find the lengths of the sides as requested.

a Find *x*.

A
x   6 cm
C   B

P
16 cm   12 cm
R   Q

b Find PQ.

Q
2.5 cm
A   B
2 cm
C

P
6 cm
R

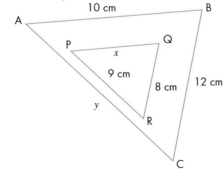

c Find *x* and *y*.

10 cm
A   B
P
x   Q
9 cm
8 cm   12 cm
y
R
C

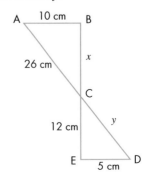

d Find *x* and *y*.

A   10 cm   B
26 cm   *x*
C
12 cm   *y*
E   5 cm   D

e Find AB and PQ.

f Find QR.

7 **a** Explain why these two triangles are similar.

b What is the ratio of their sides?

c Use Pythagoras' theorem to calculate the length of side AC of triangle ABC.

d Write down the length of the side PR of triangle PQR.

8 A model railway is made to a scale of 1 : 40. If the model bridge is 12 cm high, how high would a real railway bridge be? Give your answer in metres.

Special cases of similar triangles

EXAMPLE 2

Find the sides marked x and y in these triangles (not drawn to scale).

Triangles AED and ABC are similar. So using the corresponding sides CB, DE with AC, AD gives

$$\frac{x}{5} = \frac{10}{4}$$

$$\Rightarrow \quad x = \frac{10 \times 5}{4} = 12.5$$

Using the corresponding sides AE, AB with AD, AC gives

$$\frac{y + 6}{6} = \frac{10}{4} \quad \Rightarrow \quad y + 6 = \frac{10 \times 6}{4} = 15$$

$$\Rightarrow \quad y = 15 - 6 = 9$$

EXAMPLE 3

Ahmed wants to work out the height of a tall building. He walks 100 paces from the building and sticks a pole, 2 metres long, vertically into the ground. He then walks another 10 paces on the same line and notices that when he looks from ground level, the top of the pole and the top of the building are in line. How tall is the building?

First, draw a diagram of the situation and label it.

Using corresponding sides ED, CB with AD, AB gives

$$\frac{x}{2} = \frac{110}{10}$$

$$\Rightarrow \quad x = \frac{110 \times 2}{10} = 22 \text{ m}$$

Hence the building is 22 metres high.

EXERCISE 14B

1 In each of the cases below, state a pair of similar triangles and find the length marked x. Separate the similar triangles if it makes it easier for you.

a

b

2 In the diagrams **a** to **e**, find the lengths of the sides as requested.

a Find x.

b Find CE.

c Find x and y.

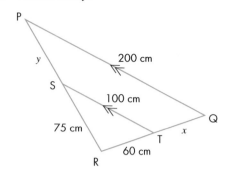

d Find x and y.

e Find DC and EB.

3 This diagram shows a method of working out the height of a tower.

A stick, 2 metres long, is placed vertically 120 metres from the base of a tower so that the top of the tower and the top of the stick is in line with a point on the ground 3 metres from the base of the stick. How high is the tower?

4 It is known that a factory chimney is 330 feet high. Patrick paces out distances as shown in the diagram, so that the top of the chimney and the top of the flag pole are in line with each other. How high is the flag pole?

5 The shadow of a tree and the shadow of a golf flag coincide, as shown in the diagram. How high is the tree?

6 Find the height of a pole which casts a shadow of 1.5 metres when at the same time a man of height 165 cm casts a shadow of 75 cm.

7 Andrew, who is about 120 cm tall, notices that when he stands at the bottom of his garden, which is 20 metres away from his house, his dad, who is about 180 cm tall, looks as big as the house when he is about 2.5 metres away from Andrew. How high is the house?

More complicated problems

The information given in a similar triangle situation can be more complicated than anything you have so far met, and you will need to have good algebraic skills to deal with it. Example 4 is typical of the more complicated problem you may be asked to solve, so follow it through carefully.

EXAMPLE 4

Find the value of x in this triangle.

You know that triangle ABC is similar to triangle ADE.

Splitting up the triangles may help you to see what will be needed.

So your equation will be

$$\frac{x + 15}{x} = \frac{30}{20}$$

Cross multiplying (moving each of the two bottom terms to the opposite side and multiplying) gives

$$20x + 300 = 30x$$

$$\Rightarrow \quad 300 = 10x \quad \Rightarrow \quad x = 30 \text{ cm}$$

Find the lengths x or x and y in the diagrams **1** to **6**.

1

2

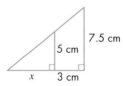

7.5 cm

5 cm

x 3 cm

3

x

5 cm   6 cm

8 cm

4

20 cm

7.5 cm

10 cm

y

x

6 cm

5

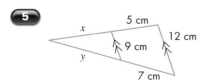

5 cm

x 12 cm

9 cm

y

7 cm

6

1 cm

x 2 cm

1.5 cm

y 0.8 cm

This section will show you how to:

- do problems involving the area and volume of similar shapes

Key words

area ratio
area scale factor
length ratio
linear scale
  factor
volume ratio
volume scale
  factor

There are relationships between the lengths, areas and volumes of similar shapes.

You saw on pages 182–184 that when a plane shape is enlarged by a given scale factor to form a new, similar shape, the corresponding lengths of the original shape and the new shape are all in the same ratio, which is equal to the scale factor. This scale factor of the lengths is called the **length ratio** or **linear scale factor**.

Two similar shapes also have an **area ratio**, which is equal to the ratio of the squares of their corresponding lengths. The area ratio, or **area scale factor**, is the square of the length ratio.

Likewise, two 3-D shapes are similar if their corresponding lengths are in the same ratio. Their **volume ratio** is equal to the ratio of the cubes of their corresponding lengths. The volume ratio, or **volume scale factor**, is the cube of the length ratio.

Generally, the relationship between similar shapes can be expressed as

Length ratio $x : y$

Area ratio $x^2 : y^2$

Volume ratio $x^3 : y^3$

EXAMPLE 5

A model yacht is made to a scale of $\frac{1}{20}$ of the size of the real yacht. The area of the sail of the model is 150 cm^2. What is the area of the sail of the real yacht?

At first sight, it may appear that you do not have enough information to solve this problem, but it can be done as follows.

Linear scale factor $= 1 : 20$

Area scale factor $= 1 : 400$ (square of the linear scale factor)

Area of real sail $= 400 \times$ area of model sail

$= 400 \times 150$ cm^2

$= 60\ 000$ cm$^2 = 6$ m^2

EXAMPLE 6

A bottle has a base radius of 4 cm, a height of 15 cm and a capacity of 650 cm^3. A similar bottle has a base radius of 3 cm.

a What is the length ratio?

b What is the volume ratio?

c What is the volume of the smaller bottle?

a The length ratio is given by the ratio of the two radii, that is 4 : 3.

b The volume ratio is therefore $4^3 : 3^3 = 64 : 27$.

c Let v be the volume of the smaller bottle. Then the volume ratio is

$$\frac{\text{Volume of smaller bottle}}{\text{Volume of larger bottle}} = \frac{v}{650} = \frac{27}{64}$$

$$\Rightarrow v = \frac{27 \times 650}{64} = 274 \text{ cm}^3 \text{ (3 significant figures)}$$

EXAMPLE 7

The cost of a paint can, height 20 cm, is £2.00 and its label has an area of 24 cm^2.

a If the cost is based on the amount of paint in the can, what is the cost of a similar can, 30 cm high?

b Assuming the labels are similar, what will be the area of the label on the larger can?

a The cost of the paint is proportional to the volume of the can.

Length ratio $= 20 : 30 = 2 : 3$

Volume ratio $= 2^3 : 3^3 = 8 : 27$

Let P be the cost of the larger can. Then the cost ratio is

$$\frac{\text{Cost of larger can}}{\text{Cost of smaller can}} = \frac{P}{2}$$

Therefore,

$$\frac{P}{2} = \frac{27}{8}$$

$$\Rightarrow P = \frac{27 \times 2}{8} = £6.75$$

b Area ratio $= 2^2 : 3^2 = 4 : 9$

Let A be the area of the larger label. Then the area ratio is

$$\frac{\text{Larger label area}}{\text{Smaller label area}} = \frac{A}{24}$$

Therefore,

$$\frac{A}{24} = \frac{9}{4}$$

$$\Rightarrow A = \frac{9 \times 24}{4} = 54 \text{ cm}^2$$

EXERCISE 14D

1 The length ratio between two similar solids is 2 : 5.

   a What is the area ratio between the solids?

   b What is the volume ratio between the solids?

2 The length ratio between two similar solids is 4 : 7.

   a What is the area ratio between the solids?

   b What is the volume ratio between the solids?

3 Copy and complete this table.

Linear scale factor	Linear ratio	Linear fraction	Area scale factor	Volume scale factor
2	1 : 2	$\frac{2}{1}$		
3				
$\frac{1}{4}$	4 : 1	$\frac{1}{4}$		$\frac{1}{64}$
			25	
				$\frac{1}{1000}$
	1 : 7			
	5 : 1			
			$\frac{1}{4}$	

4 Some years ago, a famous beer advertisement showed a bar attendant taking an ordinary pint glass and filling it with beer underneath the counter. When the glass reappeared, it was full of beer and its width and height were twice those of the original glass. The slogan on the advertisement was "The pint that thinks it's a quart". (A quart is 2 pints.)

   a What was the length ratio of the two glasses used in the advertisement?

   b What was the volume ratio of the two glasses?

   c The smaller glass held a pint. How much would the larger glass have held?

   d Is the advertisement fair?

5 A shape has an area of 15 cm². What is the area of a similar shape whose lengths are three times the corresponding lengths of the first shape?

6 A toy brick has a surface area of 14 cm². What would be the surface area of a similar toy brick whose lengths are?

   a twice the corresponding lengths of the first brick?

   b three times the corresponding lengths of the first brick?

7 A sheepskin rug covers 12 ft² of floor. What area would be covered by rugs with these lengths?

   a twice the corresponding lengths of the first rug

   b half the corresponding lengths of the first rug

8 A brick has a volume of 300 cm³. What would be the volume of a similar brick whose lengths are

    a twice the corresponding lengths of the first brick?

    b three times the corresponding lengths of the first brick?

9 Thirty cubic centimetres of clay were used to make a model sheep. What volume of clay would be needed to make a similar model sheep with these lengths?

    a five times the corresponding lengths of the first model

    b one half of the corresponding lengths of the first model

10 A can of paint, 6 cm high, holds a half a litre of paint. How much paint would go into a similar can which is 12 cm high?

11 It takes 1 litre of paint to fill a can of height 10 cm. How much paint does it take to fill a similar can of height 45 cm?

12 It takes 1.5 litres of paint to fill a can of height 12 cm.

    a How much paint does it take to fill a similar can whose dimensions are $1\frac{1}{2}$ times the corresponding dimensions of the first can?

    b Which of the information given is not needed to be able to answer part a?

13 To make a certain dress, it took 2.4 m² of material. How much material would a similar dress need if its lengths were

    a 1.5 times the corresponding lengths of the first dress?

    b three quarters of the corresponding lengths of the first dress?

14 A model statue is 10 cm high and has a volume of 100 cm³. The real statue is 2.4 m high. What is the volume of the real statue? Give your answer in m³.

15 A small can of paint costs 75p. What is the cost of a larger similar can whose circumference is twice that of the smaller can? Assume that the cost is based only on the volume of paint in the can.

16 A triangle has sides of 3, 4 and 5 cm. Its area is 6 cm². How long are the sides of a similar triangle that has an area of 24 cm²?

17 A ball with a radius of *r* cm has a volume of 10 cm³. What is the radius of a ball with a volume of 270 cm³?

A*

18 Calculate the area of each of the shaded faces and hence calculate the volume of each of these solids. (They are not drawn to scale.)

a

b

c

d

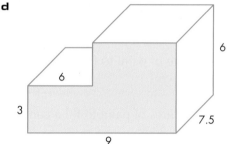

e Which two solids are similar?

Using area and volume ratios

In some problems involving similar shapes, the length ratio is not given, so we have to start with the area ratio or the volume ratio. We usually then need first to find the length ratio in order to proceed with the solution.

EXAMPLE 8

A manufacturer makes a range of clown hats that are all similar in shape. The smallest hat is 8 cm tall and uses 180 cm^2 of card. What will be the height of a hat made from 300 cm^2 of card?

The area ratio is 180 : 300

Therefore, the length ratio is $\sqrt{180} : \sqrt{300}$ (do not calculate these yet)

Let the height of the larger hat be H, then

$$\frac{H}{8} = \frac{\sqrt{300}}{\sqrt{180}} = \sqrt{\frac{300}{180}}$$

$$\Rightarrow H = 8 \times \sqrt{\frac{300}{180}} = 10.3 \text{ cm (1 decimal place)}$$

EXAMPLE 9

A supermarket stocks similar small and large cans of soup. The areas of their labels are 110 cm^2 and 190 cm^2 respectively. The weight of a small can is 450 g. What is the weight of a large can?

The area ratio is 110 : 190

Therefore, the length ratio is $\sqrt{110} : \sqrt{190}$ (do not calculate these yet)

So the volume (weight) ratio is $(\sqrt{110})^3 : (\sqrt{190})^3$.

Let the weight of a large can be W, then

$$\frac{W}{450} = \frac{(\sqrt{190})^3}{(\sqrt{110})^3} = \left(\sqrt{\frac{190}{110}}\right)^3$$

$$\Rightarrow \quad W = 450 \times \left(\sqrt{\frac{190}{110}}\right)^3 = 1020 \text{ g} \qquad \text{(3 significant figures)}$$

EXAMPLE 10

Two similar cans hold respectively 1.5 litres and 2.5 litres of paint. The area of the label on the smaller can is 85 cm^2. What is the area of the label on the larger can?

The volume ratio is 1.5 : 2.5

Therefore, the length ratio is $\sqrt[3]{1.5} : \sqrt[3]{2.5}$ (do not calculate these yet)

So the area ratio is $(\sqrt[3]{1.5})^2 : (\sqrt[3]{2.5})^2$

Let the area of the label on the larger can be A, then

$$\frac{A}{85} = \frac{(\sqrt[3]{2.5})^2}{(\sqrt[3]{1.5})^2} = \left(\sqrt[3]{\frac{2.5}{1.5}}\right)^2$$

$$\Rightarrow \quad A = 85 \times \left(\sqrt[3]{\frac{2.5}{1.5}}\right)^2 = 119 \text{ cm}^2 \qquad \text{(3 significant figures)}$$

EXERCISE 14E

1 A firm produces three sizes of similarly shaped labels for its products. Their areas are 150 cm^2, 250 cm^2 and 400 cm^2. The 250 cm^2 label just fits around a can of height 8 cm. Find the heights of similar cans around which the other two labels would just fit.

2 A firm makes similar gift boxes in three different sizes: small, medium and large. The areas of their lids are as follows.

   small: 30 cm^2,   medium: 50 cm^2,   large: 75 cm^2

The medium box is 5.5 cm high. Find the heights of the other two sizes.

A*

3 A cone, height 8 cm, can be made from a piece of card with an area of 140 cm^2. What is the height of a similar cone made from a similar piece of card with an area of 200 cm^2?

4 It takes 5.6 litres of paint to paint a chimney which is 3 m high. What is the tallest similar chimney that can be painted with 8 litres of paint?

5 A man takes 45 minutes to mow a lawn 25 m long. How long would it take him to mow a similar lawn only 15 m long?

6 A piece of card, 1200 cm^2 in area, will make a tube 13 cm long. What is the length of a similar tube made from a similar piece of card with an area of 500 cm^2?

7 All television screens (of the same style) are similar. If a screen of area 220 cm^2 has a diagonal length of 21 cm, what will be the diagonal length of a screen of area 350 cm^2?

8 Two similar statues, made from the same bronze, are placed in a school. One weighs 300 g, the other weighs 2 kg. The height of the smaller statue is 9 cm. What is the height of the larger statue?

9 A supermarket sells similar cans of pasta rings in three different sizes: small, medium and large. The sizes of the labels around the cans are as follows.

   small can: 24 cm^2,   medium can: 46 cm^2,   large can: 78 cm^2

   The medium size can is 6 cm tall with a weight of 380 g. Calculate these quantities.

   a the heights of the other two sizes

   b the weights of the other two sizes

10 Two similar bottles are 20 cm and 14 cm high. The smaller bottle holds 850 ml. Find the capacity of the larger one.

11 A statue weighs 840 kg. A similar statue was made out of the same material but two fifths the height of the first one. What was the weight of the smaller statue?

12 A model stands on a base of area 12 cm^2. A smaller but similar model, made of the same material, stands on a base of area 7.5 cm^2. Calculate the weight of the smaller model if the larger one is 3.5 kg.

13 A solid silver statue was melted down to make 100 000 similar miniatures, each 2 cm high. How tall was the original statue?

14 Two similar models have volumes 12 m^3 and 30 m^3. If the surface area of one of them is 2.4 m^2, what are the possible surface areas of the other model?

1 Two rectangles have the dimensions shown.

12 cm

8 cm

20 cm

16 cm

Are the rectangles similar?
Explain your answer clearly.

2 Triangle ABC is similar to triangle CDE.

Calculate the length of CD.

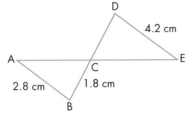

D

4.2 cm

A

E

C

2.8 cm   1.8 cm

B

3 In the triangle PQR, AB is parallel to QR. AB = 10 cm, QR = 16 cm and BR = 12 cm. Find the length PB.

P

B

A

R

Q

4 PQR and PXY are similar triangles.

Calculate the length of RY.

X

Q

15 cm

2.5 cm

P

4 cm   R   Y

5 A new AQA sign is to be erected on the Examination Board's offices in Manchester. The two As in the sign are similar in shape.

The cost of each letter A is proportional to its area. The large A costs £250 and is 250 cm high. The small A is 150 cm high. How much does the small letter cost?

NEAB, Question 18, Paper 2 Higher, June 2000

6 **a** Explain why the volume of a cube increases by a factor of 8 when the side length is doubled.

b June recently bought a small toy in the local shop.

ALIEN

Place in water and it becomes 6 times bigger!

It was originally 8 cm tall. After she placed it in water it grew to a similarly shaped alien. The height was then 14.5 cm. Is the claim on the pack justified?

AQA, Question 21, Paper 2 Higher, June 2005

WORKED EXAM QUESTION

A camping gas container is in the shape of a cylinder with a hemispherical top. The dimensions of the container are shown in the diagram.

It is decided to increase the volume of the container by 20%. The new container is mathematically similar to the old one.

Calculate the base diameter of the new container.

8 cm

8 cm

Solution

Old Volume : New volume = 100% : 120% = 1 : 1.2

First find the volume scale factor.

$\sqrt[3]{1} : \sqrt[3]{1.2} = 1 : 1.06265$

Take the cube root to get the linear scale factor.

New diameter = Old diameter × 1.06265 = 8 × 1.06265 = 8.5 cm

Multiply the old diameter by the linear scale factor to get the new diameter.

Bright Ideas

Martin works for a light company called "Bright Ideas". He has been asked to calculate accurate measurements for a new table lamp the company are going to produce.

The three main components are the base, the stem and the shade. Below is a sketch of the side view, and an "exploded" diagram which shows the lamp in more detail.

Side view

The base and stem are made from a material which has a density of 10 g/cm³. Help Martin complete the table to find the total weight of the stem and the base.

volume of stem		cm³
weight of stem		g
volume of base		cm³
weight of base		g
total weight		g

The lampshade is the frustum of a cone. It is to be made from a fire-proof material. Martin draws a sketch showing the dimensions he knows.

Help him to calculate the missing dimensions and then the surface area of the shade.

length of x		cm
length of L		cm
length of L		cm
surface area of small cone		cm²
surface area of large cone		cm²
surface area of lampshade		cm²

"Exploded" diagram

0.5cm

0.5cm

Martin knows a cone is made from the sector of a circle, but he needs to calculate the angle of the sector θ.

He draws this diagram of the large cone to help.

Find the angle θ for Martin.

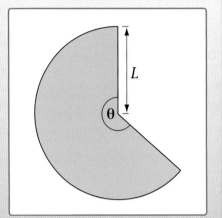

L

θ

A material trim is to go around the bottom and top circles of the lampshade.

Help Martin use this diagram to calculate the total length of trim needed.

Trim

L

θ

L

Draw an accurate scale drawing for Martin of the side view of the lamp using a scale of 3 : 1.

GRADE YOURSELF

C Know why two shapes are similar

C Able to work out unknown sides using scale factors and ratios

B Able to set up equations to find missing sides in similar triangles

A Able to solve problems using area and volume scale factors

A Able to solve practical problems using similar triangles

A* Able to solve related problems involving, for example, capacity, using area and volume scale factors

What you should know now

- How to find the ratios between two similar shapes
- How to work out unknown lengths, areas and volumes of similar 3-D shapes
- How to solve practical problems using similar shapes
- How to solve problems using area and volume ratios

Trigonometry

1 Some 2-D problems

2 Some 3-D problems

3 Trigonometric ratios of angles between 90° and 360°

4 Solving any triangle

5 Sine, cosine and tangent of 30°, 45° and 60°

6 Using sine to find the area of a triangle

This chapter will show you ...

- how to use trigonometric relationships to solve more complex 2-D problems and 3-D problems
- how to use the sine and cosine rules to solve problems involving non right-angled triangles
- how to find the area of a triangle using the rule Area = $\frac{1}{2}ab \sin C$

What you should already know

- How to find the sides of right-angled triangles using Pythagoras' theorem
- How to find angles and sides of right-angled triangles using sine, cosine and tangent

Quick check

1 Find the side x in this triangle.

17 cm

11 cm

x

2 Find the angle x in this triangle.

19 cm

7 cm

x

In this section you will learn how to:

- use trigonometric ratios and Pythagoras' theorem to solve more complex two-dimensional problems

Key words

area
length
perpendicular

EXAMPLE 1

In triangle ABC, AB = 6 cm, BC = 9 cm and angle ABC = 52°. Calculate the following.

a the **length** of the **perpendicular** from A to BC

b the **area** of the triangle

a Drop the perpendicular from A to BC to form the right-angled triangle ADB.

Let h be the length of the perpendicular AD. Then

$h = 6 \sin 52° = 4.73$ (3 significant figures)

b The area of triangle ABC is given by

Area = $\frac{1}{2}$ × base × height

= $\frac{1}{2}$ × 9 × h = 21.3 cm² (3 significant figures)

EXAMPLE 2

SR is a diameter of a circle whose radius is 25 cm. PQ is a chord at right angles to SR. X is the midpoint of PQ. The length of XR is 1 cm. Calculate the length of the arc PQ.

To find the length of the arc PQ, you need first to find the angle it subtends at the centre of the circle. (See page 157.)

So join P to the centre of the circle O to obtain the angle POX, which is equal to half the angle subtended by PQ at O.

In right-angled triangle POX

OX = OR − XR
OX = 25 − 1 = 24 cm

Therefore,

$\cos x = \dfrac{24}{25}$

$\Rightarrow x = \cos^{-1} 0.96 = 16.26°$

So, the angle subtended at the centre by the arc PQ is 2 × 16.26° = 32.52°, giving the length of the arc PQ as

$\dfrac{32.52}{360} × 2 × \pi × 25 = 14.2$ cm   (3 significant figures)

EXERCISE 15A

1 AC and BC are tangents to a circle of radius 7 cm. Calculate the length of AB.

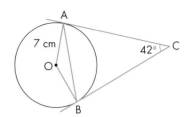

2 CD, length 20 cm, is a diameter of a circle. AB, length 12 cm, is a chord at right angles to DC. Calculate the angle AOB.

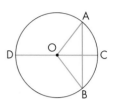

3 Calculate the length of AB.

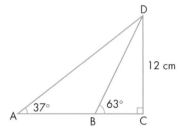

4 A building has a ledge halfway up, as shown in the diagram. Alf measures the length AB as 100 m, the angle CAB as 31° and the angle EAB as 42°. Use this information to calculate the width of the ledge CD.

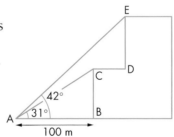

5 AB and CD are two equal, perpendicular chords of a circle that intersect at X. The circle is of radius 6 cm and the angle COA is 113°. Calculate these.

a the length AC

b the angle XAO

c the length XB

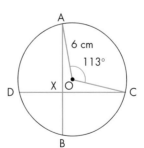

6 A vertical flagpole PQ is held by a wooden framework, as shown in the diagram. The framework is in the same vertical plane. Angle SRP = 25°, SQ = 6 m and PR = 4 m. Calculate the size of the angle QRP.

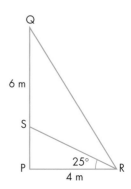

Some 3-D problems

In this section you will learn how to:

- use trigonometric ratios and Pythagoras' theorem to solve more complex three-dimensional problems

Solving a problem set in three dimensions nearly always involves identifying a right-angled triangle that contains the length or angle required. This triangle will have to contain (apart from the right angle) two known measures from which the required calculation can be made.

It is essential to extract the triangle you are going to use from its 3-D situation and redraw it as a separate, plain, right-angled triangle. (It is rarely the case that the required triangle appears as a true right-angled triangle in its 3-D representation. Even if it does, it should still be redrawn as a separate figure.)

The redrawn triangle should be annotated with the known quantities and the unknown quantity to be found.

EXAMPLE 3

A, B and C are three points at ground level. They are in the same horizontal plane. C is 50 km east of B. B is north of A. C is on a bearing of 050° from A.

An aircraft, flying in an easterly direction, passes over B and over C at the same height. When it passes over B, the angle of elevation from A is 12°. Find the angle of elevation of the aircraft from A when it is over C.

First, draw a diagram containing all the known information.

Next, use the right-angled triangle ABC to calculate AB and AC.

$$AB = \frac{50}{\tan 50°} = 41.95 \text{ km} \qquad \text{(4 significant figures)}$$

$$AC = \frac{50}{\sin 50°} = 65.27 \text{ km} \qquad \text{(4 significant figures)}$$

Then use the right-angled triangle ABX to calculate BX, and hence CY.

$$BX = 41.95 \tan 12° = 8.917 \text{ km} \quad \text{(4 significant figures)}$$

Finally, use the right-angled triangle ACY to calculate the required angle of elevation, θ.

$$\tan \theta = \frac{8.917}{65.27} = 0.1366$$

$$\Rightarrow \theta = \tan^{-1} 0.1366 = 7.8° \qquad \text{(one decimal place)}$$

Always write down working values to at least 4 significant figures, to avoid inaccuracy in the final answer.

EXAMPLE 4

The diagram shows a cuboid 22.5 cm by 40 cm by 30 cm.
M is the midpoint of FG.

Calculate these angles.

a ABE

b ECA

c EMH

a The right-angled triangle containing the angle
required is ABE.

Solving for α gives

$$\tan \alpha = \frac{40}{22.5} = 1.7777$$

$$\Rightarrow \quad \alpha = \tan^{-1} 1.7777 = 60.6° \qquad \text{(3 significant figures)}$$

b The right-angled triangle containing the angle
required is ACE, but for which only AE is known.
Therefore, you need to find AC by applying
Pythagoras to the right-angled triangle ABC.

$$x^2 = (22.5)^2 + (30)^2 \text{ cm}^2$$

$$\Rightarrow x = 37.5 \text{ cm}$$

Returning to triangle ACE, you obtain

$$\tan \beta = \frac{40}{37.5} = 1.0666$$

$$\Rightarrow \quad \beta = 46.8° \qquad \text{(3 significant figures)}$$

c EMH is an isosceles triangle.

Drop the perpendicular from M to N, the midpoint of HE,
to form two right-angled triangles. Angle HMN equals
angle EMN, and HN = NE = 15 cm.

Taking triangle MEN, you obtain

$$\tan \theta = \frac{15}{22.5} = 0.66666$$

$$\Rightarrow \quad \theta = \tan^{-1} 0.66666 = 33.7°$$

Therefore, angle HME is 2 × 33.7° = 67.4°   (3 significant figures)

EXERCISE 15B

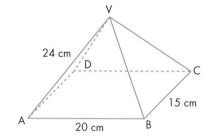

1 The diagram shows a pyramid. The base is a horizontal rectangle ABCD, 20 cm by 15 cm. The length of each sloping edge is 24 cm. The apex, V, is over the centre of the rectangular base. Calculate these.

 a the size of the angle VAC

 b the height of the pyramid

 c the volume of the pyramid

 d the size of the angle between the face VAD and the base ABCD

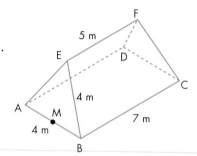

2 The diagram shows the roof of a building. The base ABCD is a horizontal rectangle 7 m by 4 m. The triangular ends are equilateral triangles. Each side of the roof is an isosceles trapezium. The length of the top of the roof, EF, is 5 m. Calculate these.

 a the length EM, where M is the midpoint of AB

 b the size of angle EBC

 c the size of the angle between the face EAB and the base ABCD

 d the surface area of the roof (excluding the base)

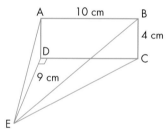

3 ABCD is a vertical rectangular plane. EDC is a horizontal triangular plane. Angle CDE = 90°, AB = 10 cm, BC = 4 cm and ED = 9 cm. Calculate these.

 a angle AED   **b** angle DEC

 c EC   **d** angle BEC

4 The diagram shows a tetrahedron. The base ABC is a horizontal equilateral triangle of side 8 cm. The vertex D is 5 cm directly above the point B. Calculate these angles.

 a DCB

 b the angle between the face ADC and the face ABC

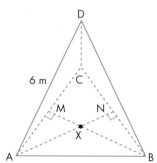

5 The diagram shows a tetrahedron, each face of which is an equilateral triangle of side 6 m. The lines AN and BM meet the sides CB and AC at a right angle. The lines AN and BM intersect at X, which is directly below the vertex, D. Calculate these.

 a the distance AX

 b the angle between the side DBC and the base ABC

Trigonometric ratios of angles between 90° and 360°

This section will show you how to:

- find the sine, cosine and tangent of any angle from 0° to 360°

Key words

cosine
sine
tangent

ACTIVITY

a Copy and complete this table using your calculator and rounding off to three decimal places.

x	$\sin x$	x	$\sin x$	x	$\sin x$	x	$\sin x$
0°		180°		180°		360°	
15°		165°		195°		335°	
30°		150°		210°		320°	
45°		135°		225°		315°	
60°		120°		240°		300°	
75°		105°		255°		285°	
90°		90°		270°		270°	

b Comment on what you notice about the **sine** of each acute angle, and the sines of its corresponding non-acute angles.

c Draw a graph of $\sin x$ against x. Take x from 0° to 360° and $\sin x$ from −1 to 1.

d Comment on any symmetries your graph has.

You should have discovered these three facts.

- When $90° < x < 180°$, $\sin x = \sin (180° − x)$
  For example, $\sin 153° = \sin (180° − 153°) = \sin 27° = 0.454$

- When $180° < x < 270°$, $\sin x = − \sin (x − 180°)$
  For example, $\sin 214° = − \sin (214° − 180°) = − \sin 34° = − 0.559$

- When $270° < x < 360°$, $\sin x = − \sin (360° − x)$
  For example, $\sin 287° = − \sin (360° − 287°) = − \sin 73° = − 0.956$

Note:

• Each and every value of sine between –1 and 1 gives *two* angles between 0° and 360°.

• When the value of sine is positive, both angles are between 0° and 180°.

• When the value of sine is negative, both angles are between 180° and 360°.

• You can use the sine graph from 0° to 360° to check values approximately.

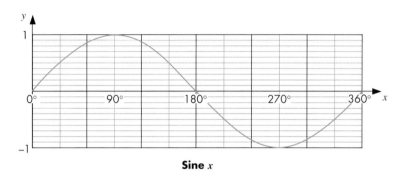

Sine x

EXAMPLE 5

Find the angles with a sine of 0.56.

You know that both angles are between 0° and 180°.

Using your calculator to find $\sin^{-1} 0.56$, you obtain 34.1°.

The other angle is, therefore,

   180° – 34.1° = 145.9°

So, the angles are 34.1° and 145.9°.

EXAMPLE 6

Find the angles with a sine of –0.197.

You know that both angles are between 180° and 360°.

Using your calculator to find $\sin^{-1} 0.197$, you obtain 11.4°.

So the angles are

   180° + 11.4° and 360° – 11.4°

which give 191.4° and 348.6°.

You can always use your calculator to check your answer to this type of problem by first keying in the angle and the appropriate trigonometric function (which would be sine in the above examples).

EXERCISE 15C

State the two angles between 0° and 360° for each of these sine values.

1 0.6   **2** 0.8   **3** 0.75   **4** –0.7

5 –0.25   **6** –0.32   **7** –0.175   **8** –0.814

9 0.471   **10** –0.097   **11** 0.553   **12** –0.5

ACTIVITY

a Copy and complete this table using your calculator and rounding off to three decimal places.

x	$\cos x$	x	$\cos x$	x	$\cos x$	x	$\cos x$
0°		180°		180°		360°	
15°		165°		195°		335°	
30°		150°		210°		320°	
45°		135°		225°		315°	
60°		120°		240°		300°	
75°		105°		255°		285°	
90°		90°		270°		270°	

b Comment on what you notice about the **cosines** of the angles.

c Draw a graph of cos x against x. Take x from 0° to 360° and cos x from –1 to 1.

d Comment on the symmetry of the graph.

You should have discovered these three facts.

- When 90° < x < 180°, cos x = – cos (180 – x)°
  For example, cos 161° = – cos (180° – 161°) = – cos 19° = – 0.946 (3 significant figures)

- When 180° < x < 270°, cos x = – cos (x – 180°)
  For example, cos 245° = – cos (245° – 180°) = – cos 65° = – 0.423 (3 significant figures)

- When 270° < x < 360°, cos x = cos (360° – x)
  For example, cos 310° = cos (360° – 310°) = cos 50° = 0.643 (3 significant figures)

Note:

- Each and every value of cosine between –1 and 1 gives *two* angles between 0° and 360°.

- When the value of cosine is positive, one angle is between 0° and 90°, and the other is between 270° and 360°.

- When the value of cosine is negative, both angles are between 90° and 270°.

- You can use the cosine graph from 0° to 360° to check values approximately.

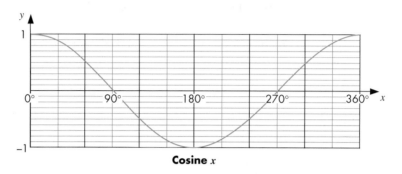

Cosine *x*

EXAMPLE 7

Find the angles with a cosine of 0.75.

One angle is between 0° and 90°, and that the other is between 270° and 360°.

Using your calculator to find $\cos^{-1} 0.75$, you obtain 41.4°.

The other angle is, therefore,

360° – 41.4° = 318.6°

So, the angles are 41.4° and 318.6°.

EXAMPLE 8

Find the angles with a cosine of –0.285.

You know that both angles are between 90° and 270°.

Using your calculator to find $\cos^{-1} 0.285$, you obtain 73.4°.

The two angles are, therefore,

180° – 73.4° and 180° + 73.4°

which give 106.6° and 253.4°.

Here again, you can use your calculator to check your answer, by keying in cosine.

EXERCISE 15D

State the two angles between 0° and 360° for each of these cosine values.

 0.6   0.58   0.458   0.575

5 0.185   **6** –0.8   **7** –0.25   **8** –0.175

9 –0.361   **10** –0.974   **11** 0.196   **12** 0.714

EXERCISE 15E

1 Write down the sine of each of these angles.

  a 135°   **b** 269°   **c** 305°   **d** 133°

2 Write down the cosine of each of these angles.

  a 129°   **b** 209°   **c** 95°   **d** 357°

3 Write down the two possible values of x ($0° < x < 360°$) for each equation. Give your answers to one decimal place.

  a $\sin x = 0.361$ **b** $\sin x = -0.486$

  c $\cos x = 0.641$ **d** $\cos x = -0.866$

  e $\sin x = 0.874$ **f** $\cos x = 0.874$

4 Find two angles such that the sine of each is 0.5.

5 $\cos 41° = 0.755$. What is $\cos 139°$?

6 Write down the value of each of the following, correct to three significant figures.

  a $\sin 50° + \cos 50°$ **b** $\cos 120° - \sin 120°$

  c $\sin 136° + \cos 223°$ **d** $\sin 175° + \cos 257°$

  e $\sin 114° - \sin 210°$ **f** $\cos 123° + \sin 177°$

7 It is suggested that $(\sin x)^2 + (\cos x)^2 = 1$ is true for all values of x. Test out this suggestion to see if you agree.

8 Suppose the sine key on your calculator is broken, but not the cosine key. Show how you could calculate these.

  a $\sin 25°$

  b $\sin 130°$

9 Find a solution to each of these equations.

  a $\sin (x + 20°) = 0.5$

  b $\cos (5x) = 0.45$

10 By any suitable method, find the solution to the equation $\sin x = (\cos x)^2$.

a Try to find tan 90°. What do you notice?

Which is the closest angle to 90° for which you can find the **tangent** on your calculator?

What is the largest value for tangent that you can get on your calculator?

b Find values of tan x where 0° < x < 360°. Draw a graph of your results.

State some rules for finding both angles between 0° and 360° that have any given tangent.

EXAMPLE 9

Find the angles between 0° and 360° with a tangent of 0.875.

One angle is between 0° and 90°, and the other is between 180° and 270°.

Using your calculator to find $\tan^{-1} 0.875$, you obtain 41.2°.

The other angle is, therefore,

180° + 41.2° = 221.2°

So, the angles are 41.2° and 221.2°.

EXAMPLE 10

Find the angles between 0° and 360° with a tangent of –1.5.

We know that one angle is between 90° and 180°, and that the other is between 270° and 360°.

Using your calculator to find $\tan^{-1} 1.5$, you obtain 56.3°.

The angles are, therefore,

180° – 56.3° and 360° – 56.3°

which give 123.7° and 303.7°.

State the angles between 0° and 360° which have each of these tangent values.

1 0.258   **2** 0.785   **3** 1.19   **4** 1.875

5 2.55   **6** –0.358   **7** –0.634   **8** –0.987

9 –1.67   **10** –3.68   **11** 1.397   **12** 0.907

13 –0.355   **14** –1.153   **15** 4.15   **16** –2.05

17 –0.098   **18** 0.998   **19** 1.208   **20** –2.5

15.4 Solving any triangle

This section will show you how to:
- find the sides and angles of any triangle whether it has a right angle or not

Key words
cosine rule
included
  angle
sine rule

We have already established that any triangle has six elements: three sides and three angles. To solve a triangle (that is, to find any unknown angles or sides), we need to know at least three of the elements. Any combination of three elements – *except that of all three angles* – is enough to work out the rest. In a right-angled triangle, one of the known elements is, of course, the right angle.

When we need to solve a triangle which contains no right angle, we can use one or the other of two rules, depending on what is known about the triangle. These are the **sine rule** and the **cosine rule**.

The sine rule

Take a triangle ABC and draw the perpendicular from A to the opposite side BC.

From right-angled triangle ADB

$$h = c \sin B$$

From right-angled triangle ADC

$$h = b \sin C$$

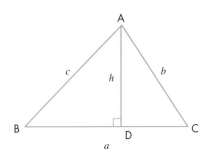

Therefore,

$$c \sin B = b \sin C$$

which can be rearranged to give

$$\frac{c}{\sin C} = \frac{b}{\sin B}$$

By drawing a perpendicular from each of the other two vertices
to the opposite side (or by algebraic symmetry), we see that

$$\frac{a}{\sin A} = \frac{c}{\sin C} \quad \text{and that} \quad \frac{a}{\sin A} = \frac{b}{\sin B}$$

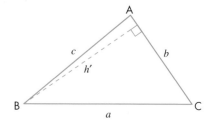

These are usually combined in the form

$$\frac{a}{\sin A} = \frac{b}{\sin B} = \frac{c}{\sin C}$$

which can be inverted to give

$$\frac{\sin A}{a} = \frac{\sin B}{b} = \frac{\sin C}{c}$$

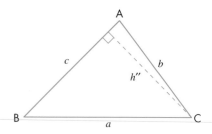

Usually, a triangle is not conveniently labelled as in these diagrams. So, when using the sine rule,
it is easier to remember to proceed as follows: take each side in turn, divide it by the sine of the angle
opposite, and then equate the resulting quotients.

Note:

• When you are calculating a *side*, use the rule with the *sides on top.*

• When you are calculating an *angle*, use the rule with the *sines on top.*

EXAMPLE 11

In triangle ABC, find the value of x.

Use the sine rule with sides on top, which gives

$$\frac{x}{\sin 84°} = \frac{25}{\sin 47°}$$

$$\Rightarrow \quad x = \frac{25 \sin 84°}{\sin 47°} = 34.0 \text{ cm} \quad \text{(3 significant figures)}$$

EXAMPLE 12

In the triangle ABC, find the value of the acute angle x.

Use the sine rule with sines on top, which gives

$$\frac{\sin x}{7} = \frac{\sin 40°}{6}$$

$$\Rightarrow \sin x = \frac{7 \sin 40°}{6} = 0.7499$$

$$\Rightarrow \quad x = \sin^{-1} 0.7499 = 48.6° \qquad \text{(3 significant figures)}$$

The ambiguous case

EXAMPLE 13

In triangle ABC, AB = 9 cm, AC = 7 cm and angle ABC = 40°. Find the angle ACB.

As you sketch triangle ABC, note that C can have two positions, giving two different configurations.

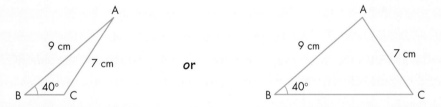

But you still proceed as in the normal sine rule situation, obtaining

$$\frac{\sin C}{9} = \frac{\sin 40°}{7}$$

$$\Rightarrow \sin C = \frac{9 \sin 40°}{7}$$

$$= 0.8264$$

Keying inverse sine on our calculator gives C = 55.7°. But there is another angle with a sine of 0.8264, given by (180° − 55.7°) = 124.3°.

These two values for C give the two different situations shown above.

When an illustration of the triangle is given, it will be clear whether the required angle is acute or obtuse. When an illustration is not given, the more likely answer is an acute angle.

Examiners will not try to catch you out with the ambiguous case. They will indicate clearly, either with the aid of a diagram or by stating it, what is required.

EXERCISE 15G

1 Find the length x in each of these triangles.

a

b

c

2 Find the angle x in each of these triangles.

a

b

c

3 In triangle ABC, the angle at A is 38°, the side AB is 10 cm and the side BC is 8 cm. Find the two possible values of the angle at C.

4 In triangle ABC, the angle at A is 42°, the side AB is 16 cm and the side BC is 14 cm. Find the two possible values of the side AC.

5 To find the height of a tower standing on a small hill, Mary made some measurements (see diagram).

From a point B, the angle of elevation of C is 20°, the angle of elevation of A is 50°, and the distance BC is 25 m.

a Calculate these angles.

   i ABC

   ii BAC

b Using the sine rule and triangle ABC, calculate the height h of the tower.

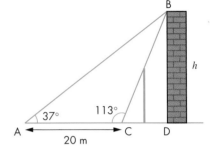

6 Use the information on this sketch to calculate the width, *w*, of the river.

7 An old building is unsafe, so it is protected by a fence. To work out the height of the building, Annie made the measurements shown on the diagram.

 a Use the sine rule to work out the distance AB.

 b Calculate the height of the building, BD.

8 A weight is hung from a horizontal beam using two strings. The shorter string is 2.5 m long and makes an angle of 71° with the horizontal. The longer string makes an angle of 43° with the horizontal. What is the length of the longer string?

9 An aircraft is flying over an army base. Suddenly, two searchlights, 3 km apart, are switched on. The two beams of light meet on the aircraft at an angle of 125° vertically above the line joining the searchlights. One of the beams of light makes an angle of 31° with the horizontal. Calculate the height of the aircraft.

10 Two ships leave a port in directions that are 41° from each other. After half an hour, the ships are 11 km apart. If the speed of the slower ship is 7 km/h, what is the speed of the faster ship?

11 For any triangle ABC, prove the sine rule

$$\frac{a}{\sin A} = \frac{b}{\sin B} = \frac{c}{\sin C}$$

The cosine rule

Take the triangle, shown on the right, where D is the foot of the perpendicular to BC from A.

Using Pythagoras on triangle BDA

$$h^2 = c^2 - x^2$$

Using Pythagoras on triangle ADC

$$h^2 = b^2 - (a - x)^2$$

Therefore,

$$c^2 - x^2 = b^2 - (a - x)^2$$

$$c^2 - x^2 = b^2 - a^2 + 2ax - x^2$$

$$\Rightarrow \quad c^2 = b^2 - a^2 + 2ax$$

From triangle BDA, $x = c \cos B$.

Hence

$$c^2 = b^2 - a^2 + 2ac \cos B$$

Rearranging gives

$$b^2 = a^2 + c^2 - 2ac \cos B$$

By algebraic symmetry

$$a^2 = b^2 + c^2 - 2bc \cos A \quad \text{and} \quad c^2 = a^2 + b^2 - 2ab \cos C$$

This is the cosine rule, which can be best remembered by
the diagram on the right, where

$$a^2 = b^2 + c^2 - 2bc \cos A$$

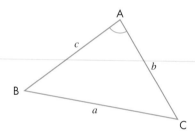

Note the symmetry of the rule and how the rule works using two
adjacent sides and the angle between them.

The formula can be rearranged to find any of the three angles

$$\cos A = \frac{b^2 + c^2 - a^2}{2bc}$$

$$\cos B = \frac{a^2 + c^2 - b^2}{2ac}$$

$$\cos C = \frac{a^2 + b^2 - c^2}{2ab}$$

Note that the cosine rule $a^2 = b^2 + c^2 - 2bc \cos A$ is given in the formula sheets in the GCSE examination
but the rearranged formula for the angle is not given. You are advised to learn this as trying to rearrange
usually ends up with an incorrect formula.

EXAMPLE 14

Find x in this triangle.

By the cosine rule

$$x^2 = 6^2 + 10^2 - 2 \times 6 \times 10 \times \cos 80°$$

$$x^2 = 115.16$$

$$\Rightarrow \quad x = 10.7 \qquad \text{(3 significant figures)}$$

EXAMPLE 15

Find x in this triangle.

By the cosine rule

$$\cos x = \frac{5^2 + 7^2 - 8^2}{2 \times 5 \times 7} = 0.1428$$

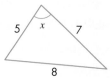

$$\Rightarrow \quad x = 81.8° \qquad \text{(3 significant figures)}$$

EXAMPLE 16

A ship sails from a port on a bearing of 055° for 40 km. It then changes course to 123° for another 50 km. On what course should the ship be steered to get it straight back to the port?

Previously, you have solved this type of problem using right-angled triangles. This method could be applied here but it would involve at least six separate calculations.

With the aid of the cosine and sine rules, however, you can reduce the solution to two separate calculations, as follows.

The course diagram gives the triangle PAB (on the right), where angle PAB is found by using alternate angles and angles on a line. 55° + (180° − 123°) = 112°

Let ϕ be the bearing to be steered, then

$$\phi = \theta + 55° + 180°$$

To find θ, you first have to obtain PB($= x$), using the cosine rule.

$$x^2 = 40^2 + 50^2 - 2 \times 40 \times 50 \times \cos 112° \text{ km}^2$$

(Remember: the cosine of 112° is negative.)

$$\Rightarrow x^2 = 5598.43 \text{ km}^2$$

$$\Rightarrow x = 74.82 \text{ km}$$

You can now find θ from the sine rule.

$$\frac{\sin \theta}{50} = \frac{\sin 112°}{74.82}$$

$$\Rightarrow \sin \theta = \frac{50 \times \sin 112°}{74.82} = 0.6196$$

$$\Rightarrow \quad \theta = 38.3°$$

So the ship should be steered on a bearing of

$$38.3° + 55° + 180° = 273.3°$$

EXERCISE 15H

1 Find the length x in each of these triangles.

a

b

c

2 Find the angle x in each of these triangles.

a

b

c

d Explain the significance of the answer to part c.

3 In triangle ABC, AB = 5 cm, BC = 6 cm and angle ABC = 55°. Find AC.

4 A triangle has two sides of length 40 cm and an angle of 110°. Work out the length of the third side of the triangle.

5 The diagram shows a trapezium ABCD. AB = 6.7 cm, AD = 7.2 cm, CB = 9.3 cm and angle DAB = 100°. Calculate these.

    a length DB

    b angle DBA

    c angle DBC

    d length DC

    e area of the trapezium

6 A quadrilateral ABCD has AD = 6 cm, DC = 9 cm, AB = 10 cm and BC = 12 cm. Angle ADC = 120°. Calculate angle ABC.

7 A triangle has two sides of length 30 cm and an angle of 50°. Unfortunately, the position of the angle is not known. Sketch the two possible triangles and use them to work out the two possible lengths of the third side of the triangle.

8 A ship sails from a port on a bearing of 050° for 50 km then turns on a bearing of 150° for 40 km. A crewman is taken ill, so the ship drops anchor. What course and distance should a rescue helicopter from the port fly to reach the ship in the shortest possible time?

9 The three sides of a triangle are given as $3a$, $5a$ and $7a$. Calculate the smallest angle in the triangle.

10 ABCD is a trapezium where AB is parallel to CD. AB = 4 cm, BC = 5 cm, CD = 8 cm, DA = 6 cm. A line BX is parallel to AD and cuts DC at X. Calculate these.

   a angle BCD

   b length BD

11 For any triangle ABC prove the cosine rule

$$a^2 = b^2 + c^2 - 2bc \cos A$$

Choosing the correct rule

When solving triangles, there are only four situations that can occur, each of which can be solved completely in three stages.

Two sides and the included angle

1 Use the cosine rule to find the third side.

2 Use the sine rule to find either of the other angles.

3 Use the sum of the angles in a triangle to find the third angle.

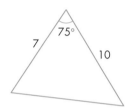

Two angles and a side

1   Use the sum of the angles in a triangle to find the third angle.

2, 3 Use the sine rule to find the other two sides.

Three sides

1 Use the cosine rule to find one angle.

2 Use the sine rule to find another angle.

3 Use the sum of the angles in a triangle to find the third angle.

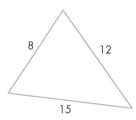

Two sides and a non-included angle

This is the ambiguous case already covered (page 347).

1 Use the sine rule to find the two possible values of the appropriate angle.

2 Use the sum of the angles in a triangle to find the two possible values of the third angle.

3 Use the sine rule to find the two possible values for the length of the third side.

Note: Apply the sine rule wherever you can – it is always easier to use than the cosine rule. The cosine rule should never need to be used more than once.

EXERCISE 15I

1 Find the length or angle x in each of these triangles.

a

b

c

d

e

f

g

h

i

2 The hands of a clock have lengths 3 cm and 5 cm. Find the distance between the tips of the hands at 4 o'clock.

3 A spacecraft is seen hovering at a point which is in the same vertical plane as two towns, X and F. Its distances from X and F are 8.5 km and 12 km respectively. The angle of elevation of the spacecraft when observed from F is 43°. Calculate the distance between the two towns.

4 Two boats, Mary Jo and Suzie, leave port at the same time. Mary Jo sails at 10 knots on a bearing of 065°. Suzie sails on a bearing of 120° and after 1 hour Mary Jo is on a bearing of 330° from Suzie. What is Suzie's speed? (A knot is a nautical mile per hour.)

5 Two ships leave port at the same time, Darling Dave sailing at 12 knots on a bearing of 055°, and Merry Mary at 18 knots on a bearing of 280°.

a How far apart are the two ships after 1 hour?

b What is the bearing of Merry Mary from Darling Dave?

Sine, cosine and tangent of 30°, 45° and 60°

In this section you will learn how to:

● work out the trigonometric ratios of 30°, 45° and 60° in surd form

EXAMPLE 17

Using an equilateral triangle whose sides are 2 units, write down expressions for the sine, cosine and tangent of 60° and 30°.

Divide the equilateral triangle into two equal right-angled triangles. Taking one of them, use Pythagoras and the definition of sine, cosine and tangent to obtain

$$\sin 60° = \frac{\sqrt{3}}{2} \qquad \cos 60° = \frac{1}{2} \qquad \tan 60° = \sqrt{3}$$

and

$$\sin 30° = \frac{1}{2} \qquad \cos 30° = \frac{\sqrt{3}}{2} \qquad \tan 30° = \frac{1}{\sqrt{3}} = \frac{\sqrt{3}}{3}$$

EXAMPLE 18

Using a right-angled isosceles triangle whose equal sides are 1 unit, find the sine, cosine and tangent of 45°.

By Pythagoras, the hypotenuse of the triangle is $\sqrt{2}$ units.

From the definition of sine, cosine and tangent, you obtain

$$\sin 45° = \frac{1}{\sqrt{2}} = \frac{\sqrt{2}}{2} \qquad \cos 45° = \frac{1}{\sqrt{2}} = \frac{\sqrt{2}}{2} \qquad \tan 45° = 1$$

EXERCISE 15J

1. The sine of angle x is $\frac{4}{5}$. Work out the cosine of angle x.

2. The cosine of angle x is $\dfrac{3}{\sqrt{15}}$. Work out the sine of angle x.

3. The two short sides of a right-angled triangle are $\sqrt{6}$ and $\sqrt{13}$. Write down the exact value of the hypotenuse of this triangle, and the exact value of the sine, cosine and tangent of the smallest angle in the triangle.

4. The tangent of angle A is $\frac{6}{11}$. Use this fact to label two sides of the triangle.

   a Calculate the third side of the triangle.

   b Write down the exact values of sin A and cos A.

5. Calculate the exact value of the area of an equilateral triangle of side 6 cm.

6. Work out the exact value of the area of a right-angled isosceles triangle whose hypotenuse is 40 cm.

15.6 Using sine to find the area of a triangle

This section will show you how to:

- work out the area of a triangle if you know two sides and the included angle

Take triangle ABC, whose vertical height is BD and whose base is AC.

Let BD = h and AC = b, then the area of the triangle is given by

$$\tfrac{1}{2} \times \text{AC} \times \text{BD} = \tfrac{1}{2}bh$$

However, in triangle BCD

$$h = \text{BC}\sin C = a\sin C$$

where BC = a.

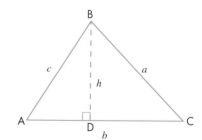

Substituting into $\frac{1}{2}bh$ gives

$$\tfrac{1}{2}b \times (a \sin C) = \tfrac{1}{2}ab \sin C$$

as the area of the triangle.

By taking the perpendicular from A to its opposite side BC, and the perpendicular from C to its opposite side AB, we can show that the area of the triangle is also given by

$$\tfrac{1}{2}ac \sin B \quad \text{and} \quad \tfrac{1}{2}bc \sin A$$

Note the pattern: the area is given by the product of two sides multiplied by the sine of the included angle.

EXAMPLE 19

Find the area of triangle ABC.

Area = $\frac{1}{2}ab \sin C$

Area = $\frac{1}{2} \times 5 \times 7 \times \sin 38° = 10.8$ cm^2 (3 significant figures)

EXAMPLE 20

Find the area of triangle ABC.

You have all three sides but no angle. So first you must find an angle in order to apply the area sine rule.

Find angle C, using the cosine rule.

$$\cos C = \frac{a^2 + b^2 - c^2}{2ab}$$

$$= \frac{13^2 + 19^2 - 8^2}{2 \times 13 \times 19} = 0.9433$$

$$\Rightarrow \quad C = \cos^{-1} 0.9433 = 19.4°$$

(Keep the exact value in your calculator memory.)

Now you apply the area sine rule

$$\tfrac{1}{2}ab \sin C = \tfrac{1}{2} \times 13 \times 19 \times \sin 19.4°$$

$$= 41.0 \text{ cm}^2 \qquad \text{(3 significant figures)}$$

EXERCISE 15K

A

1. Find the area of each of the following triangles.

   a Triangle ABC where BC = 7 cm, AC = 8 cm and angle ACB = 59°

   b Triangle ABC where angle BAC = 86°, AC = 6.7 cm and AB = 8 cm

   c Triangle PQR where QR = 27 cm, PR = 19 cm and angle QRP = 109°

   d Triangle XYZ where XY = 231 cm, XZ = 191 cm and angle YXZ = 73°

   e Triangle LMN where LN = 63 cm, LM = 39 cm and angle NLM = 85°

2. The area of triangle ABC is 27 cm². If BC = 14 cm and angle BCA = 115°, find AC.

3. The area of triangle LMN is 113 cm², LM = 16 cm and MN = 21 cm. Angle LMN is acute. Calculate these angles.

   a LMN   **b** MNL

A*

4. In a quadrilateral ABCD, DC = 4 cm, BD = 11 cm, angle BAD = 32°, angle ABD = 48° and angle BDC = 61°. Calculate the area of the quadrilateral.

5. A board is in the shape of a triangle with sides 60 cm, 70 cm and 80 cm. Find the area of the board.

6. Two circles, centres P and Q, have radii of 6 cm and 7 cm respectively. The circles intersect at X and Y. Given that PQ = 9 cm, find the area of triangle PXQ.

7. The points A, B and C are on the circumference of a circle, centre O and radius 7 cm. AB = 4 cm and BC = 3.5 cm. Calculate these.

   a angle AOB

   b area of quadrilateral OABC

8. Prove that for any triangle ABC

   Area = $\frac{1}{2}ab \sin C$

9. **a** ABC is a right-angled isosceles triangle with short sides of 1 cm. Write down the value of sin 45°.

   b Calculate the area of triangle PQR.

1 a ABC is a right-angled triangle.
AC = 19 cm and AB = 9 cm.

Calculate the length of BC.

b PQR is a right-angled triangle.
PQ = 11 cm and QR = 24 cm.

Calculate the size of angle PRQ.

c ABC and ACD are right-angled triangles.
AD is parallel to BC.
AB = 12 cm, BC = 5 cm and AD = 33.8 cm.

Calculate the size of angle ADC.

AQA, Question 10, Paper 2 Higher, June 2005

2 ABD and BCD are two right-angled triangles.
AB = 12 cm, CD = 8 cm, ∠BAD = 30°.

The two triangles are joined together as shown in the diagram. ADC is a straight line. Calculate the length BC, marked *x* on the diagram.

AQA, Question 7, Paper 2 Higher, June 2002

3 ABC is a right-angled triangle.
AB = 7 cm, ∠CAB = 52°.
Find the length of BC (marked *x* in the diagram).
Give your answer to a suitable degree of accuracy.

4 PQR is a triangle.
PQ = 12 cm, PR = 15cm, QR = 20 cm.

Calculate the angle QPR.

5 A ruined tower is fenced off for safety reasons. To find the height of the tower Rashid stands at a point A and measures the angle of elevation as 18°. He then walks 20 metres directly towards the base of the tower to point B where the angle of elevation is 31°.

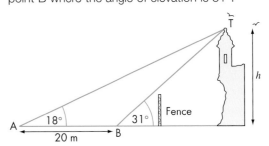

Calculate the height *h*, of the tower.

AQA, Question 17, Paper 2 Higher, November 2004

6 In triangle PQR, PQ = 13 cm, QR = 11 cm and PR = 12 cm.

Find the area of triangle PQR.

Two ships, A and B, leave port at 13:00 hours. Ship A travels at a constant speed of 18 km per hour on a bearing of 070°. Ship B travels at a constant speed of 25 km per hour on a bearing of 152°.

Calculate the distance between A and B at 14:00 hours.

AQA, Question 18, Paper 2 Higher, June 2003

 ABCDEFGH is a cuboid with sides of 5 cm, 5 cm and 12 cm as shown.

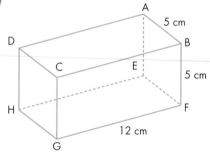

Calculate angle DFH.

AQA, Question 17, Paper 2 Higher, June 2003

 In triangle PQR, PR = 6 cm, PQ = 10 cm and angle PRQ = 105°.

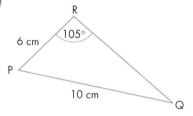

Calculate the area of triangle PQR.

 VABCD is a right pyramid with a square base. V is vertically above the centre of the square. All the slant lengths are 30 cm. The square base has a side of 20 cm.

Calculate the angle between the face VAB and the base ABCD.

 ABCD is a quadrilateral. AB = 7 cm, AD = 6 cm and BC = 9 cm. Angle ABC = 75° and angle ADC = 90°.

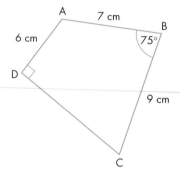

Calculate the perimeter of ABCD.

AQA, Question 21, Paper 2 Higher, June 2004

 A rectangular based pyramid has a base of length 6 cm and width 4 cm.

The vertex of the pyramid is directly over the midpoint of the base.

The volume of the pyramid is 200 cm³.

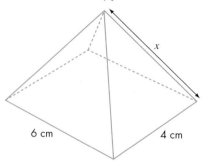

Find the length of the slant edge of the pyramid.

WORKED EXAM QUESTIONS

The diagram represents a level triangular piece of land. AB = 61 metres, AC = 76 metres, and the area of the land is 2300 m². Angle BAC is acute.

Calculate the length of BC. Give your answer to an appropriate degree of accuracy.

Solution

$\frac{1}{2} \times 61 \times 76 \times \sin$ BAC = 2300

$\therefore$ sin BAC = 0.9922 ...

$\therefore$ Angle BAC = 82.9°

Use Area $= \frac{1}{2}bc$ sin A to set up an equation and solve it to get angle A. You are given that A is acute so there is no problem with any ambiguity.

BC² = 61² + 76² − 2 × 61 × 76 × cos 82.9 = 8343.75

BC = 91.3 m

Use the cosine rule to work out the side BC. If possible keep values in your calculator display but if you have to write down values then use at least 4 significant figures for trig ratios and at least 1 decimal place for angles. This will avoid any inaccuracy in the final answer.

A tetrahedron has one face which is an equilateral triangle of side 6 cm and three faces which are isosceles triangles with sides 6 cm, 9 cm and 9 cm.

Calculate the surface area of the tetrahedron.

Solution

First work out the area of the base, which has angles of 60°.

Area base $= \frac{1}{2} \times 6 \times 6 \times \sin 60° = 15.59$ cm² (4 significant figures)

Next, work out the vertex angle of one side triangle using the cosine rule.

$\cos x = \dfrac{9^2 + 9^2 - 6^2}{2 \times 9 \times 9} = 0.7778$

So $x = 38.9°$ (Keep the exact value in your calculator.)

Work out the area of one side face and then add all faces together.

Area side face $= \frac{1}{2} \times 9 \times 9 \times \sin 38.9° = 25.46$ cm² (4 significant figures)

Total area = 3 × 25.46 + 15.59 = 92.0 cm² (3 significant figures)

GRADE YOURSELF

A Able to solve more complex 2-D problems using Pythagoras' theorem and trigonometry

A Able to use the sine and cosine rules to calculate missing angles or sides in non right-angled triangles

A Able to find the area of a triangle using the formula Area $= \frac{1}{2}ab \sin C$

A* Able to use the sine and cosine rules to solve more complex problems involving non right-angled triangles

A* Able to solve 3-D problems using Pythagoras' theorem and trigonometric ratios

A* Able to find two angles between 0° and 360° for any given value of a trigonometric ratio (positive or negative)

A* Able to solve simple equations where the trigonometric ratio is the subject

What you should know now

- How to use the sine and cosine rules
- How to find the area of a triangle using Area $= \frac{1}{2}ab \sin C$

Linear graphs and equations

1 Linear graphs

2 Finding the equation of a line from its graph

3 Uses of graphs

4 Parallel and perpendicular lines

This chapter will show you ...

● how to draw and find the equations of linear graphs

● how to use graphs to find exact or approximate solutions to equations

What you should already know

● How to read and plot coordinates

● How to substitute into simple algebraic functions

● How to plot a graph from a given table of values

Quick check

1 This table shows values of $y = 2x + 3$ for $-2 \leqslant x \leqslant 5$.

x	-2	-1	0	1	2	3	4	5
y	-1	1	3	5	7	9	11	

a Complete the table for $x = 5$

b Copy these axes and plot the points to draw the graph of $y = 2x + 3$.

In this section you will learn how to:

- draw linear graphs without using flow diagrams

Key words

axis
  (pl: axes)
coefficient
gradient-
  intercept
linear
  graphs

This chapter is concerned with drawing straight-line graphs. These graphs are usually referred to as **linear graphs**.

The minimum number of points needed to draw a linear graph is two but three or more are better because that gives at least one point to act as a check. There is no rule about how many points to plot but here are some tips.

- Use a sharp pencil and mark each point with an accurate cross.

- Get your eyes directly over the graph. If you look from the side, you will not be able to line up your ruler accurately.

Drawing graphs by finding points

This method is a bit quicker and does not need flow diagrams. However, if you prefer flow diagrams, use them. Follow through Example 1 to see how to draw a graph by finding points.

EXAMPLE 1

Draw the graph of $y = 4x - 5$ for values of x from 0 to 5. This is usually written as $0 \leqslant x \leqslant 5$.

Choose three values for x: these should be the highest and lowest x-values and one in between.

Work out the y-values by substituting the x-values into the equation.

When $x = 0$, $y = 4(0) - 5 = -5$. This gives the point $(0, -5)$.

When $x = 3$, $y = 4(3) - 5 = 7$. This gives the point $(3, 7)$.

When $x = 5$, $y = 4(5) - 5 = 15$. This gives the point $(5, 15)$.

Keep a record of your calculations in a table.

x	0	3	5
y	−5	7	15

You now have to decide the extent (range) of the **axes**. You can find this out by looking at the coordinates that you have so far. The smallest x-value is 0, the largest is 5. The smallest y-value is −5, the largest is 15.

Now draw the axes, plot the points and complete the graph. It is usually a good idea to choose 0 as one of the x-values. In an examination, the range for the x-values will usually be given and the axes already drawn.

Read through these hints before drawing the linear graphs required in Exercise 16A.

- Use the highest and lowest values of x given in the range.

- Don't pick x-values that are too close together, for example, 1 and 2. Try to space them out so that you can draw a more accurate graph.

- Always label your graph with its equation. This is particularly important when you are drawing two graphs on the same set of axes.

- If you want to use a flow diagram, use one.

- Create a table of values. You will often have to complete these in your examinations.

EXERCISE 16A

1 Draw the graph of $y = 3x + 4$ for x-values from 0 to 5 ($0 \leqslant x \leqslant 5$).

2 Draw the graph of $y = 2x - 5$ for $0 \leqslant x \leqslant 5$.

3 Draw the graph of $y = \frac{x}{2} - 3$ for $0 \leqslant x \leqslant 10$.

4 Draw the graph of $y = 3x + 5$ for $-3 \leqslant x \leqslant 3$.

5 Draw the graph of $y = \frac{x}{3} + 4$ for $-6 \leqslant x \leqslant 6$.

6 **a** On the same set of axes, draw the graphs of $y = 3x - 2$ and $y = 2x + 1$ for $0 \leqslant x \leqslant 5$.

b At which point do the two lines intersect?

7 **a** On the same axes, draw the graphs of $y = 4x - 5$ and $y = 2x + 3$ for $0 \leqslant x \leqslant 5$.

b At which point do the two lines intersect?

8 **a** On the same axes, draw the graphs of $y = \frac{x}{3} - 1$ and $y = \frac{x}{2} - 2$ for $0 \leqslant x \leqslant 12$.

b At which point do the two lines intersect?

9 **a** On the same axes, draw the graphs of $y = 3x + 1$ and $y = 3x - 2$ for $0 \leqslant x \leqslant 4$.

b Do the two lines intersect? If not, why not?

10 **a** Copy and complete the table to draw the graph of $x + y = 5$ for $0 \leqslant x \leqslant 5$.

x	0	1	2	3	4	5
y	5		3		1	

b Now draw the graph of $x + y = 7$ for $0 \leqslant x \leqslant 7$ on the same axes.

Gradient

The slope of a line is called its gradient. The steeper the slope of the line, the larger the value of the gradient.

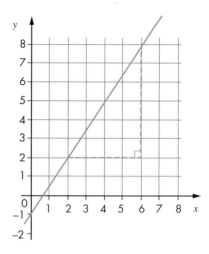

The gradient of the line shown here can be measured by drawing, as large as possible, a right-angled triangle which has part of the line as its hypotenuse (sloping side). The gradient is then given by:

$$\text{gradient} = \frac{\text{distance measured up}}{\text{distance measured along}}$$

$$= \frac{\text{difference on } y\text{-axis}}{\text{difference on } x\text{-axis}}$$

For example, to measure the steepness of the line in the next figure, you first draw a right-angled triangle whose hypotenuse is part of this line. It does not matter where you draw the triangle but it makes the calculations much easier if you choose a sensible place. This usually means using existing grid lines, so that you avoid fractional values.

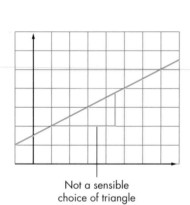

Not a sensible
choice of triangle

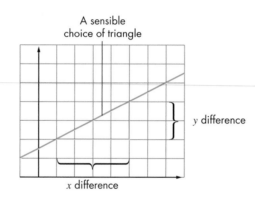

A sensible
choice of triangle

y difference

x difference

After you have drawn the triangle, you measure (or count) how many squares there are on the vertical side. This is the difference between your *y*-coordinates. In the case above, this is 2.

You then measure (or count) how many squares there are on the horizontal side. This is the difference between your *x*-coordinates. In the case above, this is 4.

To work out the gradient, you do the following calculation.

$$\text{gradient} = \frac{\text{difference of the } y\text{-coordinates}}{\text{difference of the } x\text{-coordinates}} = \frac{2}{4} = \frac{1}{2} \text{ or } 0.5$$

Note that the value of the gradient is not affected by where the triangle is drawn. As we are calculating the ratio of two sides of the triangle, the gradient will always be the same wherever we draw the triangle.

Remember: When a line slopes down from left to right, the gradient is negative, so a minus sign must be placed in front of the calculated fraction.

EXAMPLE 2

Find the gradient of each of these lines.

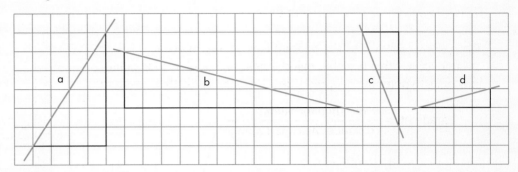

In each case, a sensible choice of triangle has already been made.

a y difference = 6, x difference = 4   Gradient = $6 \div 4 = \dfrac{3}{2} = 1.5$

b y difference = 3, x difference = 12   Line slopes down left to right,

so gradient = $-(3 \div 12) = -\dfrac{1}{4} = -0.25$

c y difference = 5, x difference = 2   Line slopes down from left to right,

so gradient = $-(5 \div 2) = -\dfrac{5}{2} = -2.5$

d y difference = 1, x difference = 4   Gradient = $1 \div 4 = \dfrac{1}{4} = 0.25$

Drawing a line with a certain gradient

To draw a line with a certain gradient, you reverse the process described above. That is, you first draw the right-angled triangle using the given gradient. For example, take a gradient of 2.

Start at a convenient point (A in the diagrams below). A gradient of 2 means for an x-step of 1 the y-step must be 2 (because 2 is the fraction $\frac{2}{1}$). So, move one square across and two squares up, and mark a dot.

Repeat this as many times as you like and draw the line. You can also move one square back and two squares down, which gives the same gradient, as the third diagram shows.

Stage 1

Stage 2

Stage 3

EXAMPLE 3

Draw lines with these gradients.   **a** $\frac{1}{3}$ **b** -3 **c** $-\frac{1}{4}$

a This is a fractional gradient which has a y-step of 1 and an x-step of 3. Move three squares across and one square up every time.

b This is a negative gradient, so for every one square across, move three squares down.

c This is also a negative gradient and it is a fraction. So for every four squares across, move one square down.

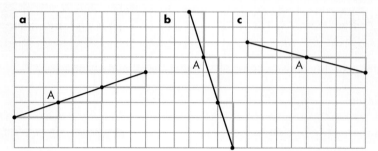

EXERCISE 16B

1 Find the gradient of each of these lines.

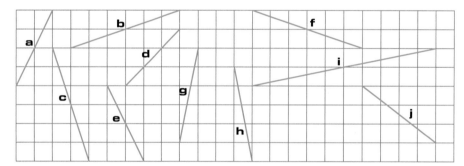

2 Draw lines with these gradients.

    a 4   **b** $\frac{2}{3}$ **c** -2 **d** $-\frac{4}{5}$ **e** 6   **f** -6

3 Find the gradient of each of these lines. What is special about these lines?

    a   **b**

4 The line on grid **e** is horizontal. The lines on grids **a** to **d** get nearer and nearer to the horizontal.

a   b   c   d   e

Find the gradient of each line in grids **a** to **d**. By looking at the values you obtain, what do you think the gradient of a horizontal line is?

5 The line on grid **e** is vertical. The lines on grids **a** to **d** get nearer and nearer to the vertical.

a   b   c   d   e

Find the gradient of each line in grids **a** to **d**. By looking at the values you obtain, what do you think the gradient of a vertical line is?

Gradient-intercept method for drawing graphs

The ideas that you have discovered in the last activity lead to another way of plotting lines, known as the **gradient-intercept** method.

EXAMPLE 4

Draw the graph of $y = 3x - 1$, using the gradient-intercept method.

- Because the constant term is −1, we know that the graph goes through the y-axis at −1. We mark this point with a dot or a cross (**A** on diagram **i**).

- The number in front of x (called the **coefficient** of x) gives the relationship between y and x. Because the coefficient of x is 3, this tells us that y is 3 times the x value, so the gradient of the line is 3. For an x-step of one unit, there is a y-step of three. Starting at −1 on the y-axis, we move one square across and three squares up and mark this point with a dot or a cross (**B** on diagram **i**).

Repeat this from every new point. You can also move one square back and three squares down. When enough points have been marked, join the dots (or crosses) to make the graph (diagram **ii**). Note that if the points are not in a straight line, a mistake has been made.

i   ii

EXERCISE 16C

1 Draw these lines using the gradient-intercept method. Use the same grid, taking x from -10 to 10 and y from -10 to 10. If the grid gets too "crowded", draw another one.

a $y = 2x + 6$　　　　**b** $y = 3x - 4$　　　　**c** $y = \frac{1}{2}x + 5$

d $y = x + 7$　　　　**e** $y = 4x - 3$　　　　**f** $y = 2x - 7$

g $y = \frac{1}{4}x - 3$　　　　**h** $y = \frac{2}{3}x + 4$　　　　**i** $y = 6x - 5$

j $y = x + 8$　　　　**k** $y = \frac{4}{5}x - 2$　　　　**l** $y = 3x - 9$

2 a Using the gradient-intercept method, draw the following lines on the same grid. Use axes with ranges $-6 \leqslant x \leqslant 6$ and $-8 \leqslant y \leqslant 8$.

　　i $y = 3x + 1$　　　　**ii** $y = 2x + 3$

　b Where do the lines cross?

3 a Using the gradient-intercept method, draw the following lines on the same grid. Use axes with ranges $-14 \leqslant x \leqslant 4$ and $-2 \leqslant y \leqslant 6$.

　　i $y = \frac{x}{3} + 3$　　　　**ii** $y = \frac{x}{4} + 2$

　b Where do the lines cross?

4 a Using the gradient-intercept method draw the following lines on the same grid. Use axes with ranges $-4 \leqslant x \leqslant 6$ and $-6 \leqslant y \leqslant 8$.

　　i $y = x + 3$　　　　**ii** $y = 2x$

　b Where do the lines cross?

Cover-up method for drawing graphs

The x-axis has the equation $y = 0$. This means that all points on the x-axis have a y-value of 0.

The y-axis has the equation $x = 0$. This means that all points on the y-axis have an x-value of 0.

We can use these facts to draw any line that has an equation of the form:

$$ax + by = c.$$

EXAMPLE 5

Draw the graph of $4x + 5y = 20$.

Because the value of x is 0 on the y-axis, we can solve the equation for y:

$$4(0) + 5y = 20$$
$$5y = 20$$
$$\Rightarrow \quad y = 4$$

Hence, the line passes through the point $(0, 4)$ on the y-axis (diagram **A**).

Because the value of y is 0 on the x-axis, we can also solve the equation for x:

$$4x + 5(0) = 20$$
$$4x = 20$$
$$\Rightarrow \quad x = 5$$

Hence, the line passes through the point $(5, 0)$ on the x-axis (diagram **B**). We need only two points to draw a line. (Normally, we would like a third point but in this case we can accept two.) The graph is drawn by joining the points $(0, 4)$ and $(5, 0)$ (diagram **C**).

This type of equation can be drawn very easily, without much working at all, using the cover-up method.

Start with the equation $\qquad\qquad\qquad\qquad\qquad 4x + 5y = 20$

Cover up the x-term: $\qquad\qquad\qquad\qquad\qquad$ $+ 5y = 20$

Solve the equation (when $x = 0$): $\qquad\qquad\qquad\qquad y = 4$

Now cover up the y-term: $\qquad\qquad\qquad\qquad\quad 4x + $ $= 20$

Solve the equation (when $y = 0$): $\qquad\qquad\qquad\qquad x = 5$

This gives the points $(0, 4)$ on the y-axis and $(5, 0)$ on the x-axis.

EXAMPLE 6

Draw the graph of $2x - 3y = 12$.

Start with the equation $\qquad\qquad\qquad 2x - 3y = 12$

Cover up the x-term: $\qquad\qquad\qquad$ $- 3y = 12$

Solve the equation (when $x = 0$): $\qquad\qquad y = -4$

Now cover up the y-term: $\qquad\qquad\quad 2x + $ $= 12$

Solve the equation (when $y = 0$): $\qquad\qquad x = 6$

This gives the points $(0, -4)$ on the y-axis and $(6, 0)$ on the x-axis.

EXERCISE 16D

1 Draw these lines using the cover-up method. Use the same grid, taking x from –10 to 10 and y from –10 to 10. If the grid gets too "crowded", draw another.

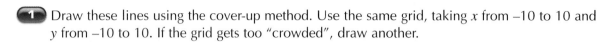

a $3x + 2y = 6$	**b** $4x + 3y = 12$	**c** $4x - 5y = 20$
d $x + y = 10$	**e** $3x - 2y = 18$	**f** $x - y = 4$
g $5x - 2y = 15$	**h** $2x - 3y = 15$	**i** $6x + 5y = 30$
j $x + y = -5$	**k** $x + y = 3$	**l** $x - y = -4$

2 a Using the cover-up method, draw the following lines on the same grid. Use axes with ranges $-2 \leqslant x \leqslant 6$ and $-2 \leqslant y \leqslant 6$.

    i $2x + y = 4$ **ii** $x - 2y = 2$

  b Where do the lines cross?

3 a Using the cover-up method, draw the following lines on the same grid. Use axes with ranges $-2 \leqslant x \leqslant 6$ and $-3 \leqslant y \leqslant 6$.

    i $x + 2y = 6$ **ii** $2x - y = 2$

  b Where do the lines cross?

4 a Using the cover-up method, draw the following lines on the same grid. Use axes with ranges $-6 \leqslant x \leqslant 8$ and $-2 \leqslant y \leqslant 8$.

    i $x + y = 6$ **ii** $x - y = 2$

  b Where do the lines cross?

16.2 Finding the equation of a line from its graph

In this section you will learn how to:
- find the equation of a line using its gradient and intercept

Key words
coefficient
gradient
intercept

The equation $y = mx + c$

When a graph can be expressed in the form $y = mx + c$, the **coefficient** of x, m, is the **gradient**, and the constant term, c, is the **intercept** on the y-axis.

This means that if we know the gradient, m, of a line and its intercept, c, on the y-axis, we can write down the equation of the line immediately.

For example, if $m = 3$ and $c = -5$, the equation of the line is $y = 3x - 5$.

All linear graphs can be expressed in the form $y = mx + c$.

This gives us a method of finding the equation of any line drawn on a pair of coordinate axes.

EXAMPLE 7

Find the equation of the line shown in diagram **A**.

First, we find where the graph crosses the y-axis (diagram **B**).

So $c = 2$.

Next, we measure the gradient of the line (diagram **C**).

y-step = 8
x-step = 2
gradient = $8 \div 2 = 4$

So $m = 4$.

Finally, we write down the equation of the line: $y = 4x + 2$.

EXERCISE 16E

1 Give the equation of each of these lines, all of which have positive gradients. (Each square represents 1 unit.)

a   **b**   **c**

d   **e**   **f**

2 In each of these grids, there are two lines. (Each square represents 1 unit.)

a   **b**   **c**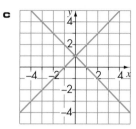

For each grid:

i find the equation of each of the lines,

ii describe any symmetries that you can see,

iii what connection is there between the gradients of each pair of lines?

3 Give the equation of each of these lines, all of which have negative gradients. (Each square represents 1 unit.)

a   **b**   **c**

d   **e**

4 In each of these grids, there are three lines. One of them is $y = x$. (Each square represents one unit.)

a   **b**   **c**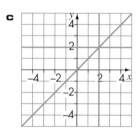

For each grid:

i find the equation of each of the other two lines,

ii describe any symmetries that you can see,

iii what connection is there between the gradients of each group of lines?

Uses of graphs

In this section you will learn how to:
- use straight-line graphs to find formulae
- solve simultaneous linear equations using graphs

Key words
formula
(pl: formulae)
rule

On page 310, you met two uses of graphs in kinematics, and the use of graphs to represent mortgage repayment and the rate of change of depth as a container is filled with water. Two other uses of graphs which we will now consider are finding formulae and solving simultaneous equations. Solving quadratic and other equations by graphical methods is covered in Chapter 17.

Finding formulae or rules

EXAMPLE 8

A taxi fare will cost more the further you go. The graph on the right illustrates the fares in one part of England.

The taxi company charges a basic hire fee to start with of £2.00. This is shown on the graph as the point where the line cuts through the hire-charge axis (when distance travelled is 0).

The gradient of the line is:

$$\frac{8-2}{4} = \frac{6}{4} = 1.5$$

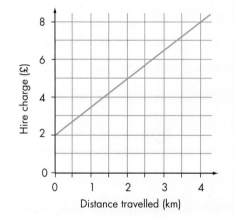

This represents the hire charge per kilometre travelled.

So the total hire charge is made up of two parts: a basic hire charge of £2.00 and an additional charge of £1.50 per kilometre travelled. This can be put in a formula as

   Hire charge = £2.00 + £1.50 per kilometre.

In this example, £2.00 is the constant term in the formula (the equation of the graph).

B

1 This graph is a conversion graph between °C and °F.

   a How many °F are equivalent to a temperature of 0 °C?

   b What is the gradient of the line?

   c From your answers to parts **a** and **b**, write down a rule which can be used to convert °C to °F.

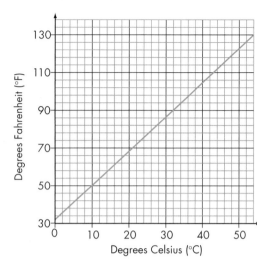

2 This graph illustrates charges for fuel.

   a What is the gradient of the line?

   b The standing charge is the basic charge before the cost per unit is added. What is the standing charge?

   c Write down the rule used to work out the total charge for different amounts of units used.

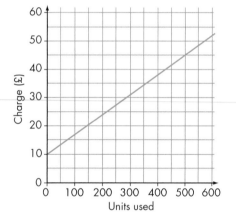

3 This graph shows the hire charge for heaters over so many days.

   a Calculate the gradient of the line.

   b What is the basic charge before the daily hire charge is added on?

   c Write down the rule used to work out the total hire charge.

4 This graph shows the hire charge for a conference centre depending on the number of people at the conference.

   a Calculate the gradient of the line.

   b What is the basic fee for hiring the conference centre?

   c Write down the rule used to work out the total hire charge for the centre.

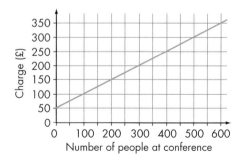

5 This graph shows the length of a spring when different weights are attached to it.

a Calculate the gradient of the line.

b How long is the spring when no weight is attached to it?

c By how much does the spring extend per kilogram?

d Write down the rule for finding the length of the spring for different weights.

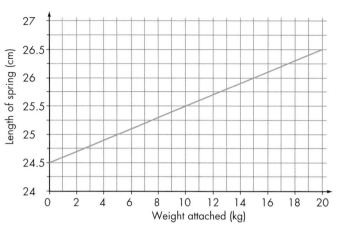

Solving simultaneous equations

By drawing their graphs on the same grid, find the solution of these simultaneous equations.

a $3x + y = 6$ b $y = 4x - 1$

a The first graph is drawn using the cover-up method. It crosses the x-axis at $(2, 0)$ and the y-axis at $(0, 6)$.

b This graph can be drawn by finding some points or by the gradient-intercept method. If you use the gradient-intercept method, you find the graph crosses the y-axis at -1 and has a gradient of 4.

The point where the graphs intersect is $(1, 3)$. So the solution to the simultaneous equations is $x = 1$, $y = 3$.

EXERCISE 16G

By drawing their graphs, find the solution of each of these pairs of simultaneous equations.

1 $x + 4y = 8$
$x - y = 3$

2 $y = 2x - 1$
$3x + 2y = 12$

3 $y = 2x + 4$
$y = x + 7$

4 $y = x$
$x + y = 10$

5 $y = 2x + 3$
$5x + y = 10$

6 $y = 5x + 1$
$y = 2x + 10$

7 $y = x + 8$
$x + y = 4$

8 $y - 3x = 9$
$y = x - 3$

9 $y = -x$
$y = 4x - 5$

10 $3x + 2y = 18$
$y = 3x$

11 $y = 3x + 2$
$y + x = 10$

12 $y = \dfrac{x}{3} + 1$
$x + y = 11$

Parallel and perpendicular lines

This section will show you how to:

- draw linear graphs parallel or perpendicular to other lines and passing through a specific point

Key words

negative reciprocal
parallel
perpendicular

EXAMPLE 10

In each of these grids, there are two lines.

a

b

c
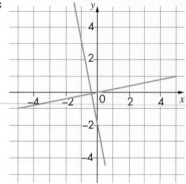

For each grid:

i   find the equation of each line,

ii describe the geometrical relationship between the lines,

iii describe the numerical relationships between their gradients.

i   Grid a: the lines have equations $y = 2x + 1$, $y = -\frac{1}{2}x - 1$

   Grid b: the lines have equations $y = \frac{3}{2}x - 2$, $y = -\frac{2}{3}x + 1$

   Grid c: the lines have equations $y = \frac{1}{5}x$, $y = -5x - 2$

ii In each case the lines are perpendicular (at right angles)

iii In each case the gradients are reciprocals of each other but with different signs.

Note: If two lines are **parallel**, then their gradients are equal.

If two lines are **perpendicular**, their gradients are **negative reciprocals** of each other.

EXAMPLE 11

Find the line that is perpendicular to the line $y = \frac{1}{2}x - 3$ and passes through $(0, 5)$.

The gradient of the new line will be the negative reciprocal of $\frac{1}{2}$ which is -2.

The point $(0, 5)$ is the intercept on the y-axis so the equation of the line is $y = -2x + 5$.

EXAMPLE 12

The point A is $(2, -1)$ and the point B is $(4, 5)$.

a Find the equation of the line parallel to AB and passing through $(2, 8)$.

b Find the equation of the line perpendicular to the midpoint of AB.

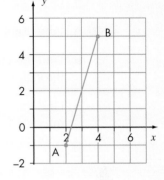

a The gradient of AB is 3, so the new equation is of the form

$$y = 3x + c.$$

The new line passes through $(2, 8)$, so $8 = 3 \times 2 + c$

$$\Rightarrow c = 2$$

Hence the line is $y = 3x + 2$.

b The midpoint of AB is $(3, 2)$.

The gradient of the perpendicular line is the negative reciprocal of 3, which is $-\frac{1}{3}$.

We could find c as in part **a** but we can also do a sketch on the grid. This will show that the perpendicular line passes through $(0, 3)$.

Hence the equation of the line is $y = -\frac{1}{3}x + 3$.

EXERCISE 16H

1 Write down the negative reciprocals of the following numbers.

a 2　　　　**b** -3　　　　**c** 5　　　　**d** -1

e $\frac{1}{2}$　　　　**f** $\frac{1}{4}$　　　　**g** $-\frac{1}{3}$　　　　**h** $-\frac{2}{3}$

i 1.5　　　　**j** 10　　　　**k** -6　　　　**l** $\frac{4}{3}$

2 Write down the equation of the line perpendicular to each of the following lines and which passes through the same point on the y-axis.

a $y = 2x - 1$　　　**b** $y = -3x + 1$　　　**c** $y = x + 2$　　　**d** $y = -x + 2$

e $y = \frac{1}{2}x + 3$　　　**f** $y = \frac{1}{4}x - 3$　　　**g** $y = -\frac{1}{3}x$　　　**h** $y = -\frac{2}{3}x - 5$

A

3 Write down the equations of these lines.

   a parallel to $y = 4x - 5$ and passes through $(0, 1)$

   b parallel to $y = \frac{1}{2}x + 3$ and passes through $(0, -2)$

   c parallel to $y = -x + 2$ and passes through $(0, 3)$

4 Write down the equations of these lines.

   a perpendicular to $y = 3x + 2$ and passes through $(0, -1)$

   b perpendicular to $y = -\frac{1}{3}x - 2$ and passes through $(0, 5)$

   c perpendicular to $y = x - 5$ and passes through $(0, 1)$

A*

5 A is the point $(1, 5)$. B is the point $(3, 3)$.

   a Find the equation of the line parallel to AB and passing through $(5, 9)$.

   b Find the equation of the line perpendicular to AB and passing through the midpoint of AB.

6 Find the equation of the line that passes through the midpoint of AB, where A is $(-5, -3)$ and B is $(-1, 3)$, and has a gradient of 2.

7 Find the equation of the line perpendicular to $y = 4x - 3$, passing though $(-4, 3)$.

8 A is the point $(0, 6)$, B is the point $(5, 5)$ and C is the point $(4, 0)$.

   a Write down the point where the line BC intercepts the y-axis.

   b Work out the equation of the line AB.

   c Write down the equation of the line BC.

9 Find the equation of the perpendicular bisector of the points A $(1, 2)$ and B $(3, 6)$.

10 A is the point $(0, 4)$, B is the point $(4, 6)$ and C is the point $(2, 0)$.

   a Find the equation of the line BC.

   b Show that the point of intersection of the perpendicular bisectors of AB and AC is $(3, 3)$.

   c Show algebraically that this point lies on the line BC.

1
  a Draw the graph of $y = 2x + 3$ for values of x from 0 to 5. Use a grid with axes covering $0 \leqslant x \leqslant 6$ and $0 \leqslant y \leqslant 14$.
  b Use your graph to solve $6.5 = 2x + 3$.

2
The diagram shows a sketch of the graph of $y = 3x + 1$.
Copy the diagram, and draw and label sketch graphs of these.
  a $y = 1$
  b $y = x + 1$

3
  a Find the equation of the line AB.

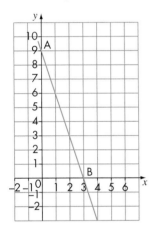

  b Give the y-coordinate of the point on the line with an x-coordinate of 6.
  c Write down the gradient of a line perpendicular to AB.

AQA, Question 7, Paper 2 Higher, November 2004

4
Here are the equations of six lines.
  i $y = 2x + 1$ **ii** $y = -\frac{1}{3}x - 3$
  iii $y = \frac{1}{3}x - 1$ **iv** $y = 2x - 2$
  v $y = 3x + 2$ **vi** $y = \frac{1}{2}x - 2$
  a Which two lines are parallel?
  b Which pairs of lines are perpendicular?
  a Which two lines intersect on the y-axis?

5
The diagram shows the points A(–1, 7), B(0, 5) and C(4, –3).

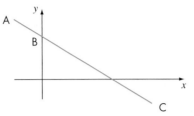

Find the equation of the straight line which passes through A, B and C.

6 Find the equation of the straight line through the point (0, 3) which is perpendicular to the line $y = \frac{3}{5}x + 5$.

7 A is the point (5, 5). B is the point (3, 1). Find the equation of the line perpendicular to AB and passing through the midpoint of AB.

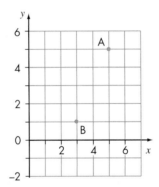

8 Find the equation of the line parallel to the line $y = 3x + 5$ passing through the point (2, 9).

9 Find the equation of the perpendicular bisector of the points A(4, 3) and B(8, 5).

10 A is the point (6, 3), B is the point (0, 5). Find algebraically, the point of intersection of the line perpendicular to AB passing through the midpoint and the line $2y + x = 4$.

WORKED EXAM QUESTION

a   Find the equation of the line shown.

b   Find the equation of the line perpendicular to the line shown and passing through $(0, -5)$.

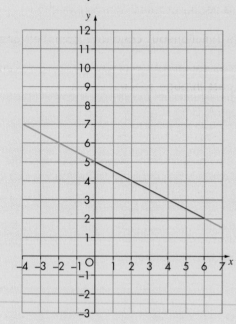

Solution

a   Intercept is at $(0, 5)$

First identify the point where the line crosses the y-axis. This is the intercept, c.

Gradient $= -\dfrac{3}{6} = -\dfrac{1}{2}$

Draw a right-angled triangle using grid lines as two sides of the triangle and part of the line as the hypotenuse. (Shown in red on diagram.)

Measure the y-step and the x-step of the triangle and divide the y-step by the x-step to get the gradient, m.

As the line slopes down from left to right the gradient is negative.

Equation of the line is $y = -\dfrac{1}{2}x + 5$

Put the two numbers into the equation $y = mx + c$ to get the equation of the line.

b   Gradient is 2

Gradient of y a perpendicular line is the negative reciprocal of $-\frac{1}{2}$.

Intercept is $(0, -5)$

Intercept is given.

Equation is $y = 2x - 5$

Give equation in the form $y = mx + c$.

GRADE YOURSELF

D Able to draw straight lines by plotting points

C Able to draw straight lines using the gradient-intercept method

B Able to solve a pair of linear simultaneous equations from their graphs

A Able to find the equations of linear graphs parallel and perpendicular to other linear graphs, that pass through specific points

What you should know now

- How to draw linear graphs
- How to solve simultaneous linear equations by finding the intersection point of the graphs of the equations or other related equations
- How to use gradients to find equations of parallel and perpendicular graphs

Chapter

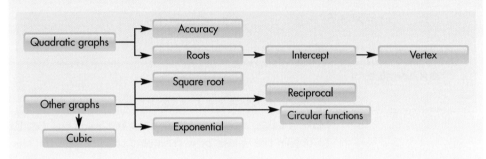

17

More graphs and equations

1 Quadratic graphs

2 Other graphs

3 Solving equations by the method of intersection

This chapter will show you ...

- how to draw quadratic, cubic, reciprocal and exponential graphs
- how to use graphs to find exact or approximate solutions to equations

What you should already know

- How to draw linear graphs
- How to find the equation of a graph using the gradient-intercept method

Quick check

1 Draw the graph of $y = 3x - 1$ for values of x from -2 to $+3$.

2 Give the equation of the graph shown.

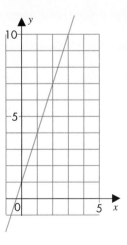

This section will show you how to:
- draw and read values from quadratic graphs

Key words
intercept
maximum
minimum
quadratic
roots
vertex

A **quadratic** graph has a term in x^2 in its equation. All of the following are quadratic equations and each would produce a quadratic graph.

$$y = x^2 \qquad\qquad y = x^2 + 5 \qquad\qquad y = x^2 - 3x$$

$$y = x^2 + 5x + 6 \qquad\qquad y = 3x^2 - 5x + 4$$

EXAMPLE 1

Draw the graph of $y = x^2 + 5x + 6$ for $-5 \leqslant x \leqslant 3$.

Make a table, as shown below. Work out each row (x^2, $5x$, 6) separately, adding them together to obtain the values of y. Then plot the points from the table.

x	−5	−4	−3	−2	−1	0	1	2	3
x^2	25	16	9	4	1	0	1	4	9
$5x$	−25	−20	−15	−10	−5	0	5	10	15
6	6	6	6	6	6	6	6	6	6
y	6	2	0	0	2	6	12	20	30

Note that in an examination paper you may be given only the first and last rows, with some values filled in. For example,

x	−5	−4	−3	−2	−1	0	1	2	3
y	6		0		2				30

In this case, you would either construct your own table, or work out the remaining y-values with a calculator.

EXAMPLE 2

a Complete the table for $y = 3x^2 - 5x + 4$ for $-1 \leqslant x \leqslant 3$, then draw the graph.

x	−1	−0.5	0	0.5	1	1.5	2	2.5	3
y	12			2.25	2			10.25	16

b Use your graph to find the value of y when $x = 2.2$.

c Use your graph to find the values of x that give a y-value of 9.

a The table gives only some values. So you either set up your own table with $3x^2$, $-5x$ and $+4$, or calculate each y-value. For example, on the majority of scientific calculators, the value for -0.5 will be worked out as

3	**×**	**0**	**•**	**5**	**+/−**	**x²**	**−**	**5**	**×**	**0**	**•**	**5**	**+/−**	**+**	**4**	**=**

Check that you get an answer of 7.25.

If you want to make sure that you are doing the correct arithmetic with your calculator, try some values for x for which you know the answer. For example, try $x = 0.5$, and see whether your answer is 2.25.

The complete table should be:

x	−1	−0.5	0	0.5	1	1.5	2	2.5	3
y	12	7.25	4	2.25	2	3.25	6	10.25	16

The graph is shown on the right.

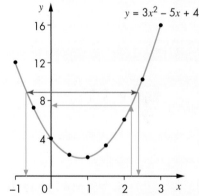

b To find the corresponding y-value for any value of x, you start on the x-axis at that x-value, go up to the curve, across to the y-axis and read off the y-value. This procedure is marked on the graph with arrows.

Always show these arrows because even if you make a mistake and misread the scales, you may still get a mark.

When $x = 2.2$, $y = 7.5$.

c This time start at 9 on the y-axis and read off the two x-values that correspond to a y-value of 9. Again, this procedure is marked on the graph with arrows.

When $y = 9$, $x = -0.7$ or $x = 2.4$.

Drawing accurate graphs

Note that although it is difficult to draw accurate curves, examiners work to a *tolerance of only 1 mm*.

Here are some of the more common ways in which marks are lost in an examination (see also diagrams on the following page).

- When the points are too far apart, a curve tends to "wobble".

- Drawing curves in small sections leads to "feathering".

- The place where a curve should turn smoothly is drawn "flat".

- A line is drawn through a point which, clearly, has been incorrectly plotted.

A quadratic curve drawn correctly will always give a smooth curve.

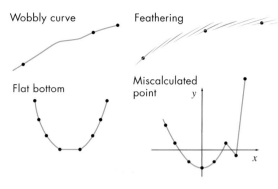

Here are some tips which will make it easier for you to draw smooth, curved lines.

- If you are *right-handed*, turn your piece of paper or your exercise book round so that you draw from left to right. Your hand is steadier this way than trying to draw from right to left or away from your body. If you are *left-handed*, you should find drawing from right to left the more accurate way.

- Move your pencil over the points as a practice run without drawing the curve.

- Do one continuous curve and only stop at a plotted point.

- Use a *sharp* pencil and do not press too heavily, so that you may easily rub out mistakes.

Normally in an examination, grids are provided with the axes clearly marked. This is so that the examiner can place a transparent master over a graph and see immediately whether any lines are badly drawn or points are misplotted. Remember that a tolerance of 1 mm is all that you are allowed. In the exercises below, suitable ranges are suggested for the axes. You can use any type of graph paper to draw the graphs.

Also you do not need to work out all values in a table. If you use a calculator, you need only to work out the y-value. The other rows in the table are just working lines to break down the calculation.

EXERCISE 17A

1 **a** Copy and complete the table for the graph of $y = 3x^2$ for values of x from -3 to 3.

x	-3	-2	-1	0	1	2	3
y	27		3			12	

b Use your graph to find the value of y when $x = -1.5$.

c Use your graph to find the values of x that give a y-value of 10.

2 **a** Copy and complete the table for the graph of $y = x^2 + 2$ for values of x from -5 to 5.

x	-5	-4	-3	-2	-1	0	1	2	3	4	5
$y = x^2 + 2$	27		11					6			

b Use your graph to find the value of y when $x = -2.5$.

c Use your graph to find the values of x that give a y-value of 14.

3 **a** Copy and complete the table for the graph of $y = x^2 - 2x - 8$ for values of x from -5 to 5.

x	-5	-4	-3	-2	-1	0	1	2	3	4	5
x^2	25		9					4			
$-2x$	10							-4			
-8	-8							-8			
y	27							-8			

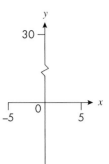

b Use your graph to find the value of y when $x = 0.5$.

c Use your graph to find the values of x that give a y-value of -3.

4 **a** Copy and complete the table for the graph of $y = x^2 + 2x - 1$ for values of x from -3 to 3.

x	-3	-2	-1	0	1	2	3
x^2	9				1	4	
$+2x$	-6		-2			4	
-1	-1	-1				-1	
y	2					7	

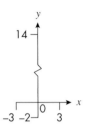

b Use your graph to find the y-value when $x = -2.5$.

c Use your graph to find the values of x that give a y-value of 1.

d On the same axes, draw the graph of $y = \dfrac{x}{2} + 2$.

e Where do the graphs $y = x^2 + 2x - 1$ and $y = \dfrac{x}{2} + 2$ cross?

5 **a** Copy and complete the table for the graph of $y = x^2 - x + 6$ for values of x from -3 to 3.

x	-3	-2	-1	0	1	2	3
x^2	9				1	4	
$-x$	3					-2	
$+6$	6					6	
y	18					8	

b Use your graph to find the y-value when $x = 2.5$.

c Use your graph to find the values of x that give a y-value of 8.

d Copy and complete the table to draw the graph of $y = x^2 + 5$ on the same axes.

x	-3	-2	-1	0	1	2	3
y	14		6				14

e Where do the graphs $y = x^2 - x + 6$ and $y = x^2 + 5$ cross?

6 **a** Copy and complete the table for the graph of $y = x^2 + 2x + 1$ for values of x from -3 to 3.

x	-3	-2	-1	0	1	2	3
x^2	9				1	4	
$+2x$	-6					4	
$+1$	1					1	
y	4						

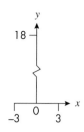

b Use your graph to find the y-value when $x = 1.7$.

c Use your graph to find the values of x that give a y-value of 2.

d On the same axes, draw the graph of $y = 2x + 2$.

e Where do the graphs $y = x^2 + 2x + 1$ and $y = 2x + 2$ cross?

7 **a** Copy and complete the table for the graph of $y = 2x^2 - 5x - 3$ for values of x from -2 to 4.

x	-2	-1.5	-1	-0.5	0	0.5	1	1.5	2	2.5	3	3.5	4
y	15	9			-3	-5				-3			9

b Where does the graph cross the x-axis?

The significant points of a quadratic graph

A quadratic graph has four points that are of interest to a mathematician. These are the points A, B, C and D on the diagram. A and B are called the **roots**, and are where the graph crosses the x-axis, C is the point where the graph crosses the y-axis (the **intercept**) and D is the **vertex**, and is the lowest or highest point of the graph.

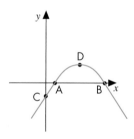

The roots

If you look at your answer to question **7** in Exercise 17A, you will see that the graph crosses the x-axis at $x = -0.5$ and $x = 3$. Since the x-axis is the line $y = 0$, the y-value at any point on the x-axis is zero. So, you have found the solution to the equation

$$0 = 2x^2 - 5x - 3 \quad \text{that is} \quad 2x^2 - 5x - 3 = 0$$

You met equations of this type in Chapter 12. They are known as quadratic equations.

You solved them either by factorisation or by using the quadratic formula. That is, you found the values of x that made them true. Such values are called the roots of an equation. So in the case of the quadratic equation $2x^2 - 5x - 3 = 0$, its roots are -0.5 and 3.

Let's check these values:

For $x = 3.0$ $2(3)^2 - 5(3) - 3 = 18 - 15 - 3 = 0$

For $x = 0.5$ $2(-0.5)^2 - 5(-0.5) - 3 = 0.5 + 2.5 - 3 = 0$

We can find the roots of a quadratic equation by drawing its graph and finding where the graph crosses the x-axis.

EXAMPLE 3

    a   Draw the graph of $y = x^2 - 3x - 4$ for $-2 \leqslant x \leqslant 5$.

    b   Use your graph to find the roots of the equation $x^2 - 3x - 4 = 0$.

    a   Set up a table.

x	-2	-1	0	1	2	3	4	5
x^2	4	1	0	1	4	9	16	25
$-3x$	6	3	0	-3	-6	-9	-12	-15
-4	-4	-4	-4	-4	-4	-4	-4	-4
y	6	0	-4	-6	-6	-4	0	6

Draw the graph.

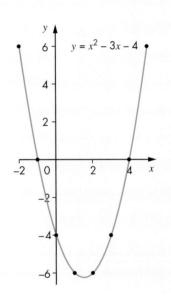

    b   The points where the graph crosses the x-axis are -1 and 4.

        So, the roots of $x^2 - 3x - 4 = 0$ are $x = -1$ and $x = 4$.

Note that sometimes the quadratic graph may not cross the x-axis. In this case there are no roots. This was dealt with in section 12.6.

The y-intercept

If you look at all the quadratic graphs we have drawn so far you will see a connection between the equation and the point where the graph crosses the y-axis. Very simply, the constant term of the equation $y = ax^2 + bx + c$ (that is, the value c) is where the graph crosses the y-axis. The intercept is at $(0, c)$.

The vertex

The lowest (or highest) point of a quadratic graph is called the vertex.

If it is the highest point, it is called the **maximum**.

If it is the lowest point, it is called the **minimum**.

It is difficult to find a general rule for the point, but the x-coordinate is always half-way between the roots.

The easiest way to find the y-value is to substitute the x-value into the original equation.

Another way to find the vertex is to use completing the square (see section 12.5, page 293).

EXAMPLE 4

a Write the equation $x^2 - 3x - 4 = 0$ in the form $(x - p)^2 - q = 0$

b What is the least value of the graph $y = x^2 - 3x - 4$?

a $x^2 - 3x - 4 = (x - 1\frac{1}{2})^2 - 2\frac{1}{4} - 4$

$= (x - 1\frac{1}{2})^2 - 6\frac{1}{4}$

b Looking at the graph drawn in Example 3 you can see that the minimum point is at $(1\frac{1}{2}, -6\frac{1}{4})$, so the least value is $-6\frac{1}{4}$.

You should be able to see the connection between the vertex point and the equation written in completing the square form.

As a general rule when a quadratic is written in the form $(x - p)^2 + q$ then the minimum point is (p, q). Note the sign change of p.

Note: If the x^2 term is negative then the graph will be inverted and the vertex will be a maximum.

EXERCISE 17B

1 a Copy and complete the table to draw the graph of $y = x^2 - 4$ for $-4 \leqslant x \leqslant 4$.

x	−4	−3	−2	−1	0	1	2	3	4
y	12			−3				5	

b Use your graph to find the roots of $x^2 - 4 = 0$.

2 a Copy and complete the table to draw the graph of $y = x^2 - 9$ for $-4 \leqslant x \leqslant 4$.

x	−4	−3	−2	−1	0	1	2	3	4
y	7				−9			0	

b Use your graph to find the roots of $x^2 - 9 = 0$.

3 a Look at the equations of the graphs you drew in questions **1** and **2**. Is there a connection between the numbers in each equation and its roots?

b Before you draw the graphs in parts **c** and **d**, try to predict what their roots will be ($\sqrt{5} \approx 2.2$).

c Copy and complete the table to draw the graph of $y = x^2 - 1$ for $-4 \leqslant x \leqslant 4$.

x	−4	−3	−2	−1	0	1	2	3	4
y	15				−1			8	

d Copy and complete the table to draw the graph of $y = x^2 - 5$ for $-4 \leqslant x \leqslant 4$.

x	−4	−3	−2	−1	0	1	2	3	4
y	11		−1					4	

e Were your predictions correct?

4 **a** Copy and complete the table to draw the graph of $y = x^2 + 4x$ for $-5 \leqslant x \leqslant 2$.

x	−5	−4	−3	−2	−1	0	1	2
x^2	25			4			1	
$+4x$	−20			−8			4	
y	5			−4			5	

b Use your graph to find the roots of the equation $x^2 + 4x = 0$.

5 **a** Copy and complete the table to draw the graph of $y = x^2 - 6x$ for $-2 \leqslant x \leqslant 8$.

x	−2	−1	0	1	2	3	4	5	6	7	8
x^2	4			1			16				
$-6x$	12			−6			−24				
y	16			−5			−8				

b Use your graph to find the roots of the equation $x^2 - 6x = 0$.

6 **a** Copy and complete the table to draw the graph of $y = x^2 + 3x$ for $-5 \leqslant x \leqslant 3$.

x	−5	−4	−3	−2	−1	0	1	2	3
y	10			−2				10	

b Use your graph to find the roots of the equation $x^2 + 3x = 0$.

7 **a** Look at the equations of the graphs you drew in questions **4**, **5** and **6**. Is there a connection between the numbers in each equation and the roots?

b Before you draw the graphs in parts **c** and **d**, try to predict what their roots will be.

c Copy and complete the table to draw the graph of $y = x^2 - 3x$ for $-2 \leqslant x \leqslant 5$.

x	−2	−1	0	1	2	3	4	5
y	10			−2				10

d Copy and complete the table to draw the graph of $y = x^2 + 5x$ for $-6 \leqslant x \leqslant 2$.

x	−6	−5	−4	−3	−2	−1	0	1	2
y	6			−6				6	

e Were your predictions correct?

8 **a** Copy and complete the table to draw the graph of $y = x^2 - 4x + 4$ for $-1 \leqslant x \leqslant 5$.

x	−1	0	1	2	3	4	5
y	9				1		

b Use your graph to find the roots of the equation $x^2 - 4x + 4 = 0$.

c What happens with the roots?

9 **a** Copy and complete the table to draw the graph of $y = x^2 - 6x + 3$ for $-1 \leqslant x \leqslant 7$.

x	−1	0	1	2	3	4	5	6	7
y	10			−5			−2		

b Use your graph to find the roots of the equation $x^2 - 6x + 3 = 0$.

10 **a** Copy and complete the table to draw the graph of $y = 2x^2 + 5x - 6$ for $-5 \leqslant x \leqslant 2$.

x	−5	−4	−3	−2	−1	0	1	2
y								

b Use your graph to find the roots of the equation $2x^2 + 5x - 6 = 0$.

11 For questions **1** to **7** write down the following.

a the point of intersection of the graph with the y-axis

b the coordinates of the minimum point (vertex) of each graph

c Explain the connection between these points and the original equation.

12 **a** Write the equation $y = x^2 - 4x + 4$ in the form $y = (x - p)^2 + q$.

b Write down the minimum value of the equation $y = x^2 - 4x + 4$.

13 **a** Write the equation $y = x^2 - 6x + 3$ in the form $y = (x - p)^2 + q$.

b Write down the minimum value of the equation $y = x^2 - 6x + 3$.

14 **a** Write the equation $y = x^2 - 8x + 2$ in the form $y = (x - p)^2 + q$.

b Write down the minimum value of the equation $y = x^2 - 8x + 2$.

15 **a** Write the equation $y = -x^2 + 2x - 6$ in the form $y = -(x - p)^2 + q$.

b Write down the minimum value of the equation $y = -x^2 + 2x - 6$.

Other graphs

This section will show you how to:

● recognise important graphs that you will meet in higher GCSE

Key words

asymptote
cosine
cubic
exponential
    functions
reciprocal
sine
square root

Square-root graphs

The graph of $y^2 = x$ is one you should be able to recognise and draw.

When you are working out coordinates in order to plot $y = \sqrt{x}$, remember that for every value of x (except $x = 0$) there are two **square roots**, one positive and the other negative, which give pairs of coordinates. For example,

when $x = 1$, $y = \pm1$ giving coordinates $(1, -1)$ and $(1, 1)$

when $x = 4$, $y = \pm2$ giving coordinates $(4, -2)$ and $(4, 2)$

In the case of $x = 0$, $y = 0$ and so there is only one coordinate: $(0, 0)$.

Using these five points, you can draw the graph.

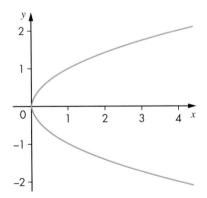

Reciprocal graphs

A **reciprocal** equation has the form $y = \dfrac{a}{x}$.

Examples of reciprocal equations are:

$$y = \frac{1}{x} \qquad y = \frac{4}{x} \qquad y = -\frac{3}{x}$$

All reciprocal graphs have a similar shape and some symmetry properties.

EXAMPLE 5

Complete the table to draw the graph of $y = \dfrac{1}{x}$ for $-4 \leqslant x \leqslant 4$.

x	−4	−3	−2	−1	1	2	3	4
y								

Values are rounded off to two decimal places, as it is unlikely that you could plot a value more accurately than this. The completed table is

x	−4	−3	−2	−1	1	2	3	4
y	−0.25	−0.33	−0.5	−1	1	0.5	0.33	0.25

The graph plotted from these values is shown in **A**. This is not much of a graph and does not show the properties of the reciprocal function. If we take x-values from −0.8 to 0.8 in steps of 0.2, we get the next table.

Note that we cannot use $x = 0$ since $\dfrac{1}{0}$ is infinity.

x	−0.8	−0.6	−0.4	−0.2	0.2	0.4	0.6	0.8
y	−1.25	−1.67	−2.5	−5	5	2.5	1.67	1.25

Plotting these points as well gives the graph in **B**.

A

B

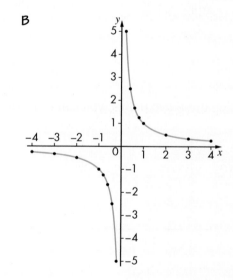

From the graph in **B**, the following properties can be seen.

● The lines $y = x$ and $y = -x$ are lines of symmetry.

● The closer x gets to zero, the nearer the graph gets to the y-axis.

● As x increases, the graph gets closer to the x-axis.

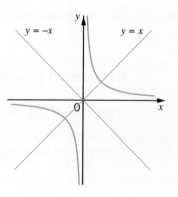

The graph never actually touches the axes, it just gets closer and closer to them. A line to which a graph gets closer but never touches or crosses is called an **asymptote**.

These properties are true for *all* reciprocal graphs.

EXERCISE 17C

1 a Copy and complete the table to draw the graph of $y = \dfrac{2}{x}$ for $-4 \leqslant x \leqslant 4$.

x	0.2	0.4	0.5	0.8	1	1.5	2	3	4
y	10		4	2.5			1		0.5

b Use your graph to find the following.

i the y-value when $x = 2.5$ **ii** the x-value when $y = -1.25$

2 a Copy and complete the table to draw the graph of $y^2 = 25x$ for $0 \leqslant x \leqslant 5$.

x	0	1	2	3	4	5
$\sqrt{x}$					2 and -2	
$y = 5\sqrt{x}$					10 and -10	

b Use your graph to find the following.

i the values of y when $x = 3.5$ **ii** the value of x when $y = 8$

3 a Copy and complete the table to draw the graph of $4y^2 = x$ for $0 \leqslant x \leqslant 5$.

x	0	1	2	3	4	5
$\sqrt{x}$					2 and -2	
$y = \frac{1}{2}\sqrt{x}$					1 and -1	

b Use your graph to find the following.

i the values of y when $x = 2.5$ **ii** the value of x when $y = 0.75$

4 a Copy and complete the table to draw the graph of $y = \dfrac{1}{x}$ for $-5 \leqslant x \leqslant 5$.

x	0.1	0.2	0.4	0.5	1	2	2.5	4	5
y	10		2.5		1				0.2

b On the same axes, draw the line $x + y = 5$.

c Use your graph to find the x-values of the points where the graphs cross.

5 a Copy and complete the table to draw the graph of $y = \dfrac{5}{x}$ for $-20 \leqslant x \leqslant 20$.

x	0.2	0.4	0.5	1	2	5	10	15	20
y	25		10						0.25

b On the same axes, draw the line $y = x + 10$.

c Use your graph to find the x-values of the points where the graphs cross.

Cubic graphs

A **cubic** function or graph is one which contains a term in x^3. The following are examples of cubic graphs:

$$y = x^3 \qquad y = x^3 - 2x^2 - 3x - 4 \qquad y = x^3 - x^2 - 4x + 4 \qquad y = x^3 + 3x$$

The techniques used to draw them are exactly the same as those for quadratic and reciprocal graphs.

EXAMPLE 6

a Complete the table to draw the graph of $y = x^3 - x^2 - 4x + 4$ for $-3 \leqslant x \leqslant 3$.

x	-3	-2.5	-2	-1.5	-1	-0.5	0	0.5	1	1.5	2	2.5	3
y	-20.00		0.00		6.00		4.00	1.88				3.38	10.00

b By drawing a suitable line on the graph find the solution of the equation $x^3 - x^2 - 4x - 1 = 0$.

a The completed table (to 2 decimal places) is given below and the graph is shown below right.

x	-3	-2.5	-2	-1.5	-1	-0.5	0	0.5	1	1.5	2	2.5	3
y	-20.00	-7.88	0.00	4.38	6.00	5.63	4.00	1.88	0.00	-0.88	0.00	3.38	10.00

b Can you see the similarity between the equation of the graph, $y = x^3 - x^2 - 4x + 4$, and the equation to be solved, $x^3 - x^2 - 4x - 1 = 0$?

Rearrange the equation to be solved as $x^3 - x^2 - 4x + 4 = something$.

That is, make the left-hand side of the equation to be solved the same as the right-hand side of the equation of the graph. You can do this by adding 5 to the -1 to make $+4$. So add 5 to both sides of the equation to be solved

$$x^3 - x^2 - 4x - 1 + 5 = 0 + 5$$

$$x^3 - x^2 - 4x + 4 = 5$$

Hence, you simply need to draw the straight line $y = 5$ and find the x-coordinates of the points where it crosses

$$y = x^3 - x^2 - 4x + 4.$$

The solutions can now be read from the graph as

$$x = -1.4, -0.3 \text{ and } 2.7.$$

1 **a** Copy and complete the table to draw the graph of $y = x^3 + 3$ for $-3 \leqslant x \leqslant 3$.

x	−3	−2.5	−2	−1.5	−1	−0.5	0	0.5	1	1.5	2	2.5	3
y	−24.00	−12.63			2.00		3.00	3.13			11.00		30.00

b Use your graph to find the y-value for an x-value of 1.2.

2 **a** Copy and complete the table to draw the graph of $y = 2x^3$ for $-3 \leqslant x \leqslant 3$.

x	−3	−2.5	−2	−1.5	−1	−0.5	0	0.5	1	1.5	2	2.5	3
y		−31.25		−6.75			0.00	0.25			16.00		

b Use your graph to find the y-value for an x-value of 2.7.

3 **a** Copy and complete the table to draw the graph of $y = -x^3$ for $-3 \leqslant x \leqslant 3$.

x	−3	−2.5	−2	−1.5	−1	−0.5	0	0.5	1	1.5	2	2.5	3
y	27.00		8.00	3.38			0.00	−0.13			−8.00	−15.63	

b Use your graph to find the y-value for an x-value of −0.6.

4 **a** Copy and complete the table to draw the graph of $y = x^3 + 3x$ for $-3 \leqslant x \leqslant 3$.

x	−3	−2.5	−2	−1.5	−1	−0.5	0	0.5	1	1.5	2	2.5	3
y	−36.00		−14.00	−7.88			0.00	1.63				23.13	

b Use your graph to find the x-value for a y-value of 2.

5 **a** Copy and complete the table to draw the graph of $y = x^3 - 3x^2 - 3x$ for $-3 \leqslant x \leqslant 3$.

x	−3	−2.5	−2	−1.5	−1	−0.5	0	0.5	1	1.5	2	2.5	3
y	−45.00		−14.00	−5.63			0.00	−0.63				−10.63	

b Use your graph to find the y-value for an x-value of 1.8.

6 **a** Copy and complete the table to draw the graph of $y = x^3 - 2x + 5$ for $-3 \leqslant x \leqslant 3$.

x	−3	−2.5	−2	−1.5	−1	−0.5	0	0.5	1	1.5	2	2.5	3
y	−16.00		1.00	4.63			5.00	4.13				15.63	

b On the same axes, draw the graph of $y = x + 6$.

c Use your graph to find the x-values of the points where the graphs cross.

7 **a** Complete the table to draw the graph of $y = x^3 - 2x + 1$ for $-3 \leqslant x \leqslant 3$.

x	-3	-2.5	-2	-1.5	-1	-0.5	0	0.5	1	1.5	2	2.5	3
y	-20.00		-3.00	0.63			1.00	0.13				11.63	

b On the same axes, draw the graph of $y = x$.

c Use your graph to find the x-values of the points where the graphs cross.

8 Write down whether each of these graphs are "linear", "quadratic", "reciprocal", "cubic" or "none of these".

a

b

c

d

e

f

g

h

i
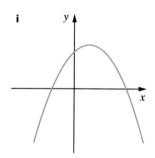

Exponential graphs

Equations which have the form $y = k^x$, where k is a positive number, are called **exponential functions**.

Exponential functions share the following properties.

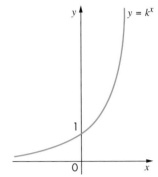

- When k is greater than 1, the value of y increases steeply as x increases, which you can see from the graph on the right.

- Also when k is greater than 1, as x takes on increasingly large negative values, the closer y gets to zero, and so the graph gets nearer and nearer to the negative x-axis. y never actually becomes zero and so the graph never actually touches the negative x-axis. That is, the negative x-axis is an asymptote to the graph. (See also page 396.)

- Whatever the value of k, the graph always intercepts the y-axis at 1, because here $y = k^0$.

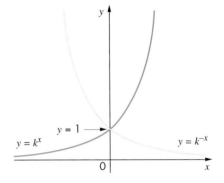

- The reciprocal graph, $y = k^{-x}$, is the reflection in the y-axis of the graph of $y = k^x$, as you can see from the graph (on the right).

EXAMPLE 7

a Complete the table below for $y = 2^x$ for values of x from -5 to $+5$. (Values are rounded to 2 decimal places.)

x	-5	-4	-3	-2	-1	0	1	2	3	4	5
$y = 2^x$	0.03	0.06	0.13				1	2	4			32

b Plot the graph of $y = 2^x$ for $-5 \leqslant x \leqslant 5$.

c Use your graph to estimate the value of y when $x = 2.5$.

d Use your graph to estimate the value of x when $y = 0.75$.

a The values missing from the table are: 0.25, 0.5, 8 and 16.

b Part of the graph (drawn to scale) is shown on the next page.

c Draw a line vertically from $x = 2.5$ until it meets the graph and then read across. The y-value is 5.7.

d Draw a line horizontally from $y = 0.75$, the x-value is -0.4.

EXERCISE 17E

1 **a** Complete the table below for $y = 3^x$ for values of x from -4 to $+3$. (Values are rounded to 2 decimal places.)

x	-4	-3	-2	-1	0	1	2	3
$y = 3^x$	0.01	0.04			1	3		

b Plot the graph of $y = 3^x$ for $-4 \leqslant x \leqslant 3$. (Take the y-axis from 0 to 30.)

c Use your graph to estimate the value of y when $x = 2.5$.

d Use your graph to estimate the value of x when $y = 0.5$.

2 **a** Complete the table below for $y = (\frac{1}{2})^x$ for values of x from -5 to $+5$. (Values are rounded to 2 decimal places.)

x	-5	-4	-3	-2	-1	0	1	2	3	4	5
$y = (\frac{1}{2})^x$			8			1				0.06	0.03

b Plot the graph of $y = (\frac{1}{2})^x$ for $-5 \leqslant x \leqslant 5$. (Take the y-axis from 0 to 35.)

c Use your graph to estimate the value of y when $x = 2.5$.

d Use your graph to estimate the value of x when $y = 0.75$.

3 One grain of rice is placed on the first square of a chess board. Two grains of rice are placed on the second square, four grains on the third square and so on.

a Explain why $y = 2^{(n-1)}$ gives the number of grains of rice on the nth square.

b Complete the table for the number of grains of rice on the first 10 squares

Square	1	2	3	4	5	6	7	8	9	10
Grains	1	2	4							

c Use the rule to work out how many grains of rice there are on the 64th square.

d If 1000 grains of rice are worth 5p, how much is the rice on the 64th square worth?

4 An extremely large sheet of paper is 0.01 cm thick. It is torn in half and one piece placed on top of the other. These two pieces are then torn in half and one half is placed on top of the other half to give a pile 4 sheets thick. This process is repeated 50 times.

a Complete the table to show how many pieces there are in the pile after each tear.

Tears	1	2	3	4	5	6	7	8
Pieces	2	4						

b Write down a rule for the number of pieces after n tears.

c How many pieces will there be piled up after 50 tears?

d How thick is this pile?

The circular function graphs

You saw the graphs of $y = \sin x$ and $y = \cos x$ in Chapter 15.

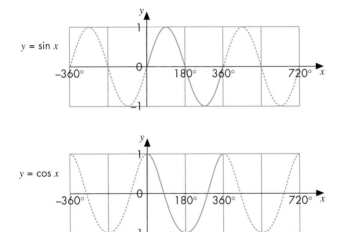

These graphs have some special properties.

- They are cyclic. This means that they repeat indefinitely in both directions.

- For every value of **sine** or **cosine** between –1 and 1 there are 2 angles between 0° and 360°, and an infinite number of angles altogether.

- The sine graph has rotational symmetry about (180°, 0) and has line symmetry between 0° and 180° about $x = 90°$, and between 180° and 360° about $x = 270°$.

- The cosine graph has line symmetry about $x = 180°$, and has rotational symmetry between 0° and 180° about (90°, 0) and between 180° and 360° about (270°, 0).

The graphs can be used to find angles with certain values of sine and cosine.

EXAMPLE 8

Given that sin 42° = 0.669, find another angle between 0° and 360° that also has a sine of 0.669.

Plot the approximate value 0.669 on the sine graph and use the symmetry to work out the other value.

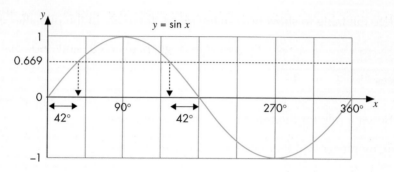

The other value is 180° − 42° = 138°.

EXAMPLE 9

Given that cos 110° = −0.342, find two angles between 0° and 360° that have a cosine of +0.342.

Plot the approximate values −0.342 and 0.342 on the cosine graph and use the symmetry to work out the values.

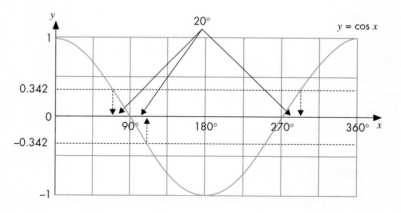

The required values are 90° − 20° = 70° and 270° + 20° = 290°.

EXERCISE 17F

1. Given that sin 65° = 0.906, find another angle between 0° and 360° that also has a sine of 0.906.

2. Given that sin 213° = –0.545, find another angle between 0° and 360° that also has a sine of –0.545.

3. Given that cos 36° = 0.809, find another angle between 0° and 360° that also has a cosine of 0.809.

4. Given that cos 165° = –0.966, find another angle between 0° and 360° that also has a cosine of –0.966.

5. Given that sin 30° = 0.5, find two angles between 0° and 360° that have a sine of –0.5.

6. Given that cos 45° = 0.707, find two angles between 0° and 360° that have a cosine of –0.707.

7. Given that sin 26° = 0.438

   a   write down an angle between 0° and 90° that has a cosine of 0.438,

   b   find two angles between 0° and 360° that have a sine of –0.438,

   c   find two angles between 0° and 360° that have a cosine of –0.438.

17.3 Solving equations by the method of intersection

This section will show you how to:
- solve equations by the method of intersecting graphs

Many equations can be solved by drawing two intersecting graphs on the same axes and using the x-value(s) of their point(s) of intersection. (In the GCSE examination, you are very likely to be presented with one drawn graph and asked to draw a straight line to solve a new equation.)

EXAMPLE 10

Show how each equation given below can be solved using the graph of $y = x^3 - 2x - 2$ and its intersection with another graph. In each case, give the equation of the other graph and the solution(s).

   a $x^3 - 2x - 4 = 0$ b $x^3 - 3x - 1 = 0$

   a   This method will give the required graph.

   Step 1: Write down the original (given) equation.

   $y = x^3 - 2x - 2$

   Step 2: Write down the (new) equation to be solved in reverse.

   $0 = x^3 - 2x - 4$

   Step 3: Subtract these equations.

   $y = \qquad\ + 2$

   Step 4: Draw this line on the original graph to solve the new equation.

The graphs of $y = x^3 - 2x - 2$ and $y = 2$ are drawn on the same axes.

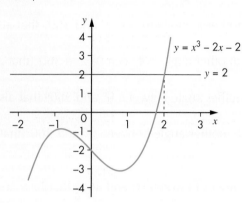

The intersection of these two graphs is the solution of $x^3 - 2x - 4 = 0$.

The solution is $x = 2$.

This works because you are drawing a straight line along with the original graph, and solving where they intersect.

At the points of intersection you can say:
   original equation = straight line

Rearranging this gives:
   (original equation) − (straight line) = 0

You have been asked to solve:
   (new equation) = 0

So (original equation) − (straight line) = (new equation)

Rearranging this again gives:
   (original equation) − (new equation) = straight line

Note: In GCSE exams the curve is always drawn already and you will only have to draw the straight line.

b Write down given graph: $\qquad\qquad\qquad\qquad\qquad\quad y = x^3 - 2x - 2$

Write down new equation: $\qquad\qquad\qquad\quad \underline{0 = x^3 - 3x - 1}$

Subtract: $\qquad\qquad\qquad\qquad\qquad\qquad\quad y = \qquad\ + x - 1$

The graphs of $y = x^3 - 2x - 2$ and $y = x - 1$ are then drawn on the same axes.

The intersection of the two graphs is the solution of $x^3 - 3x - 1 = 0$.

The solutions are $x = -1.5$, -0.3 and 1.9.

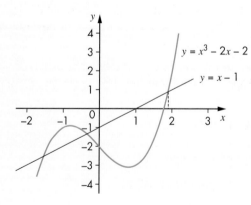

EXAMPLE 11

The graph shows the curve $y = x^2 + 3x - 2$.

By drawing a suitable straight line, solve these equations.

a $x^2 + 3x - 1 = 0$

b $x^2 + 2x - 3 = 0$

a Given graph: $\qquad y = x^2 + 3x - 2$

New equation: $\qquad 0 = x^2 + 3x - 1$

Subtract: $\qquad y = \qquad -1$

Draw: $\qquad y = -1$

Solutions: $\qquad x = 0.3, -3.3$

b Given graph: $\qquad y = x^2 + 3x - 2$

New equation: $\qquad 0 = x^2 + 2x - 3$

Subtract: $\qquad y = \quad + x\ + 1$

Draw: $\qquad y = x + 1$

Solutions: $\qquad x = 1, -3$

EXERCISE 17G

In questions **1** to **5**, use the graphs given here. Trace the graphs or place a ruler over them in the position of the line. Solution values only need to be given to 1 decimal place. In questions **6** to **10**, either draw the graphs yourself or use a graphics calculator to draw them.

1 On the following page is the graph of $y = x^2 - 3x - 6$.

   a Solve these equations.

     i $x^2 - 3x - 6 = 0$

     ii $x^2 - 3x - 6 = 4$

     iii $x^2 - 3x - 2 = 0$

b By drawing a suitable straight line solve $2x^2 - 6x + 2 = 0$.

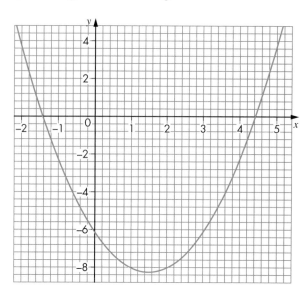

2 Below is the graph of $y = x^2 + 4x - 5$.

a Solve $x^2 + 4x - 5 = 0$.

b By drawing suitable straight lines solve these equations.

  i $x^2 + 4x - 5 = 2$

  ii $x^2 + 4x - 4 = 0$

  iii $3x^2 + 12x + 6 = 0$

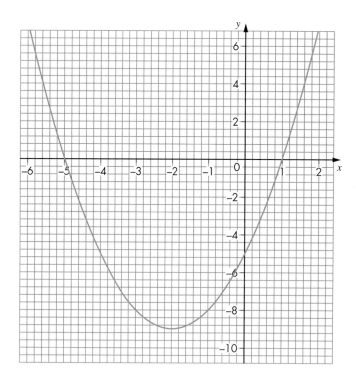

3 Below are the graphs of $y = x^2 - 5x + 3$ and $y = x + 3$.

  a Solve these equations. **i** $x^2 - 6x = 0$ **ii** $x^2 - 5x + 3 = 0$

  b By drawing suitable straight lines solve these equations.

  i $x^2 - 5x + 3 = 2$ **ii** $x^2 - 5x - 2 = 0$

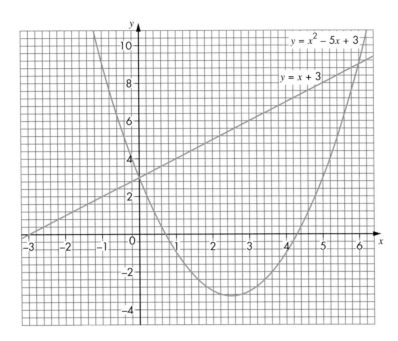

4 Below are the graphs of $y = x^2 - 2$ and $y = x + 2$.

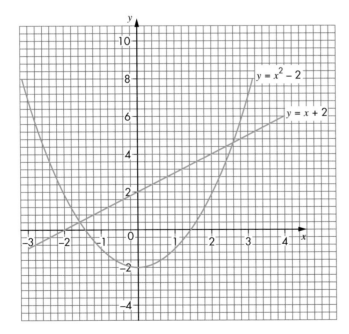

  a Solve these equations. **i** $x^2 - x - 4 = 0$ **ii** $x^2 - 2 = 0$

  b By drawing suitable straight lines solve these equations.

  i $x^2 - 2 = 3$ **ii** $x^2 - 4 = 0$

5 Below are the graphs of $y = x^3 - 2x^2$, $y = 2x + 1$ and $y = x - 1$.

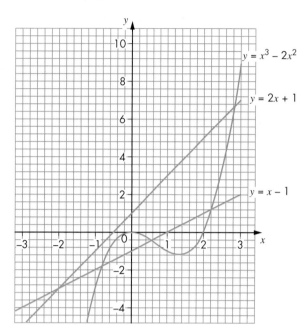

Solve these equations.

a $x^3 - 2x^2 = 0$ **b** $x^3 - 2x^2 = 3$ **c** $x^3 - 2x^2 + 1 = 0$

d $x^3 - 2x^2 - 2x - 1 = 0$ **e** $x^3 - 2x^2 - x + 1 = 0$

6 Draw the graph of $y = x^2 - 4x - 2$.

    a Solve $x^2 - 4x - 2 = 0$.

    b By drawing a suitable straight line solve $x^2 - 4x - 5 = 0$.

7 Draw the graph of $y = 2x^2 - 5$.

    a Solve $2x^2 - 5 = 0$.

    b By drawing a suitable straight line solve $2x^2 - 3 = 0$.

8 Draw the graphs of $y = x^2 - 3$ and $y = x + 2$ on the same axes. Use the graphs to solve these equations.

    a $x^2 - 5 = 0$ **b** $x^2 - x - 5 = 0$

9 Draw the graphs of $y = x^2 - 3x - 2$ and $y = 2x - 3$ on the same axes. Use the graphs to solve these equations.

    a $x^2 - 3x - 1 = 0$ **b** $x^2 - 5x + 1 = 0$

10 Draw the graphs of $y = x^3 - 2x^2 + 3x - 4$ and $y = 3x - 1$ on the same axes. Use the graphs to solve these equations.

    a $x^3 - 2x^2 + 3x - 6 = 0$ **b** $x^3 - 2x^2 - 3 = 0$

1 **a** Copy and complete the table of values for
$y = 2x^2 - 4x - 1$.

x	–2	–1	0	1	2	3
y	15		–1		–1	5

b Draw the graph of $y = 2x^2 - 4x - 1$ for values of x from –2 to +3. Use a grid with an x-axis from –2 to 3 and a y-axis from –3 to 15.

c An approximate solution of the equation $2x^2 - 4x - 1 = 0$ is $x = 2.2$.

   i Explain how you can find this from the graph.

   ii Use your graph to write down another solution of this equation.

AQA, Question 7, Paper 1 Higher, June 2004

2 **a** Copy and complete the table of values for
$y = (x + 3)(2 - x)$.

x	–3	–2	–1	0	1	2	3
y		4	6	6	4		

b Draw the graph of $y = (x + 3)(2 - x)$ for values of x from –3 to +3. Use a grid with an x-axis from –4 to 4 and a y-axis from –8 to 8.

c Use the graph to solve the equation $(x + 3)(2 - x) = 2$.

3 **a** Four graphs are sketched.

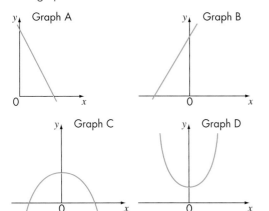

Complete the following statements.

$y = 2x + 4$ matches graph ....

$y = x^2 + 4$ matches graph ....

$y + 2x = 4$ matches graph ....

b Sketch the graph of $y = x^3$

AQA, Question 7, Paper 2 Higher, June 2005

4 **a** Complete the table of values for $y = (0.8)^x$

x	0	1	2	3	4
y	1	0.8	0.64		0.41

b Draw the graph of $y = (0.8)^x$ for values of x from 0 to 4. Use a grid with an x-axis from 0 to 5 and a y-axis from 0 to 1, marked off every 0.1 units.

c Use your graph to solve the equation $(0.8)^x = 0.76$

AQA, Question 15, Paper 2 Higher, June 2004

5 The grid below shows the graphs of
$y = x^2 - x - 6$ and $y = x + 2$.

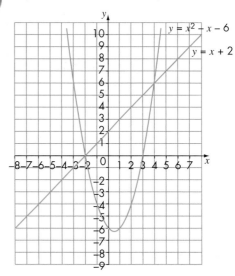

a Deduce the coordinates of the minimum point of the graph $y = x^2 - x - 12$.

b Find the quadratic equation whose solutions are the x-coordinates of the points of intersection of $y = x^2 - x - 6$ and $y = x + 2$.

AQA, Question 24, Paper 2 Higher, November 2003

6 The grid below shows the graph of $y = x^2 + 3x - 2$.

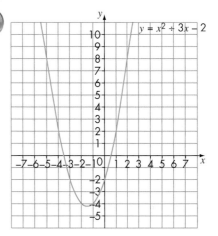

a By drawing an appropriate straight line on the graph solve this equation.

$$x^2 + 3x - 3 = 0$$

b By drawing an appropriate straight line on the graph solve this equation.

$$x^2 + 2x - 1 = 0$$

AQA, Question 22, Paper 2 Higher, June 2005

411

WORKED EXAM QUESTION

The diagram right shows the graph of

$$y = x^3 - 12x$$

for values of x from -4 to 4.

a   Use the graph to find estimates of the three
solutions of the equation

$$x^3 - 12x = 0$$

b   By drawing a suitable straight line on the grid,
find estimates of the solutions of the equation

$$x^3 - 12x - 5 = 0$$

Label clearly the straight line that you have drawn.

c   By drawing a suitable straight line on the grid,
find estimates of the solutions of the equation

$$x^3 - 14x + 5 = 0$$

Label clearly the straight line that you have drawn.

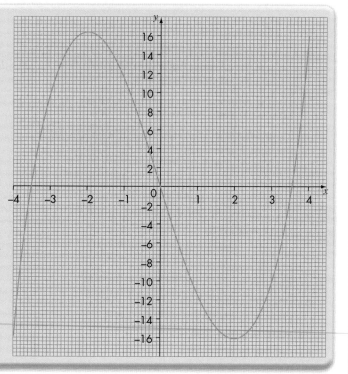

Solution

a -3.5, 0 and 3.5

> To find the values where the given graph
> is equal to zero read from the x-axis.
> These are the roots of the equation.

b -3.3, -0.5, 3.7

> To find the straight line subtract the
> required curve from the given curve.
> Given curve $y = x^3 - 12x$
> New curve $0 = x^3 - 12x - 5$
> Subtract $\overline{y = \qquad + 5}$
> Draw $y = 5$

c -3.9, 0.4, 3.5

> To find the straight line subtract the
> required curve from the given curve.
> Given curve $y = x^3 - 12x$
> New curve $0 = x^3 - 14x + 5$
> Subtract $\overline{y = \quad + 2x \; -5}$
> Draw $y = 2x - 5$

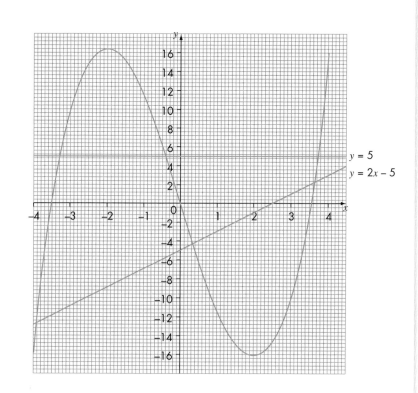

$y = 5$

$y = 2x - 5$

GRADE YOURSELF

C Able to draw quadratic graphs using a table of values

B Able to solve quadratic equations from their graphs

B Plot cubic graphs using a table of values

B Recognise the shapes of the graphs $y = x^3$ and $y = \dfrac{1}{x}$

A Able to draw a variety of graphs such as exponential graphs and reciprocal graphs using a table of values

A* Able to solve equations using the intersection of two graphs

A* Use trigonometric graphs to solve sine and cosine problems

What you should know now

● How to draw non-linear graphs

● How to solve equations by finding the intersection points of the graphs of the equations with the x-axis or other related equations

Statistics 2

This chapter will show you ...

- how to interpret and draw line graphs and stem-and-leaf diagrams
- how to draw scatter diagrams and lines of best fit
- how to interpret scatter diagrams and the different types of correlation
- how to draw and interpret cumulative frequency diagrams
- how to draw and interpret box plots
- how to calculate the standard deviation of a set of data

Visual overview

What you should already know

- How to plot coordinate points
- How to read information from charts and tables
- How to calculate the mean of a set of data from a frequency table
- How to recognise a positive or negative gradient

Quick check

1 The table shows the number of children in 10 classes in a primary school.

Calculate the mean number of children in each class.

Number of children	27	28	29	30	31
Frequency	1	2	4	2	1

Line graphs

Line graphs are usually used in statistics to show how data changes over a period of time. One use is to indicate **trends**: for example, line graphs can be used to show whether the Earth's temperature is increasing as the concentration of carbon dioxide builds up in the atmosphere, or whether a firm's profit margin is falling year on year.

Line graphs are best drawn on graph paper.

EXAMPLE 1

This line graph shows the profit made each year by a company over a five-year period.

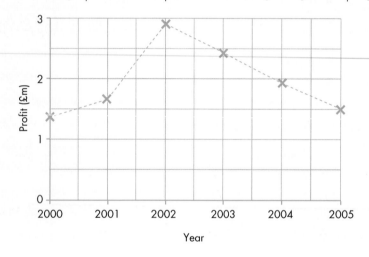

For this graph, the values between the plotted points have no meaning because the profit of the company would have been calculated at the end of every year. In cases like this, the lines are often dashed. Although the trend appears to be that profits have fallen after 2002, it would not be sensible to try to predict what will happen after 2005.

EXERCISE 18A

1 The table shows the estimated number of tourists world wide.

Year	1970	1975	1980	1985	1990	1995	2000	2005
No. of tourists (millions)	60	100	150	220	280	290	320	340

a Draw a line graph for the data.

b From your graph estimate the number of tourists in 2002.

c In which five-year period did world tourism increase the most?

d Explain the trend in world tourism. What reasons can you give to explain this trend?

2 The table shows the maximum and minimum daily temperatures for London over a week.

Day	Sunday	Monday	Tuesday	Wednesday	Thursday	Friday	Saturday
Maximum (°C)	12	14	16	15	16	14	10
Minimum (°C)	4	5	7	8	7	4	3

a Draw line graphs on the *same axes* to show the maximum and minimum temperatures.

b Find the smallest and greatest difference between the maximum and minimum temperatures.

Stem-and-leaf diagrams

In this section you will learn how to:

- draw and read information from an ordered stem-and-leaf diagram

Key words

discrete data
ordered
raw data
unordered

Raw data

If you are recording the ages of the first 20 people who line up at a bus stop in the morning, the **raw data** might look like this.

23, 13, 34, 44, 26, 12, 41, 31, 20, 18, 19, 31, 48, 32, 45, 14, 12, 27, 31, 19

This data is **unordered** and is difficult to read and analyse. When the data is **ordered**, it looks like this.

12, 12, 13, 14, 18, 19, 19, 20, 23, 26, 27, 31, 31, 31, 32, 34, 41, 44, 45, 48

This is easier to read and analyse.

Another method for displaying **discrete data** such as this, is a stem-and-leaf diagram. The tens values will be the "stem" and the units values will be the "leaves".

Key: 1 │ 2 represents 12

```
1 │ 2   2   3   4   8   9   9
2 │ 0   3   6   7
3 │ 1   1   1   2   4
4 │ 1   4   5   8
```

This is called an ordered stem-and-leaf diagram and gives a better idea of how the data is distributed.

A stem-and-leaf diagram should always have a key.

EXAMPLE 2

Put the following data into an ordered stem-and-leaf diagram.

45, 62, 58, 58, 61, 49, 61, 47, 52, 58, 48, 56, 65, 46, 54

a What is the modal value?

b What is the median value?

c What is the range of the values?

First decide on the stem and leaf.

In this case, the tens digit will be the stem and the units digit will be the leaf.

Key: 4 | 5 represents 45

4	5	6	7	8	9	
5	2	4	6	8	8	8
6	1	1	2	5		

a The modal value is the most common, which is 58.

b There are 15 values, so the median will be the (15 + 1) ÷ 2th value, or 8th value. Counting from either the top or the bottom, the median is 56.

c The range is the difference between the largest and the smallest value, which is 65 − 45 = 20.

EXERCISE 18B

1 The heights of 15 tulips are measured.

43 cm, 39 cm, 41 cm, 29 cm, 36 cm,

34 cm, 43 cm, 48 cm, 38 cm, 35 cm,

41 cm, 38 cm, 43 cm, 28 cm, 48 cm

a Show the results in an ordered stem-and-leaf diagram, using this key.

Key: 4 | 3 represents 43 cm

b What is the modal height?

c What is the median height?

d What is the range of the heights?

2 A student records the number of text messages she receives each day for two weeks.

12, 18, 21, 9, 17, 23, 8, 2, 20, 13, 17, 22, 9, 9

a Show the results in an ordered stem-and-leaf diagram, using this key.

Key: 1 | 2 represents 12 messages

b What was the modal number of text messages received in a day?

c What was the median number of text messages received in a day?

In this section you will learn how to:
- draw, interpret and use scatter diagrams

Key words
line of best fit
negative
    correlation
no correlation
positive
    correlation
scatter
    diagram
variable

A **scatter diagram** (also called a scattergraph or scattergram) is a method of comparing two **variables** by plotting on a graph their corresponding values (usually taken from a table). In other words, the variables are treated just like a set of (x, y) coordinates.

In the scatter diagram below, the marks scored by pupils in an English test are plotted against the marks they scored in a mathematics test. This graph shows positive **correlation**. This means that the pupils who got high marks in the mathematics test also tended to get high marks in the English test.

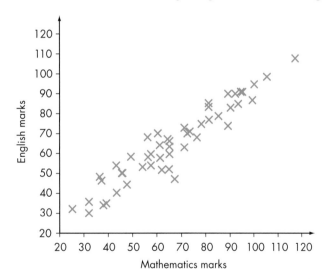

Correlation

This section will explain the different types of correlation.

Here are three statements that may or may not be true.

> The taller people are, the wider their arm span is likely to be.

> The older a car is, the lower its value will be.

> The distance you live from your place of work will affect how much you earn.

These relationships could be tested by collecting data and plotting the data on a scatter diagram.

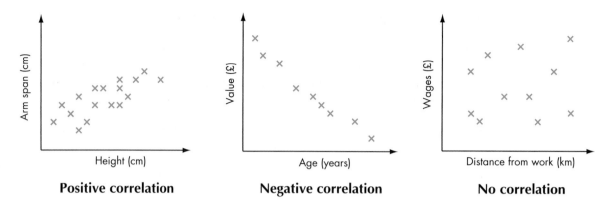

Positive correlation   **Negative correlation**   **No correlation**

For example, the first statement may give a scatter diagram like the first diagram above. This diagram has positive correlation because as one quantity increases so does the other. From such a scatter diagram we could say that the taller someone is, the wider the arm span.

Testing the second statement may give a scatter diagram like the second one. This diagram has **negative correlation** because as one quantity increases, the other quantity decreases. From such a scatter diagram we could say that as a car gets older, its value decreases.

Testing the third statement may give a scatter diagram like the third one. This scatter diagram has **no correlation**. There is no relationship between the distance a person lives from his or her work and how much the person earns.

EXAMPLE 3

The graphs show the relationship between the temperature and the amount of ice cream sold, and that between the age of people and the amount of ice cream they eat.

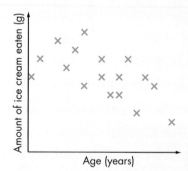

a Comment on the correlation of each graph.

b What does each graph tell you?

The first graph has positive correlation and tells us that as the temperature increases, the amount of ice cream sold increases.

The second graph has negative correlation and tells us that as people get older, they eat less ice cream.

Line of best fit

This section will explain how to draw and use a line of best fit.

The **line of best fit** is a straight line that goes between all the points on a scatter diagram, passing as close as possible to all of them. You should try to have the same number of points on both sides of the line. Because you are drawing this line by eye, examiners make a generous allowance around the correct answer. The line of best fit for the scatter diagram on page 419 is shown below.

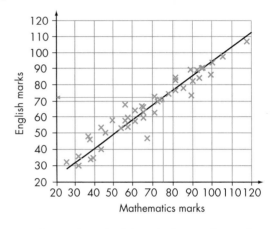

The line of best fit can be used to answer the following type of question: A girl took the mathematics test and scored 75 marks, but was ill for the English test. How many marks was she likely to have scored?

The answer is found by drawing a line up from 75 on the mathematics axis to the line of best fit and then drawing a line across to the English axis. This gives 73, which is the mark she is likely to have scored in the English test.

EXERCISE 18C

1 Describe the correlation of each of these four graphs and write in words what each graph tells you.

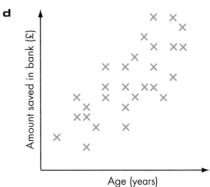

2 The table shows the results of a science experiment in which a ball is rolled along a desk top. The speed of the ball is measured at various points.

Distance from start (cm)	10	20	30	40	50	60	70	80
Speed (cm/s)	18	16	13	10	7	5	3	0

a Plot the data on a scatter diagram.

b Draw the line of best fit.

c If the ball's speed had been measured at 5 cm from the start, what is it likely to have been?

d How far from the start was the ball when its speed was 12 cm/s?

> **HINTS AND TIPS**
>
> Usually in exams axes are given and most, if not all, of the points are plotted.

3 The table shows the marks for ten pupils in their mathematics and geography examinations.

Pupil	Anna	Beryl	Cath	Dema	Ethel	Fatima	Greta	Hannah	Imogen	Joan
Maths	57	65	34	87	42	35	59	61	25	35
Geog	45	61	30	78	41	36	35	57	23	34

a Plot the data on a scatter diagram. Take the x-axis for the mathematics scores and mark it from 20 to 100. Take the y-axis for the geography scores and mark it from 20 to 100.

b Draw the line of best fit.

c One of the pupils was ill when she took the geography examination. Which pupil was it most likely to be?

d If another pupil, Kate, was absent for the geography examination but scored 75 in mathematics, what mark would you expect her to have got in geography?

e If another pupil, Lynne, was absent for the mathematics examination but scored 65 in geography, what mark would you expect her to have got in mathematics?

4 The heights, in centimetres, of twenty mothers and their 15-year-old daughters were measured. These are the results.

Mother	153	162	147	183	174	169	152	164	186	178
Daughter	145	155	142	167	167	151	145	152	163	168
Mother	175	173	158	168	181	173	166	162	180	156
Daughter	172	167	160	154	170	164	156	150	160	152

a Plot these results on a scatter diagram. Take the x-axis for the mothers' heights from 140 to 200. Take the y-axis for the daughters' heights from 140 to 200.

b Is it true that the tall mothers have tall daughters?

5 A form teacher carried out a survey of his class. He asked pupils to say how many hours per week they spent playing sport and how many hours per week they spent watching TV. This table shows the results of the survey.

Pupil	1	2	3	4	5	6	7	8	9	10
Hours playing sport	12	3	5	15	11	0	9	7	6	12
Hours watching TV	18	26	24	16	19	27	12	13	17	14

Pupil	11	12	13	14	15	16	17	18	19	20
Hours playing sport	12	10	7	6	7	3	1	2	0	12
Hours watching TV	22	16	18	22	12	28	18	20	25	13

a Plot these results on a scatter diagram. Take the *x*-axis as the number of hours playing sport and mark it from 0 to 20. Take the *y*-axis as the number of hours watching TV and mark it from 0 to 30.

b If you knew that another pupil from the form watched 8 hours of TV a week, would you be able to predict how long she or he spent playing sport? Explain why.

18.4 Cumulative frequency diagrams

In this section you will learn how to:

● find a measure of dispersion (the interquartile range) and a measure of location (the median) using a graph

Key words

cumulative
   frequency
   diagram
dispersion
interquartile
   range
lower quartile
median
upper quartile

The **interquartile range** is a measure of the **dispersion** of a set of data. The advantage of the interquartile range is that it eliminates extreme values, and bases the measure of spread on the middle 50% of the data. This section will show how to find the interquartile range, and the median, of a set of data by drawing a **cumulative frequency diagram**.

Look back at the marks of the 50 pupils in the mathematics test (see page 419). These can be put into a grouped table, as shown on the next page. Note that it includes a column for the cumulative frequency, which is found by adding each frequency to the sum of all preceding frequencies.

Mark	Number of pupils	Cumulative frequency
21 to 30	1	1
31 to 40	6	7
41 to 50	6	13
51 to 60	8	21
61 to 70	8	29
71 to 80	6	35
81 to 90	7	42
91 to 100	6	48
101 to 110	1	49
111 to 120	1	50

This data can then be used to plot a graph of the top value of each group against its cumulative frequency. The points to be plotted are (30, 1), (40, 7), (50, 13), (60, 21), etc., which will give the graph shown below. Note that the cumulative frequency is *always* the vertical (*y*) axis.

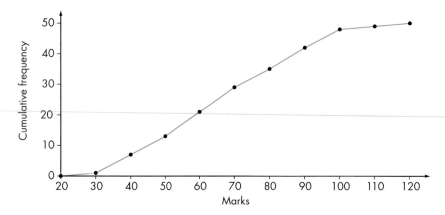

Also note that the scales on both axes are labelled at each graduation mark, in the usual way. Do not label the scales as shown here – it is wrong.

21–30	31–40	41–50

The plotted points can be joined in two different ways:

- by straight lines, to give a cumulative frequency polygon

- by a freehand curve, to give a cumulative frequency curve or ogive.

They are both called cumulative frequency diagrams.

In an examination you are most likely to be asked to draw a cumulative frequency diagram, and the type (polygon or curve) is up to you. Both will give similar results. The cumulative frequency diagram can be used in several ways, as you will now see.

The median

The **median** is the middle item of data once all the items have been put in order of size, from lowest to highest. So, if you have *n* items of data plotted as a cumulative frequency diagram, the median can be found from the middle value of the cumulative frequency, that is the $\frac{n}{2}$th value.

But remember, if you want to find the median from a simple list of discrete data, you *must* use the $(\frac{n+1}{2})$th value. The reason for the difference is that the cumulative frequency diagram treats the data as continuous, even when using data such as examination marks which are discrete. The reason you can use the $\frac{n}{2}$th value when working with cumulative frequency diagrams is that you are only looking for an estimate of the median.

There are 50 values in the table on page 424. The middle value will be the 25th value. Draw a horizontal line from the 25th value to meet the graph then go down to the horizontal axis. This will give an estimate of the median. In this example, the median is about 65 marks.

The interquartile range

By dividing the cumulative frequency into four parts, we obtain quartiles and the interquartile range.

The **lower quartile** is the item one quarter of the way up the cumulative frequency axis and is found by looking at the $\frac{n}{4}$th value.

The **upper quartile** is the item three-quarters of the way up the cumulative frequency axis and is found by looking at the $\frac{3n}{4}$th value.

The **interquartile range** is the difference between the lower and upper quartiles.

These are illustrated on the graph below.

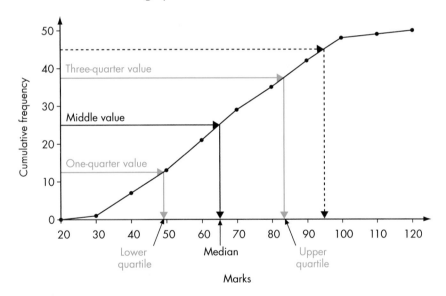

The quarter and three-quarter values out of 50 values are the 12.5th value and the 37.5th value. Draw lines across to the cumulative frequency curve from these values and down to the horizontal axis. These give the lower and upper quartiles. In this example, the lower quartile is 49 marks, the upper quartile is 83 marks, and the interquartile range is 83 − 49 = 34 marks.

Note that problems like these are often followed up with an extra question such as: The Head of Mathematics decides to give a special award to the top 10% of pupils. What would the cut-off mark be?

The top 10% would be the top 5 pupils (10% of 50 is 5). Draw a line across from the 45th pupil to the graph and down to the horizontal axis. This gives a cut-off mark of 95.

EXAMPLE 4

The table below shows the marks of 100 pupils in a mathematics SAT.

a Draw a cumulative frequency curve.

b Use your graph to find the median and the interquartile range.

c Pupils who score less than 44 do not get a SAT level awarded. How many pupils will not get a SAT level?

Mark	Number of pupils	Cumulative frequency
$21 \leqslant x \leqslant 30$	3	3
$31 \leqslant x \leqslant 40$	9	12
$41 \leqslant x \leqslant 50$	12	24
$51 \leqslant x \leqslant 60$	15	39
$61 \leqslant x \leqslant 70$	22	61
$71 \leqslant x \leqslant 80$	16	77
$81 \leqslant x \leqslant 90$	10	87
$91 \leqslant x \leqslant 100$	8	95
$101 \leqslant x \leqslant 110$	3	98
$111 \leqslant x \leqslant 120$	2	100

The groups are given in a different way to those in the table on page 424. You will meet several ways of giving groups (for example, 21–30, $20 < x \leqslant 30$, $21 < x < 30$) but the important thing to remember is to plot the top point of each group against the corresponding cumulative frequency.

a and **b** Draw the graph and put on the lines for the median (50th value), lower and upper quartiles (25th and 75th values).

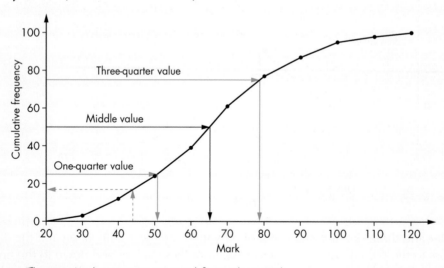

The required answers are read from the graph.

Median = 65 marks
Lower quartile = 51 marks
Upper quartile = 79 marks
Interquartile range = 79 − 51 = 28 marks

c At 44 on the mark axis draw a perpendicular line to intersect the graph, and at the point of intersection draw a horizontal line across to the cumulative frequency axis, as shown. Number of pupils without a SAT level = 18

Note, an alternative way in which the table in Example 4 could have been set out is shown below. This arrangement has the advantage that the points to be plotted are taken straight from the last two columns. You have to decide which method you prefer. In examination papers, the columns of tables are sometimes given without headings, so you will need to be familiar with all the different ways in which the data can be set out.

Mark	Number of pupils	Less than	Cumulative frequency
$21 \leqslant x \leqslant 30$	3	30	3
$31 \leqslant x \leqslant 40$	9	40	12
$41 \leqslant x \leqslant 50$	12	50	24
$51 \leqslant x \leqslant 60$	15	60	39
$61 \leqslant x \leqslant 70$	22	70	61
$71 \leqslant x \leqslant 80$	16	80	77
$81 \leqslant x \leqslant 90$	10	90	87
$91 \leqslant x \leqslant 100$	8	100	95
$101 \leqslant x \leqslant 110$	3	110	98
$111 \leqslant x \leqslant 120$	2	120	100

EXERCISE 18D

1 A class of 30 children was asked to estimate one minute. The teacher recorded the times the pupils actually said. The table on the right shows the results.

a Copy the table and complete a cumulative frequency column.

b Draw a cumulative frequency diagram.

c Use your diagram to estimate the median time and the interquartile range.

Time (seconds)	Number of pupils
$20 < x \leqslant 30$	1
$30 < x \leqslant 40$	3
$40 < x \leqslant 50$	6
$50 < x \leqslant 60$	12
$60 < x \leqslant 70$	3
$70 < x \leqslant 80$	3
$80 < x \leqslant 90$	2

2 A group of 50 pensioners was given the same task as the children in question 1. The results are shown in the table on the right.

a Copy the table and complete a cumulative frequency column.

b Draw a cumulative frequency diagram.

c Use your diagram to estimate the median time and the interquartile range.

d Which group, the children or the pensioners, would you say was better at estimating time? Give a reason for your answer.

Time (seconds)	Number of pensioners
$10 < x \leqslant 20$	1
$20 < x \leqslant 30$	2
$30 < x \leqslant 40$	2
$40 < x \leqslant 50$	9
$50 < x \leqslant 60$	17
$60 < x \leqslant 70$	13
$70 < x \leqslant 80$	3
$80 < x \leqslant 90$	2
$90 < x \leqslant 100$	1

3 The sizes of 360 secondary schools in South Yorkshire are recorded in the table on the right.

a Copy the table and complete a cumulative frequency column.

b Draw a cumulative frequency diagram.

c Use your diagram to estimate the median size of the schools and the interquartile range.

d Schools with less than 350 pupils are threatened with closure. About how many schools are threatened with closure?

Number of pupils	Number of schools
100–199	12
200–299	18
300–399	33
400–499	50
500–599	63
600–699	74
700–799	64
800–899	35
900–999	11

4 The temperature at a seaside resort was recorded over a period of 50 days. The temperature was recorded to the nearest degree. The table on the right shows the results.

a Copy the table and complete a cumulative frequency column.

b Draw a cumulative frequency diagram. Note that as the temperature is to the nearest degree the top values of the groups are 7.5°C, 10.5°C, 13.5°C, 16.5°C, etc.

c Use your diagram to estimate the median temperature and the interquartile range.

Temperature (°C)	Number of days
5–7	2
8–10	3
11–13	5
14–16	6
17–19	6
20–22	9
23–25	8
26–28	6
29–31	5

5 At the school charity fête, a game consists of throwing three darts and recording the total score. The results of the first 80 people to throw are recorded in the table on the right.

a Draw a cumulative frequency diagram to show the data.

b Use your diagram to estimate the median score and the interquartile range.

Total score	Number of players
$1 \leqslant x \leqslant 20$	9
$21 \leqslant x \leqslant 40$	13
$41 \leqslant x \leqslant 60$	23
$61 \leqslant x \leqslant 80$	15
$81 \leqslant x \leqslant 100$	11
$101 \leqslant x \leqslant 120$	7
$121 \leqslant x \leqslant 140$	2

c People who score over 90 get a prize. About what percentage of the people get a prize?

6 One hundred pupils in a primary school were asked to say how much pocket money they each get in a week. The results are in the table on the right.

a Copy the table and complete a cumulative frequency column.

b Draw a cumulative frequency diagram.

c Use your diagram to estimate the median amount of pocket money and the interquartile range.

Amount of pocket money (p)	No. of pupils
51–100	6
101–150	10
151–200	20
201–250	28
251–300	18
301–350	11
351–400	5
401–450	2

In this section you will learn how to:

- draw and read box plots

Key words

box plot
highest value
lower quartile
lowest value
median
upper quartile

Another way of displaying data for comparison is by means of a box-and-whisker plot (or just **box plot**). This requires five pieces of data. These are the **lowest value**, the **lower quartile** (Q_1), the **median** (Q_2), the **upper quartile** (Q_3) and the **highest value**. They are drawn in the following way.

These data are always placed against a scale so that their values are accurately plotted.

The following diagrams show how the cumulative frequency curve, the frequency curve and the box plot are connected for three common types of distribution.

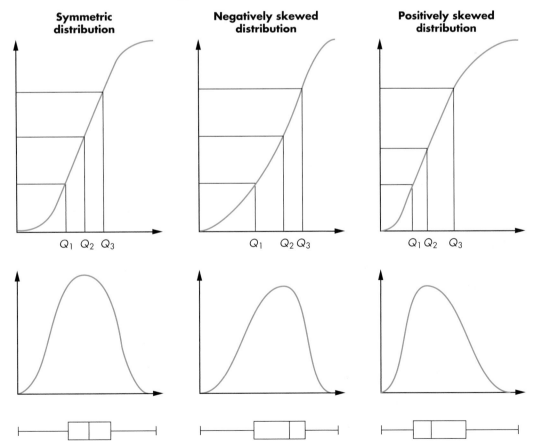

EXAMPLE 5

The box plot for the girls' marks in last year's SATs is shown on the grid below.

SATs mark

The boys' results for the same SATs are: lowest mark 39; lower quartile 65; median 78; upper quartile 87; highest mark 112.

a On the same grid, plot the box plot for the boys' marks.

b Comment on the differences between the two distributions of marks.

a The data for boys and girls is plotted on the grid below.

SATs mark

b The girls and boys have the same median mark but both the lower and upper quartiles for the girls are higher than those for the boys, and the girls' range is slightly smaller than the boys'. This suggests that the girls did better than the boys overall, even though a boy got the highest mark.

EXERCISE 18E

1 The box plot shows the times taken for a group of pensioners to do a set of ten long-division calculations.

Time (minutes)

The same set of calculations was given to some students in Year 11. Their results are: shortest time 3 minutes 20 seconds; lower quartile 6 minutes 10 seconds; median 7 minutes; upper quartile 7 minutes 50 seconds; longest time 9 minutes 40 seconds.

a Copy the diagram and draw a box plot for the students' times.

b Comment on the differences between the two distributions.

2 The box plot shows the sizes of secondary schools in Dorset.

Size (number of pupils)

The data for schools in Rotherham is: smallest 280 pupils: lower quartile 1100 pupils; median 1400 pupils; upper quartile 1600 pupils; largest 1820 pupils.

a Copy the diagram and draw a box plot for the sizes of schools in Rotherham.

b Comment on the diferences between the two distributions.

3 The box plots for the noon temperature at two resorts, recorded over a year, are shown on the grid below.

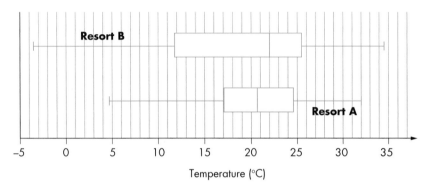

Temperature (°C)

a Comment on the differences in the two distributions.

b Mary wants to go on holiday in July. Which resort would you recommend and why?

4 The following table shows some data on the annual salary for 100 men and 100 women.

	Lowest salary	Lower quartile	Median salary	Upper quartile	Highest salary
Men	£6500	£16 000	£20 000	£22 000	£44 500
Women	£7000	£14 000	£16 000	£21 500	£33 500

a Draw box plots to compare both sets of data.

b Comment on the differences between the distributions.

5 The table shows the monthly salaries of 100 families.

a Draw a cumulative frequency diagram to show the data.

b Estimate the median monthly salary and the interquartile range.

c The lowest monthly salary was £1480 and the highest was £1740.

    i Draw a box plot to show the distribution of salaries.

    ii Is the distribution symmetric, negatively skewed or positively skewed?

Monthly salary (£)	No. of families
1451–1500	8
1501–1550	14
1551–1600	25
1601–1650	35
1651–1700	14
1701–1750	4

6 Indicate whether the following sets of data are likely to be symmetric, negatively skewed or positively skewed.

   a heights of adult males

   b annual salaries of adult males

   c shoe sizes of adult males

   d weights of babies born in Britain

   e speeds of cars on a motorway in the middle of the night

   f speeds of cars on a motorway in the rush hour

   g shopping bills in a supermarket the week before Christmas

   h number of letters in the words in a teenage magazine

   i time taken for students to get to school in the morning

   j time taken for students to run one mile

18.6 Measures of dispersion

In this section you will learn how to:
● calculate standard deviation for a set of data

Key words
dispersion
measure of
   spread
standard
   deviation

Note: This section is no longer in the specification and will not be examined in either the modular or the end-of-course examination papers. However, you may find it to be useful for the data handling task needed for coursework.

Another method commonly used to compare data is the measure of **dispersion**, also called the **measure of spread**.

You have already met two measures of dispersion:

● range, which is calculated by subtracting the smallest value in the set of data from the largest

● interquartile range, which is the difference between the upper and lower quartiles.

The range is not a good measure of dispersion, as it does not eliminate extreme values. The interquartile range is a better measure, as it takes the central half of the data. The only drawback is that it is centred about the median which may not be the best measure of location.

A much better measure of dispersion centred about the mean is the **standard deviation**.

There are two tabular methods for calculating standard deviation, but it is easier and quicker to use a calculator.

Separate values (ungrouped data)

First put your calculator into statistics mode by pressing one of the following keys.

SD or SAT will usually appear on the display. (On a graphics calculator, the operation mode key is different but the method is similar.)

Enter each number followed by

The mean, $\bar{x}$, and the standard deviation, σ, are found by pressing $\boxed{\bar{x}}$ or $\boxed{\sigma_n}$ or $\boxed{\sigma_x}$. But you may have to use $\boxed{\text{INV}}$ or $\boxed{\text{2ndF}}$ first.

Some calculators have a $\boxed{\sigma_{n-1}}$ key. Be careful *not* to use it.

Your calculator will also have $\boxed{\Sigma x}$, $\boxed{\Sigma x^2}$ and $\boxed{n}$ keys.

After each calculation remember to clear your data. On most calculators this is done by pressing $\boxed{\text{SAC}}$ or $\boxed{\text{CA}}$.

EXAMPLE 6

Find the mean and the standard deviation for 3, 8, 5 and 7.

First key

$\boxed{3}$ $\boxed{\text{DATA}}$ $\boxed{8}$ $\boxed{\text{DATA}}$ $\boxed{5}$ $\boxed{\text{DATA}}$ $\boxed{7}$ $\boxed{\text{DATA}}$

Then press $\boxed{\bar{x}}$. (You may first have to use $\boxed{\text{INV}}$ or $\boxed{\text{2ndF}}$.) You should get 5.75.

Finally, press $\boxed{\sigma_n}$. You should get 1.92 (2 decimal places).

EXAMPLE 7

Calculate the mean and the standard deviation of the heights of the people in group A.

Group A

| 1.62 m | 1.73 m | 1.60 m | 1.75 m | 1.75 m |

Check that you get $\bar{x}$ = 1.69 m and σ = 0.0660 m (3 significant figures).

EXAMPLE 8

Calculate the mean and the standard deviation of the heights of the people in group B.

Group B

| 1.79 m | 1.84 m | 1.56 m | 1.74 m | 2.20 m | 1.35 m | 1.35 m |

Check that you get $\bar{x}$ = 1.69 m and σ = 0.28 m (2 decimal places).

Use of standard deviation

Using standard deviation, we can compare, for example, the two groups A and B.

Although both groups have the same mean height, we can see that group B has a much greater variation in the heights of its members than group A. Hence, the heights of the members of group B deviate much more from the mean, while the members of group A are all very similar in height.

EXERCISE 18F

Use your calculator to work out the answers to these.

1 Find the mean and the standard deviation of the following sets of data.

    a 2, 5, 6, 8, 9

    b 7, 9, 11, 13, 18

    c 102, 105, 108, 110, 115

    d 201, 202, 203, 204, 205

    e 68.6, 72.3, 75.6, 78.1

    f −2, −1, −1, 0, 2, 4, 5

    g 71, 72, 78, 80, 85

    h 29.3, 31.8, 33.9, 34.9, 40.0, 40.1

2 Five numbers, 4, 5, 7, 8 and x, have a mean of 6.

    a What is the value of x?

    b What is the standard deviation of the numbers?

3 **a** Calculate the mean and the standard deviation of 4, 7, 8, 9, 12.

    b Calculate the mean and standard deviation of 14, 17, 18, 19, 22.

    c Using your answers to parts a and b, write down the mean and the standard deviation of 24, 27, 28, 29, 32.

4 The captain of the netball team needs to pick a player for an important match. She has to choose between Paula and Rose. She has a list of the number of points they have scored in their last few matches.

    Paula 7, 8, 6, 8, 7, 12, 6, 10

    Rose 2, 4, 4, 4, 6, 8, 10, 10, 16, 16

    a Calculate the mean and the standard deviation for Paula.

    b Calculate the mean and standard deviation for Rose.

    c Who would you pick and why?

Mean and standard deviation from a frequency table of data

Large sets of data often contain repeated values. For example, these are the marks of 20 pupils in a mathematics test.

    4, 5, 6, 5, 5, 4, 4, 7, 8, 10, 7, 4, 7, 8, 5, 6, 6, 5, 9, 6

Normally, they would be put in a frequency table like that shown on the right.

Follow through the next example, noting especially the *strict order* in which the input must be keyed. For example, each item of the data *always precedes* its frequency.

x	f
4	4
5	5
6	4
7	3
8	2
9	1
10	1
Total	20

EXAMPLE 9

Find the mean and the standard deviation for the frequency table on the right.

x	f
4	2
5	3
6	4
7	1

Enter as

| 4 | × | 2 | DATA | 5 | × | 3 | DATA | 6 | × | 4 |

| DATA | 7 | × | 1 | DATA |

Then $\bar{x}$ = 5.4   and σ_n = 0.92 (2 decimal places)

Note: Always clear your calculator of old data before starting a new calculation, by pressing SAC or CA

Some later models have a different way of inputting data from a frequency table.

They use a comma or a colon to separate the data from each frequency. These will appear in the display of the calculator. For example, you might see

| 4:2 | | M+ | | 5:3 | | M+ | | 6:4 | | M+ | | 7:1 | | M+ |

EXERCISE 18G

Use your calculator to work out the answers to these.

1 The times (to the nearest minute) of the first 20 phone calls made from an office one morning are

2, 5, 5, 7, 3, 4, 5, 6, 7, 8, 2, 12, 2, 5, 2, 5, 7, 9, 10, 2

Put these times into a frequency table and calculate the mean and the standard deviation of the call times.

2 Calculate the mean and the standard deviation of the data in these tables.

a

x	f
0	2
1	4
2	6
3	5
4	3

b

x	f
22	4
23	6
24	7
25	6
26	4
27	3

c

x	f
100	2
101	4
102	6
103	5
104	3

d

x	f
6.7	12
7.3	41
7.8	66
8.1	43
8.5	27

e

x	f
2.2	8
3.2	13
4.2	16
5.2	3

f

x	f
0.07	12
0.09	17
0.14	25
0.17	36
0.26	17
0.27	13

3 a A dice is thrown 120 times. The results are shown in the table.

Score	1	2	3	4	5	6
Frequency	21	20	19	20	19	21

    i Calculate the mean and the standard deviation of the scores from the dice.

    ii Square the standard deviation.

b Two dice are thrown 180 times. The results are shown in the table.

Score	2	3	4	5	6	7	8	9	10	11	12
Frequency	5	11	15	20	25	31	24	19	16	9	5

    i Calculate the mean and the standard deviation of the scores from the two dice.

    ii Square the standard deviation.

c What is the approximate relationship between the answers to parts **a** and **b**?

d If three dice are thrown, estimate the mean and the standard deviation of the total scores from all three dice.

4 a Calculate the mean and the standard deviation of the data in this table.

Mark, x	121	126	131	136	141	146
Frequency, f	2	3	5	6	5	4

b 121 is subtracted from each of the values in the table above and the result is divided by 5. This gives the table below.

Mark, x	0	1	2	3	4	5
Frequency, f	2	3	5	6	5	4

Calculate the mean and the standard deviation for this table.

    i Multiply the mean by 5 and add 121.

    ii Multiply the standard deviation by 5.

c What connects your answers to parts **b i** and **b ii** and your answers to part **a**?

d What advantage does the second table have over the first?

1 The table shows the times taken for a certain train journey on 20 different occasions.

Time taken, t (min)	Frequency
$18 < t \leq 20$	4
$20 < t \leq 22$	6
$22 < t \leq 24$	5
$24 < t \leq 26$	3
$26 < t \leq 28$	2

Calculate an estimate of the mean journey time.

2 Brian and George played 40 games of golf. The cumulative frequency diagram shows information about Brian's scores. The box plot shows information about George's scores.

a Showing your method clearly, find

i Brian's median score

ii Brian's interquartile range.

b Use the cumulative frequency diagram and the box plot to answer the following.

i Which player is the more consistent in his scoring?

ii The winner of a game of golf is the player who has the lowest score. Who do you think is the better player? Give a reason for your choice.

AQA, Question 12, Paper 2 Higher, November 2003

3 56 boys and 52 girls took an English test. The box plots show the distributions of their marks.

Give *two* differences between the boys' marks and the girls' marks.

AQA, Question 6, Paper 1 Higher, November 2004

4 The length of time, in minutes, of 40 telephone calls was recorded. A cumulative frequency diagram of this data is shown on the grid below.

Use the diagram to find the limits between which the middle 50% of the times lie.

AQA, Question 12, Paper 2 Higher, June 2003

WORKED EXAM QUESTION

Derek makes men's and women's shirts. He needs to know the range of collar sizes so he measures 100 men's necks.
The results are shown in the table.

a   Draw a cumulative frequency diagram to show this information
b   Use the diagram to find
   i   the median
   ii the interquartile range
c   The box plot shows the neck sizes of 100 women.

Neck size, n (cm)	Frequency
$12 < n \leqslant 13$	5
$13 < n \leqslant 14$	16
$14 < n \leqslant 15$	28
$15 < n \leqslant 16$	37
$16 < n \leqslant 17$	10
$17 < n \leqslant 18$	4

Neck size, cm

Comment on the differences in the distribution of neck sizes for men and women.

Solution

a   Cumulative Frequencies: 5, 21, 49, 86, 96, 100

> First work out the cumulative frequencies. The easiest way to do this is with another column on the table.

b

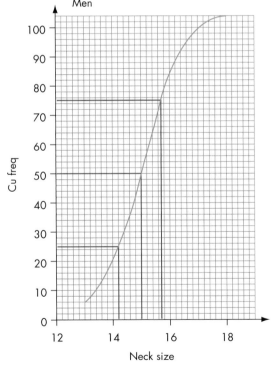

Men

Neck size

> Plot the points (13, 5), (14, 21), etc.
> i.e the top value of each group against the cumulative frequency.

> Draw lines from 50 (median), 25 (lower quartile) and 75 (upper quartile) from the vertical axis across to the graph and down to the horizontal axis. Subtract lower quartile from upper quartile for the inter-quartile range.

Median = 15 cm

IQR = 15.7 − 14.2 = 1.5 cm

c   The men have a higher median (about 1.5 cm higher) and the women have a larger interquartile range
(About 2.5 cm compared to 1.5 cm)

> Comment on the differences between The medians and the interquartile ranges. Use numerical values to show you know how to read the box plot.

Michael Jones is a journalist. He writes articles for a monthly magazine.

He is asked to write a report on the changes in the population of the UK over the 25 years from 1976 to 2001.

Michael does some research, and finds the following figures for 1976 and 2001.

He calculates the percentage change for each age group to the nearest percent. Help him to complete the table.

Age distribution in the UK (numbers in millions)			
Age (a) in years	1976	2001	% change
$0 \le a < 15$	12.9	11.1	−14%
$15 \le a < 25$	8.1	7.2	
$25 \le a < 35$	7.9	8.4	
$35 \le a < 45$	6.4	8.8	
$45 \le a < 55$	9.8	7.8	
$55 \le a < 65$	3.1	6.2	
$65 \le a < 75$	5.1	4.9	
$75 \le a < 85$	2.3	3.3	
$85 \le a < 105$	0.5	1.1	

He also decides to find an estimate of the mean in 1976 and 2001.

He uses this table to help. Complete the calculations for him.

Midpoint of ages	1976 frequency (millions)	midpoint x frequency	2001 frequency (millions)	midpoint x frequency
7.5	12.9	96.75	11.1	83.25
20	8.1		7.2	
	7.9		8.4	
	6.4		8.8	
	9.8		7.8	
	3.1		6.2	
	5.1		4.9	
	2.3		3.3	
	0.5		1.1	
Totals				
Mean age				

Finally he wants to find the median ages and interquartile ranges (IQR).

Complete the cumulative frequencies below, then draw cumulative frequency graphs and use them to find the median and IQR for both years.

Cumulative frequencies for age distributions (in millions)									
	< 15	< 25	< 35	< 45	< 55	< 65	< 75	< 85	<105
1976	12.9	21	28.9						
2001	11.1	18.3							

Michael summarises the statistical data in a table. He rounds every answer to the nearest whole number of years.

Complete the table for him.

	1976	2001
mean		
median		
upper quartile		
lower quartile		
IQR		

He writes the following article. Write down the words that should go in the spaces.

Are we living longer?

Michael Jones reports on the change in the population of the UK from 1976 to 2001.

The total population for the UK in 1976 was approximately 56.1 million, which increased to 58.8 million in 2001. This means that over 25 years, the population has grown by _____ million people. During this time period, the largest percentage increase occurred in the age group _____ with a staggering _____% increase.

However the largest percentage decrease of _____% occurred in the age group _____. The reasons for this could possibly be due to rationing and a shortage of men in the decade following the second world war.

The mean age of the population has increased from _____ years old to _____ years old (both values are given to the nearest whole year).

This increase of _____ years appears to reinforce the claim made by politicians that as medical science advances and our standard of living and diet improve, it means that we are living longer.

The median age for the two years shows a slightly larger increase than the mean, going from _____ years up to _____ years. The lower and upper quartiles also increase by _____ years, thus showing a shift upwards by _____ years of the central 50% of the population.

So, does this show a healthier, happier Britain?

Well, it certainly appears that we are on average living longer. The mean and median both show the average age increasing. But, will the trend continue? Certainly our standard of living has improved, and the treatment of illnesses is improving at a rapid rate, but what about our eating habits? These too are changing.

Fast food + less exercise = obesity. Is this the maths equation that will reverse the trend in the age of the population?

Read next months article, **We are what we eat – true or false?** which looks more closely at the UK's expanding waistlines.

Do you think this article is well written? Is it misleading in any way? Can you write a better article for him?

GRADE YOURSELF

D Able to draw an ordered stem-and-leaf diagram

D Able to draw a line of best fit on a scatter diagram

C Recognise the different types of correlation

C Able to interpret a line of best fit

B Able to draw a cumulative frequency diagram

B Able to find medians and quartiles from cumulative frequency diagrams

B Able to draw and interpret box plots

What you should know now

- How to read information from statistical diagrams including stem-and-leaf diagrams

- How to plot scatter diagrams, recognise correlation, draw lines of best fit and use them to predict values

- How to construct a cumulative frequency diagram

- How to draw and interpret box plots

Probability

This chapter will show you ...

- how to work out the probability of events, either using theoretical models or experimental models
- how to predict outcomes using theoretical models and compare experimental and theoretical data
- how to calculate probabilities for combined events

What you should already know

- That the probability scale goes from 0 to 1
- How to use the probability scale and to assess the likelihood of events depending on their position on the scale
- How to cancel, add and subtract factors

Quick check

1 Draw a probability scale and put an arrow to show approximately the probability of each of the following events happening.

a The next TV programme you watch will have been made in Britain.

b A person in your class will have been born in April.

c It will snow in July in Spain.

d In the next Olympic Games, a man will run the 100 m race in less than 20 seconds.

e During this week, you will drink some water or pop.

Terminology

The topic of probability has its own special terminology, which will be explained as it arises. For example, a **trial** is one go at performing something, such as throwing a dice or tossing a coin. So, if we throw a dice 10 times, we perform 10 trials.

Two other probability terms are **event** and **outcome**. An event is anything whose probability we want to measure. An outcome is any way in which an event can happen.

Another probability term is **at random**. This means "without looking" or "not knowing what the outcome is in advance".

Note: "Dice" is used in this book in preference to "die" for the singular form of the noun, as well as for the plural. This is in keeping with growing common usage, including in examination papers.

Probability facts

The probability of a *certain* event is 1 and the probability of an *impossible* event is 0.

Probability is never greater than 1 or less than 0.

Many probability examples involve coins, dice and packs of cards. Here is a reminder of their outcomes.

- A coin has two outcomes: head or tail.

- An ordinary six-sided dice has six outcomes: 1, 2, 3, 4, 5, 6.

- A pack of cards consists of 52 cards divided into four suits: Hearts (red), Spades (black), Diamonds (red), and Clubs (black). Each suit consists of 13 cards bearing the following values: 2, 3, 4, 5, 6, 7, 8, 9, 10, Jack, Queen, King and Ace. The Jack, Queen and King are called "picture cards". (The Ace is sometimes also called a picture card.) So the total number of outcomes is 52.

Probability is defined as

$$P(\text{event}) = \frac{\text{Number of ways the event can happen}}{\text{Total number of all possible outcomes}}$$

This definition always leads to a fraction which should be cancelled down to its simplest form. Make sure that you know how to cancel down fractions with or without a calculator. It is acceptable to give a probability as a decimal or a percentage but a fraction is better.

This definition can be used to work out the probability of events, as the following example shows.

EXAMPLE 1

A card is drawn from a pack of cards. What is the probability that it is one of the following?

a a red card   **b** a Spade   **c** a seven

d a picture card   **e** a number less than 5   **f** a red King

a There are 26 red cards, so P(red card) $= \frac{26}{52} = \frac{1}{2}$

b There are 13 Spades, so P(Spade) $= \frac{13}{52} = \frac{1}{4}$

c There are four sevens, so P(seven) $= \frac{4}{52} = \frac{1}{13}$

d There are 12 picture cards, so P(picture card) $= \frac{12}{52} = \frac{3}{13}$

e If you count the value of an Ace as 1, there are 16 cards with a value less than 5.
So, P(number less than 5) $= \frac{16}{52} = \frac{4}{13}$

f There are 2 red Kings, so P(red King) $= \frac{2}{52} = \frac{1}{26}$

19.1 Experimental probability

In this section you will learn how to:
- calculate experimental probabilities and relative frequencies
- estimate probabilities from experiments
- use different methods to estimate probabilities

Key words

experimental probability
relative frequency
trials

The value of number of heads ÷ number of tosses is called an **experimental probability**. As the number of **trials** or experiments increases, the value of the experimental probability gets closer to the true or theoretical probability.

Experimental probability is also known as the **relative frequency** of an event. The relative frequency of an event is an estimate for the theoretical probability. It is given by

$$\text{Relative frequency of an event} = \frac{\text{Frequency of the event}}{\text{Total number of trials}}$$

EXAMPLE 2

The frequency table shows the speeds of 160 vehicles which pass a radar speed check on a dual carriageway.

Speed (mph)	20–29	30–39	40–49	50–59	60–69	70+
Frequency	14	23	28	35	52	8

a What is the experimental probability that a vehicle is travelling faster than 70 mph?

b If 500 vehicles pass the speed check, estimate how many will be travelling faster than 70 mph.

a The experimental probability is the relative frequency, which is $\frac{8}{160} = \frac{1}{20}$

b The number of vehicles travelling faster than 70 mph will be $\frac{1}{20}$ of 500.

That is, $500 \div 20 = 25$ vehicles

Finding probabilities

There are three ways in which the probability of an event can be found.

• If we can work out the theoretical probability of an event – for example, drawing a King from a pack of cards – this is called using equally likely outcomes.

• Some events, such as buying a certain brand of dog food, cannot be calculated using equally likely outcomes. To find the probability of such an event, we can perform an experiment or conduct a survey. This is called collecting experimental data. The more data we collect, the better the estimate is.

• The probability of some events, such as an earthquake occurring in Japan, cannot be found by either of the above methods. One of the things we can do is to look at data collected over a long period of time and make an estimate (sometimes called a best guess) at the chance of the event happening. This is called looking at historical data.

EXAMPLE 3

Which method (A, B or C) would you use to estimate the probabilities of the events a to e?

A: Use equally likely outcomes

B: Conduct a survey/collect data

C: Look at historical data

a Someone in your class will go abroad for a holiday this year.

b You will win the National Lottery.

c Your bus home will be late.

d It will snow on Christmas Day.

e You will pick a red seven from a pack of cards.

a You would have to ask all the members of your class what they intended to do for their holidays this year. You would therefore conduct a survey, method B.

b The odds on winning are about 14 million to 1. This is an equally likely outcome, method A.

c If you catch the bus every day, you can collect data over several weeks. This would be method C.

d If you check whether it snowed on Christmas Day for the last few years you would be able to make a good estimate of the probability. This would be method C.

e There are two red sevens out of 52 cards, so the probability of picking one can be calculated: $P(\text{red seven}) = \frac{2}{52} = \frac{1}{26}$

This is method A.

EXERCISE 19A

1 Naseer throws a dice and records the number of sixes that he gets after various numbers of throws. The table shows his results.

Number of throws	10	50	100	200	500	1000	2000
Number of sixes	2	4	10	21	74	163	329

a Calculate the experimental probability of a six at each stage that Naseer recorded his results.

b How many ways can a dice land?

c How many of these ways give a six?

d What is the theoretical probability of throwing a six with a dice?

e If Naseer threw the dice a total of 6000 times, how many sixes would you expect him to get?

2 Marie made a five-sided spinner, like the one shown in the diagram. She used it to play a board game with her friend Sarah. The girls thought that the spinner wasn't very fair as it seemed to land on some numbers more than others. They spun the spinner 200 times and recorded the results. The results are shown in the table.

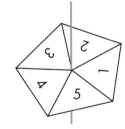

Side spinner lands on	1	2	3	4	5
Number of times	19	27	32	53	69

a Work out the experimental probability of each number.

b How many times would you expect each number to occur if the spinner is fair?

c Do you think that the spinner is fair? Give a reason for your answer.

Sarah thought she could make a much more accurate spinner. After she had made it, she tested it and recorded how many times she scored a 5. Her results are shown in the table.

Number of spins	10	50	100	500
Number of fives	3	12	32	107

a Sarah made a mistake in recording the number of fives. Which number in the second row above is wrong? Give a reason for your answer.

b These are the full results for 500 spins.

Side spinner lands on	1	2	3	4	5
Number of times	96	112	87	98	107

Do you think the spinner is fair? Give a reason for your answer.

4 A sampling bottle contains 20 balls. The balls are either black or white. (A sampling bottle is a sealed bottle with a clear plastic tube at one end into which one of the balls can be tipped.) Kenny conducts an experiment to see how many black balls are in the bottle. He takes various numbers of samples and records how many of them showed a black ball. The results are shown in the table.

Number of samples	Number of black balls	Experimental probability
10	2	
100	25	
200	76	
500	210	
1000	385	
5000	1987	

a Copy the table and calculate the experimental probability of getting a black ball at each stage.

b Using this information, how many black balls do you think are in the bottle?

5 Another sampling bottle contains red, white and blue balls. It is known that there are 20 balls in the bottle altogether. Carrie performs an experiment to see how many of each colour are in the bottle. She starts off putting down a tally each time a colour shows in the clear plastic tube.

Red	White	Blue
⦀⦀ ⦀⦀ ⦀⦀ ⦀⦀ II	⦀⦀ ⦀⦀ ⦀⦀ III	⦀⦀ ⦀⦀ II

Unfortunately, she forgets to count how many times she performs the experiment, so every now and again she counts up the tallies and records them in a table (see below).

Red	White	Blue	Total
22	18	12	52
48	31	16	95
65	37	24	126
107	61	32	200
152	93	62	307
206	128	84	418

The relative frequency of the red balls is calculated by dividing the frequency of red by the total number of trials, so at each stage these are

  0.423 0.505 0.516 0.535 0.495 0.493

These answers are rounded off to three significant figures.

 a Calculate the relative frequencies of the white balls at each stage to three significant figures.

 b Calculate the relative frequencies of the blue balls at each stage to three significant figures.

 c Round off the final relative frequencies for Carrie's 418 trials to one decimal place.

 d What is the total of the answers in part **c**?

 e How many balls of each colour do you think are in the bottle? Explain your answer.

6 Using card and a cocktail stick, make a six-sided spinner, as shown below.

When you have made the spinner, spin it 120 times and record your results in a table like the one below.

Number	Tally	Total
1	⊮⊮ ‖	
2	‖‖‖	

 a Which number occurred the most?

 b How many times would you expect to get each number?

 c Is your spinner fair?

 d Explain your answer to part **c**.

7 Use a set of number cards from 1 to 10 (or make your own set) and work with a partner. Take it in turns to choose a card and keep a record each time of what card you get. Shuffle the cards each time and repeat the experiment 60 times. Put your results in a copy of this table.

Score	1	2	3	4	5	6	7	8	9	10
Total										

 a How many times would you expect to get each number?

 b Do you think you and your partner conducted this experiment fairly?

 c Explain your answer to part **b**.

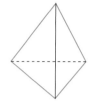

8 A four-sided dice has faces numbered 1, 2, 3 and 4. The score is the face on which it lands. Five pupils throw the dice to see if it is biased. They each throw it a different number of times. Their results are shown in the table.

Pupil	Total number of throws	Score			
		1	2	3	4
Alfred	20	7	6	3	4
Brian	50	19	16	8	7
Caryl	250	102	76	42	30
Deema	80	25	25	12	18
Emma	150	61	46	26	17

a Which pupil will have the most reliable set of results? Why?

b Add up all the score columns and work out the relative frequency of each score. Give your answers to two decimal places.

c Is the dice biased? Explain your answer.

9 Which of these methods would you use to estimate or state the probability of each of the events **a** to **h**?

Method A: Equally likely outcomes

Method B: Survey or experiment

Method C: Look at historical data

a How people will vote in the next election.

b A drawing pin dropped on a desk will land point up.

c A Premiership football team will win the FA Cup.

d You will win a school raffle.

e The next car to drive down the road will be red.

f You will throw a "double six" with two dice.

g Someone in your class likes classical music.

h A person picked at random from your school will be a vegetarian.

10 If you were about to choose a card from a pack of yellow cards numbered from 1 to 10, what would be the chance of each of the events **a** to **i** occurring? Copy and complete each of these statements with a word or phrase chosen from "impossible", "not likely", "50–50 chance", "quite likely", or "certain".

a The likelihood that the next card chosen will be a four is ......

b The likelihood that the next card chosen will be pink is ......

c The likelihood that the next card chosen will be a seven is ......

d The likelihood that the next card chosen will be a number less than 11 is ......

e The likelihood that the next card chosen will be a number bigger than 11 is ......

f The likelihood that the next card chosen will be an even number is ......

g The likelihood that the next card chosen will be a number more than 5 is ......

h The likelihood that the next card chosen will be a multiple of 1 is ......

i The likelihood that the next card chosen will be a prime number is ......

19.2 Mutually exclusive and exhaustive events

In this section you will learn how to:

● recognise mutually exclusive, complementary and exhaustive events

Key words

complementary
exhaustive
mutually
    exclusive

If a bag contains three black, two yellow and five white balls and only one ball is allowed to be taken at random from the bag, then by the basic definition of probability

$$P(\text{black ball}) = \frac{3}{10}$$

$$P(\text{yellow ball}) = \frac{2}{10} = \frac{1}{5}$$

$$P(\text{white ball}) = \frac{5}{10} = \frac{1}{2}$$

We can also say that the probability of choosing a black ball or a yellow ball is $= \frac{5}{10} = \frac{1}{2}$

The events "picking a yellow ball" and "picking a black ball" can never happen at the same time when only one ball is taken out: that is, a ball can be either black or yellow. Such events are called **mutually exclusive**. Other examples of mutually exclusive events are tossing a head or a tail with a coin, drawing a King or an Ace from a pack of cards and throwing an even or an odd number with a dice.

An example of events that are not mutually exclusive would be drawing a red card and a King from a pack of cards. There are two red Kings, so these events could be true at the same time.

EXAMPLE 4

An ordinary dice is thrown.

a What is the probability of throwing

    i an even number?   **ii** an odd number?

b What is the total of the answers to part **a**?

c Is it possible to get a score on a dice that is both odd and even?

  a **i** $P(\text{even}) = \dfrac{1}{2}$ **ii** $P(\text{odd}) = \dfrac{1}{2}$ **b** $\dfrac{1}{2} + \dfrac{1}{2} = 1$ **c** No

Events such as those in Example 4 are mutually exclusive because they can never happen at the same time. Because there are no other possibilities, they are also called **exhaustive** events. The probabilities of exhaustive events add up to 1.

EXAMPLE 5

A bag contains only black and white balls. The probability of picking at random a black ball from the bag is $\dfrac{7}{10}$.

a What is the probability of picking a white ball from the bag?

b Can you say how many black and white balls are in the bag?

a As the event "picking a white ball" and the event "picking a black ball" are mutually exclusive and exhaustive then

$$P(\text{white}) = 1 - P(\text{black}) = 1 - \frac{7}{10} = \frac{3}{10}$$

b You cannot say precisely what the number of balls is although you can say that there could be seven black and three white, fourteen black and six white, or any combination of black and white balls in the ratio 7 : 3.

Complementary event

If there is an event A, the **complementary** event of A is

    Event A *not* happening

Any event is mutually exclusive and exhaustive to its complementary event. That is,

    P(event A not happening) = 1 – P(event A happening)

which can be stated as

    P(event) + P(complementary event) = 1

For example, the probability of getting a King from a pack of cards is $\dfrac{4}{52} = \dfrac{1}{13}$, so the probability of *not* getting a King is

$$1 - \frac{1}{13} = \frac{12}{13}$$

EXERCISE 19B

1 Say whether these pairs of events are mutually exclusive or not.

 a tossing a head with a coin/tossing a tail with a coin

 b throwing a number less than 3 with a dice/throwing a number greater than 3 with a dice

 c drawing a Spade from a pack of cards/drawing an Ace from a pack of cards

 d drawing a Spade from a pack of cards/drawing a red card from a pack of cards

 e if two people are to be chosen from three girls and two boys: choosing two girls/choosing two boys

 f drawing a red card from a pack of cards/drawing a black card from a pack of cards

2 Which of the pairs of mutually exclusive events in question **1** are also exhaustive?

3 Each morning I run to work or get a lift. The probability that I run to work is $\frac{2}{5}$.
What is the probability that I get a lift?

4 A letter is to be chosen at random from this set of letter-cards.

 a What is the probability the letter is

  i an S?   **ii** a T?   **iii** a vowel?

 b Which of these pairs of events are mutually exclusive?

  i picking an S / picking a T   **ii** picking an S / picking a vowel

  iii picking an S / picking another consonant   **iv** picking a vowel / picking a consonant

 c Which pair of mutually exclusive events in part **b** is also exhaustive?

5 Two people are to be chosen for a job from this set of five people.

 a List all of the possible pairs (there are 10 altogether).

 b What is the probability that the pair of people chosen will

  i both be female?   **ii** both be male?

  iii both have the same initial?   **iv** have different initials?

Jane   Dave   Anne   Jack   John

 c Which of these pairs of events are mutually exclusive?

  i picking two women/picking two men

  ii picking two people of the same sex/picking two people of opposite sex

  iii picking two people with the same initial/picking two men

  iv picking two people with the same initial/picking two women

 d Which pair of mutually exclusive events in part **c** is also exhaustive?

6 A spinner consists of an outer ring of coloured sectors and an inner circle of numbered sectors, as shown.

a The probability of getting 2 is $\frac{1}{4}$. The probabilities of getting 1 or 3 are equal. What is the probability of getting 3?

b The probability of getting blue is $\frac{1}{4}$. The probability of getting white $\frac{1}{4}$. The probability of getting green is $\frac{3}{8}$. What is the probability of getting red?

c Which of these pairs of events are mutually exclusive?

   i getting 3/getting 2   **ii** getting 3/getting green

   iii getting 3/getting blue   **iv** getting blue/getting red

d Explain why it is not possible to get a colour that is mutually exclusive to the event "getting an odd number".

7 At the morning break, I have the choice of coffee, tea or hot chocolate. If the probability I choose coffee is $\frac{3}{5}$, the probability I choose tea is $\frac{1}{4}$, what is the probability I choose hot chocolate?

8 Assemblies at school are always taken by the head, the deputy head or the senior teacher. If the head takes the assembly, the probability that she goes over time is $\frac{1}{2}$. If the deputy takes the assembly, the probability that he goes over time is $\frac{1}{4}$. Explain why it is not necessarily true to say that the probability that the senior teacher goes over time is $\frac{1}{4}$.

9 A hotelier conducted a survey of guests staying at her hotel. The table shows some of the results of her survey.

Type of guest	Probability
Man	0.7
Woman	0.3
American man	0.2
American woman	0.05
Vegetarian	0.3
Married	0.6

a A guest was chosen at random. From the table, work out these probabilities.

   i the guest was American

   ii the guest was single

   iii the guest was not a vegetarian

b Explain why it is not possible to work out from the table the probability of a guest being a married vegetarian.

c From the table, give two examples of pairs of types of guest that would form a pair of mutually exclusive events.

d From the table, give one example of a pair of types of guest that would form a pair of exhaustive events.

Expectation

In this section you will learn how to:

- predict the likely number of successful events given the number of trials and the probability of any one event

Key word

expectation

When we know the probability of an event, we can predict how many times we would expect that event to happen in a certain number of trials.

Note that this is what we *expect*. It is not what is going to happen. If what we expected always happened, life would be very dull and boring and the National Lottery would be a waste of time.

EXAMPLE 6

A bag contains 20 balls, nine of which are black, six white and five yellow. A ball is drawn at random from the bag, its colour noted and then it is put back in the bag. This is repeated 500 times.

a How many times would you expect a black ball to be drawn?

b How many times would you expect a yellow ball to be drawn?

c How many times would you expect a black or a yellow ball to be drawn?

a P(black ball) = $\frac{9}{20}$

Expected number of black balls = $\frac{9}{20} \times 500 = 225$

b P(yellow ball) = $\frac{5}{20} = \frac{1}{4}$

Expected number of yellow balls = $\frac{1}{4} \times 500 = 125$

c Expected number of black or yellow balls = 225 + 125 = 350

EXAMPLE 7

Four in 10 cars sold in Britain are made by Japanese companies.

a What is the probability that the next car to drive down your road will be Japanese?

b If there are 2000 cars in a multistorey car park, how many of them would you expect to be Japanese?

a P(Japanese car) = $\frac{4}{10} = \frac{2}{5} = 0.4$

b Expected number of Japanese cars in 2000 cars = 0.4 × 2000 = 800 cars

EXERCISE 19C

 1 I throw an ordinary dice 150 times. How many times can I expect to get a score of 6?

 2 I toss a coin 2000 times. How many times can I expect to get a head?

 3 I draw a card from a pack of cards and replace it. I do this 520 times. How many times would I expect to get these?

    a a black card   **b** a King

    c a Heart   **d** the King of Hearts

 4 The ball in a roulette wheel can land in 37 spaces which are the numbers between 0 and 36 inclusive. I always bet on the same number, 13. If I play all evening and there is a total of 185 spins of the wheel in that time, how many times could I expect to win?

 5 In a bag there are 30 balls, 15 of which are red, 5 yellow, 5 green, and 5 blue. A ball is taken out at random and then replaced. This is repeated 300 times. How many times would I expect to get these outcomes?

    a a red ball   **b** a yellow or blue ball

    c a ball that is not blue   **d** a pink ball

 6 The same experiment described in question **5** is carried out 1000 times. Approximately how many times would you expect to get **a** a green ball, **b** a ball that is not blue?

 7 A sampling bottle (as described in question **4** of Exercise 19A) contains red and white balls. It is known that the probability of getting a red ball is 0.3. 1500 samples are taken. How many of them would you expect to give a white ball?

 8 Josie said: "When I throw a dice, I expect to get a score of 3.5."

"Impossible," said Paul, "you can't score 3.5 with a dice."

"Do this and I'll prove it," said Josie.

    a An ordinary dice is thrown 60 times. Fill in the table for the expected number of times each score will occur.

Score						
Expected occurrences						

    b Now work out the average score that is expected over 60 throws.

    c There is an easy way to get an answer of 3.5 for the expected average score. Can you see what it is?

  9 I have 20 tickets for a raffle and I know that the probability of my winning the prize is 0.05. How many tickets were sold altogether in the raffle?

Two-way tables

A **two-way table** is a table that links together two variables. For example, the following table shows how many boys and girls are in a form and whether they are left- or right-handed.

	Boys	Girls
Left-handed	2	4
Right-handed	10	13

This table shows the colour and make of cars in the school car park.

	Red	Blue	White
Ford	2	4	1
Vauxhall	0	1	2
Toyota	3	3	4
Peugeot	2	0	3

One variable is written in the rows of the table and the other variable is written in the columns of the table.

EXAMPLE 8

Using the first two-way table above, answer these questions.

a If a pupil is selected at random from the form what is the probability that the pupil is a left-handed boy?

b It is known that a pupil selected at random is a girl. What is the probability that she is right-handed?

a $\frac{2}{29}$

b $\frac{13}{17}$

EXAMPLE 9

Using the second two-way table above, answer these questions.

a What percentage of the cars in the car park are red?

b What percentage of the white cars are Vauxhalls?

a 28%. Seven out of 25 is the same as 28 out of 100.

b 20%. Two out of 10 is 20%.

1 The two-way table shows the age and sex of a sample of 50 pupils in a school.

	Age (years)					
	11	**12**	**13**	**14**	**15**	**16**
Number of boys	4	3	6	2	5	4
Number of girls	2	5	3	6	4	6

a How many pupils are aged 13 years or less?

b What percentage of the pupils in the table are 16?

c A pupil from the table is selected at random. What is the probability that the pupil will be 14 years of age. Give your answer as a fraction in its lowest form.

d There are 1000 pupils in the school. Use the table to estimate how many boys are in the school altogether.

2 The two-way table shows the number of adults and the number of cars in 50 houses in one street.

		Number of adults			
		1	**2**	**3**	**4**
Number of cars	**0**	2	1	0	0
	1	3	13	3	1
	2	0	10	6	4
	3	0	1	4	2

a How many houses have exactly two adults and two cars?

b How many houses altogether have three cars?

c What percentage of the houses have three cars?

d What percentage of the houses with just one car have three adults living in the house?

3 Jane has two four-sided spinners. One has the numbers 1 to 4 and the other has the numbers 5 to 8.

Spinner A   Spinner B

Both spinners are spun together.

The two-way table (on the next page) shows all the ways the two spinners can land.

Some of the total scores are filled in.

		Score on spinner A			
		1	**2**	**3**	**4**
	5	6	7		
Score on spinner B	**6**	7			
	7				
	8				

a   Complete the table to show all the possible total scores.

b   How many of the total scores are 9?

c   When the two spinners are spun together what is the probability that the total score will be

   i   9?

   ii   8?

   iii   a prime number?

4   The table shows information about the number of items in Flossy's music collection.

		Type of music		
		Pop	**Folk**	**Classical**
	Tape	16	5	2
Format	**CD**	51	9	13
	Mini disc	9	2	0

a   How many pop tapes does Flossy have?

b   How many items of folk music does Flossy have?

c   How many CDs does Flossy have?

d   If a CD is chosen at random from all the CDs, what is the probability that it will be a pop CD?

5   Zoe throws a fair coin and rolls a fair dice.

   If the coin shows a head she records the score on the dice.

   If the coin shows tails she doubles the number on the dice.

a   Complete the two-way table to show Zoe's possible scores.

		Number on dice					
		1	**2**	**3**	**4**	**5**	**6**
Coin	**Head**	1	2				
	Tail	2	4				

b   How many of the scores are square numbers?

c   What is the probability of getting a score that is a square number?

6 A gardener plants some sunflower seeds in a greenhouse and plants some in the garden. After they have fully grown, he measures the diameter of the sunflower heads. The table shows his results.

	Greenhouse	Garden
Mean diameter	16.8 cm	14.5 cm
Range of diameter	3.2 cm	1.8 cm

a The gardener who wants to enter competitions says "the sunflowers from the greenhouse are better".

Using the data in the table, give a reason to justify this statement.

b The gardener's wife, who does flower arranging says "the sunflowers from the garden are better".

Using the data in the table, give a reason to justify this statement.

7 The two-way table shows the wages for the men and women in a factory.

Wage, w, (£) per week	Men	Women
£100 < w ≤ £150	3	4
£150 < w ≤ £200	7	5
£200 < w ≤ £250	23	12
£250 < w ≤ £300	48	27
£300 < w ≤ £350	32	11
More than £350	7	1

a What percentage of the men earn between £250 and £300 per week?

b What percentage of the women earn between £250 and £300 per week?

c Is it possible to work out the mean wage of the men and women? Explain your answer.

19.5 Addition rule for events

In this section you will learn how to:
● work out the probability of two events such as P(event A) or P(event B)

Key word
either

We have used the addition rule already but it has not yet been formally defined.

When two events are mutually exclusive, we can work out the probability of **either** of them occurring by adding up the separate probabilities.

EXAMPLE 10

A bag contains twelve red balls, eight green balls, five blue balls and fifteen black balls. A ball is drawn at random. What is the probability of it being each of these?

a red b black c red or black

d not green e neither green nor blue

a $P(\text{red}) = \dfrac{12}{40} = \dfrac{3}{10}$ b $P(\text{black}) = \dfrac{15}{40} = \dfrac{3}{8}$

c $P(\text{red or black}) = P(\text{red}) + P(\text{black}) = \dfrac{3}{10} + \dfrac{3}{8} = \dfrac{27}{40}$

d $P(\text{not green}) = \dfrac{32}{40} = \dfrac{4}{5}$

e $P(\text{neither green nor blue}) = P(\text{red or black}) = \dfrac{27}{40}$

The last part of Example 10 is another illustration of how confusing probability can be. You might think

$$P(\text{neither green nor blue}) = P(\text{not green}) + P(\text{not blue}) = \dfrac{32}{40} + \dfrac{35}{40} = \dfrac{67}{40}$$

This cannot be correct, as the answer is greater than 1. In fact, the events "not green" and "not blue" are not mutually exclusive, as there are lots of balls that are true for both events.

EXERCISE 19E

1 Iqbal throws an ordinary dice. What is the probability that he throws these scores?

a 2 b 5 c 2 or 5

2 Jennifer draws a card from a pack of cards. What is the probability that she draws these?

a a Heart b a Club c a Heart or a Club

3 Jasper draws a card from a pack of cards. What is the probability that he draws one of the following numbers?

a 2 b 6 c 2 or 6

4 A letter is chosen at random from the letters on these cards. What is the probability of choosing each of these?

a a B b a vowel c a B or a vowel

5 A bag contains 10 white balls, 12 black balls and 8 red balls. A ball is drawn at random from the bag. What is the probability of each of these outcomes?

a white   b black

c black or white   d not red

e not red or black

6 At the School Fayre the tombola stall gives out a prize if you draw from the drum a numbered ticket that ends in 0 or 5. There are 300 tickets in the drum altogether and the probability of getting a winning ticket is 0.4.

a What is the probability of getting a losing ticket?

b How many winning tickets are there in the drum?

7 John needs his calculator for his mathematics lesson. It is either in his pocket, bag or locker. The probability it is in his pocket is 0.35; the probability it is in his bag is 0.45. What is the probability that

a he will have the calculator for the lesson?

b it is in his locker?

8 A spinner has numbers and colours on it, as shown in the diagram. Their probabilities are given in the tables.

When the spinner is spun what is the probability of each of the following?

a red or green

b 2 or 3

c 3 or green

d 2 or green

e i Explain why the answer to P(1 or red) is not 0.9.

    ii What is the answer to P(1 or red)?

Red	0.5
Green	0.25
Blue	0.25

1	0.4
2	0.35
3	0.25

9 Debbie has 20 unlabelled pirate CDs, 12 of which are rock, 5 are pop and 3 are classical. She picks a CD at random. What is the probability of these outcomes?

a rock or pop

b pop or classical

c not pop

10 The probability that it rains on Monday is 0.5. The probability that it rains on Tuesday is 0.5 and the probability that it rains on Wednesday is 0.5. Kelly argues that it is certain to rain on Monday, Tuesday or Wednesday because 0.5 + 0.5 + 0.5 = 1.5, which is bigger than 1 so that it is a certain event. Explain why she is wrong.

Combined events

In this section you will learn how to:
- work out the probability of two events occurring at the same time

Key words

probability
space
diagram
sample space
diagram

There are many situations where two events occur together. Some examples are given below. Note that in each case all the possible outcomes of the events are shown in diagrams. These are called **probability space diagrams** or **sample space diagrams**.

Throwing two dice

Imagine that two dice, one red and one blue, are thrown. The red dice can land with any one of six scores: 1, 2, 3, 4, 5 or 6. The blue dice can also land with any one of six scores. This gives a total of 36 possible combinations. These are shown in the left-hand diagram, where each combination is given as (2, 3), etc. The first number is the score on the blue dice and the second number is the score on the red dice.

The combination (2, 3) gives a total score of 5. The total scores for all the combinations are shown in the right-hand diagram.

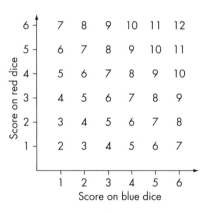

From the diagram on the right, we can see that there are two ways to get a score of 3. This gives a probability of

$$P(3) = \frac{2}{36} = \frac{1}{18}$$

From the diagram on the left, we can see that there are six ways to get a "double". This gives a probability of

$$P(double) = \frac{6}{36} = \frac{1}{6}$$

Throwing coins

Throwing one coin

There are two equally likely outcomes, head or tail

Throwing two coins together

There are four equally likely outcomes

$P(\text{2 heads}) = \dfrac{1}{4}$

$P(\text{head and tail}) = 2 \text{ ways out of } 4 = \dfrac{2}{4} = \dfrac{1}{2}$

Dice and coins

Throwing a dice and a coin

$$
\begin{array}{c|cccccc}
\text{H} & (1, H) & (2, H) & (3, H) & (4, H) & (5, H) & (6, H) \\
\text{T} & (1, T) & (2, T) & (3, T) & (4, T) & (5, T) & (6, T) \\
\hline
 & 1 & 2 & 3 & 4 & 5 & 6
\end{array}
$$

Outcome on coin — Score on dice

$P(\text{head and an even number}) = 3 \text{ ways out of } 12 = \dfrac{3}{12} = \dfrac{1}{4}$

EXERCISE 19F

1 To answer these questions, use the right-hand diagram on page 463 for the total scores when two dice are thrown together.

  a What is the most likely score?

  b Which two scores are least likely?

  c Write down the probabilities of all scores from 2 to 12.

  d What is the probability of each of these scores?

   i bigger than 10   **ii** between 3 and 7   **iii** even

   iv a square number   **v** a prime number   **vi** a triangular number

2 Using the left-hand diagram on page 463 that shows, as coordinates, the outcomes when two dice are thrown together, what is the probability of each of these?

  a the score is an even "double"

  b at least one of the dice shows 2

  c the score on one dice is twice the score on the other dice

  d at least one of the dice shows a multiple of 3

3 Using the left-hand diagram on page 463 that shows, as coordinates, the outcomes when two dice are thrown together, what is the probability of each of these?

a both dice show a 6

b at least one of the dice shows a six

c exactly one dice shows a six

4 The diagram shows the score for the event "the difference between the scores when two dice are thrown". Copy and complete the diagram.

For the event described above, what is the probability of a difference of each of these?

a 1   **b** 0   **c** 4

d 6   **e** an odd number

5 When two coins are thrown together, what is the probability of each of these outcomes?

a 2 heads   **b** a head and a tail

c at least 1 tail   **d** no tails

Use the diagram of the outcomes when two coins are thrown together, on page 464.

6 Two five-sided spinners are spun together and the total score of the faces that they land on is worked out. Copy and complete this probability space diagram.

a What is the most likely score?

b When two five-sided spinners are spun together, what is the probability of each of these?

    i the total score is 5   **ii** the total score is an even number

    iii the score is a "double"   **iv** the score is less than 7

7 When three coins are tossed together, what is the probability of each of these outcomes?

a three heads   **b** two heads and one tail

c at least one tail   **d** no tails

8 When one coin is tossed there are two outcomes. When two coins are tossed, there are four outcomes. When three coins are tossed, there are eight outcomes.

a How many outcomes will there be when four coins are tossed?

b How many outcomes will there be when five coins are tossed?

c How many outcomes will there be when ten coins are tossed?

d How many outcomes will there be when n coins are tossed?

When a dice and a coin are thrown together, what is the probability of each of the following outcomes?

a You get a head on the coin and a 6 on the dice.

b You get a tail on the coin and an even number on the dice.

c You get a head on the coin and a square number on the dice.

Use the diagram on page 464 that shows the outcomes when a dice and a coin are thrown together.

19.7 Tree diagrams

In this section you will learn how to:
- use sample space diagrams and tree diagrams to work out the probability of combined events

Key words
combined
    events
space
    diagram
tree diagram

Imagine we have to draw two cards from this pack of six cards, but we must replace the first card before we select the second card.

One way we could show all the outcomes of this experiment is to construct a **probability space diagram**. For example, this could be an array set in a pair of axes, like those used for the two dice (see page 463), or a pictogram, like those used for the coins, or simply a list of all the outcomes. By showing all the outcomes of our experiment as an array, we obtain the diagram below.

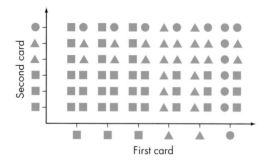

From the diagram, we can see immediately that the probability of picking, say, two squares is 9 out of 36 pairs of cards. So,

$$P(2 \text{ squares}) = \frac{9}{36} = \frac{1}{4}$$

EXAMPLE 11

Using the probability space diagram on page 466, what is the probability of getting each of these outcomes?

a a square and a triangle (in any order)

b two circles

c two shapes the same

a There are 12 combinations which give a square and a triangle together. There are six when a square is chosen first and six when a triangle is chosen first. So,

$$P(\text{square and triangle, in any order}) = \frac{12}{36} = \frac{1}{3}$$

b There is only one combination which gives two circles. So,

$$P(\text{two circles}) = \frac{1}{36}$$

c There are nine combinations of two squares together, four combinations of two triangles together, and one combination of two circles together. These give a total of 14 combinations with two shapes the same. So,

$$P(\text{two shapes the same}) = \frac{14}{36} = \frac{7}{18}$$

An alternative method to tackling problems involving **combined events** is to use a **tree diagram**.

When we pick the first card, there are three possible outcomes: a square, a triangle or a circle. For a single event,

$$P(\text{square}) = \frac{1}{2} \qquad P(\text{triangle}) = \frac{1}{3} \qquad P(\text{circle}) = \frac{1}{6}$$

We can show this by depicting each event as a branch and writing its probability on the branch.

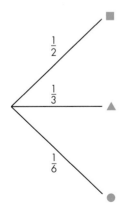

The diagram can then be extended to take into account a second choice. Because the first card has been replaced, we can still pick a square, a triangle or a circle. This is true no matter what is chosen the first time. We can demonstrate this by adding three more branches to the "squares" branch in the diagram.

Here is the complete tree diagram.

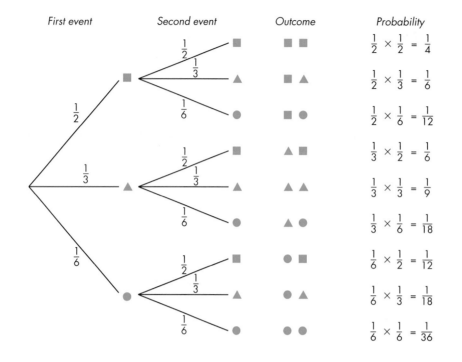

First event	Second event	Outcome	Probability

The probability of any outcome is calculated by multiplying together the probabilities on its branches. For instance,

$$P(\text{two squares}) = \frac{1}{2} \times \frac{1}{2} = \frac{1}{4}$$

$$P(\text{triangle followed by circle}) = \frac{1}{3} \times \frac{1}{6} = \frac{1}{18}$$

EXAMPLE 12

Using the tree diagram above, what is the probability of obtaining each of the following?

a two triangles

b a circle followed by a triangle

c a square and a triangle, in any order

d two circles

e two shapes the same

a $P(\text{two triangles}) = \frac{1}{9}$

b $P(\text{circle followed by triangle}) = \frac{1}{18}$

c There are two places in the outcome column which have a square and a triangle. These are the second and fourth rows. The probability of each is $\frac{1}{6}$. Their combined probability is given by the addition rule.

$$P(\text{square and triangle, in any order}) = \frac{1}{6} + \frac{1}{6} = \frac{1}{3}$$

d $P(\text{two circles}) = \dfrac{1}{36}$

e There are three places in the outcome column which have two shapes the same. These are the first, fifth and last rows. The probabilities are respectively $\frac{1}{4}, \frac{1}{9}$ and $\frac{1}{36}$. Their combined probability is given by the addition rule.

$$P(\text{two shapes the same}) = \frac{1}{4} + \frac{1}{9} + \frac{1}{36} = \frac{7}{18}$$

Note that the answers to parts **c, d** and **e** are the same as the answers obtained in Example 11.

EXERCISE 19G

1 A coin is tossed twice. Copy and complete the tree diagram below to show all the outcomes.

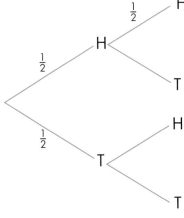

| First event | Second event | Outcome | Probability |

$$\frac{1}{2} \times \frac{1}{2} = \frac{1}{4}$$

Use your tree diagram to work out the probability of each of these outcomes.

a getting two heads

b getting a head and a tail

c getting at least one tail

2 A card is drawn from a pack of cards. It is replaced, the pack is shuffled and another card is drawn.

a What is the probability that either card was an Ace?

b What is the probability that either card was not an Ace?

c Draw a tree diagram to show the outcomes of two cards being drawn as described. Use the tree diagram to work out the probability of each of these.

  i both cards will be Aces

  ii at least one of the cards will be an Ace

On my way to work, I drive through two sets of road works with traffic lights which only show green or red. I know that the probability of the first set being green is $\frac{1}{3}$ and the probability of the second set being green is $\frac{1}{2}$.

a What is the probability that the first set of lights will be red?

b What is the probability that the second set of lights will be red?

c Copy and complete the tree diagram below, showing the possible outcomes when passing through both sets of lights.

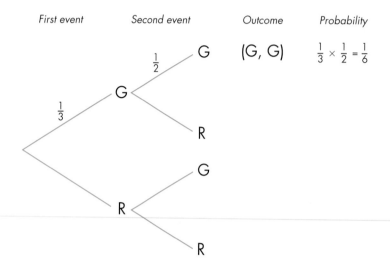

| First event | Second event | Outcome | Probability |

$\frac{1}{3}$ $\frac{1}{2}$ G   (G, G) $\frac{1}{3} \times \frac{1}{2} = \frac{1}{6}$

d Using the tree diagram, what is the probability of each of the following outcomes?

  i I do not get held up at either set of lights

  ii I get held up at exactly one set of lights

  iii I get held up at least once

e Over a school term I make 90 journeys to work. On how many days can I expect to get two green lights?

 Six out of every 10 cars in Britain are foreign made.

a What is the probability that any car will be British made?

b Two cars can be seen approaching in the distance. Draw a tree diagram to work out the probability of each of these outcomes.

  i both cars will be British made

  ii one car will be British and the other car will be foreign made

5 Three coins are tossed. Complete the tree diagram below and use it to answer the questions.

First event   Second event   Third event   Outcome   Probability

(H, H, H) $\frac{1}{2} \times \frac{1}{2} \times \frac{1}{2} = \frac{1}{8}$

If a coin is tossed three times, what is the probability that you get each of these outcomes?

a three heads

b two heads and a tail

c at least one tail

6 Thomas has to take a three-part language examination paper. The first part is speaking. He has a 0.4 chance of passing this part. The second is listening. He has a 0.5 chance of passing this part. The third part is writing. He has a 0.7 chance of passing this part. Draw a tree diagram covering three events where the first event is passing or failing the speaking part of the examination, the second event is passing or failing the listening part, and the third event is passing or failing the writing part.

a If he passes all three parts, his father will give him £20. What is the probability that he gets the money?

b If he passes two parts only, he can resit the other part. What is the chance he will have to resit?

c If he fails all three parts, he will be thrown off the course. What is the chance he is thrown off the course?

7 In a group of ten girls, six like the pop group Smudge and four like the pop group Mirage. Two girls are to be chosen for a pop quiz.

a What is the probability that the first girl chosen will be a Smudge fan?

b Draw a tree diagram to show the outcomes of choosing two girls and which pop groups they like. (Remember, once a girl has been chosen the first time she cannot be chosen again.)

c Use your tree diagram to work out the probability of each of these.

i both girls chosen will like Smudge

ii both girls chosen will like the same group

iii both girls chosen will like different groups

8 Look at all the tree diagrams that have been drawn so far.

   a What do the probabilities across any set of branches (outlined in the diagram below) always add up to?

   b What do the final probabilities (outlined in the diagram below) always add up to?

   c You should now be able to fill in all of the missing values in the diagram.

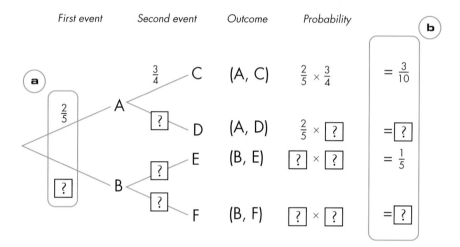

19.8 Independent events

In this section you will learn how to:

- use the connectors "and" and "or" to find the probability of combined events

Key words

and
independent events
or

If the outcome of event A does not effect the outcome of event B, then events A and B are called **independent events**. Most of the combined events we have looked at so far have been independent events.

It is possible to work out problems on combined events without using tree diagrams. The method explained in Example 13 is basically the same as that of a tree diagram but uses the words **and** and **or**.

EXAMPLE 13

The chance that Ashley hits a target with an arrow is $\frac{1}{4}$. He has two shots at the target. What is the probability of each of these?

a He hits the target both times.

b He hits the target once only.

c He hits the target at least once.

a P(hits both times) = P(first shot hits **and** second shot hits) = $\frac{1}{4} \times \frac{1}{4} = \frac{1}{16}$

b P(hits the target once only) = P (first hits **and** second misses **or** first misses **and** second hits) = $\left(\frac{1}{4} \times \frac{3}{4}\right) + \left(\frac{3}{4} \times \frac{1}{4}\right) = \frac{3}{8}$

c P(hits at least once) = P(both hit **or** one hits) = $\frac{1}{16} + \frac{3}{8} = \frac{7}{16}$

Note the connections between the word "and" and the operation "times", and the word "or" and the operation "add".

EXERCISE 19H

1 Alf tosses a coin twice. The coin is biased so it has a probability of $\frac{2}{3}$ of landing on a head. What is the probability that he gets

a two heads? **b** a head and a tail (in any order)?

2 Bernice draws a card from a pack of cards, replaces it, shuffles the pack and then draws another card. What is the probability that the cards are

a both Aces? **b** an Ace and a King (in any order)?

3 A dice is thrown twice. What is the probability that both scores are

a even? **b** one even and one odd (in any order)?

4 I throw a dice three times. What is the probability of getting three sixes?

5 A bag contains 15 white beads and 10 black beads. I take out a bead at random, replace it and take out another bead. What is the probability of each of these?

a both beads are black

b one bead is black and the other white (in any order)

6 The probability that I am late for work on Monday is 0.4. The probability that I am late on Tuesday is 0.2. What is the probability of each of the following outcomes?

a I am late for work on Monday and Tuesday.

b I am late for work on Monday and on time on Tuesday.

c I am on time on both Monday and Tuesday.

7 Ronda has to take a three-part language examination paper. The first part is speaking. She has a 0.7 chance of passing this part. The second part is listening. She has a 0.6 chance of passing this part. The third part is writing. She has a 0.8 chance of passing this part.

a If she passes all three parts, her father will give her £20. What is the probability that she gets the money?

b If she passes two parts only, she can resit the other part. What is the chance she will have to resit?

c If she fails all three parts, she will be thrown off the course. What is the chance she is thrown off the course?

"At least" problems

In examination questions concerning combined events, it is common to ask for the probability of at least one of the events occurring. There are two ways to solve such problems.

- All possibilities can be written out, which takes a long time.

- Use P(at least one) = 1 − P(none)

The second option is much easier to work out and there is less chance of making a mistake.

EXAMPLE 14

A bag contains seven red and three black balls. A ball is taken out and replaced. This is repeated three times. What is the probability of getting each of these?

a no red balls

b at least one red ball

a P(no reds) = P(black, black, black) = $\frac{7}{10} \times \frac{7}{10} \times \frac{7}{10} = 0.343$

b P(at least one red) = 1 − P(no reds) = 1 − 0.343 = 0.657

Note that the answer to part **b** is 1 minus the answer to part **a**. Examination questions often build up answers in this manner.

EXERCISE 19I

1 A dice is thrown three times.

a What is the probability of not getting a 2?

b What is the probability of at least one 2?

2 Four coins are thrown. What is the probability of

a 4 tails?

b at least 1 head?

3 Adam, Bashir and Clem take a mathematics test. The probability that Adam passes is 0.6, the probability that Bashir passes is 0.9, and the probability that Clem passes is 0.7. What is the probability of each of these outcomes?

  a all three pass

  b Bashir and Adam pass but Clem does not

  c all three fail

  d at least one passes

4 A bag contains 4 red and 6 blue balls. A ball is taken out and replaced. Another ball is taken out. What is the probability of each of these?

  a both balls are red   **b** both balls are blue   **c** at least one is red

5 **a** A dice is thrown three times. What is the probability of

    i 3 sixes?   **ii** no sixes?   **iii** at least one six?

  b A dice is thrown four times. What is the probability of

    i 4 sixes?   **ii** no sixes?   **iii** at least one six?

  c A dice is thrown five times. What is the probability of

    i 5 sixes?   **ii** no sixes?   **iii** at least one six?

  d A dice is thrown n times. What is the probability of

    i n sixes?   **ii** no sixes?   **iii** at least one six?

6 The probability that the school canteen serves chips on any day is $\frac{2}{3}$. In a week of five days, what is the probability of each of these?

  a chips are served every day

  b chips are not served on any day

  c chips are served on at least one day

7 The probability that Steve is late for work is $\frac{5}{6}$. The probability that Nigel is late for work is $\frac{9}{10}$. The probability that Gary is late for work is $\frac{1}{2}$. What is the probability that on a particular day

  a all three are late?   **b** none of them are late?   **c** at least one is late?

More advanced use of *and* and *or*

We have already seen how certain probability problems can be solved either by tree diagrams or by the use of the *and/or* method. Both methods are basically the same but the *and/or* method works better in the case of three events following one another or in situations where the number of outcomes of one event is greater than two. This is simply because the tree diagram would get too large and involved.

EXAMPLE 15

Three cards are to be drawn from a pack of cards. Each card is to be replaced before the next one is drawn. What is the probability of drawing each of these combinations?

a three Kings

b exactly two Kings and one other card

c no Kings

d at least one King

Let K be the event "Drawing a King". Let N be the event "Not drawing a King". Then you obtain

a $P(KKK) = \frac{1}{13} \times \frac{1}{13} \times \frac{1}{13} = \frac{1}{2197}$

b $P(\text{exactly two Kings}) = P(KKN) \text{ or } P(KNK) \text{ or } P(NKK)$

$$= \left(\frac{1}{13} \times \frac{1}{13} \times \frac{12}{13}\right) + \left(\frac{1}{13} \times \frac{12}{13} \times \frac{1}{13}\right) + \left(\frac{12}{13} \times \frac{1}{13} \times \frac{1}{13}\right) = \frac{36}{2197}$$

c $P(\text{no Kings}) = P(NNN) = \frac{12}{13} \times \frac{12}{13} \times \frac{12}{13} = \frac{1728}{2197}$

d $P(\text{at least one King}) = 1 - P(\text{no Kings}) = 1 - \frac{1728}{2197} = \frac{469}{2197}$

Note that in part **b** the notation stands for the probability that the first card is a King, the second is a King and the third is not a King; or the first is a King, the second is not a King and the third is a King; or the first is not a King, the second is a King and the third is a King.

Note also that the probability of each component of part **b** is exactly the same. So we could have done the calculation as

$$3 \times \frac{1}{13} \times \frac{1}{13} \times \frac{12}{13} = \frac{36}{2197}$$

Patterns of this kind often occur in probability.

EXERCISE 19J

1 A bag contains three black balls and seven red balls. A ball is taken out and replaced. This is repeated twice. What is the probability of each of these outcomes?

a all three are black

b exactly two are black

c exactly one is black

d none are black

2 A dice is thrown four times. What is the probability of each of these?

a four sixes are thrown

b no sixes are thrown

c exactly one six is thrown

3 On my way to work I pass three sets of traffic lights. The probability that the first is green is $\frac{1}{2}$. The probability that the second is green is $\frac{1}{3}$. The probability that the third is green is $\frac{2}{3}$. What is the probability of each of these?

a all three are green

b exactly two are green

c exactly one is green

d none are green

e at least one is green

4 Alf is late for school with a probability of 0.9. Bert is late with a probability of 0.7. Chas is late with a probability of 0.6. On any particular day what is the probability of each of these?

a exactly one of them being late

b exactly two of them being late

5 Daisy takes four A-levels. The probability that she will pass English is 0.7. The probability that she will pass history is 0.6. The probability she will pass geography is 0.8. The probability that she will pass general studies is 0.9. What is the probability of each of these?

a she passes all four subjects

b she passes exactly three subjects

c she passes at least three subjects

6 The driving test is in two parts, a written test and a practical test. It is known that 90% of people who take the written test pass, and 60% of people who take the practical test pass. A person who passes the written test does not have to take it again. A person who fails the practical test does have to take it again.

a What is the probability that someone passes the written test?

b What is the probability that someone passes the practical test?

c What is the probability that someone passes both tests?

d What is the probability that someone passes the written test but takes two attempts to pass the practical test?

7 Six out of ten cars in Britain are made by foreign manufacturers. Three cars can be seen approaching in the distance.

a What is the probability that the first one is foreign?

b The first car is going so fast that its make could not be made out. What is the probability that the second car is foreign?

c What is the probability that exactly two of the three cars are foreign?

d Explain why, if the first car is foreign, the probability of the second car being foreign is still 6 out of 10.

8 Each day Mr Smith runs home. He has a choice of three routes: the road, the fields or the canal path. The road route is 4 miles, the fields route is 6 miles and the canal route is 5 miles. In a three-day period, what is the probability that Mr Smith runs a total distance of

a exactly 17 miles

b exactly 13 miles

c exactly 15 miles

d over 17 miles?

9 A rock climber attempts a difficult route. There are three hard moves at points A, B and C in the climb. The climber has a probability of 0.6, 0.3 and 0.7 respectively of completing each of these moves. What is the probability that the climber

a completes the climb

b fails at move A

c fails at move B

d fails at move C

19.9 Conditional probability

In this section you will learn how to:
- work out the probability of combined events when the probabilities change after each event

Key word
conditional probability

The term **conditional probability** is used to describe the situation when the probability of an event is dependent on the outcome of another event. For instance, if a card is taken from a pack and not returned, then the probabilities for the next card drawn will be altered. The following example illustrates this situation.

EXAMPLE 16

A bag contains nine balls, of which five are white and four are black.

A ball is taken out and not replaced. Another is then taken out. If the first ball removed is black, what is the probability of each of these outcomes?

a the second ball will be black

b both balls will be black

When a black ball is removed, there are five white balls and three black balls left, reducing the total to eight.

Hence, when the second ball is taken out,

a P(second ball black) = $\frac{3}{8}$

b P(both balls black) = $\frac{4}{9} \times \frac{3}{8} = \frac{1}{6}$

EXERCISE 19K

1 I put six CDs in my multi-player and put it on random play. Each CD has 10 tracks. Once a track is played, it is not played again.

   a What is the chance that track 5 on CD 6 is the first one played?

   b What is the maximum number of tracks that could be played before a track from CD 6 is played?

2 There are five white and one brown eggs in an egg box. Kate decides to make a two-egg omelette. She takes each egg from the box without looking at its colour.

   a What is the probability that the first egg taken is brown?

   b If the first egg taken is brown, what is the probability that the second egg taken will be brown?

   c What is the probability that Kate gets an omelette made from each of these combinations?

      i two white eggs   **ii** one white and one brown egg   **iii** two brown eggs

3 A box contains 10 red and 15 yellow balls. One is taken out and not replaced. Another is taken out.

   a If the first ball taken out is red, what is the probability that the second ball is

      i red?   **ii** yellow?

   b If the first ball taken out is yellow, what is the probability that the second ball is

      i red?   **ii** yellow?

4 A fruit bowl contains six Granny Smith apples and eight Golden Delicious apples. Kevin takes two apples at random.

   a If the first apple is a Granny Smith, what is the probability that the second is

      i a Granny Smith?   **ii** a Golden Delicious?

   b What is the probability that

      i both are Granny Smiths?   **ii** both are Golden Delicious?

5 Ann has a bargain box of tins. They are unlabelled but she knows that six tins contain soup and four contain peaches.

   a She opens two tins. What is the probability that

      i they are both soup?   **ii** they are both peaches?

   b What is the probability that she has to open two tins before she gets a tin of peaches?

   c What is the probability that she has to open three tins before she gets a tin of peaches?

   d What is the probability that she will get a tin of soup if she opens five tins?

6 One in three cars on British roads is made in Britain. A car comes down the road. It is a British-made car. John says that the probability of the next car being British made is one in two because a British-made car has just gone past. Explain why he is wrong.

7 A bag contains three black balls and seven red balls. A ball is taken out and not replaced. This is repeated twice. What is the probability of each of these outcomes?

a all three are black

b exactly two are black

c exactly one is black

d none are black

8 One my way to work, I pass two sets of traffic lights. The probability that the first is green is $\frac{1}{3}$. If the first is green, the probability that the second is green is $\frac{1}{3}$. If the first is red, the probability that the second is green is $\frac{2}{3}$. What is the probability of each of these?

a both are green

b none are green

c exactly one is green

d at least one is green

9 A hand of five cards is dealt. What is the probability of each of these outcomes?

a all five are Spades

b all five are the same suit

c they are four Aces and any other card

d they are four of a kind and any other card

10 An engineering test is in two parts, a written test and a practical test. It is known that 90% who take the written test pass. When a person passes the written test, the probability that he/she will also pass the practical test is 60%. When a person fails the written test, the probability that he/she will pass the practical test is 20%.

a What is the probability that someone passes both tests?

b What is the probability that someone passes one test?

c What is the probability that someone fails both tests?

d What is the combined probability of the answers to parts **a**, **b** and **c**?

11 Each day Mr Smith runs home from work. He has a choice of three routes. The road, the fields or the canal path. On Monday, each route has an equal probability of being chosen. The route chosen on any day will not be picked the next day and so each of the other two routes has an equal probability of being chosen.

a Write down all the possible combinations so that Mr Smith runs home via the canal path on Wednesday (there are four of them).

b Calculate the probability that Mr Smith runs home via the canal path on Wednesday.

c Calculate the probability that Mr Smith runs home via the canal path on Tuesday.

d Using your results from parts **b** and **c**, write down the probability that Mr Smith runs home via the canal path on Thursday.

e Explain the answers to parts **b**, **c** and **d**.

1 The probabilities of whether a student, picked at random from a school, is vegetarian or not are shown in this table.

	Boys	Girls
Vegetarian	0.08	0.2
Non-vegetarian	0.4	0.32

a What is the probability that a student chosen at random from the school is vegetarian?

b There are 320 girls in the school who are vegetarian. How many students are there in the school altogether?

AQA, Question 3, Paper 2 Higher, November 2003

2 a Jonathan has a bag containing 10 balls. The balls are red, green or blue. He takes a ball at random from the bag and notes its colour. He then replaces the ball in the bag and repeats the experiment 500 times.

The results are

Red	Green	Blue
235	168	97

i What is the relative frequency of picking a red ball?

ii How many of each coloured ball are in the bag?

b Matthew takes a ball at random from another bag and replaces it. He does this 10 times and gets 6 reds and 4 greens. He claims that there are no blue balls in the bag.

Explain why he could be wrong.

 3 A bag contains 4 red balls and 6 blue balls. A ball is taken from the bag at random and replaced. Another ball is then taken from the bag at random.

a Complete the tree diagram.

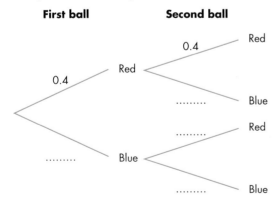

b What is the probability that both balls are the same colour?

AQA, Question 10, Paper 2 Higher, November 2004

 4 Arthur has a box of 10 unlabelled CDs. The CDs are pop, classical or dance. The table shows the probability of each type of music if a CD is taken out at random.

Type of music	Probability
Pop	0.6
Classical	0.1
Dance	

a What is the probability that a CD chosen at random is a dance CD?

b How many classical CDs are in the box?

c Arthur picks a CD at random and puts it in a 2-disc CD player. He then picks another CD at random and puts it in the player. Complete the tree diagram

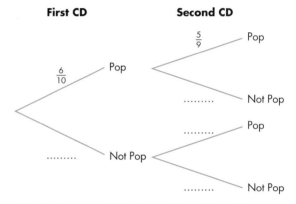

d What is the probability that neither of the CDs is pop?

 5 At the end of a training programme, students have to pass an exam to gain a certificate. The probability of passing the exam at the first attempt is 0.75.
Those who fail are allowed to re-sit.
The probability of passing the re-sit is 0.6.
No further attempts are allowed.

a i Complete the tree diagram.

1st attempt   **2nd attempt**

```
        0.75  Pass
      <
                    0.6   Pass
   .........  Fail <
                    .........  Fail
```

ii What is the probability that a student fails to gain a certificate?

b Three students take the exam.
What is the probability that all of them gain a certificate?

AQA, Question 20, Paper 1 Higher, June 2005

6 A bag contains 8 balls. 5 are black and 3 are white.

A ball is taken out of the bag at random and *not* replaced. Another ball is taken out of the bag at random. What is the probability that both of the balls are the same colour?

AQA, Question 23, Paper 2 Higher, November 2003

7 A drinks machine uses cartridges to supply the drink. Billy has a job lot of eight cartridges which have lost their labels. He knows he has three teas and five coffees. He makes three drinks with the cartridges.

a What is the probability he gets three teas?

b What is the probability he gets exactly two coffees?

c What is the probability that he gets at least one coffee?

d Billy makes the three drinks and leaves the room. Betty comes in, tastes one of the drinks. She finds it is tea. What is the probability that the other two drinks are also tea?

WORKED EXAM QUESTION

Harry is a pensioner. The probability that Harry goes into town on a Tuesday is $\frac{2}{5}$. The probability that Harry goes into town on a Tuesday and visits the library is $\frac{3}{20}$.

a One Tuesday Harry is in town. Calculate the probability that he visits the library.

b Calculate the probability that Harry goes into town on a Tuesday and does not visit the library.

SEG/Mod Math, Question 7, Paper 15, November 1999

Solution

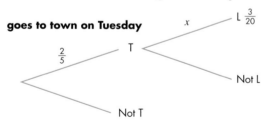

goes to library

goes to town on Tuesday

$\frac{2}{5}$ T x L $\frac{3}{20}$

Not L

Not T

> Draw the part of the probability tree that you know about.

a P(Harry goes to town on Tuesday) $\times x = \frac{3}{20}$

> Set up an equation.

$$\frac{2}{5} \times x = \frac{3}{20}$$

P(Harry visits the library when in town on Tuesday) $= \frac{3}{20} \div \frac{2}{5}$

> Substitute in the probabilities and solve the equation. Remember to turn the fraction upside down and multiply by it when you divide.

$$= \frac{3}{20} \times \frac{5}{2} = \frac{3}{8}$$

b P(Harry does not visit the library) $= 1 - \frac{3}{8} = \frac{5}{8}$

P(Harry goes into town and does not visit the library) $= \frac{2}{5} \times \frac{5}{8} = \frac{1}{4}$

> First work out the probability of the complementary event then use the 'and' rule for combined events.

GRADE YOURSELF

D Able to calculate the probability of an event happening when you know the probability that the event does not happen and that the total probability of all possible outcomes is 1

D Able to predict the expected number of successes from a given number of trials if you know the probability of one success

C Able to calculate relative frequency from experimental evidence and compare this with the theoretical probability

B Able to draw a tree diagram to work out the probability of combined events

A Able to use *and/or* or a tree diagram to work out probabilities of specific outcomes of combined events

A* Able to work out the probabilities of combined events when the probability of each event changes depending on the outcome of the previous event

What you should know now

● How to calculate theoretical probabilities from different situations

Chapter

20

Algebra 3

1 Algebraic fractions

2 Linear and non-linear simultaneous equations

3 Number sequences

4 General rules from given patterns

5 Quadratic sequences

6 Changing the subject of a formula

This chapter will show you ...

- how to combine fractions algebraically and solve equations with algebraic fractions
- how to solve linear and non-linear simultaneous equations
- some of the common sequences of numbers
- how to express a rule for a sequence in words and algebraically
- how to transpose a formula where the subject appears twice

What you should already know

- How to state a rule for a simple linear sequence in words
- How to substitute numbers into an algebraic expression
- How to factorise simple linear expressions
- How to expand a pair of linear brackets to get a quadratic equation

Quick check

1 Write down the next three terms of these sequences.

    a 2, 5, 8, 11, 14, ...   **b** 1, 3, 6, 10, 15, 21, ...

    c 40, 35, 30, 25, 20, ...   **d** 1, 4, 9, 16, 25, 36, ...

2 Work out the value of the expression $3n - 2$ for

    a $n = 1$ **b** $n = 2$ **c** $n = 3$

3 Factorise

    a $2x + 6$ **b** $x^2 - x$ **c** $10x^2 + 2x$

4 Expand

    a $(x + 6)(x + 2)$ **b** $(2x + 1)(x - 3)$ **c** $(x - 2)^2$

5 Make x the subject of

    a $2y + x = 3$ **b** $x - 3y = 4$ **c** $4y - x = 3$

Algebraic fractions

In this section you will learn how to:
- simplify algebraic fractions
- solve equations containing algebraic fractions

Key words
brackets
cancel
cross-multiply
expression
factorise

The following four rules are used to work out the value of fractions.

Addition: $\dfrac{a}{b} + \dfrac{c}{d} = \dfrac{ad + bc}{bd}$

Subtraction: $\dfrac{a}{b} - \dfrac{c}{d} = \dfrac{ad - bc}{bd}$

Multiplication: $\dfrac{a}{b} \times \dfrac{c}{d} = \dfrac{ac}{bd}$

Division: $\dfrac{a}{b} \div \dfrac{c}{d} = \dfrac{ad}{bc}$

Note that a, b, c and d can be numbers, other letters or algebraic **expressions**. Remember:

- use **brackets**, if necessary

- **factorise** if you can

- **cancel** if you can.

EXAMPLE 1

Simplify   **a** $\dfrac{1}{x} + \dfrac{x}{2y}$ **b** $\dfrac{2}{b} - \dfrac{a}{2b}$

a Using the addition rule: $\dfrac{1}{x} + \dfrac{x}{2y} = \dfrac{(1)(2y) + (x)(x)}{(x)(2y)} = \dfrac{2y + x^2}{2xy}$

b Using the subtraction rule: $\dfrac{2}{b} - \dfrac{a}{2b} = \dfrac{(2)(2b) - (a)(b)}{(b)(2b)} = \dfrac{4b - ab}{2b^2}$

$= \dfrac{b(4 - a)}{2b^{\cancel{2}}} = \dfrac{4 - a}{2b}$

Note: There are different ways of working out fraction calculations. Part **b** could have been done by making the denominator of each fraction the same. Namely,

$\dfrac{(2)2}{(2)b} - \dfrac{a}{2b} = \dfrac{4 - a}{2b}$

EXAMPLE 2

Simplify   **a** $\dfrac{x}{3} \times \dfrac{x+2}{x-2}$ **b** $\dfrac{x}{3} \div \dfrac{2x}{7}$

a Using the multiplication rule: $\dfrac{x}{3} \times \dfrac{x+2}{x-2} = \dfrac{(x)(x+2)}{(3)(x-2)} = \dfrac{x^2+2x}{3x-6}$

Remember that the line that separates the top from the bottom of an algebraic fraction acts as a bracket as well as a divide sign. Note that it is sometimes preferable to leave an algebraic fraction in a factorised form.

b Using the division rule: $\dfrac{x}{3} \div \dfrac{2x}{7} = \dfrac{(\cancel{x})(7)}{(3)(2\cancel{x})} = \dfrac{7}{6}$

EXAMPLE 3

Solve this equation. $\dfrac{x+1}{3} - \dfrac{x-3}{2} = 1$

Use the rule for combining fractions, and also **cross-multiply** the denominator of the left-hand side to the right-hand side.

$$\dfrac{(2)(x+1) - (3)(x-3)}{(2)(3)} = 1$$

$$2(x+1) - 3(x-3) = 6 \;(= 1 \times 2 \times 3)$$

Note the brackets. These will avoid problems with signs and help you to expand to get a linear equation.

$$2x + 2 - 3x + 9 = 6 \quad \Rightarrow \quad -x = -5 \quad \Rightarrow \quad x = 5$$

EXAMPLE 4

Solve this equation. $\dfrac{3}{x-1} - \dfrac{2}{x+1} = 1$

Use the rule for combining fractions, and cross multiply the denominator as in Example 3. Use brackets to help with expanding and to avoid problems with minus signs.

$$3(x+1) - 2(x-1) = (x-1)(x+1)$$

$$3x + 3 - 2x + 2 = x^2 - 1 \quad \text{(Right-hand side is the difference of two squares.)}$$

Rearrange into the general quadratic form (see Chapter 12).

$$x^2 - x - 6 = 0$$

Factorise and solve $(x-3)(x+2) = 0 \quad \Rightarrow \quad x = 3 \text{ or } -2$

Note that when your equation is rearranged into the quadratic form it should factorise. If it doesn't, then you have almost certainly made a mistake. If the question required an answer as a decimal or a surd it would say so.

EXAMPLE 5

Simplify: $\dfrac{2x^2 + x - 3}{4x^2 - 9}$

Factorise the numerator and denominator: $\dfrac{(2x + 3)(x - 1)}{(2x + 3)(2x - 3)}$

Denominator is the difference of two squares.

Cancel any common factors: $\dfrac{\cancel{(2x + 3)}(x - 1)}{\cancel{(2x + 3)}(2x - 3)}$

If at this stage there isn't a common factor on top and bottom, you should check your factorisations.

Remaining term is the answer: $\dfrac{(x - 1)}{(2x - 3)}$

EXERCISE 20A

1 Simplify each of these.

a $\dfrac{x}{2} + \dfrac{x}{3}$

b $\dfrac{3x}{4} + \dfrac{x}{5}$

c $\dfrac{3x}{4} + \dfrac{2x}{5}$

d $\dfrac{x}{2} + \dfrac{y}{3}$

e $\dfrac{xy}{4} + \dfrac{2}{x}$

f $\dfrac{x + 1}{2} + \dfrac{x + 2}{3}$

g $\dfrac{2x - 1}{2} + \dfrac{3x - 1}{4}$

h $\dfrac{x}{5} + \dfrac{2x - 1}{3}$

i $\dfrac{x - 2}{2} + \dfrac{x + 3}{4}$

j $\dfrac{x - 4}{5} + \dfrac{2x - 3}{2}$

2 Simplify each of these.

a $\dfrac{x}{2} - \dfrac{x}{3}$

b $\dfrac{3x}{4} - \dfrac{x}{5}$

c $\dfrac{3x}{4} - \dfrac{2x}{5}$

d $\dfrac{x}{2} - \dfrac{y}{3}$

e $\dfrac{xy}{4} - \dfrac{2}{y}$

f $\dfrac{x + 1}{2} - \dfrac{x + 2}{3}$

g $\dfrac{2x + 1}{2} - \dfrac{3x + 3}{4}$

h $\dfrac{x}{5} - \dfrac{2x + 1}{3}$

i $\dfrac{x - 2}{2} - \dfrac{x - 3}{4}$

j $\dfrac{x - 4}{5} - \dfrac{2x - 3}{2}$

3 Solve the following equations.

a $\dfrac{x + 1}{2} + \dfrac{x + 2}{5} = 3$

b $\dfrac{x + 2}{4} + \dfrac{x + 1}{7} = 3$

c $\dfrac{4x + 1}{3} - \dfrac{x + 2}{4} = 2$

d $\dfrac{2x - 1}{3} + \dfrac{3x + 1}{4} = 7$

e $\dfrac{2x + 1}{2} - \dfrac{x + 1}{7} = 1$

f $\dfrac{3x + 1}{5} - \dfrac{5x - 1}{7} = 0$

4 Simplify each of these.

a $\dfrac{x}{2} \times \dfrac{x}{3}$

b $\dfrac{2x}{7} \times \dfrac{3y}{4}$

c $\dfrac{4x}{3y} \times \dfrac{2y}{x}$

d $\dfrac{4y^2}{9x} \times \dfrac{3x^2}{2y}$

e $\dfrac{x}{2} \times \dfrac{x-2}{5}$

f $\dfrac{x-3}{15} \times \dfrac{5}{2x-6}$

g $\dfrac{2x+1}{2} \times \dfrac{3x+1}{4}$

h $\dfrac{x}{5} \times \dfrac{2x+1}{3}$

i $\dfrac{x-2}{2} \times \dfrac{4}{x-3}$

j $\dfrac{x-5}{10} \times \dfrac{5}{x^2-5x}$

5 Simplify each of these.

a $\dfrac{x}{2} \div \dfrac{x}{3}$

b $\dfrac{2x}{7} \div \dfrac{4y}{14}$

c $\dfrac{4x}{3y} \div \dfrac{x}{2y}$

d $\dfrac{4y^2}{9x} \div \dfrac{2y}{3x^2}$

e $\dfrac{x}{2} \div \dfrac{x-2}{5}$

f $\dfrac{x-3}{15} \div \dfrac{5}{2x-6}$

g $\dfrac{2x+1}{2} \div \dfrac{4x+2}{4}$

h $\dfrac{x}{6} \div \dfrac{2x^2+x}{3}$

i $\dfrac{x-2}{12} \div \dfrac{4}{x-3}$

j $\dfrac{x-5}{10} \div \dfrac{x^2-5x}{5}$

6 Simplify each of these. Factorise and cancel where appropriate.

a $\dfrac{3x}{4} + \dfrac{x}{4}$

b $\dfrac{3x}{4} - \dfrac{x}{4}$

c $\dfrac{3x}{4} \times \dfrac{x}{4}$

d $\dfrac{3x}{4} \div \dfrac{x}{4}$

e $\dfrac{3x+1}{2} + \dfrac{x-2}{5}$

f $\dfrac{3x+1}{2} - \dfrac{x-2}{5}$

g $\dfrac{3x+1}{2} \times \dfrac{x-2}{5}$

h $\dfrac{x^2-9}{10} \times \dfrac{5}{x-3}$

i $\dfrac{2x+3}{5} \div \dfrac{6x+9}{10}$

j $\dfrac{2x^2}{9} - \dfrac{2y^2}{3}$

7 Show that each algebraic fraction simplifies to the given expression.

a $\dfrac{2}{x+1} + \dfrac{5}{x+2} = 3$ simplifies to $3x^2 + 2x - 3 = 0$

b $\dfrac{4}{x-2} + \dfrac{7}{x+1} = 3$ simplifies to $3x^2 - 14x + 4 = 0$

c $\dfrac{3}{4x+1} - \dfrac{4}{x+2} = 2$ simplifies to $8x^2 + 31x + 2 = 0$

d $\dfrac{2}{2x-1} - \dfrac{6}{x+1} = 11$ simplifies to $22x^2 + 21x - 19 = 0$

e $\dfrac{3}{2x-1} - \dfrac{4}{3x-1} = 1$ simplifies to $x^2 - x = 0$

8 Solve the following equations.

a $\dfrac{4}{x+1} + \dfrac{5}{x+2} = 2$

b $\dfrac{18}{4x-1} - \dfrac{1}{x+1} = 1$

c $\dfrac{2x-1}{2} - \dfrac{6}{x+1} = 1$

d $\dfrac{3}{2x-1} - \dfrac{4}{3x-1} = 1$

9 Simplify the following expressions.

a $\dfrac{x^2 + 2x - 3}{2x^2 + 7x + 3}$

b $\dfrac{4x^2 - 1}{2x^2 + 5x - 3}$

c $\dfrac{6x^2 + x - 2}{9x^2 - 4}$

d $\dfrac{4x^2 + x - 3}{4x^2 - 7x + 3}$

e $\dfrac{4x^2 - 25}{8x^2 - 22x + 5}$

20.2 Linear and non-linear simultaneous equations

In this section you will learn how to:

- solve linear and non-linear simultaneous equations

Key words

linear
non-linear
substitute

You have already seen the method of substitution for solving **linear** simultaneous equations (see page 98). Example 6 is a reminder.

EXAMPLE 6

Solve these simultaneous equations.

$2x + 3y = 7$ (1)

$x - 4y = 9$ (2)

First, rearrange equation (2) to obtain:

$x = 9 + 4y$

Substitute the expression for x into equation (1), which gives:

$2(9 + 4y) + 3y = 7$

Expand and solve this equation to obtain:

$18 + 8y + 3y = 7$

$\Rightarrow \quad 11y = -11$

$\Rightarrow \quad y = -1$

Now substitute y into either equation (1) or (2) to find x. Using equation (1), we have

$\Rightarrow 2x - 3 = 7$

$\Rightarrow \quad x = 5$

We can use a similar method when we need to solve a pair of equations, one of which is linear and the other of which is **non-linear**. But we must *always* **substitute** from the linear into the non-linear.

EXAMPLE 7

Solve these simultaneous equations.

$$x^2 + y^2 = 5$$
$$x + y = 3$$

Call the equations (1) and (2):

$$x^2 + y^2 = 5 \ (1)$$
$$x + y = 3 \ (2)$$

Rearrange equation (2) to obtain:

$$x = 3 - y$$

Substitute this into equation (1), which gives:

$$(3 - y)^2 + y^2 = 5$$

Expand and rearrange into the general form of the quadratic equation:

$$9 - 6y + y^2 + y^2 = 5$$
$$2y^2 - 6y + 4 = 0$$

Cancel by 2:

$$y^2 - 3y + 2 = 0$$

Factorise:

$$(y - 1)(y - 2) = 0$$
$$\Rightarrow \qquad y = 1 \text{ or } 2$$

Substitute for y in equation (2):

When $y = 1$, $x = 2$; and when $y = 2$, $x = 1$.

Note you should always give answers as a pair of values in x and y.

 EXERCISE 20B

1 Solve these pairs of linear simultaneous equations using the substitution method.

a $2x + y = 9$
   $x - 2y = 7$

b $3x - 2y = 10$
   $4x + y = 17$

c $x - 2y = 10$
   $2x + 3y = 13$

2 Solve these pairs of simultaneous equations.

a $xy = 2$
   $y = x + 1$

b $xy = -4$
   $2y = x + 6$

A

3 Solve these pairs of simultaneous equations.

   a $x^2 + y^2 = 25$
      $x + y = 7$

   b $x^2 + y^2 = 9$
      $y = x + 3$

   c $x^2 + y^2 = 13$
      $5y + x = 13$

4 Solve these pairs of simultaneous equations.

   a $y = x^2 + 2x - 3$
      $y = 2x + 1$

   b $y = x^2 - 2x - 5$
      $y = x - 1$

   c $y = x^2 - 2x$
      $y = 2x - 3$

5 Solve these pairs of simultaneous equations.

   a $y = x^2 + x - 2$
      $y = 5x - 6$

   b $y = x^2 + 2x - 3$
      $y = 4x - 4$

   c What is the geometrical significance of the answers to parts **a** and **b**?

20.3 Number sequences

In this section you will learn how to:	Key words
• recognise how number sequences are built up • find the nth term of a sequence • recognise some special sequences	coefficient consecutive difference nth term sequence term

A number **sequence** is an ordered set of numbers with a rule to find every number in the sequence. The rule which takes you from one number to the next could be a simple addition or multiplication, but often it is more tricky than that. So you need to look most carefully at the pattern of a sequence.

Each number in a sequence is called a **term** and is in a certain position in the sequence.

Look at these sequences and their rules.

   3, 6, 12, 24, … doubling the last term each time … 48, 96, …

   2, 5, 8, 11, … adding 3 to the last term each time … 14, 17, …

   1, 10, 100, 1000, … multiplying the last term by 10 each time … 10 000, 100 000, …

   1, 8, 15, 22, … adding 7 to the last term each time … 29, 36, …

These are all quite straightforward once you have looked for the link from one term to the next (**consecutive** terms).

Differences

For some sequences we need to look at the **differences** between consecutive terms to determine the pattern.

EXAMPLE 8

Find the next two terms of the sequence 1, 3, 6, 10, 15, ...

Looking at the differences between each pair of consecutive terms, we notice:

```
1    3    6    10    15
  ↑    ↑    ↑    ↑
  2    3    4    5
```

So, we can continue the sequence as follows:

```
1    3    6    10    15    21    28
  ↑    ↑    ↑    ↑
  2    3    4    5   +6    +7
```

The differences usually form a number sequence of their own, so you need to find out the sequence of the differences before you can expand the original sequence.

Generalising to find the rule

When using a number sequence, we sometimes need to know, say, its 50th term, or even a later term in the sequence. To do so, we need to find the rule which produces the sequence in its general form.

Let's first look at the problem backwards. That is, we'll take a rule and see how it produces a sequence.

EXAMPLE 9

A sequence is formed by the rule $3n + 1$, where $n = 1, 2, 3, 4, 5, 6, ...$. Write down the first five terms of the sequence.

Substituting $n = 1, 2, 3, 4, 5$ in turn, we get:

$(3 \times 1 + 1), (3 \times 2 + 1), (3 \times 3 + 1), (3 \times 4 + 1), (3 \times 5 + 1), ...$

$\qquad 4 \qquad\quad 7 \qquad\quad 10 \qquad\quad 13 \qquad\quad 16$

So the sequence is 4, 7, 10, 13, 16, ...

Notice that the difference between each term and the next is always 3, which is the **coefficient** of n (the number attached to n). The constant term is the difference between the first term and the coefficient (in this case, $4 - 3 = 1$).

EXAMPLE 10

The **nth term** of a sequence is $4n - 3$. Write down the first five terms of the sequence.

Substituting $n = 1, 2, 3, 4, 5$ in turn, we get

$$(4 \times 1 - 3), (4 \times 2 - 3), (4 \times 3 - 3), (4 \times 4 - 3), (4 \times 5 - 3)$$
$$1 \qquad 5 \qquad 9 \qquad 13 \qquad 17$$

So the sequence is $1, 5, 9, 13, 17, \ldots$

Notice that the difference between each term and the next is always 4, which is the coefficient of n. The constant term is the difference between the first term and the coefficient $(1 - 4 = -3)$.

EXERCISE 20C

1 Look carefully at each number sequence below. Find the next two numbers in the sequence and try to explain the pattern.

a $1, 1, 2, 3, 5, 8, 13, \ldots$ **b** $1, 4, 9, 16, 25, 36, \ldots$

c $3, 4, 7, 11, 18, 29, \ldots$

2 Triangular numbers are found as follows.

1   3   6   10

Find the next four triangular numbers.

3 Hexagonal numbers are found as follows.

1   7   19   37

Find the next three hexagonal numbers.

4 The first two terms of the sequence of fractions $\dfrac{n-1}{n+1}$ are:

$$n = 1: \frac{1-1}{1+1} = \frac{0}{2} = 0 \qquad n = 2: \frac{2-1}{2+1} = \frac{1}{3}$$

Work out the next five terms of the sequence.

5 A sequence is formed by the rule $\frac{1}{2} \times n \times (n + 1)$ for $n = 1, 2, 3, 4, \dots$

The first term is given by $n = 1$: $\frac{1}{2} \times 1 \times (1 + 1) = 1$

The second term is given by $n = 2$: $\frac{1}{2} \times 2 \times (2 + 1) = 3$

a Work out the next five terms of this sequence.

b This is a well-known sequence you have met before. What is it?

6 5! means "factorial 5", which is $5 \times 4 \times 3 \times 2 \times 1 = 120$

In the same way 7! means $7 \times 6 \times 5 \times 4 \times 3 \times 2 \times 1 = 5040$

a Calculate 2!, 3!, 4! and 6!

b If your calculator has a factorial button, check that it gives the same answers as you get for part **a**. What is the largest factorial you can work out with your calculator before you get an error?

Finding the nth term of a linear sequence

A linear sequence has the *same difference* between each term and the next.

For example:

2, 5, 8, 11, 14, … difference of 3

The nth term of this sequence is given by $3n - 1$.

Here is another linear sequence:

5, 7, 9, 11, 13, … difference of 2

The nth term of this sequence is given by $2n + 3$.

So, you can see that the nth term of a linear sequence is *always* of the form $An + b$, where:

- A, the coefficient of n, is the difference between each term and the next term (consecutive terms)

- b is the difference between the first term and A.

EXAMPLE 11

Find the nth term of the sequence 5, 7, 9, 11, 13, …

The difference between consecutive terms is 2. So the first part of the nth term is $2n$.

Subtract the difference, 2, from the first term, 5, which gives $5 - 2 = 3$.

So the nth term is given by $2n + 3$.

(You can test it by substituting $n = 1, 2, 3, 4, \dots$.)

EXAMPLE 12

Find the nth term of the sequence 3, 7, 11, 15, 19, ...

The difference between consecutive terms is 4. So the first part of the nth term is $4n$.

Subtract the difference 4 from the first term 3, which gives $3 - 4 = -1$.

So the nth term is given by $4n - 1$.

EXAMPLE 13

From the sequence 5, 12, 19, 26, 33, ... find the following.

    a the nth term   **b** the 50th term   **c** the first term that is greater than 1000

a The difference between consecutive terms is 7. So the first part of the nth term is $7n$.

    Subtract the difference 7 from the first term 5, which gives $5 - 7 = -2$.

    So the nth term is given by $7n - 2$.

b The 50th term is found by substituting $n = 50$ into the rule, $7n - 2$.

    So 50th term $= 7 \times 50 - 2 = 350 - 2$

                    $= 348$

c The first term that is greater than 1000 is given by

$$7n - 2 > 1000$$
$$\Rightarrow \quad 7n > 1000 + 2$$
$$\Rightarrow \quad n > \frac{1002}{7}$$
$$n > 143.14$$

So the first term (which has to be a whole number) over 1000 is the 144th.

Special sequences

There are some number sequences that occur frequently. It is useful to know these as they are very likely to occur in examinations.

Even numbers

The even numbers are 2, 4, 6, 8, 10, 12, ...

The nth term of this sequence is $2n$

Odd numbers

The odd numbers are 1, 3, 5, 7, 9, 11, ...

The nth term of this sequence is $2n - 1$

Square numbers

The square numbers are 1, 4, 9, 16, 25, 36, ...

The nth term of this sequence is n^2

Triangular numbers

The triangular numbers are 1, 3, 6, 10, 15, 21, ...

The nth term of this sequence is $\frac{1}{2}n(n + 1)$

Powers of 2

The powers of 2 are 2, 4, 8, 16, 32, 64, ...

The nth term of this sequence is 2^n

Powers of 10

The powers of 10 are 10, 100, 1000, 10 000, 100 000, 1 000 000, ...

The nth term of this sequence is 10^n

Prime numbers

The first 20 prime numbers are 2, 3, 5, 7, 11, 13, 17, 19, 23, 29, 31, 37, 41, 43, 47, 53, 59, 61, 67, 71

A prime number is a number that only has two factors, 1 and itself.

There is no pattern to the prime numbers so they do not have an nth term.

One important fact that you should remember is that there is only one even prime number, 2.

EXERCISE 20D

1 Find the next two terms and the nth term in each of these linear sequences.

HINTS AND TIPS
Remember to look at the differences and the first term.

a 3, 5, 7, 9, 11, ...

b 5, 9, 13, 17, 21, ...

c 8, 13, 18, 23, 28, ...

d 2, 8, 14, 20, 26, ...

e 5, 8, 11, 14, 17, ...

f 2, 9, 16, 23, 30, ...

g 1, 5, 9, 13, 17, ...

h 3, 7, 11, 15, 19, ...

i 2, 5, 8, 11, 14, ...

j 2, 12, 22, 32, ...

k 8, 12, 16, 20, ...

l 4, 9, 14, 19, 24, ...

2 Find the nth term and the 50th term in each of these linear sequences.

a 4, 7, 10, 13, 16, ...

b 7, 9, 11, 13, 15, ...

c 3, 8, 13, 18, 23, ...

d 1, 5, 9, 13, 17, ...

e 2, 10, 18, 26, ...

f 5, 6, 7, 8, 9, ...

g 6, 11, 16, 21, 26, ...

h 3, 11, 19, 27, 35, ...

i 1, 4, 7, 10, 13, ...

j 21, 24, 27, 30, 33, ...

k 12, 19, 26, 33, 40, ...

l 1, 9, 17, 25, 33, ...

3 **a** Which term of the sequence 5, 8, 11, 14, 17, … is the first one to be greater than 100?

b Which term of the sequence 1, 8, 15, 22, 29, … is the first one to be greater than 200?

c Which term of the sequence 4, 9, 14, 19, 24, … is the closest to 500?

4 For each sequence **a** to **j**, find

i the nth term   **ii** the 100th term   **iii** the term closest to 100.

a 5, 9, 13, 17, 21, …   **b** 3, 5, 7, 9, 11, 13, …

c 4, 7, 10, 13, 16, …   **d** 8, 10, 12, 14, 16, …

e 9, 13, 17, 21, …   **f** 6, 11, 16, 21, …

g 0, 3, 6, 9, 12, …   **h** 2, 8, 14, 20, 26, …

i 7, 15, 23, 31, …   **j** 25, 27, 29, 31, …

5 A sequence of fractions is $\frac{3}{4}, \frac{5}{7}, \frac{7}{10}, \frac{9}{13}, \frac{11}{16}, \dots$

a Find the nth term in the sequence.

b By changing each fraction to a decimal, can you see a pattern?

c What, as a decimal, will be the value of the

i 100th term?   **ii** 1000th term?

d Use your answers to part **c** to predict what the 10 000th term and the millionth term are. (Check these out on your calculator.)

6 Repeat question **5** for $\frac{3}{6}, \frac{7}{11}, \frac{11}{16}, \frac{15}{21}, \frac{19}{26}, \dots$

7 The powers of 2 are $2^1, 2^2, 2^3, 2^4, 2^5, \dots$

This gives the sequence 2, 4, 8, 16, 32, …

The nth term is given by 2^n.

a Continue the sequence for another five terms.

b Give the nth term of these sequences.

i 1, 3, 7, 15, 31, …

ii 3, 5, 9, 17, 33, …

iii 6, 12, 24, 48, 96, …

8 The powers of 10 are $10^1, 10^2, 10^3, 10^4, 10^5, \dots$

This gives the sequence 10, 100, 1000, 10 000, 100 000, …

The nth term is given by 10^n.

a Describe the connection between the numbers of zeros in each term and the power of the term.

b If $10^n = 1\,000\,000$, what is the value of n?

c Give the *n*th term of these sequences.

   i 9, 99, 999, 9 999, 99 999, ...

   ii 20, 200, 2000, 20 000, 200 000, ...

9 **a** Pick any odd number.

Pick any other odd number.

Add the two numbers together. Is the answer odd or even?

Complete this table.

+	Odd	Even
Odd	Even	
Even		

b Pick any odd number.

Pick any other odd number.

Multiply the two numbers together. Is the answer odd or even?

Complete this table.

×	Odd	Even
Odd	Odd	
Even		

10 The square numbers are 1, 4, 9, 16, 25, ...

The *n*th term of this sequence is n^2.

a Continue the sequence for another five terms.

b Give the *n*th term of these sequences.

   i 2, 5, 10, 17, 26, ...

   ii 2, 8, 18, 32, 50, ...

   iii 0, 3, 8, 15, 24, ...

11 Write down the next two lines of this number pattern.

$$1 = 1 = 1^2$$
$$1 + 3 = 4 = 2^2$$
$$1 + 3 + 5 = 9 = 3^2$$

12 The triangular numbers are 1, 3, 6, 10, 15, 21, ...

a Continue the sequence for another four terms.

b The *n*th term of this sequence is given by $\frac{1}{2}n(n + 1)$.

Use the formula to find:

i The 20th triangular number

ii the 100th triangular number

c Add consecutive terms of the triangular number sequence.

For example, $1 + 3 = 4$, $3 + 6 = 9$, etc.

What do you notice?

13 *p* is an odd number, *q* is an even number. State if the following are odd or even.

a $p + 1$	**b** $q + 1$	**c** $p + q$
d p^2	**e** $qp + 1$	**f** $(p + q)(p - q)$
g $q^2 + 4$	**h** $p^2 + q^2$	**i** p^3

14 *p* is a prime number, *q* is an even number.

State if the following are odd or even, or could be either odd or even.

a $p + 1$	**b** $p + q$	**c** p^2
d $qp + 1$	**e** $(p + q)(p - q)$	**f** $2p + 3q$

20.4 General rules from given patterns

In this section you will learn how to:

● find the *n*th term from practical problems

Key words

difference
pattern
rule

Many problem-solving situations that you are likely to meet involve number sequences. So you need to be able to formulate general **rules** from given number **patterns**.

EXAMPLE 14

The diagram shows a pattern of squares building up.

a How many squares will be on the base of the nth pattern?

b Which pattern has 99 squares in its base?

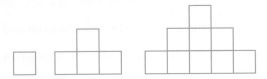

a First, we build up the following table for the patterns.

Pattern number	1	2	3	4	5
Number of squares in base	1	3	5	7	9

Looking at the **difference** between consecutive patterns, we see it is always two squares. So, we use $2n$.

Subtract the difference 2 from the first number, which gives $1 - 2 = -1$.

So the number of squares on the base of the nth pattern is $2n - 1$.

b We have to find n when $2n - 1 = 99$:

$2n - 1 = 99$

$2n = 99 + 1 = 100$

$n = 100 \div 2 = 50$

The pattern with 99 squares in its base is the 50th.

EXERCISE 20E

 A pattern of squares is built up from matchsticks as shown.

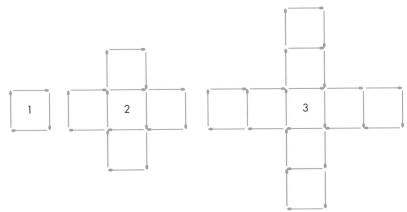

a Draw the 4th diagram.

b How many squares are in the nth diagram?

c How many squares are in the 25th diagram?

d With 200 squares, which is the biggest diagram that could be made?

HINTS AND TIPS

Write out the number sequences to help you see the patterns.

2 A pattern of triangles is built up from matchsticks.

1   2   3   4

a Draw the 5th set of triangles in this pattern.

b How many matchsticks are needed for the nth set of triangles?

c How many matchsticks are needed to make the 60th set of triangles?

d If there are only 100 matchsticks, which is the largest set of triangles that could be made?

3 A conference centre had tables each of which could sit six people. When put together, the tables could seat people as shown.

1   2   3

a How many people could be seated at four tables put together this way?

b How many people could be seated at n tables put together in this way?

c A conference had 50 people who wished to use the tables in this way. How many tables would they need?

4 Prepacked fencing units come in the shape shown on the right, made of four pieces of wood. When you put them together in stages to make a fence, you also need joining pieces, so the fence will start to build up as shown below.

2   3

a How many pieces of wood would you have in a fence made up in:

   i five stages   **ii** n stages   **iii** 45 stages?

b I made a fence out of 124 pieces of wood. How many stages did I use?

5 Regular pentagons of side length 1 cm are joined together to make a pattern as shown.

Copy this pattern and write down the perimeter of each shape.

1   2   3   4

a What is the perimeter of patterns like this made from

   i six pentagons?   **ii** n pentagons?   **iii** 50 pentagons?

b What is the largest number of pentagons that can be put together like this to have a perimeter less than 1000 cm?

6 Lamp-posts are put at the end of every 100 m stretch of a motorway, as shown.

1   2   3

a How many lamp-posts are needed for

   i 900 m of this motorway?   **ii** 8 km of this motorway?

b The M99 is a motorway being built. The contractor has ordered 1598 lamp-posts. How long is this motorway?

7 A school dining hall had tables in the shape of a trapezium. Each table could seat five people, as shown on the right. When the tables were joined together as shown below, each table could not seat as many people.

  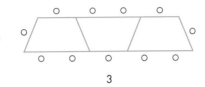

1   2   3

a In this arrangement, how many could be seated if there were:

   i four tables?   **ii** n tables?   **iii** 13 tables?

b For an outside charity event, up to 200 people had to be seated. How many tables arranged like this did they need?

8 When setting out tins to make a display of a certain height, you need to know how many tins to start with at the bottom.

a How many tins are needed on the bottom if you wish the display to be:

   i five tins high?   **ii** n tins high?   **iii** 18 tins high?

b I saw a shop assistant starting to build a display, and noticed he was starting with 20 tins on the bottom. How high was the display when it was finished?

9 a The values of 2 raised to a positive whole-number power are 2, 4, 8, 16, 32, …

What is the nth term of this sequence?

b A supermarket sells four different sized bottles of water: pocket size, 100 ml; standard size, 200 ml; family size, 400 ml; giant size, 800 ml.

   i Describe the number pattern that the contents follow.

   ii The supermarket introduces a super giant size, which is the next sized bottle in the pattern. How much does this bottle hold?

Quadratic sequences

In this section you will learn how to:
- work out the nth term of a non-linear rule

Some problem-solving situations involve number sequences which are governed by a **quadratic rule**.

You can always identify a pattern as being quadratic from its **second differences**, which are *constant*. (A second difference is the result of subtracting one difference between consecutive terms from the next difference.)

The simpler rules

These sequences will nearly always be based on n^2 alone. So you do need to recognise the pattern 1, 4, 9, 16, 25, ...

The differences between consecutive terms of this pattern are the odd numbers 3, 5, 7, 9, ... So if you find that the differences form an odd-number sequence, you know the pattern is based on n^2.

EXAMPLE 15

Find the nth term in the sequence 2, 5, 10, 17, 26, ...

The differences are the odd numbers 3, 5, 7, 9, ... so we know the rule is based on n^2.

The second differences are 2, a constant.

Next, we look for a link with the square numbers. We do this by subtracting from each term the corresponding square number:

2	5	10	17	26
−1	−4	−9	−16	−25
1	1	1	1	1

Clearly, the link is +1, so the nth term is $n^2 + 1$.

(You should always quickly check the generalisation by substituting $n = 1, 2, 3, 4$ to see whether it does work.)

EXAMPLE 16

Find the nth term in the sequence 1, 6, 13, 22, 33, ...

The differences are 5, 7, 9, 11, ... so we know the pattern is based on n^2.

The second differences are 2, a constant.

Next, we have to find the link. We notice that the first difference is 5 not 3, which means that the series of square numbers we use starts at 4, not at 1.

It follows that to obtain 4, 9, 16, 25, ... from the original sequence simply add 3 to each term of that sequence.

So to get from the square numbers to the sequence 1, 6, 13, 22, 33, ... we have to use $(n + 1)^2$, since the sequence is based on 4, 9, 16, ...

The final step in finding the rule is to take away the 3, which gives the nth term as $(n + 1)^2 - 3$.

More complicated rules

EXAMPLE 17

Find the *n*th term in the sequence 2, 6, 12, 20, 30, ...

Looking at the differences tells us that the sequence is non-linear, and is not based on n^2.

So we split each term into factors to see whether we can find a pattern which shows how the numbers have been formed. Constructing a table like the one below can help us to sort out which factors to use when we have a choice.

Term	2	6	12	20	30
Factors	1×2	2×3	3×4	4×5	5×6

We can break down the factors to obtain:

$1 \times (1 + 1)$ $2 \times (2 + 1)$ $3 \times (3 + 1)$ $4 \times (4 + 1)$ $5 \times (5 + 1)$

We can now see quite easily that the pattern is $n \times (n + 1)$. That is the *n*th term is $n(n + 1)$.

EXAMPLE 18

Find the *n*th term in the sequence of the triangular numbers 1, 3, 6, 10, 15, ...

Looking at the differences tells us that the sequence is non-linear and is not based on n^2.

So we split each term into factors and construct a table. (We have no problem with the choice of factors.)

Term	1	3	6	10	15
Factors	1×1	1×3	2×3	2×5	3×5

At this stage, we may not yet have spotted a pattern. So we investigate the effect of multiplying the smaller of each pair of factors by 2, and obtain an interesting pattern.

Term	1	3	6	10	15
Factors	1×1	1×3	2×3	2×5	3×5
Smaller $\times$ 2	2×1	2×3	4×3	4×5	6×5

That is:

1×2 2×3 3×4 4×5 5×6

We can further break down this last set of numbers to obtain:

$1 \times (1 + 1)$ $2 \times (2 + 1)$ $3 \times (3 + 1)$ $4 \times (4 + 1)$ $5 \times (5 + 1)$

the pattern of which is given by $n \times (n + 1)$.

This gives terms twice the size of those in the sequence 1, 3, 6, 10, 15, ... so we need to change the expression to $\frac{1}{2} \times n (n + 1)$.

So the *n*th term is $\frac{1}{2}n(n + 1)$.

Expressions of the form $an^2 + bn + c$

These expressions are unlikely to appear in a GCSE exam but could easily appear in an AO1 coursework task. This method will give an algebraic means of showing a sequence.

EXAMPLE 19

Find the nth term of the sequence 5, 15, 31, 53, ...

Set up a difference table.

n	1	2	3	4
nth term	5	15	31	53
1st difference		10	16	22
2nd difference			6	6

Now extend the table backwards to get the term for $n = 0$ and call the three lines of the table c, $a + b$ and $2a$.

n	0	1	2	3	4
c	1	5	15	31	53
$a + b$		4	10	16	22
$2a$			6	6	6

This gives $2a = 6 \Rightarrow a = 3,$ $a + b = 4 \Rightarrow b = 1,$ $c = 1$

Giving the nth term as: $3n^2 + n + 1$

EXAMPLE 20

Find the nth term of the sequence 3, 5, 8, 12, 17, ...

Set up a difference table.

n	0	1	2	3	4	5
c	2	3	5	8	12	17
$a + b$		1	2	3	4	5
$2a$			1	1	1	1

This gives $2a = 1 \Rightarrow a = \frac{1}{2},$ $a + b = 1 \Rightarrow b = \frac{1}{2},$ $c = 2$

Giving the nth term as: $\frac{1}{2}n^2 + \frac{1}{2}n + 2$

1 For each of the sequences **a** to **e**   **i** write down the next two terms   **ii** find the nth term.

   a 0, 3, 8, 15, 24, …   **b** 3, 6, 11, 18, 27, …   **c** 4, 7, 12, 19, 28, …

   d −1, 2, 7, 14, 23, …   **e** 11, 14, 19, 26, …

 2 For each of the sequences **a** to **e**   **i** write down the next two terms   **ii** find the nth term.

   a 5, 10, 17, 26, …   **b** 3, 8, 15, 24, …   **c** 9, 14, 21, 30, …

   d 10, 17, 26, 37, …   **e** 8, 15, 24, 35, …

 3 Look at each of the following sequences to see whether the rule is linear, quadratic on n^2 alone or fully quadratic. Then

   i write down the nth term   **ii** write down the 50th term.

   a 5, 8, 13, 20, 29, …   **b** 5, 8, 11, 14, 17, …   **c** 3, 8, 15, 24, 35, …

   d 5, 12, 21, 32, 45, …   **e** 3, 6, 11, 18, 27, …   **f** 1, 6, 11, 16, 21, …

 4 Find the nth terms of the following sequences in the form $an^2 + bn + c$.

   a 1, 4, 11, 22, 37, ….   **b** 2, 13, 30, 53, 82, ….   **c** 4, 8, 13, 19, 26, …..

20.6 Changing the subject of a formula

In this section you will learn how to:	Key words
• change the subject of a formula where the subject occurs more than once	subject transpose

You already have met changing the **subject** of a formula in which the subject appears only once (see page 104). This is like solving an equation but using letters. You have also solved equations in which the unknown appears on both sides of the equation. This requires the unknown (usually x) terms to be collected on one side and the numbers to be collected on the other.

We can do something similar, to **transpose** formulae in which the subject appears more than once. The principle is the same. Collect all the subject terms on the same side and everything else on the other side. Most often, we then need to factorise the subject out of the resulting expression.

EXAMPLE 21

Make x the subject of this formula.

$$ax + b = cx + d$$

First, rearrange the formula to get all the x terms on the left-hand side and all the other terms on the right-hand side. (The rule "change sides – change signs" still applies.)

$$ax - cx = d - b$$

Factorise x out of left-hand side to get:

$$x(a - c) = d - b$$

Divide by the bracket, which gives:

$$x = \frac{d - b}{a - c}$$

EXAMPLE 22

Make p the subject of this formula.

$$5 = \frac{ap + b}{cp + d}$$

First, multiply both sides by the denominator of the algebraic fraction, which gives:

$$5(cp + d) = ap + b$$

Expand the bracket to get:

$$5cp + 5d = ap + b$$

Now continue as in Example 21:

$$5cp - ap = b - 5d$$

$$p(5c - a) = b - 5d$$

$$p = \frac{b - 5d}{5c - a}$$

EXERCISE 20G

In questions **1** to **10**, make the letter in brackets the subject of each formula.

1 $3(x + 2y) = 2(x - y)$ (x)

2 $3(x + 2y) = 2(x - y)$ (y)

3 $5 = \dfrac{a + b}{a - c}$ (a)

4 $p(a + b) = q(a - b)$ (a)

5 $p(a + b) = q(a - b)$ (b)

6 $A = 2\pi rh + \pi rk$ (r)

7 $v^2 = u^2 + av^2$ (v)

8 $s(t - r) = 2r - 3$ (r)

9 $s(t - r) = 2(r - 3)$ (r)

10 $R = \dfrac{x - 3}{x - 2}$ (x)

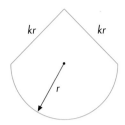

11 **a** The perimeter of the shape shown on the right is given by the formula $P = \pi r + 2kr$. Make r the subject of this formula.

b The area of the same shape is given by $A = \frac{1}{2}[\pi r^2 + r^2\sqrt{(k^2 - 1)}]$ Make r the subject of this formula.

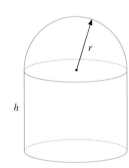

12 When £P is invested for Y years at a simple interest rate of R, the following formula gives the amount, A, at any time:

$$A = P + \frac{PRY}{100}$$

Make P the subject of this formula.

13 When two resistors with values a and b are connected in parallel, the total resistance is given by:

$$R = \frac{ab}{a + b}$$

a Make b the subject of the formula.

b Write the formula when a is the subject.

14 **a** Make x the subject of this formula.

$$y = \frac{x + 2}{x - 2}$$

b Show that the formula $y = 1 + \dfrac{4}{x - 2}$ can be rearranged to give:

$$x = 2 + \frac{4}{y - 1}$$

c Combine the right-hand sides of each formula in part **b** into single fractions and simplify as much as possible.

d What do you notice?

15 The volume of the solid shown is given by:

$$V = \tfrac{2}{3}\pi r^3 + \pi r^2 h$$

a Explain why it is not possible to make r the subject of this formula.

b Make π the subject.

c If $h = r$, can the formula be rearranged to make r the subject? If so, rearrange it to make r the subject.

16 Make x the subject of this formula.

$$W = \tfrac{1}{2}z(x + y) + \tfrac{1}{2}y(x + z)$$

1　**a**　Here is a sequence of numbers.

　　　　29　　25　　21　　17　　13

　　　i　Write down the next two numbers in the sequence.

　　　ii　Write down the rule for continuing the sequence.

　b　Another sequence of numbers begins:

　　　　2　　5　　14　　41

　　The rule for continuing this sequence is:

> Multiply by 3 and subtract 1

　　　i　What is the next number in the sequence?

　　　ii　The same rule is used for a sequence that starts with the number 7. What is the second number in this sequence?

　　　iii　The same rule is also used for a sequence that starts with the number −2. What is the second number in this sequence?

2　The first 10 prime numbers are 2, 3, 5, 7, 11, 13, 17, 19, 23, 29.

P is a prime number.
Q is an odd number.
State whether each of the following is always odd, always even or could be either odd or even.

3　The nth term of a sequence is $3n - 1$.

　a　Write down the first and second terms of the sequence.

　b　Which term of the sequence is equal to 32?

　c　Explain why 85 is not a term in this sequence.

4　**a**　The nth term of a sequence is $4n - 1$.

　　　i　Write down the first three terms of the sequence.

　　　ii　Is 132 a term in this sequence? Explain your answer.

　b　Tom builds fencing from pieces of wood as shown.

Diagram 1　　　　　　　　Diagram 2
five pieces of wood　　　　nine pieces of wood

Diagram 3
13 pieces of wood

How many pieces of wood will be in diagram n?

5　**a**　**i**　Multiply out　　　　　　　$s(s^2 + 6)$

　　　ii　Multiply out and simplify　$4(x - 2) + 3(x + 2)$

　　　iii　Multiply out and simplify　$(n + 3)^2$

　b　Factorise completely the following expressions

　　　i　$2a^2 + a$

　　　ii　$8x^3y^2 - 4xy^3$

AQA, Question 5, Paper 2 Higher, June 2004

6　Here is a sequence made from a pattern of dots.

1st pattern　　　　2nd pattern　　　　3rd pattern

　a　Complete the table.

Pattern	1	2	3	4	5
Number of dots	5	8	11		

　b　How many dots are in the 7th pattern?

　c　How many dots are in the nth pattern?

　d　Which pattern has 62 dots in it?

7　Make x the subject of this formula.

$$w = x^2 + y$$

AQA, Question 11, Paper 2 Higher, June 2003

8　**a**　Solve the equation

$$\frac{x \div 1}{2} + \frac{x - 3}{4} = 2$$

　　You *must* show all your working.

AQA, Question 11b, Paper 2 Higher, June 2004

9　A star shape is made by cutting quadrants of a circle from a square of side $2r$.

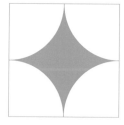

　a　Show that the shaded area is given by the formula

$$A = 4r^2 - \pi r^2$$

　b　Rearrange the formula

$$A = 4r^2 - \pi r^2$$

　　to make r the subject.

AQA, Question 22, Paper 2 (2-tier trial), June 2005

10　Make x the subject of this formula.

$$p(q - x) = px + q^2$$

11　Make x the subject of this formula.

$$y = \frac{2x + 3}{x - 5}$$

12 A straight line has the equation $\quad y = 2x + 1$

A curve has the equation $\quad\quad\quad y^2 = 8x$

Find the point of intersection of the line and the curve.

13 Solve the equation

$$\frac{4}{2x + 1} - \frac{1}{3x - 1} = 5$$

AQA, Question 19, Paper 2 Higher, June 2005

14 Simplify fully $\quad\quad\quad\dfrac{3x^2 - 5x - 2}{x^2 + x - 6}$

15 Solve the simultaneous equations

$$y = x \div 2$$
$$y = 3x^2$$

You *must* show your working. Do *not* use trial and improvement.

AQA, Question 20, Paper 2 Higher, June 2004

16 Simplify $\quad\quad\quad\dfrac{x^2 - 9}{x^2 + 3x}$

AQA, Question 18b, Paper 2 Higher, June 2004

17 Solve the equation $\quad\quad\quad\dfrac{1}{x + 2} + \dfrac{3x}{x - 1} = 3$

AQA, Question 20 (modified), Paper 2 Higher, November 2003

WORKED EXAM QUESTION

Make g the subject of the following formula.

$$\frac{t(3 + g)}{8 - g} = 2$$

$t(3 + g) = 2(8 - g)$ ——— Cross multiply to get rid of the fraction

$3t + gt = 16 - 2g$ ——— Expand the brackets

$gt + 2g = 16 - 3t$ ——— Collect all the g terms on the left-hand side and other terms on the right-hand side.

$g(t + 2) = 16 - 3t$

$g = \dfrac{16 - 3t}{t + 2}$ ——— Simplify, $gt + 2g = g(t + 2)$, and divide by $(t + 2)$.

Walking holiday

A group of friends plan an eight-day walking holiday. The profile of their first four daily walks is shown below.

For every day they work out the horizontal distance they walk in kilometres, and the height they climb in metres.

They calculate the time each day's walk will take using the formula

$$T = 15D + \frac{H}{10}$$

where: T = time in minutes D = distance in km
H = height climbed in m

This formula assumes an average walking speed of 4km/h and an extra minute for each 10 metres climbed.

Copy this table and help them complete it. Work out the time each day's walk will take, and the time that the group expects to finish.

Day	Distance in km	Height climbed in metres	Time in minutes	Time in hours and minutes	Start time	Time allowed for breaks	Finish time
1	16	250	265	4h 25m	9:30 am	2 hours	3:55 pm
2					9.00 am	2¾ hours	
3					10:00 am	2½ hours	
4					10:30 am	2¼ hours	

Do not include the height they go down in the calculation – only the height they go up

Day 3

Day 4

Distance (km)

This table shows the information for their walks from Day 5 to Day 8.

Unfortunately coffee has been spilt on the table! Help them to work out the values covered by the coffee.

Day	Distance in km	Height climbed in metres	Time in minutes	Time in hours and minutes	Start time	Time allowed for breaks	Finish time
5	18		282		10:00 am		5:12 pm
6		290	284			2 hours	5:14 pm
7		90		5h 39m	10:00 am	2¾ hours	
8	12			3h 30m	10:30 am		4:15 pm

GRADE YOURSELF

D Able to substitute numbers into an *n*th term rule

D Able to understand how odd and even numbers interact in addition, subtraction and multiplication problems

C Able to give the *n*th term of a linear sequence

C Able to give the *n*th term of a sequence of powers of 2 or 10

B Able to find the *n*th term of a quadratic sequence

B Able to solve linear equations involving algebraic fractions where the subject appears as the numerator

A Able to rearrange a formula where the subject appears twice

A Able to combine algebraic fractions using the four rules of addition, subtraction, multiplication and division

A* Able to rearrange more complicated formulae where the subject may appear twice or as a power

A* Able to solve a quadratic equation obtained from algebraic fractions where the variable appears in the denominator

A* Able to simplify algebraic fractions by factorisation and cancellation

A* Able to solve a pair of simultaneous equations where one is linear and the other is non-linear

What you should know now

- Be able to manipulate algebraic fractions and solve equations resulting from the simplified fractions

- Be able to solve a pair of simultaneous equations where one is linear and one is non-linear

- Be able to recognise a linear sequence and find its *n*th term

- Be able to recognise a sequence of powers of 2 or 10

- Be able to recognise a non-linear sequence and find its *n*th term

- Be able to rearrange a formula where the subject appears twice

1 Dimensions of length

2 Dimensions of area

3 Dimensions of volume

4 Consistent dimensions

This chapter will show you ...

● how to decide whether a formula represents a length, an area or a volume

● how to check that a formula has consistent dimensions

What you should already know

● The formulae for perimeters, areas and volumes of common shapes

● The common units used for length, area and volume

Quick check

Write down a formula for each of the following.

1 The perimeter of a square with side length l.

2 The circumference of a circle with diameter d.

3 The area of a triangle with base b and height h.

4 The area of a circle with radius r.

5 The volume of a cube with side length l.

6 The volume of a cylinder with radius r and height h.

When we have an unknown length or distance in a problem, we represent it by a single letter, followed by the unit in which it is measured. For example,

t centimetres $\qquad$ x miles $\qquad$ y kilometres

EXAMPLE 1

Find a formula the **perimeter** of each of these shapes.

a b

Shape **a** is a rectangle. Its perimeter is given by the formula

$P = x + y + x + y = 2x + 2y$

Shape **b** is an irregular quadrilateral. Its perimeter is given by the formula

$P = p + p + r + s = 2p + r + s$

In the example, each letter is a **length** and has the dimension or measure of length, i.e. centimetre, metre, kilometre, etc. The numbers or coefficients written before the letters are *not* lengths and therefore have *no* dimensions. So, for example, $2x$, $5y$ or $\frac{1}{2}p$ have the same dimension as x, y or p respectively.

When just lengths are involved in a formula, the formula is said to have one dimension or **1-D**, which is sometimes represented by the symbol [L].

EXERCISE 21A

Find a formula for the perimeter of each of these shapes. Each letter represents a length.

1

2

3

4

5

6

7

8

9

10
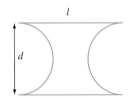

In this section you will learn how to:
- find formulae for the area of 2-D shapes

Key words
2-D
area

EXAMPLE 2

Look at these four examples of formulae for calculating area.

$A = lb$ gives the area of a rectangle

$A = x^2$ gives the area of a square

$A = 2ab + 2ac + 2bc$ gives the surface area of a cuboid

$A = \pi r^2$ gives the area of a circle

These formulae have one thing in common. They all consist of terms that are the product of two lengths. You can recognise this by counting the number of letters in each term of the formula. The first formula has two (l and b). The second has two (x and x). The third has three terms, each of two letters (a and b, a and c, b and c). The fourth also has only two letters (r and r) because π is a number (3.14159…) which has no dimension.

We can recognise formulae for **area** because they only have terms that consist of two letters – that is, two lengths multiplied together. Numbers are not defined as lengths, since they have no dimensions. These formulae therefore have two dimensions or **2-D**, which is sometimes represented by the symbol [L^2].

This confirms the units in which area is usually measured. For example,

square metres (m × m or m^2)

square centimetres (cm × cm or cm^2)

EXERCISE 21B

Find a formula for the area of each of these shapes. Each letter represents a length.

6

7

8

9

10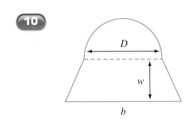

21.3 Dimensions of volume

In this section you will learn how to:

- find formulae for the volume of 3-D shapes

Key words
3-D
volume

EXAMPLE 3

Look at these three examples of formulae for calculating volume.

$V = lbh$ gives the volume of a cuboid
$V = x^3$ gives the volume of a cube
$V = \pi r^2 h + \frac{4}{3}\pi r^3$ gives the volume of a cylinder with hemispherical ends

Again, these formulae have one thing in common. They all consist of terms that are the product of three lengths. You can recognise this by counting the number of letters in each term of the formula. The first formula has three (l, b and h). The second has three (x, x and x). The third has two terms, each of three letters (r, r and h; r, r and r). Remember, π has no dimension.

We can recognise formulae for **volume** because they only have terms that consist of three letters – that is, three lengths multiplied together. They therefore have three dimensions or **3-D**, which is sometimes represented by the symbol $[L^3]$. Once more, numbers are not defined as lengths, since they have no dimensions.

This confirms the units in which volume is usually measured. For example,

cubic metres (m × m × m or m^3)

cubic centimetres (cm × cm × cm or cm^3)

EXERCISE 21C

Find a formula for the volume of each of these shapes. Each letter represents a length.

1

p

2p

3p

2

r

h

3

h

b

w

4

h

l

b

5

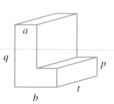

a

q

p

b

t

6

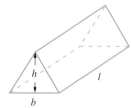

a

l

b

d

c

c

21.4 **Consistent dimensions**

In this section you will learn how to:

- check that the dimensions of a formula are consistent

Key words

consistency
dimension
formula

One way in which scientists and mathematicians check complicated **formulae** to see whether they are correct is to test for **consistency**. They check that every term in the formula is of the same **dimension**.

Each term in a formula must have the correct number of dimensions. It is not possible to have a formula with a mixture of terms, some of which have, for example, one dimension and some two dimensions. When terms are found to be mixed, the formula is said to be *inconsistent* and is not possible.

We are only concerned with lengths, areas and volumes, so it is easy for us to test for consistency.

EXAMPLE 4

Which of these expressions are consistent? If any are consistent, do they represent a length, an area or a volume?

a $a + bc$ **b** $\pi r^2 + ab$ **c** $r^3 + 2\pi r^2$ **d** $\dfrac{(ab^2 + a^2 b)}{2}$ **e** $\dfrac{\pi(R^2 + r^2)}{x}$

a is inconsistent because the first term has one letter (1-D), and the second has two letters (2-D). Hence, it is a mixture of length and area. So it has no physical meaning, i.e. $[L] + [L^2]$ is not possible.

b is consistent because the first term has two letters (r and r) multiplied by a dimensionless number (π), and the second term also has two letters (a and b). Hence the expression could represent an area, i.e. $[L^2] + [L^2] = [L^2]$ is consistent.

c is inconsistent because the first term is 3-D and the second term is 2-D. It is a mixture of volume and area, so it has no physical meaning, i.e. $[L^3] + [L^2]$ is not possible.

d is consistent. Each term is 3-D and hence the expression could represent a volume, i.e. $[L^3] + [L^3] = [L^3]$ is consistent.

e is consistent. There are two terms which are 2-D in the numerator and the term in the denominator is 1-D. The numerator can be cancelled to give two terms which are both 1-D. Hence the expression could represent a length, i.e. $[L^2]/[L] = [L]$ is consistent.

EXERCISE 21D

1 Each of these expressions represents a length, an area or a volume. Indicate which it is by writing L, A or V. Each letter represents a length.

a x^2	**b** $2y$	**c** πa	**d** πab
e xyz	**f** $3x^3$	**g** $x^2 y$	**h** $2xy$
i $4y$	**j** $3ab^2$	**k** $4xz$	**l** $5z$
m abc	**n** $ab + bc$	**o** $abc + d^3$	**p** $2ab + 3bc$
q $a^2 b + ab^2$	**r** $a^2 + b^2$	**s** πa^2	**t** $\dfrac{abc}{d}$
u $\dfrac{(ab + bc)}{d}$	**v** $\dfrac{ab}{2}$	**w** $(a + b)^2$	**x** $4a^2 + 2ab$
y $3abc + 2abd + 4bcd + 2acd$		**z** $4\pi r^3 + \pi r^2 h$	

2 Indicate whether each of these expressions is consistent (C) or inconsistent (I). Each letter represents a length.

a $a + b$	**b** $a^2 + b$	**c** $a^2 + b^2$	**d** $ab + c$
e $ab + c^2$	**f** $a^3 + bc$	**g** $a^3 + abc$	**h** $a^2 + abc$
i $3a^2 + bc$	**j** $4a^3 b + 2ab^2$	**k** $3abc + 2x^2 y$	**l** $3a(ab + bc)$
m $4a^2 + 3ab$	**n** $\pi a^2(a + b)$	**o** $\pi a^2 + 2r^2$	**p** $\pi r^2 h + \pi rh$

q $\pi r^2 (R + r)$ **r** $\dfrac{(ab + bc)}{d}$ **s** $a(b^2 + c)$ **t** $\pi ab + \pi bc$

u $(a + b)(c + d)$ **v** $\pi(a + b)(a^2 + b^2)$ **w** $\pi(a^2 + b^2)$ **x** $\pi^2(a + b)$

y $\pi r^2 h + \pi r^3$

3 Write down whether each of these expressions is consistent (C) or inconsistent (I). When it is consistent, say whether it represents a length (L), an area (A) or a volume (V). Each letter represents a length.

a $\pi a + \pi b$ **b** $2\pi r^2 + h$ **c** $\pi r^2 h + 2\pi r^3$ **d** $2\pi r + h$

e $2\pi rh + 4\pi r^3$ **f** $\dfrac{\pi r}{6} + \pi a^2$ **g** $r^2 h + \pi rh^2$ **h** $\pi r^2(r + h)$

i $\pi r^2 h + 2r^3 + \dfrac{h^2 r}{6}$ **j** $2\pi r^3 + 3\pi r^2 h$ **k** $4\pi a + 3x$ **l** $3\pi r^2 a + 2\pi r$

m $\dfrac{\pi r^2 h}{3} + \dfrac{\pi r^3}{3} + x^3$

4 What power * would make each expression consistent?

a $\pi abc + a^* b$ **b** $\dfrac{\pi r^* h}{2} + \pi h^* + \dfrac{rh^2}{2}$

c $\pi a(b^* + ac)$ **d** $a^* b + ab^* + c^3$

5 Kerry has worked out a volume formula as

$$V = \frac{(2hD^2 + hd)}{4}$$

It is wrong. Why?

6 The diagram shows a cuboid with sides a, b and c, with a circular hole radius r drilled through it. Three of the following formulae represent

    A: the total length of all straight edges

    B: the total surface area of the six flat sides

    C: the volume.

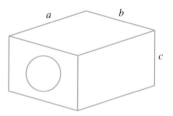

a Match the correct formula to each of the quantities A, B and C.

    F_1: $4\pi r$ F_2: $4(a + b + c)$

    F_3: $abc - \pi r^2 a$ F_4: $2a(b + c) + 2(bc - \pi r^2)$

b Say what quantity the fourth formula represents.

1 In this question, the letters x, y and z represent lengths. State whether each expression could represent a length, an area or a volume.

  a xyz

  b $\pi(x + y + z)$

AQA, Question 11, Paper 1 Intermediate, Spec B, Module 5, November 2004

2 In this question, the letters x, y and z represent lengths. State whether each expression could represent a length, an area or a volume.

  a $\pi x^2 y$

  b $x + y + z$

  c $x^2 + y^2$

AQA, Question 12, Paper 1 Intermediate, Spec B, Module 5, November 2003

3 In the formulae given below, the letters p, q and r represent lengths.

  a Grant has written down this formula

$$\text{Volume} = \frac{1}{4}\pi r^4$$

    Explain how you can tell that Grant has made a mistake.

  b Jared has this formula

$$\text{Area} = p^2 + 2q$$

    Explain how you can tell that Jared has made a mistake.

AQA, Question 5, Paper 2 Higher, Spec B, Module 5, June 2003

4 The diagram shows a hollow cylinder. It has dimensions x, y and z as marked on the diagram.

For each expression, state whether it represents a length, an area, a volume, or none of these.

  a $\pi(x^2 - y^2)z$ **b** $\pi(x + y)(x - y)$ **c** $\pi xy^3 + \pi x^2 z$

AQA, Question 10, Paper 2 Higher, June 2002

5 The diagram shows an ellipse of width $2a$ cm and height $2b$ cm.

One of the following is a formula for the area of the ellipse.

Formula 1 $\pi(a + b)$

Formula 2 πab

Formula 3 $\pi a^2 b^2$

  a What is the correct formula?

  a Explain how you can tell that this formula is correct.

AQA, Question 4, Paper 1 Higher, June 2004

6 In the following expressions r, a and b represent lengths. For each expression state whether it represents a length, an area, a volume, or none of these.

  a πab **b** $\pi r^2 a + 2\pi r$ **c** $\dfrac{\pi r a^3}{b}$

AQA, Question 11, Paper 2 Higher, June 2000

WORKED EXAM QUESTION

r, a and b are all lengths. Which of the following expressions could be a volume? Write Yes or No for each one. If the expression could not be a volume, give a reason.

$$\frac{ar}{2}(4b + \pi r) \qquad 2a^2 + \pi r^2 \qquad 4a^2 b + rb^3 \qquad 2abr + \frac{\pi ar^2}{2}$$

Solution

1   Yes, $[L^2] \times [L + L] = [L^2] \times [L] = [L^3]$

2   No, $[L^2] + [L^2]$ is an area

3   No, $[L^3] + [L^4]$ inconsistent

4   Yes, $[L^3] + [L^3] = [L^3]$

> Convert the letters in each term. If the term is a product of three letters, it can represent a volume.

GRADE YOURSELF

D Able to work out a formula for the perimeter, area or volume of simple shapes

C Able to work out a formula for the perimeter, area or volume of complex shapes

C Able to work out whether an expression or formula is dimensionally consistent and whether it represents a length, an area or a volume

What you should know now

- How to work out a formula for the length, area or volume of a shape
- How to recognise whether a formula is 1-D, 2-D or 3-D
- How to recognise when a formula or expression is consistent

Variation

1 Direct variation

2 Inverse variation

This chapter will show you ...

- how to solve problems where two variables are connected by a relationship that varies in direct or inverse proportion

Direct proportion ⟶ Inverse proportion

What you should already know

- Squares, square roots, cubes and cube roots of integers
- How to substitute values into algebraic expressions
- How to solve simple algebraic equations

Quick check

1 Write down the value of each of the following.

   a 5^2 **b** $\sqrt{81}$ **c** 3^3 **d** $\sqrt[3]{64}$

2 Calculate the value of y if $x = 4$.

   a $y = 3x^2$ **b** $y = \dfrac{1}{\sqrt{x}}$

This section will introduce you to:
- direct variation and show you how to work out the constant of proportionality

The term **direct variation** has the same meaning as **direct proportion**.

There is direct variation (or direct proportion) between two variables when one variable is a simple multiple of the other. That is, their ratio is a constant.

For example:

1 kilogram = 2.2 pounds   There is a multiplying factor of 2.2 between kilograms and pounds.

Area of a circle = πr^2 There is a multiplying factor of π between the area of a circle and the square of its radius.

An examination question involving direct variation usually requires you first to find this multiplying factor (called the **constant of proportionality**), then to use it to solve a problem.

The symbol for variation or proportion is $\propto$.

So the statement "Pay is directly proportional to time" can be mathematically written as

   Pay $\propto$ *Time*

which implies that

   Pay $= k \times$ *Time*

where k is the constant of proportionality.

There are three steps to be followed when solving a question involving proportionality.

   Step 1: set up the proportionality equation (you may have to define variables).

   Step 2: use the given information to find the constant of proportionality.

   Step 3: substitute the constant of proportionality in the original equation and use this to find unknown values.

EXAMPLE 1

The cost of an article is directly proportional to the time spent making it. An article taking 6 hours to make costs £30. Find the following.

a   the cost of an article that takes 5 hours to make

b   the length of time it takes to make an article costing £40

Step 1: Let C be the cost of making an article and t the time it takes. We then have:

$$C \propto t$$

$$\Rightarrow C = kt$$

where k is the constant of proportionality.

Note that we can "replace" the proportionality sign $\propto$ with $= k$ to obtain the proportionality equation.

Step 2: Since $C = £30$ when $t = 6$ hours, then $30 = 6k$

$$\Rightarrow \frac{30}{6} = k$$

$$\Rightarrow k = 5$$

Step 3: So the formula is $C = 5t$

a   When $t = 5$ hours $C = 5 \times 5 = 25$

So the cost is £25.

b   When $C = £40$ $40 = 5 \times t$

$$\Rightarrow \frac{40}{5} = t \Rightarrow t = 8$$

So the making time is 8 hours.

EXERCISE 22A

In each case, first find k, the constant of proportionality, and then the formula connecting the variables.

 1 T is directly proportional to M. If $T = 20$ when $M = 4$, find the following.

a T when $M = 3$ **b** M when $T = 10$

 2 W is directly proportional to F. If $W = 45$ when $F = 3$, find the following.

a W when $F = 5$ **b** F when $W = 90$

 3 Q varies directly with P. If $Q = 100$ when $P = 2$, find the following.

a Q when $P = 3$ **b** P when $Q = 300$

 4 X varies directly with Y. If $X = 17.5$ when $Y = 7$, find the following.

a X when $Y = 9$ **b** Y when $X = 30$

A

A

5 The distance covered by a train is directly proportional to the time taken. The train travels 105 miles in 3 hours.

    a What distance will the train cover in 5 hours?

    b What time will it take for the train to cover 280 miles?

6 The cost of fuel delivered to your door is directly proportional to the weight received. When 250 kg is delivered, it costs £47.50.

    a How much will it cost to have 350 kg delivered?

    b How much would be delivered if the cost were £33.25?

7 The number of children who can play safely in a playground is directly proportional to the area of the playground. A playground with an area of 210 m² is safe for 60 children.

    a How many children can safely play in a playground of area 154 m²?

    b A playgroup has 24 children. What is the smallest playground area in which they could safely play?

Direct proportions involving squares, cubes and square roots

The process is the same as for a linear direct variation, as the next example shows.

EXAMPLE 2

The cost of a circular badge is directly proportional to the square of its radius. The cost of a badge with a radius of 2 cm is 68p.

a Find the cost of a badge of radius 2.4 cm.

b Find the radius of a badge costing £1.53.

Step 1: Let C be the cost and r the radius of a badge. Then

$$C \propto r^2$$

$$\Rightarrow C = kr^2 \text{ where } k \text{ is the constant of proportionality.}$$

Step 2: $C = 68$p when $r = 2$ cm. So

$$68 = 4k$$

$$\Rightarrow \frac{68}{4} = k \Rightarrow k = 17$$

Hence the formula is $C = 17r^2$

a When $r = 2.4$ cm $C = 17 \times 2.4^2 \text{p} = 97.92\text{p}$

    Rounding off gives the cost as 98p.

b When $C = 153$p $153 = 17r^2$

$$\Rightarrow \frac{153}{17} = 9 = r^2$$

$$\Rightarrow r = \sqrt{9} = 3$$

Hence, the radius is 3 cm.

EXERCISE 22B

In each case, first find k, the constant of proportionality, and then the formula connecting the variables.

 1 T is directly proportional to x^2. If $T = 36$ when $x = 3$, find the following.

    a T when $x = 5$ **b** x when $T = 400$

 2 W is directly proportional to M^2. If $W = 12$ when $M = 2$, find the following.

    a W when $M = 3$ **b** M when $W = 75$

 3 E varies directly with $\sqrt{C}$. If $E = 40$ when $C = 25$, find the following.

    a E when $C = 49$ **b** C when $E = 10.4$

 4 X is directly proportional to $\sqrt{Y}$. If $X = 128$ when $Y = 16$, find the following.

    a X when $Y = 36$ **b** Y when $X = 48$

 5 P is directly proportional to f^3. If $P = 400$ when $f = 10$, find the following.

    a P when $f = 4$ **b** f when $P = 50$

 6 The cost of serving tea and biscuits varies directly with the square root of the number of people at the buffet. It costs £25 to serve tea and biscuits to 100 people.

    a How much will it cost to serve tea and biscuits to 400 people?

    b For a cost of £37.50, how many could be served tea and biscuits?

 7 In an experiment, the temperature, in °C, varied directly with the square of the pressure, in atmospheres. The temperature was 20 °C when the pressure was 5 atm.

    a What will the temperature be at 2 atm?   **b** What will the pressure be at 80 °C?

 8 The weight, in grams, of ball bearings varies directly with the cube of the radius measured in millimetres. A ball bearing of radius 4 mm has a weight of 115.2 g.

    a What will a ball bearing of radius 6 mm weigh?

    b A ball bearing has a weight of 48.6 g. What is its radius?

 9 The energy, in J, of a particle varies directly with the square of its speed in m/s. A particle moving at 20 m/s has 50 J of energy.

    a How much energy has a particle moving at 4 m/s?

    b At what speed is a particle moving if it has 200 J of energy?

 10 The cost, in £, of a trip varies directly with the square root of the number of miles travelled. The cost of a 100-mile trip is £35.

    a What is the cost of a 500-mile trip (to the nearest £1)?

    b What is the distance of a trip costing £70?

Inverse variation

This section will introduce you to:

● inverse variation and show you how to work out the constant of proportionality

Key words

constant of proportionality, k
inverse proportion

There is **inverse variation** between two variables when one variable is directly proportional to the reciprocal of the other. That is, the product of the two variables is constant. So, as one variable increases, the other decreases.

For example, the faster you travel over a given distance, the less time it takes. So there is an inverse variation between speed and time. We say speed is inversely proportional to time.

$$S \propto \frac{1}{T} \text{ and so } S = \frac{k}{T}$$

which can be written as $ST = k$.

EXAMPLE 3

M is **inversely proportional** to R. If $M = 9$ when $R = 4$, find the following.

a M when $R = 2$ 　　　　　　　　　 **b** R when $M = 3$

Step 1: $M \propto \frac{1}{R} \Rightarrow M = \frac{k}{R}$ where k is the **constant of proportionality**.

Step 2: When $M = 9$ and $R = 4$, we get $9 = \frac{k}{4}$

$\Rightarrow 9 \times 4 = k \Rightarrow k = 36$

Step 3: So the formula is $M = \frac{36}{R}$

a When $R = 2$, then $M = \frac{36}{2} = 18$

b When $M = 3$, then $3 = \frac{36}{R} \Rightarrow 3R = 36 \Rightarrow R = 12$

In each case, first find the formula connecting the variables.

1 T is inversely proportional to m. If $T = 6$ when $m = 2$, find the following.

a T when $m = 4$ 　　　　　　　　　 **b** m when $T = 4.8$

2 W is inversely proportional to x. If $W = 5$ when $x = 12$, find the following.

a W when $x = 3$ 　　　　　　　　　 **b** x when $W = 10$

3 Q varies inversely with $(5 - t)$. If $Q = 8$ when $t = 3$, find the following.

   a Q when $t = 10$ **b** t when $Q = 16$

4 M varies inversely with t^2. If $M = 9$ when $t = 2$, find the following.

   a M when $t = 3$ **b** t when $M = 1.44$

5 W is inversely proportional to $\sqrt{T}$. If $W = 6$ when $T = 16$, find the following.

   a W when $T = 25$ **b** T when $W = 2.4$

6 The grant available to a section of society was inversely proportional to the number of people needing the grant. When 30 people needed a grant, they received £60 each.

   a   What would the grant have been if 120 people had needed one?

   b   If the grant had been £50 each, how many people would have received it?

7 While doing underwater tests in one part of an ocean, a team of scientists noticed that the temperature in °C was inversely proportional to the depth in kilometres. When the temperature was 6 °C, the scientists were at a depth of 4 km.

   a   What would the temperature have been at a depth of 8 km?

   b   To what depth would they have had to go to find the temperature at 2 °C?

8 A new engine was being tested, but it had serious problems. The distance it went, in km, without breaking down was inversely proportional to the square of its speed in m/s. When the speed was 12 m/s, the engine lasted 3 km.

   a   Find the distance covered before a breakdown, when the speed is 15 m/s.

   b   On one test, the engine broke down after 6.75 km. What was the speed?

9 In a balloon it was noticed that the pressure, in atmospheres, was inversely proportional to the square root of the height, in metres. When the balloon was at a height of 25 m, the pressure was 1.44 atm.

   a   What was the pressure at a height of 9 m?

   b   What would the height have been if the pressure was 0.72 atm?

10 The amount of waste which a firm produces, measured in tonnes per hour, is inversely proportional to the square root of the size of the filter beds, measured in m². At the moment, the firm produces 1.25 tonnes per hour of waste, with filter beds of size 0.16 m².

   a   The filter beds used to be only 0.01 m². How much waste did the firm produce then?

   b   How much waste could be produced if the filter beds were 0.75 m²?

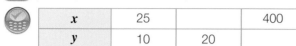

1 y is proportional to $\sqrt{x}$. Complete the table.

x	25		400
y	10	20	

2 The energy, E, of an object moving horizontally is directly proportional to the speed, v, of the object. When the speed is 10 m/s the energy is 40 000 Joules.

    a Find an equation connecting E and v.

    b Find the speed of the object when the energy is 14 400 Joules.

3 y is inversely proportional to the cube root of x. When $y = 8$, $x = \frac{1}{8}$.

    a Find an expression for y in terms of x,

    b Calculate

      i the value of y when $x = \frac{1}{125}$,

      ii the value of x when $y = 2$.

4 The mass of a cube is directly proportional to the cube of its side. A cube with a side of 4 cm has a mass of 320 grams. Calculate the side length of a cube made of the same material with a mass of 36 450 grams

5 y is directly proportional to the cube of x. When $y = 16$, $x = 3$. Find the value of y when $x = 6$.

6 y is inversely proportional to the square of x. When $y = 3$, $x = 2$. Find the value of y when $x = 4$.

AQA, Question 12, Paper 2 Higher, June 2004

7 In an experiment measurements of t and h were taken. These are the results.

t	2	5	6
h	10	62.5	90

Which of these rules fits the results?

    a $h \propto t$

    b $h \propto t^2$

    c $h \propto t^3$

You *must* show all your working.

AQA, Question 14, Paper 1 Higher, November 2003

8 Two variables, x and y, are known to be proportional to each other. When $x = 10$, $y = 25$.

Find the constant of proportionality, k, if:

    a $y \propto x$

    b $y \propto x^2$

    c $y \propto \frac{1}{x}$

    d $\sqrt{y} \propto \frac{1}{x}$

9 y is directly proportional to the cube root of x. When $x = 27$, $y = 6$.

    a Find the value of y when $x = 125$.

    b Find the value of x when $y = 3$.

10 The surface area, A, of a solid is directly proportional to the square of the depth, d. When $d = 6$, $A = 12\pi$.

    a Find the value of A when $d = 12$. Give your answer in terms of π.

    b Find the value of d when $A = 27\pi$.

11 The frequency, f, of sound is inversely proportional to the wavelength, w. A sound with a frequency of 36 hertz has a wavelength of 20.25 metres.

Calculate the frequency when the frequency and the wavelength have the same numerical value.

12 y is proportional to x^3.

    a When $x = 4$, $y = 80$. Find the value of y when $x = 8$.

Also, x is inversely proportional to the square root of z.

    b When $y = 10$, $z = 16$. Find the value of z when $x = 4$.

AQA, Question 17, Paper 2 Higher, June 2001

13 P and Q are positive quantities. P is inversely proportional to Q^2. When $P = 160$, $Q = 20$. Find the value of P when $P = Q$.

WORKED EXAM QUESTION

y is inversely proportional to the square of x. When y is 40, $x = 5$.

a Find an equation connecting x and y.

b Find the value of y when $x = 10$.

Solution

a $\qquad y \propto \dfrac{1}{x^2}$

> First set up the proportionality relationship and replace the proportionality sign with $= k$.

$\qquad y = \dfrac{k}{x^2}$

$\qquad 40 = \dfrac{k}{25}$

> Substitute the given values of y and x into the proportionality equation to find the value of k.

$\qquad \Rightarrow \quad k = 40 \times 25 = 1000$

$\qquad y = \dfrac{1000}{x^2}$

> Substitute the value of k to get the final equation connecting y and x.

$\qquad$ or $yx^2 = 1000$

b When $x = 10$, $y = \dfrac{1000}{10^2} = \dfrac{1000}{100} = 10$

> Substitute the value of x into the equation to find y.

The mass of a solid, M, is directly proportional to the cube of its height, h. When $h = 10$, $M = 4000$.

The surface area, A, of the solid is directly proportional to the square of the height, h. When $h = 10$, $A = 50$.

Find A, when $M = 32\,000$.

Solution

$M = kh^3$

$4000 = k \times 1000 \Rightarrow k = 4$

So, $M = 4h^3$

> First, find the relationship between M and h using the given information.

$A = ph^2$

$50 = p \times 100 \Rightarrow p = \dfrac{1}{2}$

So, $A = \dfrac{1}{2} h^2$

> Next, find the relationship between A and h using the given information.

$32\,000 = 4h^3$

$h^3 = 8000 \Rightarrow h = 20$

> Find the value of h when $M = 32\,000$.

$A = \dfrac{1}{2}(20)^2 = \dfrac{400}{2} = 200$

> Now find the value of A for that value of h.

An electricity company wants to build some offshore wind turbines (as shown below). The company is concerned about how big the turbines will look to a person standing on the shore. It asks an engineer to calculate the angle of elevation from the shore to the highest point of a turbine, when it is rotating, if the turbine was placed at different distances out to sea. Help the engineer to complete the first table below.

Distance of turbine out to sea	Angle of elevation from shore
3km	2.29°
4km	
5km	
6km	
7km	
8km	

50m

70m

The power available in the wind is measured in watts per metre squared of rotor area (W/m^2). Wind speed is measured in metres per second (m/s). The power available in the wind is proportional to the cube of its speed. A wind speed of 7 m/s can provide 210 W/m^2 of energy. Complete the table below to show the available power at different wind speeds.

Wind speed (m/s)	Available power (W/m^2)
6	
7	210
8	
9	
10	
11	
12	

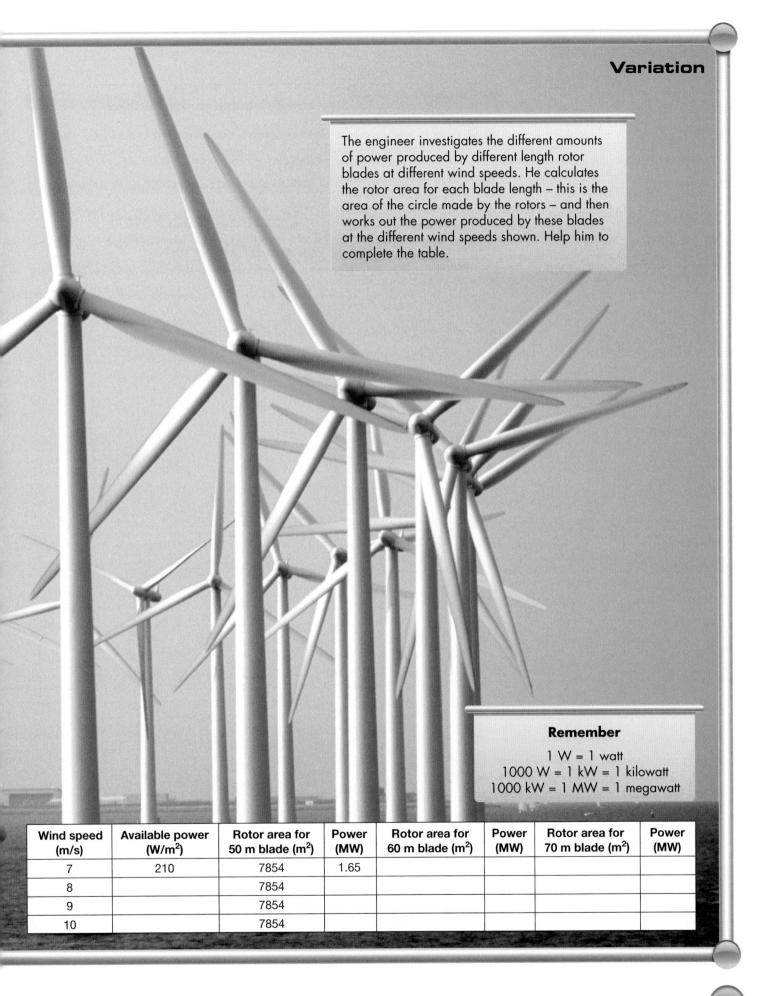

The engineer investigates the different amounts of power produced by different length rotor blades at different wind speeds. He calculates the rotor area for each blade length – this is the area of the circle made by the rotors – and then works out the power produced by these blades at the different wind speeds shown. Help him to complete the table.

Remember

1 W = 1 watt
1000 W = 1 kW = 1 kilowatt
1000 kW = 1 MW = 1 megawatt

Wind speed (m/s)	Available power (W/m²)	Rotor area for 50 m blade (m²)	Power (MW)	Rotor area for 60 m blade (m²)	Power (MW)	Rotor area for 70 m blade (m²)	Power (MW)
7	210	7854	1.65				
8		7854					
9		7854					
10		7854					

GRADE YOURSELF

A Able to find formulae describing direct or inverse variation and use them to solve problems

A* Able to solve direct and inverse variation problems involving three variables

What you should know now

- How to recognise direct and inverse variation
- What a constant of proportionality is, and how to find it
- How to find formulae describing inverse or direct variation
- How to solve problems involving direct or inverse variation

Number and limits of accuracy

1 Limits of accuracy

2 Problems involving limits of accuracy

This chapter will show you ...

- how to find the limits of numbers rounded to certain accuracies
- how to use limits of accuracy in calculations

Limits of accuracy ⟶ Calculating with limits of accuracy

What you should already know

- How to round numbers to various degrees of accuracy

Quick check

1 Round off 6374 to

  a the nearest 10,

  b the nearest 100,

  c the nearest 1000.

2 Round off 2.389 to

  a one decimal place,

  b two decimal places.

3 Round off 47.28 to

  a one significant figure,

  b three significant figures.

This section will show you how to:

- find the limits of accuracy of numbers that have been rounded to different degrees of accuracy

Key words

continuous data
discrete data
limits of accuracy
lower bound
rounding error
upper bound

Any recorded measurement will have been rounded off to some degree of accuracy. This defines the possible true value before rounding off took place, and hence the **limits of accuracy**. The range of values between the limits of accuracy is called the **rounding error**.

EXAMPLE 1

A stick of wood is measured as 32 cm to the nearest centimetre.

Between what limits does the actual length of the stick lie?

The lower limit is 31.5 cm as a halfway value is always rounded up.

The upper limit is 32.499999999... cm. In other words it can get as close to 32.5 cm as possible but not be 32.5 cm. However 32.5 cm is the upper limit. So we say

$31.5 \text{ cm} \leqslant \text{length of stick} < 32.5 \text{ cm}$.

Note the use of the strict inequality for the upper limit.

EXAMPLE 2

53.7 is accurate to one decimal place. What are the limits of accuracy?

The smallest possible value is 53.65.

The largest possible value is 53.749999999... but once again we say 53.75 is the upper limit.

Hence the limits of accuracy are $53.65 \leqslant 53.7 < 53.75$

EXAMPLE 3

A skip has a mass of 220 kg measured to three significant figures. What are the limits of accuracy of the mass of the skip?

The smallest possible value is 219.5 kg.

The largest possible value is 220.49999999... kg but once again we say 220.5 kg is the upper limit.

Hence the limits of accuracy are $219.5 \text{ kg} \leqslant \text{mass of skip} < 220.5 \text{ kg}$

Note that the limits of accuracy are always given to one more degree of accuracy than the rounded value. For example 32 is the nearest integer and the limits are to half a unit; 53.7 is to 1 decimal place and the limits are to 2 decimal places; 220 is to 3 significant figures and the limits are to 4 significant figures.

EXAMPLE 4

A coach carrying 50 people measured to the nearest 10, is travelling at 50 mph measured to the nearest 10 mph. What are the actual limits of the number of people and the speed?

This is an example of the difference between **discrete** and **continuous data**. The number of people is discrete data as it can only take integer values, but speed is continuous data as it can take any value in a range.

The limits are 45 ⩽ number of people ⩽ 54, 45 mph ⩽ speed < 55 mph.

Be careful as questions sometimes ask about the limits of discrete data.

EXERCISE 23A

1 Write down the limits of accuracy of the following.

    a 7 cm measured to the nearest centimetre

    b 120 grams measured to the nearest 10 grams

    c 3400 kilometres measured to the nearest 100 kilometres

    d 50 mph measured to the nearest mph

    e £6 given to the nearest £

    f 16.8 cm to the nearest tenth of a centimetre

    g 16 kg to the nearest kilogram

    h a football crowd of 14 500 given to the nearest 100

    i 55 miles given to the nearest mile

    j 55 miles given to the nearest 5 miles

2 Write down the limits of accuracy for each of the following values which are rounded to the given degree of accuracy.

a 6 cm (1 significant figure)	**b** 17 kg (2 significant figures)	**c** 32 min (2 significant figures)
d 238 km (3 significant figures)	**e** 7.3 m (1 decimal place)	**f** 25.8 kg (1 decimal place)
g 3.4 h (1 decimal place)	**h** 87 g (2 significant figures)	**i** 4.23 mm (2 decimal places)
j 2.19 kg (2 decimal places)	**k** 12.67 min (2 decimal places)	**l** 25 m (2 significant figures)
m 40 cm (1 significant figure)	**n** 600 g (2 significant figures)	**o** 30 min (1 significant figure)
p 1000 m (2 significant figures)	**q** 4.0 m (1 decimal place)	**r** 7.04 kg (2 decimal places)
s 12.0 s (1 decimal place)	**t** 7.00 m (2 decimal places)	

Upper and lower bounds

A journey of 26 miles measured to the nearest mile could actually be as long as 26.4999999... miles or as short as 25.5 miles. It could not be 26.5 miles, as this would round up to 27 miles. However, 26.4999999... is *virtually the same* as 26.5.

We overcome this difficulty by saying that 26.5 is the **upper bound** of the measured value and 25.5 is its **lower bound**. We can therefore write

$$25.5 \text{ miles} \leqslant \text{actual distance} < 26.5 \text{ miles}$$

which states that the actual distance is *greater than or equal to* 25.5 miles but *less than* 26.5 miles.

Although it is not wrong to give the upper bound as 26.49999... it is mathematically neater to give 26.5. It is wrong, however, to give the upper bound as 26.4 or 26.49. So, when stating an upper bound, always follow the accepted practice, as demonstrated here, which eliminates the difficulties that arise with recurring decimals.

A mathematical peculiarity

Let $x = 0.999\,999...$ (1)

Multiply by 10 $10x = 9.999\,999...$ (2)

Subtract (1) from (2) $9x = 9$

Divide by 9 $x = 1$

So, we have $0.\dot{9} = 1$

Hence, it is valid to give the upper bound without using recurring decimals.

EXERCISE 23B

1 Write down the lower and upper bounds of each of these values, rounded to the accuracy stated.

a 8 m (1 significant figure) **b** 26 kg (2 significant figures) **c** 25 min (2 significant figures)

d 85 g (2 significant figures) **e** 2.40 m (2 decimal places) **f** 0.2 kg (1 decimal place)

g 0.06 s (2 decimal places) **h** 300 g (1 significant figure) **i** 0.7 m (1 decimal place)

j 366 d (3 significant figures) **k** 170 weeks (2 significant figures) **l** 210 g (2 significant figures)

2 Billy has 40 identical marbles. Each marble weighs 65 g (to the nearest gram).

a What is the greatest possible weight of one marble?

b What is the least possible weight of one marble?

c What is the greatest possible weight of all the marbles?

d What is the least possible weight of all the marbles?

Problems involving limits of accuracy

In this section you will learn how to:

- Combine limits of two or more variables together to solve problems

Key words

limits of accuracy
maximum
minimum

When we calculate an area or a volume, the errors in the linear measures will be compounded and, hence, will produce a still larger error in the calculated value. There are four operations to perform on limits – addition, subtraction, multiplication and division.

To get the **maximum** value when adding two numbers given to a certain **limit of accuracy**, the maximum values of the two numbers should be added. However, to get the maximum value when two numbers are subtracted then the lower limit of the second number should be subtracted from the upper limit of the first number.

Let a and b be two numbers that lie within limits $a_{min} \leq a < a_{max}$ and $b_{min} \leq b < b_{max}$

The following table shows the combinations to give the maximum and **minimum** values for the four rules of arithmetic.

Operation	Maximum	Minimum
Addition ($a + b$)	$a_{max} + b_{max}$	$a_{min} + b_{min}$
Subtraction ($a - b$)	$a_{max} - b_{min}$	$a_{min} - b_{max}$
Multiplication ($a \times b$)	$a_{max} \times b_{max}$	$a_{min} \times b_{min}$
Division ($a \div b$)	$a_{max} \div b_{min}$	$a_{min} \div b_{max}$

Be very careful about the order when doing subtraction or division.

When solving problems involving limits, start by writing down the limits of the variables involved, as this will get you some credit in the exam, then think about which combination of limits is needed to get the required answer.

Sometimes, especially when dividing, the upper and lower limits will be given to many decimal places. Be careful where rounding these off as the rounded answer may be outside the acceptable range of the limits. If you do round answers off, give your answer to at least 3 significant figures.

EXAMPLE 5

A rectangle has sides given as 6 cm by 15 cm, to the nearest centimetre.

Calculate the limits of accuracy of the area of the rectangle.

Write down the limits: 5.5 cm ⩽ width < 6.5 cm, 14.5 cm ⩽ length < 15.5 cm

For maximum area, multiply maximum width by maximum length, and for minimum area, multiply minimum width by minimum length.

The upper bound of the width is 6.5 cm and of the length is 15.5 cm. Hence the upper bound of the area of the rectangle is

$$6.5 \text{ cm} \times 15.5 \text{ cm} = 100.75 \text{ cm}^2$$

The lower bound of the width is 5.5 cm and of the length is 14.5 cm. Hence the lower bound of the area of the rectangle is

$$5.5 \text{ cm} \times 14.5 \text{ cm} = 79.75 \text{ cm}^2$$

Therefore, the limits of accuracy for the area of the rectangle are

$$79.75 \text{ cm}^2 \leqslant \text{area} < 100.75 \text{ cm}^2$$

EXAMPLE 6

The distance from Barnsley to Sheffield is 15 miles to the nearest mile. The time Jeff took to drive between Barnsley and Sheffield was 40 minutes to the nearest 10 minutes.

Calculate the upper limit of Jeff's average speed.

Write down the limits: 14.5 miles ⩽ distance < 15.5 miles, 35 mins ⩽ time < 45 mins

$$\text{speed} = \text{distance} \div \text{time}$$

To get the maximum speed we need the maximum distance ÷ minimum time.

$$15.5 \text{ miles} \div 35 \text{ mins} = 0.443 \text{ (3 significant figures) miles per minute}$$

$$0.443 \text{ mph} \times 60 = 26.6 \text{ mph}$$

The upper limit of Jeff's average speed = 26.6 mph.

EXERCISE 23C

1 For each of these rectangles, find the limits of accuracy of the area. The measurements are shown to the level of accuracy indicated in brackets.

a 5 cm × 9 cm (nearest cm)

b 4.5 cm × 8.4 cm (1 decimal place)

c 7.8 cm × 18 cm (2 significant figures)

2 A rectangular garden has sides of 6 m and 4 m, measured to the nearest metre.

a Write down the limits of accuracy for each length.

b What is the maximum area of the garden?

c What is the minimum perimeter of the garden?

3 A cinema screen is measured as 6 m by 15 m, to the nearest metre. Calculate the limits of accuracy for the area of the screen.

 4 The measurements, to the nearest centimetre, of a box are given as 10 cm × 7 cm × 4 cm. Calculate the limits of accuracy for the volume of the box.

 5 The area of a field is given as 350 m², to the nearest 10 m². One length is given as 16 m, to the nearest metre. Find the limits of accuracy for the other length of the field.

 6 In triangle ABC, AB = 9 cm, BC = 7 cm, and ∠ABC = 37°. All the measurements are given to the nearest unit. Calculate the limits of accuracy for the area of the triangle.

 7 The price of pure gold is £18.25 per gram. The density of gold is 19.3 g/cm³. (Assume these figures are exact.) A solid gold bar in the shape of a cuboid has sides 4.6 cm, 2.2 cm and 6.6 cm. These measurements are made to the nearest 0.1 cm.

  a i What are the limits of accuracy for the volume of this gold bar?

    ii What are the upper and lower limits of the cost of this bar?

The gold bar was weighed and given a value of 1296 g, to the nearest gram.

  b What are the upper and lower limits for the cost of the bar now?.

  c Explain why the price ranges are so different.

 8 A stopwatch records the time for the winner of a 100-metre race as 14.7 seconds, measured to the nearest one-tenth of a second.

  a What are the greatest and least possible times for the winner?

  b The length of the 100-metre track is correct to the nearest 1 m. What are the greatest and least possible lengths of the track?

  c What is the fastest possible average speed of the winner, with a time of 14.7 seconds in the 100-metre race?

 9 A cube has a side measured as 8 cm, to the nearest millimetre. What is the greatest percentage error of the following?

  a the calculated area of one face

  b the calculated volume of the cube

 10 A cube has a volume of 40 cm³, to the nearest cm³. Find the range of possible values of the side length of the cube.

 11 A cube has a volume of 200 cm³, to the nearest 10 cm³. Find the limits of accuracy of the side length of the cube.

 12 A model car travels 40 m, measured to one significant figure, at a speed of 2 m/s, measured to one significant figure. Between what limits does the time taken lie?

1 A school has 1850 pupils to the nearest 10.
 a What is the least number of pupils at the school
 b What is the greatest number of pupils at the school?

2 The longest river in Britain is the River Severn. It is 220 miles long to the nearest 10 miles. What is the least length it could be?

3 A notice board is a rectangle with a length of 80 cm and a width of 40 cm. Both measurements are correct to the nearest centimetre.

 a What is the least possible length of the notice board?
 b What is the greatest possible width of the notice board?
 c What is the greatest possible area of the notice board?

4 The base of a triangle is 10 cm measured to the nearest centimetre. The area of the triangle is 100 cm^2 measured to the nearest square centimetre. Calculate the least and greatest values of the height of the triangle.

5 A formula used in kinematics is $s = \dfrac{v^2 - u^2}{2a}$.

Calculate the greatest possible value of a if $v = 6.2$, $u = 3.6$ and $a = 9.8$, all values accurate to 2 significant figures.

6 A circle has an area of 100 cm^2, measured to the nearest square centimetre. What is the lower bound of the radius?

AQA, Question 20, Paper 2 Higher, June 2005

7 $x = 1.8$ measured to 1 decimal place,
 $y = 4.0$ measured to 2 significant figures,
 $z = 2.56$ measured to 3 significant figures.

Calculate the upper limit of $\dfrac{x^2 + y}{z}$.

8 A crane has a cable with a breaking strain of 5300 kg measured to 2 significant figures. It is used to lift crates which weigh 100 kg measured to the nearest 10 kg.

What is the greatest number of crates that can be lifted at one time so that the cable does not break?

AQA, Question 21, Paper 1 Higher, June 2004

9 A girl runs 60 metres in a time of 8.0 seconds. The distance is measured to the nearest metre and the time is measured to 2 significant figures. What is the least possible speed ?

10 A coffee machine dispenses 130 millilitres of black coffee into cups with a capacity of 175 millilitres. These values are accurate to 3 significant figures.

Milk is supplied in small cartons which contain 21 millilitres, accurate to the nearest millilitre.

Beryl likes milky coffee and always puts two cartons of milk in her coffee.

Will Beryl's cup ever overflow? You *must* show all your working.

AQA, Question 25, Paper 2 Higher, June 2003

11 a Calculate the length of the diagonal x in this cube of side 3 m.

 b A man is carrying a pole of length 5 m down a long corridor. The pole is measured to the nearest centimetre. At the end of the corridor is a right-angled corner. The corridor is 3 m wide and 3 m high, both measurements correct to the nearest 10 cm. Will the pole be certain to get round the corner?

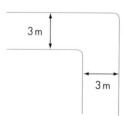

WORKED EXAM QUESTION

The magnification of a lens is given by the formula

$$m = \frac{v}{u}$$

In an experiment, u is measured as 8.5 cm and v is measured as 14.0 cm, both correct to the nearest 0.1 cm. Find the least possible value of m, You must show full details of your calculation.

Solution

$8.45 \leqslant u < 8.55$

$13.95 \leqslant v < 14.05$

> Write down the limits of both variables.

Least m = least u ÷ greatest v = 8.45 ÷ 14.05 = 0.6014234875

> As the calculation is a division the least value will be given by least u ÷ greatest v.

= 0.601 or 0.6

> Round off to a suitable degree of accuracy.

A long rod with a square cross-section is made with a side of 5 cm. A circular hole is drilled with a radius of 3.6 cm. All measurements are to the nearest $\frac{1}{10}$ cm. Will the rod fit into the circle?

Solution

Limits of side of square

   4.95 < side < 5.05

> This is a using and applying maths question. You need to have a strategy to solve it. Step 1: find the largest possible diagonal of the square using Pythagoras. Step 2: work out the smallest possible diameter of the circle. Step 3: Compare the values to see if the diagonal is smaller than the diameter. Always start with writing down the limits of the variables in the question.

Limits of radius

   3.55 < radius < 3.65

Largest diagonal = $\sqrt{(5.05^2 + 5.05^2)}$

   = 7.14177849

   = 7.142 (4 significant figures)

> Step 1: Work out the largest possible diagonal, do not round off to less than 4 significant figures.

Smallest diameter = 2 × 3.55 = 7.1

> Step 2: Work out the smallest diameter.

As 7.142 > 7.1,
the rod may not fit in the circle.

> Step 3: Compare the results.

Mr Slater buys a new house. He decides to put laminate flooring throughout the whole ground floor.

The laminate flooring he has chosen comes in packs, which cover 2 m^2.

Each room also needs an edging strip around the perimeter of the room, excluding doorways.

The edging comes in packs, which have a total length of 12 m.

The hall and bathroom are to have beech laminate flooring, and the other rooms oak.

Mr Slater works out the upper and lower bound for each length shown on the sketch. He then calculates the maximum floor area of each room and the maximum length of edging needed for every room. Help him complete the table to find the total maximum floor area and edging he needs.

Beech effect

Room	Room Maximum floor area (m^2)	Maximum edging needed (m)
Hall		
Bathroom		
Total		

Oak effect

Room	Room Maximum floor area (m^2)	Maximum edging needed (m)
Lounge		
Sitting room		
Kitchen/diner		
Conservatory		
Total		

This is a sketch showing the ground floor dimensions.

All measurements are to the nearest 0.1 m.

width of each door = 0.8m

Calculate for Mr Slater the total cost of the flooring and edging.

Oak effect

	Number of packs	Price per pack	Total cost
Beech flooring		£56.40	
Beech edging		£21.15	
Oak flooring		£61.10	
Oak edging		£25.85	
	Total:		

This total price is inclusive of VAT.

VAT is 17½%.

What is the total price, exclusive of VAT?

GRADE YOURSELF

B Able to find measures of accuracy for numbers given to whole number accuracies

A Able to find measures of accuracy for numbers given to decimal place or significant figure accuracies

A* Able to calculate the limits of compound measures

What you should know now

● How to find the limits of numbers given to various accuracies

● How to find the limits of compound measures by combining the appropriate limits of the variables involved

Inequalities and regions

1 Solving inequalities

2 Graphical inequalities

3 Problem solving

This chapter will show you ...

- how to solve a linear inequality
- how to find a region on a graph that obeys a linear inequality in two variables
- how inequalities can be used to represent and solve problems

Visual overview

Linear inequalities → Inequalities in two variables → Problem solving

What you should already know

- How to solve linear equations
- How to draw linear graphs

Quick check

1 Solve these equations.

a $\dfrac{2x + 5}{3} = 7$

b $2x - 7 = 13$

2 On a grid with x and y axes from 0 to 10, draw the graphs of these equations.

a $y = 3x + 1$

b $2x + 3y = 12$

Solving inequalities

This section will show you how to:
- solve a simple linear inequality

Key words

inequality
number line

Inequalities behave similarly to equations which you have already met. In the case of linear inequalities, we use the same rules to solve them as we use for linear equations. There are four inequality signs, $<$ which means "less than", $>$ which means "greater than", $\leq$ which means "less than or equal to" and $\geq$ which means "greater than or equal to".

EXAMPLE 1

Solve $2x + 3 < 14$.

This is rewritten as:

$$2x < 14 - 3$$
$$2x < 11$$

Divide both sides by 2:

$$\frac{2x}{2} < \frac{11}{2}$$
$$\Rightarrow x < 5.5$$

This means that x can take any value below 5.5 but not the value 5.5.

Note: The inequality sign given in the problem is the sign to give in the answer.

EXAMPLE 2

Solve $\frac{x}{2} + 4 \geq 13$.

Solve just like an equation but leave the inequality sign in place of the equals sign.

Subtract 4 from both sides:

$$\frac{x}{2} \geq 9$$

Multiply both sides by 2:

$$x \geq 18$$

This means that x can take any value above and including 18.

EXAMPLE 3

Solve $\dfrac{3x + 7}{2} < 14$.

This is rewritten as:

$$3x + 7 < 14 \times 2$$

That is:

$$3x + 7 < 28$$

$$\Rightarrow \quad 3x < 28 - 7$$

$$\Rightarrow \quad 3x < 21$$

$$\Rightarrow \quad x < 21 \div 3$$

$$\Rightarrow \quad x < 7$$

EXAMPLE 4

Solve $1 < 3x + 4 \leqslant 13$.

Divide the inequality into two parts, and treat each part separately.

$$1 < 3x + 4 \qquad\qquad\qquad 3x + 4 \leqslant 13$$

$$\Rightarrow \quad 1 - 4 < 3x \qquad\qquad \Rightarrow \quad 3x \leqslant 13 - 4$$

$$\Rightarrow \quad -3 < 3x \qquad\qquad \Rightarrow \quad 3x \leqslant 9$$

$$\Rightarrow \quad -\frac{3}{3} < x \qquad\qquad \Rightarrow \quad x \leqslant \frac{9}{3}$$

$$\Rightarrow \quad -1 < x \qquad\qquad \Rightarrow \quad x \leqslant 3$$

Hence, $-1 < x \leqslant 3$.

EXERCISE 24A

1 Solve the following linear inequalities.

a $x + 4 < 7$

b $t - 3 > 5$

c $p + 2 \geqslant 12$

d $2x - 3 < 7$

e $4y + 5 \leqslant 17$

f $3t - 4 > 11$

g $\dfrac{x}{2} + 4 < 7$

h $\dfrac{y}{5} + 3 \leqslant 6$

i $\dfrac{t}{3} - 2 \geqslant 4$

j $3(x - 2) < 15$

k $5(2x + 1) \leqslant 35$

l $2(4t - 3) \geqslant 34$

2 Write down the largest integer value of x that satisfies each of the following.

a $x - 3 \leqslant 5$, where x is positive

b $x + 2 < 9$, where x is positive and even

c $3x - 11 < 40$, where x is a square number

d $5x - 8 \leqslant 15$, where x is positive and odd

e $2x + 1 < 19$, where x is positive and prime

3 Write down the smallest integer value of x that satisfies each of the following.

    a $x - 2 \geqslant 9$, where x is positive

    b $x - 2 > 13$, where x is positive and even

    c $2x - 11 \geqslant 19$, where x is a square number

4 Solve the following linear inequalities.

    a $4x + 1 \geqslant 3x - 5$ **b** $5t - 3 \leqslant 2t + 5$ **c** $3y - 12 \leqslant y - 4$

    d $2x + 3 \geqslant x + 1$ **e** $5w - 7 \leqslant 3w + 4$ **f** $2(4x - 1) \leqslant 3(x + 4)$

5 Solve the following linear inequalities.

    a $\dfrac{x + 4}{2} \leqslant 3$ **b** $\dfrac{x - 3}{5} > 7$ **c** $\dfrac{2x + 5}{3} < 6$

    d $\dfrac{4x - 3}{5} \geqslant 5$ **e** $\dfrac{3t - 2}{7} > 4$ **f** $\dfrac{5y + 3}{5} \leqslant 2$

6 Solve the following linear inequalities.

    a $7 < 2x + 1 < 13$ **b** $5 < 3x - 1 < 14$ **c** $-1 < 5x + 4 \leqslant 19$

    d $1 \leqslant 4x - 3 < 13$ **e** $11 \leqslant 3x + 5 < 17$ **f** $-3 \leqslant 2x - 3 \leqslant 7$

The number line

The solution to a linear inequality can be shown on the **number line** by using the following conventions.

Below are five examples.

represents $x < 3$

represents $x > 1$

represents $x \leqslant -2$

represents $x \geqslant 4$

represents $-1 \leqslant x < 2$

EXAMPLE 5

a Write down the inequality shown by this diagram.

b **i** Solve the following inequality $2x + 3 < 11$.

ii Mark the solution on a number line.

c Write down the integers that satisfy both the inequalities in **a** and **b**.

a The inequality shown is $x \geqslant 1$.

b **i** $2x + 3 < 11 \quad \Rightarrow \quad 2x < 8 \quad \Rightarrow \quad x < 4$

ii

c The integers that satisfy both inequalities are 1, 2 and 3.

EXERCISE 24B

1 Write down the inequality that is represented by each diagram below.

a

b

c

d

e

f

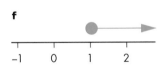

2 Draw diagrams to illustrate the following.

a $x \leqslant 3$ **b** $x > -2$ **c** $x \geqslant 0$ **d** $x < 5$

e $x \geqslant -1$ **f** $2 < x \leqslant 5$ **g** $-1 \leqslant x \leqslant 3$ **h** $-3 < x < 4$

3 Solve the following inequalities and illustrate their solutions on number lines.

a $x + 4 \geqslant 8$ **b** $x + 5 < 3$ **c** $4x - 2 \geqslant 12$ **d** $2x + 5 < 3$

e $2(4x + 3) < 18$ **f** $\dfrac{x}{2} + 3 \leqslant 2$ **g** $\dfrac{x}{5} - 2 > 8$ **h** $\dfrac{x}{3} + 5 \geqslant 3$

4 Solve the following inequalities and illustrate their solutions on number lines.

a $\dfrac{2x + 5}{3} > 3$ **b** $\dfrac{3x + 4}{2} \geqslant 11$ **c** $\dfrac{2x + 8}{3} \leqslant 2$ **d** $\dfrac{2x - 1}{3} \geqslant -3$

Inequalities involving x^2

When we have an inequality such as $x^2 < 9$, we have to think very carefully because there are two possible solutions to $x^2 = 9$. They are $x = 3$ and $x = -3$.

The solution $x = 3$ to the equation $x^2 = 9$ would suggest the condition $x < 3$ is a solution to $x^2 < 9$. Clearly, $x < 3$ does satisfy the inequality $x^2 < 9$. The condition to be obtained from the solution $x = -3$ is not $x < -3$. (Think about $(-5)^2$.) So it must be $x > -3$. That is, the inequality sign is *changed*. For convenience, $x > -3$ can be turned to give $-3 < x$.

Show this situation on a number line and the solution becomes clear.

Namely, $-3 < x < 3$.

EXAMPLE 6

Solve the inequality $x^2 > 16$ and show your solution on a number line.

The solution to $x^2 > 16$ will be $x > 4$ and $x < -4$, which is represented as

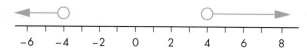

Notice the difference between inequalities of the type $x^2 < a^2$ and those of the type $x^2 > a^2$.

EXERCISE 24C

Solve the following inequalities, showing their solutions on number lines.

1 $x^2 \leqslant 4$ **2** $x^2 > 25$ **3** $x^2 < 49$

4 $x^2 \geqslant 1$ **5** $x^2 \geqslant 9$ **6** $x^2 - 1 > 8$

7 $x^2 + 2 \leqslant 6$ **8** $x^2 - 3 < 13$ **9** $x^2 + 5 > 6$

10 $x^2 - 4 \geqslant 5$ **11** $2x^2 - 1 > 7$ **12** $3x^2 - 5 < 22$

13 $5x^2 + 3 \leqslant 8$ **14** $2x^2 - 4 < 28$ **15** $3x^2 - 9 \geqslant 66$

16 $x^2 \geqslant 100$ **17** $x^2 < 2.25$ **18** $x^2 \geqslant 0.25$

19 $x^2 - 5 \leqslant 76$ **20** $x^2 > 0$

Graphical inequalities

This section will show you how to:
- show a graphical inequality and how to find regions that satisfy more than one graphical inequality

Key words
boundary
included
origin
region

A linear inequality can be plotted on a graph. The result is a **region** that lies on one side or the other of a straight line. You will recognise an inequality by the fact that it looks like an equation but instead of the equals sign it has an inequality sign: $<$, $>$, $\leq$, or $\geq$.

The following are examples of linear inequalities which can be represented on a graph.

$$y < 3 \qquad x > 7 \qquad -3 \leq y < 5 \qquad y \geq 2x + 3 \qquad 2x + 3y < 6 \qquad y \leq x$$

The method for graphing an inequality is to draw the **boundary** line that defines the inequality. This is found by replacing the inequality sign with an equals sign. When a strict inequality is stated ($<$ or $>$), the boundary line should be drawn as a *dashed* line to show that it is not included in the range of values. When $\leq$ or $\geq$ are used to state the inequality, the boundary line should be drawn as a *solid* line to show that the boundary is **included**.

After the boundary line has been drawn, the *required region is shaded*.

To confirm on which side of the line the region lies, choose any point that is not on the boundary line and test it in the inequality. If it satisfies the inequality, that is the side required. If it doesn't, the other side is required.

Work through the six inequalities on this page and the next, to see how the procedure is applied.

EXAMPLE 7

Show each of the following inequalities on a graph.

a $y \leq 3$ **b** $x > 7$ **c** $-3 \leq y < 5$ **d** $y \leq 2x + 3$ **e** $2x + 3y < 6$ **f** $y \leq x$

a Draw the line $y = 3$. Since the inequality is stated as $\leq$, the line is solid. Test a point that is not on the line. The **origin** is always a good choice if possible, as 0 is easy to test.

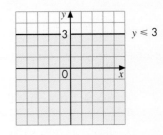

Putting 0 into the inequality gives $0 \leq 3$. The inequality is satisfied and so the region containing the origin is the side we want.

Shade it in.

b Since the inequality is stated as >, the line is *dashed*. Draw the line $x = 7$.

Test the origin $(0, 0)$, which gives $0 > 7$. This is not true, so we want the other side of the line from the origin.

Shade it in.

c Draw the lines $y = -3$ (solid for $\leq$) and $y = 5$ (dashed for <).

Test a point that is not on either line, say $(0, 0)$. Zero is between -3 and 5, so the required region lies between the lines.

Shade it in.

d Draw the line $y = 2x + 3$. Since the inequality is stated as $\leq$, the line is solid.

Test a point that is not on the line, $(0, 0)$. Putting these x and y-values in the inequality gives $0 \leq 2(0) + 3$, which is true. So the region that includes the origin is what we want.

Shade it in.

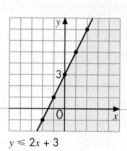

e Draw the line $2x + 3y = 6$. Since the inequality is stated as <, the line is dashed.

Test a point that is not on the line, say $(0, 0)$. Is it true that $2(0) + 3(0) < 6$? The answer is yes, so the origin is in the region that we want.

Shade it in.

f Draw the line $y = x$. Since the inequality is stated as $\leq$, the line is solid.

This time the origin is on the line, so pick any other point, say $(1, 3)$. Putting $x = 1$ and $y = 3$ in the inequality gives $3 \leq 1$. This is not true, so the point $(1, 3)$ is not in the region we want.

Shade in the other side to $(1, 3)$.

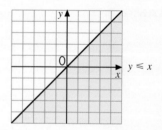

More than one inequality

When we have to show a region that satisfies more than one inequality, it is clearer to *shade* the regions *not required*, so that the *required region* is left *blank*.

EXAMPLE 8

a On the same grid, show the regions that represent the following inequalities by shading the unwanted regions.

    i $x > 2$ **ii** $y \geqslant x$ **iii** $x + y < 8$

b Are the points $(3, 4)$, $(2, 6)$ and $(3, 3)$ in the region that satisfies all three inequalities?

i   **ii**   **iii**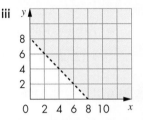

a **i** This region is shown unshaded in diagram **i**.

      The boundary line is $x = 2$ (dashed).

    ii This region is shown unshaded in diagram **ii**.

      The boundary line is $y = x$ (solid).

    iii This region is shown unshaded in diagram **iii**.

      The boundary line is $x + y = 8$ (dashed). The regions have first been drawn separately so that each may be clearly seen. The diagram on the right shows all three regions on the same grid. The white triangular area defines the region that satisfies all three inequalities.

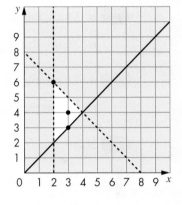

b **i** The point $(3, 4)$ is clearly within the region that satisfies all three inequalities.

    ii The point $(2, 6)$ is on the boundary lines $x = 2$ and $x + y = 8$. As these are dashed lines, they are not included in the region defined by all three inequalities. So, the point $(2, 6)$ is not in this region.

    iii The point $(3, 3)$ is on the boundary line $y = x$. As this is a solid line, it is included in the region defined by all three inequalities. So, the point $(3, 3)$ is included in this region.

EXERCISE 24D

1 **a** Draw the line $x = 2$ (as a solid line).

    b Shade the region defined by $x \leqslant 2$.

2 **a** Draw the line $y = -3$ (as a dashed line).

    b Shade the region defined by $y > -3$.

3 **a** Draw the line $x = -2$ (as a solid line).

 b Draw the line $x = 1$ (as a solid line) on the same grid.

 c Shade the region defined by $-2 \leqslant x \leqslant 1$.

4 **a** Draw the line $y = -1$ (as a dashed line).

 b Draw the line $y = 4$ (as a solid line) on the same grid.

 c Shade the region defined by $-1 < y \leqslant 4$.

5 **a** On the same grid, draw the regions defined by these inequalities.

 i $-3 \leqslant x \leqslant 6$ **ii** $-4 < y \leqslant 5$

 b Are the following points in the region defined by both inequalities?

 i $(2, 2)$ **ii** $(1, 5)$ **iii** $(-2, -4)$

6 **a** Draw the line $y = 2x - 1$ (as a dashed line).

 b Shade the region defined by $y < 2x - 1$.

7 **a** Draw the line $3x - 4y = 12$ (as a solid line).

 b Shade the region defined by $3x - 4y \leqslant 12$.

8 **a** Draw the line $y = \frac{1}{2}x + 3$ (as a solid line).

 b Shade the region defined by $y \geqslant \frac{1}{2}x + 3$.

9 Shade the region defined by $y < -3$.

10 **a** Draw the line $y = 3x - 4$ (as a solid line).

 b Draw the line $x + y = 10$ (as a solid line) on the same diagram.

 c Shade the diagram so that the region defined by $y \geqslant 3x - 4$ is left *unshaded*.

 d Shade the diagram so that the region defined by $x + y \leqslant 10$ is left *unshaded*.

 e Are the following points in the region defined by both inequalities?

 i $(2, 1)$ **ii** $(2, 2)$ **iii** $(2, 3)$

11 **a** Draw the line $y = x$ (as a solid line).

 b Draw the line $2x + 5y = 10$ (as a solid line) on the same diagram.

 c Draw the line $2x + y = 6$ (as a dashed line) on the same diagram.

 d Shade the diagram so that the region defined by $y \geqslant x$ is left *unshaded*.

 e Shade the diagram so that the region defined by $2x + 5y \geqslant 10$ is left *unshaded*.

 f Shade the diagram so that the region defined by $2x + y < 6$ is left *unshaded*.

 g Are the following points in the region defined by these inequalities?

 i $(1, 1)$ **ii** $(2, 2)$ **iii** $(1, 3)$

HINTS AND TIPS

In exams it is always made clear which region is to be labelled or shaded. Make sure you do as the question asks, and label or shade as required otherwise you could lose a mark.

12 **a** On the same grid, draw the regions defined by the following inequalities. (Shade the diagram so that the overlapping region is left blank.)

    i $y > x - 3$ **ii** $3y + 4x \leqslant 24$ **iii** $x \geqslant 2$

   b Are the following points in the region defined by all three inequalities?

    i $(1, 1)$ **ii** $(2, 2)$ **iii** $(3, 3)$ **iv** $(4, 4)$

24.3 Problem solving

This section will show you:

- some of the problems that can be solved using inequalities

Inequalities can arise in the solution of certain kinds of problem. The next example illustrates such a situation.

EXAMPLE 9

James has to buy drinks for himself and four friends. He has £2.50 to spend. A can of Cola costs 60 pence and a can of Orange costs 40 pence. He buys x cans of Cola and y cans of Orange.

   a Explain why   **i** $x + y \geqslant 5$ **ii** $6x + 4y \leqslant 25$

   b Write down all the possible numbers of each type of drink he can buy.

   a **i** James needs to buy at least five cans as there are five people. So the total number of cans of Cola and Orange must be at least five. This is expressed as $x + y \geqslant 5$.

      ii x cans of Cola cost $60x$ pence, and y cans of Orange cost $40y$ pence. So

          total cost $= 60x + 40y$

          But he has only 250 pence to spend, so total cost cannot exceed 250 pence. Hence,

          $60x + 40y \leqslant 250$

          This cancels through by 10 to give

          $6x + 4y \leqslant 25$

   b By trying different values of x and y, the following four combinations are found to satisfy the condition.

     one can of Cola and four cans of Orange

     two cans of Cola and three cans of Orange

     five or six cans of Orange

EXERCISE 24E

1 A company sells two types of bicycle, the Chapper and the Graffiti. A Chapper costs £148 and a Graffiti cost £125.

  a How much do x Chappers cost?

  b How much do y Graffitis cost?

  c How much do x Chappers and y Graffitis cost altogether?

2 A computer firm makes two types of machine. The Z210 and the Z310. The price of the Z210 is £A and that of the Z310 is £B. How much are the following?

  a x Z210s and y Z310s

  b x Z210s and twice as many Z310s

  c 9 Z210s and $(9 + y)$ Z310s

3 If $x + y > 40$, which of the following *may* be true?

  a $x > 40$ **b** $x + y \leqslant 20$ **c** $x - y = 10$ **d** $x \leqslant 5$

4 A bookshelf holds P paperback and H hardback books. The bookshelf can hold a total of 400 books. Which of the following *may* be true?

  a $P + H < 300$ **b** $P \geqslant H$ **c** $P + H > 500$

5 A school uses two coach firms, Excel and Storm, to take pupils home from school. An Excel coach holds 40 pupils and a Storm coach holds 50 pupils. 1500 pupils need to be taken home by coach. If E Excel coaches and S Storm coaches are used, explain why:

$4E + 5S \geqslant 150$

6 A boy goes to the fair with £6.00 in his pocket. He only likes rides on the big wheel and eating hot-dogs. A big wheel ride costs £1.50 and a hot-dog costs £2.00. He has W big wheel rides and D hot-dogs. Explain why:

  a $W \leqslant 4$ **b** $D \leqslant 3$ **c** $3W + 4D \leqslant 12$

  d If he cannot eat more than two hot-dogs without being ill, write down an inequality that *must* be true.

  e Which of these combinations of big wheel rides and hot-dogs are possible if they obey all of the above conditions?

    i two big wheel rides and one hot-dog

    ii three big wheel rides and two hot-dogs

    iii two big wheel rides and two hot-dogs

    iv one big wheel ride and one hot-dog

7 Pens cost 45p each and pencils cost 25p each. Jane has £2.00 with which to buy pens and pencils. She buys x pens and y pencils.

a Write down an inequality that must be true.

b She must have at least two more pencils than pens. Write down an inequality that must be true.

8 Mushtaq has to buy some apples and some pears. He has £3.00 to spend. Apples cost 30p each and pears cost 40p each. He must buy at least two apples and at least three pears, and at least seven fruits altogether. He buys x apples and y pears.

a Explain each of these inequalities.

    i $3x + 4y \leqslant 30$ **ii** $x \geqslant 2$ **iii** $y \geqslant 3$ **iv** $x + y \geqslant 7$

b Which of these combinations satisfy all of the above inequalities?

    i three apples and three pears   **ii** four apples and five pears

    iii no apples and seven pears   **iv** three apples and five pears

9 A shop decides to stock only sofas and beds. A sofa takes up 4 m^2 of floor area and is worth £300. A bed takes up 3 m^2 of floor area and is worth £500. The shop has 48 m^2 of floor space for stock. The insurance policy will allow a total of only £6000 of stock to be in the shop at any one time. The shop stocks x sofas and y beds.

a Explain each of these inequalities.

    i $4x + 3y \leqslant 48$ **ii** $3x + 5y \leqslant 60$

b Which of these combinations satisfy both of the above inequalities?

    i ten sofas and no beds   **ii** eight sofas and six beds

    iii ten sofas and five beds   **iv** six sofas and eight beds

10 The 300 pupils in Year 7 are to go on a trip to Adern Towers theme park. The local bus company has six 40-seat coaches and five 50-seat coaches. The school hires x 40-seat coaches and y 50-seat coaches.

a Explain each of these inequalities.

    i $4x + 5y \geqslant 30$ **ii** $x \leqslant 6$ **iii** $y \leqslant 5$

b Check that each of these combinations obeys each of the inequalities above.

    i six 40-seaters and two 50-seaters

    ii two 40-seaters and five 50-seaters

    iii four 40-seaters and three 50-seaters

    iv three 40-seaters and four 50-seaters

c The cost of hiring each coach is £100 for a 40-seater and £120 for a 50-seater. Which of the combinations in part **b** would be the cheapest option?

d There is one combination that is even cheaper than the answer to part **c**. What is it?

1 **a** Solve the inequality $2x + 3 \geqslant 1$

b Write down the inequality shown by the following diagram.

c Write down all the integers that satisfy both inequalities shown in parts **a** and **b**.

AQA, Question 19, Paper 2 Higher, June 2004

2 **a** Solve the inequality $4x + 3 < 13$

b Write down the largest integer that is a solution of $4x + 3 < 13$

3 **a** Solve the inequality $7y < 3y + 6$

b Make r the subject of the formula $p = 3 + 2r$

c Solve the equation $\frac{1}{2}x - 5 = \frac{1}{4}x + 3$

AQA, Question 2, Paper 1 Higher, June 2005

4 **a** Solve the inequality $5x - 9 \geqslant 6$

b **i** Solve the inequality $2x + 7 > 15 - 3x$

ii If x is an integer, what is the smallest possible value of x?

5 Find all the integer values of n that satisfy the inequality
$-3 \leqslant 2n + 1 < 9$

6 **a** Solve the inequality $4x - 9 < x + 3$

b Solve the inequality $x^2 < 25$

7 On a grid show the region that is defined by the three inequalities

$x \geqslant 1 \qquad y \leqslant 3 \qquad x + y \leqslant 5$

Mark the region with an R.

8 On a grid show the region that is defined by the three inequalities

$x \geqslant 0 \qquad y \leqslant 2x + 1 \qquad x + y \leqslant 4$

Mark the region with an R.

9 The region R is shown shaded below.

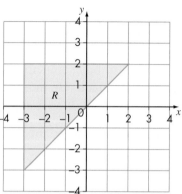

Write down three inequalities which together describe the shaded region.

AQA, Question 15, Paper 2 (2-tier trial), June 2005

10 Copy the grid below and indicate clearly on it the region defined by the three inequalities

$y \leqslant 4$

$x \geqslant -3$

$y \geqslant x + 2$

Mark the region with an R.

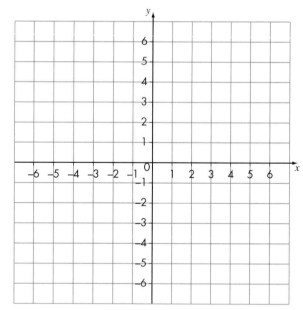

AQA, Question 11, Paper 2 Higher, November 2004

11 n is an integer that satisfies the inequality

$\dfrac{121}{n^2} \geqslant 8$

List all the possible values of n.

WORKED EXAM QUESTION

a On the number lines show the inequalities

  i $-2 \leqslant n < 4$

  ii $n < 2$

b n is an integer. Find the values of n that satisfy both inequalities in part **a**

c Solve the inequalities

  i $3x + 8 > 2$

  ii $3(x - 4) \leqslant \frac{1}{2}(x + 1)$

Solution

a i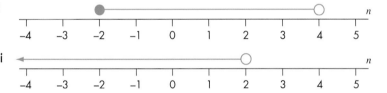

  ii

Remember that a strict inequality has an open circle to show the boundary and an inclusive inequality has a solid circle to show the boundary.

b $\{-2, -1, 0, 1\}$

The integers that satisfy both inequalities are in the overlap of both lines.

c i $3x + 8 > 2$

  $3x > -6$

  $x > -2$

As when solving an equation do the same thing to both sides. First subtract 8, then divide by 3.

  ii $3(x - 4) \leqslant \frac{1}{2}(x + 1)$

  $6(x - 4) \leqslant x + 1$

  $6x - 24 < x + 1$

  $5x < 25$

  $x < 5$

First multiply by 2 to get rid of the fraction, then expand the brackets. Then collect all the x terms on the left-hand side and the number terms on the right-hand side. Then simplify and divide by 5.

GRADE YOURSELF

C   Able to solve inequalities such as $3x + 2 < 5$ and represent the solution on a number line

B   Able to represent a region that satisfies a linear inequality graphically, and to solve more complex linear inequalities

B   Able to represent a region that simultaneously satisfies more than one linear inequality graphically

A   Able to translate a problem into inequalities

What you should know now

- How to solve simple inequalities
- How to create algebraic inequalities from verbal statements
- How to represent linear inequalities on a graph
- How to depict a region satisfying more than one linear inequality

Vectors

1 Properties of vectors

2 Vectors in geometry

This chapter will show you ...

- the properties of vectors
- how to add and subtract vectors
- how to use vectors to solve geometrical problems

Visual overview

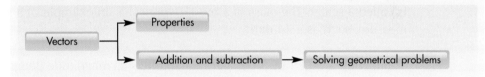

What you should already know

- Vectors are used to describe translations

Quick check

Use column vectors to describe these translations.

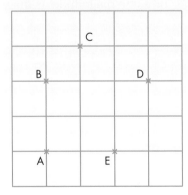

a A to C

b B to D

c C to D

d D to E

25.1

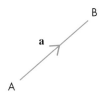

In this section you will learn how to:
● add and subtract vectors

Key words
direction
magnitude
vector

A **vector** is a quantity which has both **magnitude** and **direction**. It can be represented by a straight line which is drawn in the direction of the vector and whose length represents the magnitude of the vector. Usually, the line includes an arrowhead.

The translation or movement from A to B is represented by the vector **a**.

a is always printed in bold type, but is written as a̲.

a can also be written as $\overrightarrow{AB}$.

A quantity which is completely described by its magnitude, and has no direction associated with it, is called a scalar. The mass of a bus (10 tonnes) is an example of a scalar. Another example is a linear measure, such as 25.4 mm.

Multiplying a vector by a number (scalar) alters its magnitude (length) but not its direction. For example, the vector 2**a** is twice as long as the vector **a**, but in the same direction.

A negative vector, for example –**b**, has the same magnitude as the vector **b**, but is in the opposite direction.

Addition and subtraction of vectors

Take two non-parallel vectors **a** and **b**, then **a** + **b** is defined to be the translation of **a** followed by the translation of **b**. This can easily be seen on a vector diagram.

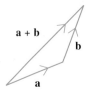

Similarly, **a** – **b** is defined to be the translation of **a** followed by the translation of –**b**.

Look at the parallelogram grid below. **a** and **b** are two independent vectors that form the basis of this grid. It is possible to define the position, with reference to O, of any point on this grid by a vector expressed in terms of **a** and **b**. Such a vector is called a position vector.

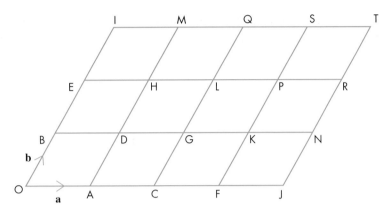

For example, the position vector of K is $\overrightarrow{OK}$ or **k** = 3**a** + **b**, the position vector of E is $\overrightarrow{OE}$ or **e** = 2**b**. The vector $\overrightarrow{HT}$ = 3**a** + **b**, the vector $\overrightarrow{PN}$ = **a** – **b**, the vector $\overrightarrow{MK}$ = 2**a** – 2**b**, and the vector $\overrightarrow{TP}$ = –**a** – **b**.

Note $\overrightarrow{OK}$ and $\overrightarrow{HT}$ are called equal vectors because they have exactly the same length and are in the same direction. $\overrightarrow{MK}$ and $\overrightarrow{PN}$ are parallel vectors but $\overrightarrow{MK}$ is twice the magnitude of $\overrightarrow{PN}$.

EXAMPLE 1

   a   Using the grid above, write down the following vectors in terms of **a** and **b**.

      i $\overrightarrow{BH}$ ii $\overrightarrow{HP}$ iii $\overrightarrow{GT}$

      iv $\overrightarrow{TI}$ v $\overrightarrow{FH}$ vi $\overrightarrow{BQ}$

   b   What is the relationship between the following vectors?

      i $\overrightarrow{BH}$ and $\overrightarrow{GT}$ ii $\overrightarrow{BQ}$ and $\overrightarrow{GT}$ iii $\overrightarrow{HP}$ and $\overrightarrow{TI}$

   c   Show that B, H and Q lie on the same straight line.

   a   i   **a** + **b**   ii   2**a**   iii   2**a** + 2**b**   iv   –4**a**   v   –2**a** + 2**b**   vi   2**a** + 2**b**

   b   i $\overrightarrow{BH}$ and $\overrightarrow{GT}$ are parallel and $\overrightarrow{GT}$ is twice the length of $\overrightarrow{BH}$.

      ii $\overrightarrow{BQ}$ and $\overrightarrow{GT}$ are equal.

      iii $\overrightarrow{HP}$ and $\overrightarrow{TI}$ are in opposite directions and $\overrightarrow{TI}$ is twice the length of $\overrightarrow{HP}$.

   c $\overrightarrow{BH}$ and $\overrightarrow{BQ}$ are parallel and start at the same point B. Therefore, B, H and Q must lie on the same straight line.

EXAMPLE 2

Use a vector diagram to show that $\quad$ **a** + **b** = **b** + **a**

Take two independent vectors **a** and **b**

a + **b** and **b** + **a** have the same magnitude and direction and are therefore equal.

EXERCISE 25A

1 On this grid, $\overrightarrow{OA}$ is **a** and $\overrightarrow{OB}$ is **b**.

a Name three other vectors equivalent to **a**.

b Name three other vectors equivalent to **b**.

c Name three vectors equivalent to –**a**.

d Name three vectors equivalent to –**b**.

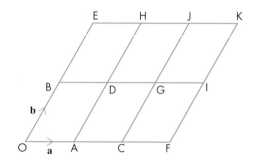

2 Using the same grid as in question **1**, give the following vectors in terms of **a** and **b**.

a $\overrightarrow{OC}$ $\qquad$ **b** $\overrightarrow{OE}$ $\qquad$ **c** $\overrightarrow{OD}$ $\qquad$ **d** $\overrightarrow{OG}$ $\qquad$ **e** $\overrightarrow{OJ}$

f $\overrightarrow{OH}$ $\qquad$ **g** $\overrightarrow{AG}$ $\qquad$ **h** $\overrightarrow{AK}$ $\qquad$ **i** $\overrightarrow{BK}$ $\qquad$ **j** $\overrightarrow{DI}$

k $\overrightarrow{GJ}$ $\qquad$ **l** $\overrightarrow{DK}$

3 a What do the answers to parts **2c** and **2g** tell you about the vectors $\overrightarrow{OD}$ and $\overrightarrow{AG}$?

b On the grid in question **1**, there are three vectors equivalent to $\overrightarrow{OG}$. Name all three.

4 a What do the answers to parts **2c** and **2e** tell you about vectors $\overrightarrow{OD}$ and $\overrightarrow{OJ}$?

b On the grid in question **1**, there is one other vector that is twice the size of $\overrightarrow{OD}$. Which is it?

c On the grid in question **1**, there are three vectors that are three times the size of $\overrightarrow{OA}$. Name all three.

5 On a copy of this grid, mark on the points C to P
to show the following.

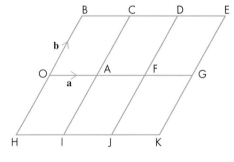

a $\overrightarrow{OC}$ = 2**a** + 3**b**   b $\overrightarrow{OD}$ = 2**a** + **b**

c $\overrightarrow{OE}$ = **a** + 2**b**   d $\overrightarrow{OF}$ = 3**b**

e $\overrightarrow{OG}$ = 4**a**   f $\overrightarrow{OH}$ = 4**a** + 2**b**

g $\overrightarrow{OI}$ = 3**a** + 3**b**   h $\overrightarrow{OJ}$ = **a** + **b**

i $\overrightarrow{OK}$ = 2**a** + 2**b**   j $\overrightarrow{OM}$ = 2**a** + $\frac{3}{2}$**b**   k $\overrightarrow{ON}$ = $\frac{1}{2}$**a** + 2**b**   l $\overrightarrow{OP}$ = $\frac{5}{2}$**a** + $\frac{3}{2}$**b**

6 a Look at the diagram in question **5**. What can you say about the points O, J, K and I?

b How could you tell this by looking at the vectors for parts **5g**, **5h** and **5i**?

c There is another point on the same straight line as O and D. Which is it?

d Copy and complete these statements and then mark the appropriate points on the diagram you
drew for question **5**.

i The point Q is on the straight line ODH. The vector $\overrightarrow{OQ}$ is given by

$\overrightarrow{OQ}$ = **a** + ... **b**

ii The point R is on the straight line ODH. The vector $\overrightarrow{OR}$ is given by

$\overrightarrow{OR}$ = 3**a** + ... **b**

e Copy and complete the following statement.

Any point on the line ODH has a vector *n***a** + ... **b**, where *n* is any number.

7 On this grid, $\overrightarrow{OA}$ is **a** and $\overrightarrow{OB}$ is **b**.

Give the following vectors in terms of **a** and **b**.

a $\overrightarrow{OH}$ b $\overrightarrow{OK}$

c $\overrightarrow{OJ}$ d $\overrightarrow{OI}$

e $\overrightarrow{OC}$ f $\overrightarrow{CO}$

g $\overrightarrow{AK}$ h $\overrightarrow{DI}$

i $\overrightarrow{JE}$ j $\overrightarrow{AB}$ k $\overrightarrow{CK}$ l $\overrightarrow{DK}$

8 a What do the answers to parts **7e** and **7f** tell you about the vectors $\overrightarrow{OC}$ and $\overrightarrow{CO}$?

b On the grid in question **7**, there are five other vectors opposite to $\overrightarrow{OC}$. Name at least three.

9 a What do the answers to parts **7j** and **7k** tell you about vectors $\overrightarrow{AB}$ and $\overrightarrow{CK}$?

b On the grid in question **7**, there are two vectors that are twice the size of $\overrightarrow{AB}$ and in the opposite
direction. Name both of them.

c On the grid in question **7**, there are three vectors that are three times the size of $\overrightarrow{OA}$ and in the
opposite direction. Name all three.

10 On a copy of this grid, mark on the points C to P to show the following.

a $\overrightarrow{OC} = 2\mathbf{a} - \mathbf{b}$ **b** $\overrightarrow{OD} = 2\mathbf{a} + \mathbf{b}$

c $\overrightarrow{OE} = \mathbf{a} - 2\mathbf{b}$ **d** $\overrightarrow{OF} = \mathbf{b} - 2\mathbf{a}$

e $\overrightarrow{OG} = -\mathbf{a}$ **f** $\overrightarrow{OH} = -\mathbf{a} - 2\mathbf{b}$

g $\overrightarrow{OI} = 2\mathbf{a} - 2\mathbf{b}$ **h** $\overrightarrow{OJ} = -\mathbf{a} + \mathbf{b}$

i $\overrightarrow{OK} = -\mathbf{a} - \mathbf{b}$ **j** $\overrightarrow{OM} = -\mathbf{a} - \frac{3}{2}\mathbf{b}$ **k** $\overrightarrow{ON} = -\frac{1}{2}\mathbf{a} - 2\mathbf{b}$ **l** $\overrightarrow{OP} = \frac{3}{2}\mathbf{a} - \frac{3}{2}\mathbf{b}$

11 This grid shows the vectors $\overrightarrow{OA} = \mathbf{a}$ and $\overrightarrow{OB} = \mathbf{b}$.

a Name three vectors equivalent to $\mathbf{a} + \mathbf{b}$.

b Name three vectors equivalent to $\mathbf{a} - \mathbf{b}$.

c Name three vectors equivalent to $\mathbf{b} - \mathbf{a}$.

d Name three vectors equivalent to $-\mathbf{a} - \mathbf{b}$.

e Name three vectors equivalent to $2\mathbf{a} - \mathbf{b}$.

f Name three vectors equivalent to $2\mathbf{b} - \mathbf{a}$.

g For each of these, name one equivalent vector.

i $3\mathbf{a} - \mathbf{b}$ **ii** $2(\mathbf{a} + \mathbf{b})$ **iii** $3\mathbf{a} - 2\mathbf{b}$

iv $3(\mathbf{a} - \mathbf{b})$ **v** $3(\mathbf{b} - \mathbf{a})$ **vi** $3(\mathbf{a} + \mathbf{b})$

vii $-3(\mathbf{a} + \mathbf{b})$ **viii** $2\mathbf{a} + \mathbf{b} - 3\mathbf{a} - 2\mathbf{b}$ **ix** $2(2\mathbf{a} - \mathbf{b}) - 3(\mathbf{a} - \mathbf{b})$

12 The points P, Q and R lie on a straight line. The vector $\overrightarrow{PQ}$ is $2\mathbf{a} + \mathbf{b}$, where $\mathbf{a}$ and $\mathbf{b}$ are vectors. Which of the following vectors could be the vector $\overrightarrow{PR}$ and which could not be the vector $\overrightarrow{PR}$ (two of each).

a $2\mathbf{a} + 2\mathbf{b}$ **b** $4\mathbf{a} + 2\mathbf{b}$ **c** $2\mathbf{a} - \mathbf{b}$ **d** $-6\mathbf{a} - 3\mathbf{b}$

13 The points P, Q and R lie on a straight line. The vector $\overrightarrow{PQ}$ is $3\mathbf{a} - \mathbf{b}$, where $\mathbf{a}$ and $\mathbf{b}$ are vectors.

a Write down any other vector that could represent $\overrightarrow{PR}$.

b How can you tell from the vector $\overrightarrow{PS}$ that S lies on the same straight line as P, Q and R?

14 Use the diagram in question **11** to prove the following results.

a KB is parallel to IE.

b L, A and F are on a straight line.

15 Use a vector diagram to show that $\mathbf{a} + (\mathbf{b} + \mathbf{c}) = (\mathbf{a} + \mathbf{b}) + \mathbf{c}$.

In this section you will learn how to:
● use vectors to solve geometrical problems

Key word
vector

Vectors can be used to prove many results in geometry, as the following examples show.

EXAMPLE 3

In the diagram, $\overrightarrow{OA} = \mathbf{a}$, $\overrightarrow{OB} = \mathbf{b}$, and $\overrightarrow{BC} = 1.5\mathbf{a}$. M is the midpoint of BC, N is the midpoint of AC and P is the midpoint of OB.

a Find these vectors in terms of $\mathbf{a}$ and $\mathbf{b}$.

   i $\overrightarrow{AC}$ **ii** $\overrightarrow{OM}$ **iii** $\overrightarrow{BN}$

b Prove that $\overrightarrow{PN}$ is parallel to $\overrightarrow{OA}$.

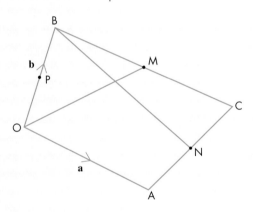

a i You have to get from A to C in terms of vectors that you know.

$$\overrightarrow{AC} = \overrightarrow{AO} + \overrightarrow{OB} + \overrightarrow{BC}$$

Now $\overrightarrow{AO} = -\overrightarrow{OA}$, so you can write

$$\overrightarrow{AC} = -\mathbf{a} + \mathbf{b} + \tfrac{3}{2}\mathbf{a}$$
$$= \tfrac{1}{2}\mathbf{a} + \mathbf{b}$$

Note that the letters "connect up" as we go from A to C, and that the negative of a vector represented by any pair of letters is formed by reversing the letters.

ii In the same way

$$\overrightarrow{OM} = \overrightarrow{OB} + \overrightarrow{BM} = \overrightarrow{OB} + \tfrac{1}{2}\overrightarrow{BC}$$
$$= \mathbf{b} + \tfrac{1}{2}(\tfrac{3}{2}\mathbf{a})$$
$$\overrightarrow{OM} = \tfrac{3}{4}\mathbf{a} + \mathbf{b}$$

iii $\overrightarrow{BN} = \overrightarrow{BC} + \overrightarrow{CN} = \overrightarrow{BC} - \frac{1}{2}\overrightarrow{AC}$

$= \frac{3}{2}\mathbf{a} - \frac{1}{2}(\frac{1}{2}\mathbf{a} + \mathbf{b})$

$= \frac{3}{2}\mathbf{a} - \frac{1}{4}\mathbf{a} - \frac{1}{2}\mathbf{b}$

$= \frac{5}{4}\mathbf{a} - \frac{1}{2}\mathbf{b}$

Note that if you did this as $\overrightarrow{BN} = \overrightarrow{BO} + \overrightarrow{OA} + \overrightarrow{AN}$, you would get the same result.

b $\overrightarrow{PN} = \overrightarrow{PO} + \overrightarrow{OA} + \overrightarrow{AN}$

$= \frac{1}{2}(-\mathbf{b}) + \mathbf{a} + \frac{1}{2}(\frac{1}{2}\mathbf{a} + \mathbf{b})$

$= -\frac{1}{2}\mathbf{b} + \mathbf{a} + \frac{1}{4}\mathbf{a} + \frac{1}{2}\mathbf{b}$

$= \frac{5}{4}\mathbf{a}$

$\overrightarrow{PN}$ is a multiple of $\mathbf{a}$ only, so must be parallel to $\overrightarrow{OA}$.

EXAMPLE 4

OACB is a parallelogram. $\overrightarrow{OA}$ is represented by the vector $\mathbf{a}$. $\overrightarrow{OB}$ is represented by the vector $\mathbf{b}$. P is a point $\frac{2}{3}$ the distance from O to C, and M is the midpoint of AC. Show that B, P and M lie on the same straight line.

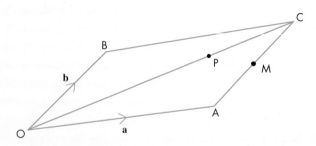

$\overrightarrow{OC} = \overrightarrow{OA} + \overrightarrow{AC} = \mathbf{a} + \mathbf{b}$

$\overrightarrow{OP} = \frac{2}{3}\overrightarrow{OC} = \frac{2}{3}\mathbf{a} + \frac{2}{3}\mathbf{b}$

$\overrightarrow{OM} = \overrightarrow{OA} + \overrightarrow{AM} = \overrightarrow{OA} + \frac{1}{2}\overrightarrow{AC} = \mathbf{a} + \frac{1}{2}\mathbf{b}$

$\overrightarrow{BP} = \overrightarrow{BO} + \overrightarrow{OP} = -\mathbf{b} + \frac{2}{3}\mathbf{a} + \frac{2}{3}\mathbf{b} = \frac{2}{3}\mathbf{a} - \frac{1}{3}\mathbf{b} = \frac{1}{3}(2\mathbf{a} - \mathbf{b})$

$\overrightarrow{BM} = \overrightarrow{BO} + \overrightarrow{OM} = -\mathbf{b} + \mathbf{a} + \frac{1}{2}\mathbf{b} = \mathbf{a} - \frac{1}{2}\mathbf{b} = \frac{1}{2}(2\mathbf{a} - \mathbf{b})$

Therefore, $\overrightarrow{BM}$ is a multiple of $\overrightarrow{BP}$ ($\overrightarrow{BM} = \frac{3}{2}\overrightarrow{BP}$).

Therefore, $\overrightarrow{BP}$ and $\overrightarrow{BM}$ are parallel and as they have a common point, B, they must lie on the same straight line.

EXERCISE 25B

1 The diagram shows the vectors $\overrightarrow{OA} = \mathbf{a}$ and $\overrightarrow{OB} = \mathbf{b}$. M is the midpoint of AB.

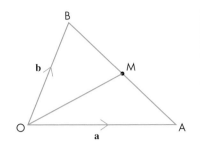

   a i Work out the vector $\overrightarrow{AB}$.

   ii Work out the vector $\overrightarrow{AM}$.

   iii Explain why $\overrightarrow{OM} = \overrightarrow{OA} + \overrightarrow{AM}$.

   iv Using your answers to parts **ii** and **iii**, work out $\overrightarrow{OM}$ in terms of **a** and **b**.

   b i Work out the vector $\overrightarrow{BA}$.

   ii Work out the vector $\overrightarrow{BM}$.

   iii Explain why $\overrightarrow{OM} = \overrightarrow{OB} + \overrightarrow{BM}$.

   iv Using your answers to parts **ii** and **iii**, work out $\overrightarrow{OM}$ in terms of **a** and **b**.

   c Copy the diagram and show on it the vector $\overrightarrow{OC}$ which is equal to **a** + **b**.

   d Describe in geometrical terms the position of M in relation to O, A, B and C.

2 The diagram shows the vectors $\overrightarrow{OA} = \mathbf{a}$ and $\overrightarrow{OC} = -\mathbf{b}$. N is the midpoint of AC.

   a i Work out the vector $\overrightarrow{AC}$.

   ii Work out the vector $\overrightarrow{AN}$.

   iii Explain why
   $$\overrightarrow{ON} = \overrightarrow{OA} + \overrightarrow{AN}.$$

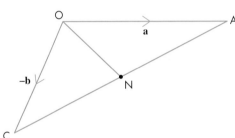

   iv Using your answers to parts **ii** and **iii**, work out $\overrightarrow{ON}$ in terms of **a** and **b**.

   b i Work out the vector $\overrightarrow{CA}$.

   ii Work out the vector $\overrightarrow{CN}$.

   iii Explain why $\overrightarrow{ON} = \overrightarrow{OC} + \overrightarrow{CN}$.

   iv Using your answers to parts **ii** and **iii**, work out $\overrightarrow{ON}$ in terms of **a** and **b**.

   c Copy the diagram above and show on it the vector $\overrightarrow{OD}$ which is equal to **a** – **b**.

   d Describe in geometrical terms the position of N in relation to O, A, C and D.

3 Copy this diagram and on it draw vectors that represent

   a a + b   **b a – b**

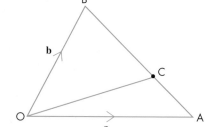

4 The diagram shows the vectors $\overrightarrow{OA} = \mathbf{a}$ and $\overrightarrow{OB} = \mathbf{b}$.

The point C divides the line AB in the ratio 1:2 (i.e. AC is $\frac{1}{3}$ the distance from A to B).

a i Work out the vector $\overrightarrow{AB}$.

ii Work out the vector $\overrightarrow{AC}$.

iii Work out the vector $\overrightarrow{OC}$ in terms of **a** and **b**.

b If C now divides the line AB in the ratio 1:3 (i.e. AC is $\frac{1}{4}$ the distance from A to B), write down the vector that represents $\overrightarrow{OC}$.

5 The diagram shows the vectors $\overrightarrow{OA} = \mathbf{a}$ and $\overrightarrow{OB} = \mathbf{b}$.

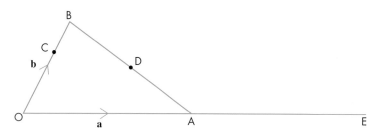

The point C divides OB in the ratio 2:1 (i.e. OC is $\frac{2}{3}$ the distance from O to B). The point E is such that $\overrightarrow{OE} = 2\overrightarrow{OA}$. D is the midpoint of AB.

a Write down (or work out) these vectors in terms of **a** and **b**.

i $\overrightarrow{OC}$ **ii** $\overrightarrow{OD}$ **iii** $\overrightarrow{CO}$

b The vector $\overrightarrow{CD}$ can be written as $\overrightarrow{CD} = \overrightarrow{CO} + \overrightarrow{OD}$. Use this fact to work out $\overrightarrow{CD}$ in terms of **a** and **b**.

c Write down a similar rule to that in part **b** for the vector $\overrightarrow{DE}$. Use this rule to work out $\overrightarrow{DE}$ in terms of **a** and **b**.

d Explain why C, D and E lie on the same straight line.

6 ABCDEF is a regular hexagon. $\overrightarrow{AB}$ is represented by the vector **a**, and $\overrightarrow{BC}$ by the vector **b**.

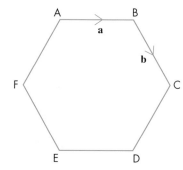

a By means of a diagram, or otherwise, explain why $\overrightarrow{CD} = \mathbf{b} - \mathbf{a}$.

b Express these vectors in terms of **a** and **b**.

i $\overrightarrow{DE}$ **ii** $\overrightarrow{EF}$ **iii** $\overrightarrow{FA}$

c Work out the answer to

$$\overrightarrow{AB} + \overrightarrow{BC} + \overrightarrow{CD} + \overrightarrow{DE} + \overrightarrow{EF} + \overrightarrow{FA}$$

Explain your answer.

d Express these vectors in terms of **a** and **b**.

i $\overrightarrow{AD}$ **ii** $\overrightarrow{BE}$ **iii** $\overrightarrow{CF}$ **iv** $\overrightarrow{AE}$ **v** $\overrightarrow{DF}$

7 ABCDEFGH is a regular octagon. $\overrightarrow{AB}$ is represented by the vector **a**, and $\overrightarrow{BC}$ by the vector **b**.

a By means of a diagram, or otherwise, explain why $\overrightarrow{CD} = \sqrt{2}\mathbf{b} - \mathbf{a}$.

b By means of a diagram, or otherwise, explain why $\overrightarrow{DE} = \mathbf{b} - \sqrt{2}\mathbf{a}$.

c Express the following vectors in terms of **a** and **b**.

   i $\overrightarrow{EF}$ **ii** $\overrightarrow{FG}$ **iii** $\overrightarrow{GH}$ **iv** $\overrightarrow{HA}$

   v $\overrightarrow{HC}$ **vi** $\overrightarrow{AD}$ **vii** $\overrightarrow{BE}$ **viii** $\overrightarrow{BF}$

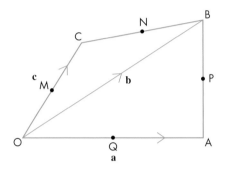

8 In the quadrilateral OABC, M, N, P and Q are the midpoints of the sides as shown. $\overrightarrow{OA}$ is represented by the vector **a**, and $\overrightarrow{OC}$ by the vector **c**. The diagonal $\overrightarrow{OB}$ is represented by the vector **b**.

a Express these vectors in terms of **a**, **b** and **c**.

   i $\overrightarrow{AB}$ **ii** $\overrightarrow{AP}$ **iii** $\overrightarrow{OP}$

   Give your answers as simply as possible.

b **i** Express the vector $\overrightarrow{ON}$ in terms of **b** and **c**.

   ii Hence express the vector $\overrightarrow{PN}$ in terms of **a** and **c**.

c **i** Express the vector $\overrightarrow{QM}$ in terms of **a** and **c**.

   ii What relationship is there between $\overrightarrow{PN}$ and $\overrightarrow{QM}$?

   iii What sort of quadrilateral is PNMQ?

d Prove that $\overrightarrow{AC} = 2\overrightarrow{QM}$.

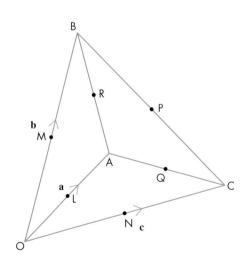

9 L, M, N, P, Q, R are the midpoints of the line segments, as shown. $\overrightarrow{OA} = \mathbf{a}$, $\overrightarrow{OB} = \mathbf{b}$, $\overrightarrow{OC} = \mathbf{c}$.

a Express these vectors in terms of **a** and **c**.

   i $\overrightarrow{OL}$ **ii** $\overrightarrow{AC}$

   iii $\overrightarrow{OQ}$ **iv** $\overrightarrow{LQ}$

b Express these vectors in terms of **a** and **b**.

   i $\overrightarrow{LM}$ **ii** $\overrightarrow{QP}$

c Prove that the quadrilateral LMPQ is a parallelogram.

d Find two other sets of four points that form parallelograms.

1 In triangle ABC, M lies on BC such that BM = $\frac{3}{4}$BC.

$\overrightarrow{AB} = \mathbf{s}$ and $\overrightarrow{AC} = \mathbf{t}$

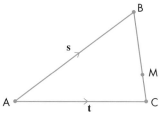

Find $\overrightarrow{AM}$ in terms of $\mathbf{s}$ and $\mathbf{t}$.

Give your answer in its simplest form.

AQA, Question 17, Paper 1 Higher, June 2005

2 In the diagram OACD, OADB and ODEB are parallelograms.

$\overrightarrow{OA} = \mathbf{a}$ and $\overrightarrow{OB} = \mathbf{b}$

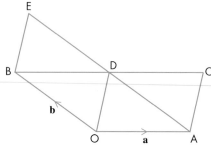

a Express, in terms of $\mathbf{a}$ and $\mathbf{b}$, the following vectors. Give your answers in their simplest form.

 i $\overrightarrow{OD}$

 ii $\overrightarrow{OC}$

 iii $\overrightarrow{AB}$

b The point F is such that OCFE is a parallelogram. Write the vector $\overrightarrow{CF}$ in terms of $\mathbf{a}$ and $\mathbf{b}$.

c What geometrical relationship is there between the points O, D and F? Justify your answer.

AQA, Question 22, Paper 2 Higher, November 2004

3 OABC is a quadrilateral.

$\overrightarrow{OA} = \mathbf{a}$, $\overrightarrow{OB} = \mathbf{b}$, $\overrightarrow{OC} = \mathbf{c}$.

The midpoints of OC, CB, BA, AO are P, Q, R and S, respectively.

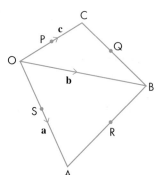

a Find these vectors in terms of $\mathbf{a}$, $\mathbf{b}$ and $\mathbf{c}$.

 i $\overrightarrow{PS}$

 ii $\overrightarrow{QB}$

 iii $\overrightarrow{BR}$

b What type of quadrilateral is PQRS? Give a reason for your answer.

AQA, Question 21, Paper 2 Higher, June 2001

4 In the diagram, $\overrightarrow{OP} = 3\mathbf{a}$, $\overrightarrow{PA} = \mathbf{a}$, $\overrightarrow{OB} = 4\mathbf{b}$ and $\overrightarrow{BR} = 2\mathbf{b}$. Q is the midpoint of AB.

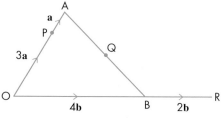

Find, in terms of $\mathbf{a}$ and $\mathbf{b}$, the following vectors.

a $\overrightarrow{AB}$

b $\overrightarrow{PQ}$

c Explain clearly why the points PQR lie on a straight line.

AQA, Question 22, Paper 2 Higher, November 2001

5

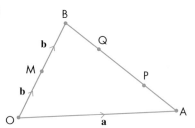

OAB is a triangle where M is the midpoint of OB.

P and Q are points on AB such that AP = PQ = QB.

$\overrightarrow{OA} = \mathbf{a}$ and $\overrightarrow{OB} = 2\mathbf{b}$

a Find, in terms of $\mathbf{a}$ and $\mathbf{b}$, expressions for these vectors.

 i $\overrightarrow{BA}$

 ii $\overrightarrow{MQ}$

 iii $\overrightarrow{OP}$

b What can you deduce about quadrilateral OMQP? Give a reason for your answer.

AQA, Question 18, Paper 1 Higher, June 2003

6 The diagram shows quadrilateral OABC.
$\overrightarrow{OA} = \mathbf{a}$, $\overrightarrow{OC} = \mathbf{c}$ and $\overrightarrow{OB} = 2\mathbf{a} + \mathbf{c}$

a Find expressions for these vectors in terms of $\mathbf{a}$ and $\mathbf{c}$.

   i $\overrightarrow{AB}$

   ii $\overrightarrow{CB}$

b What kind of quadrilateral is OABC?
Give a reason for your answer.

c Point P lies on AC and $AP = \frac{1}{3}AC$.

   i Find an expression for $\overrightarrow{OP}$ in terms of $\mathbf{a}$ and $\mathbf{c}$. Write your answer in its simplest form.

   ii Describe, as fully as possible, the position of P.

AQA, Question 23, Paper 1 Higher, May 2002

7 In the triangle OAB, P is the midpoint of AB, X is the midpoint of OB, $\overrightarrow{OA} = \mathbf{a}$ and $\overrightarrow{OB} = \mathbf{b}$. Q is the point that divides OP in the ratio 2 : 1.

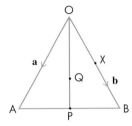

a Express these vectors in terms of $\mathbf{a}$ and $\mathbf{b}$.

   i $\overrightarrow{AB}$ **ii** $\overrightarrow{AP}$

   iii $\overrightarrow{OP}$ **iv** $\overrightarrow{OQ}$

   v $\overrightarrow{AQ}$ **vi** $\overrightarrow{AX}$

b Deduce that $\overrightarrow{AX} = k\overrightarrow{AQ}$, where k is a scalar, and find the value of k.

WORKED EXAM QUESTION

The diagram shows triangle OAB. M is the midpoint of OA. P lies on BM and $BP = \frac{2}{3}BM$. $\overrightarrow{OA} = 2\mathbf{a}$ and $\overrightarrow{OB} = 2\mathbf{b}$

a Find expressions, in terms of a and b, for **i** $\overrightarrow{BM}$ and **ii** $\overrightarrow{OP}$. Write each answer in its simplest form.

b N is the midpoint of OB. Q lies on AN and $AQ = \frac{2}{3}AN$.

   i Find an expression for $\overrightarrow{OQ}$, in terms of a and b. Write your answer in its simplest form.

   ii What do your answers for $\overrightarrow{OP}$ and $\overrightarrow{OQ}$ tell you about the points P and Q?

AQA, Question 18, Paper 1 Higher, November 2002

Solution

a i $\overrightarrow{BM} = \mathbf{a} - 2\mathbf{b}$

> Find a route from B to M in terms of known vectors. $\overrightarrow{BM} = \overrightarrow{BO} + \overrightarrow{OM}$

ii $\overrightarrow{OP} = \overrightarrow{OB} + \frac{2}{3}\overrightarrow{BM} = 2\mathbf{b} + \frac{2}{3}\mathbf{a} - \frac{4}{3}\mathbf{b} = \frac{2}{3}\mathbf{a} + \frac{2}{3}\mathbf{b}$

> Find a route from O to P in terms of known vectors. $\overrightarrow{OP} = \overrightarrow{OB} + \overrightarrow{BP}$

b i $\overrightarrow{OQ} = \overrightarrow{OA} + \overrightarrow{AQ} = \overrightarrow{OA} + \frac{2}{3}\overrightarrow{AN}$ with $\overrightarrow{AN} = \mathbf{b} - 2\mathbf{a}$

> Find a route from O to Q in terms of known vectors. $\overrightarrow{OQ} = \overrightarrow{OA} + \overrightarrow{AQ}$

So $\overrightarrow{OQ} = 2\mathbf{a} + \frac{2}{3}(\mathbf{b} - 2\mathbf{a}) = 2\mathbf{a} + \frac{2}{3}\mathbf{b} - \frac{4}{3}\mathbf{a} = \frac{2}{3}\mathbf{a} + \frac{2}{3}\mathbf{b}$

ii $\overrightarrow{OP} = \overrightarrow{OQ}$, so P and Q are the same point

GRADE YOURSELF

A Able to solve problems using addition and subtraction of vectors

A* Able to solve more complex geometrical problems

What you should know now

- How to add and subtract vectors
- How to apply vector methods to solve geometrical problems

1 Transformations
of the graph
$y = f(x)$

This chapter will show you ...

- how to transform a graph

- how to recognise the relationships between graphs and their equations

Visual overview

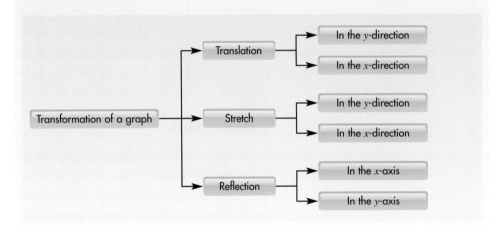

Transformation of a graph → Translation → In the y-direction / In the x-direction

Stretch → In the y-direction / In the x-direction

Reflection → In the x-axis / In the y-axis

What you should already know

- How to transform a shape by a translation and a reflection

- A translation is described by a column vector

- A reflection is described by a mirror line

continued

● The graphs of $y = x^2$, $y = x^3$, $y = \dfrac{1}{x}$, $y = \sin x$, $y = \cos x$ and $y = \tan x$

$y = x^2$

$y = \sin x$

$y = x^3$

$y = \cos x$

$y = \dfrac{1}{x}$

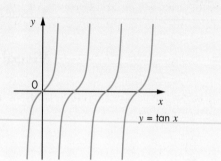
$y = \tan x$

Quick check

Starting with the shaded triangle every time, do the following transformations.

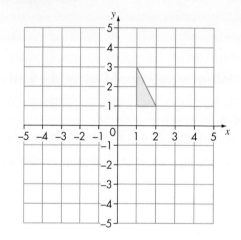

a translation

   i $\begin{pmatrix} 3 \\ 0 \end{pmatrix}$ **ii** $\begin{pmatrix} 0 \\ -2 \end{pmatrix}$

b reflection in the   **i** y-axis   **ii** x-axis

c rotation of 180° about the origin

Transformations of the graph $y = f(x)$

This section will show you how to:

● transform a graph

Key words

function
reflection
scale factor
stretch
transform
translation
vector

We use the notation $f(x)$ to represent a **function** of x. A function of x is any algebraic expression in which x is the only variable. Examples of functions are: $f(x) = x + 3$, $f(x) = 5x$, $f(x) = 2x - 7$, $f(x) = x^2$, $f(x) = x^3 + 2x - 1$, $f(x) = \sin x$ and $f(x) = \frac{1}{x}$.

Below and on page 582 are six general statements or rules about **transforming** graphs.

This work is much easier to understand if you have access to a graphics calculator or a graph-drawing computer program.

The graph on the right represents any function $y = f(x)$.

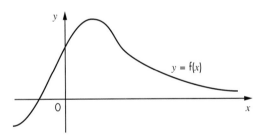

Rule 1 The graph of $y = f(x) + a$ is a **translation** of the graph of $y = f(x)$ by a **vector** $\begin{pmatrix} 0 \\ a \end{pmatrix}$.

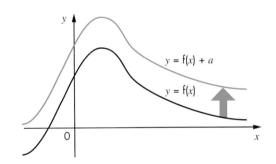

Rule 2 The graph of $y = f(x - a)$ is a translation of the graph of $y = f(x)$ by a vector $\begin{pmatrix} a \\ 0 \end{pmatrix}$.

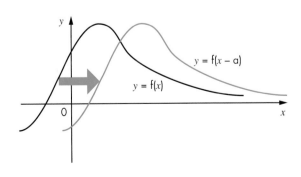

A **stretch** is an enlargement that takes place in one direction only. It is described by a **scale factor** and the direction of the stretch

Original

Stretch, scale factor 3
in x-direction

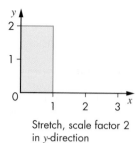

Stretch, scale factor 2
in y-direction

Rule 3 The graph of $y = kf(x)$ is a stretch of the graph $y = f(x)$ by a scale factor of k in the y-direction.

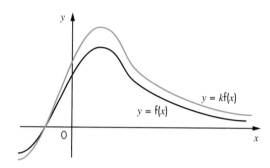

Rule 4 The graph of $y = f(tx)$ is a stretch of the graph $y = f(x)$ by a scale factor of $\dfrac{1}{t}$ in the x-direction.

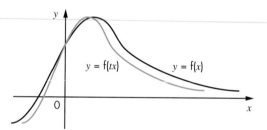

Rule 5 The graph of $y = -f(x)$ is the **reflection** of the graph $y = f(x)$ in the x-axis.

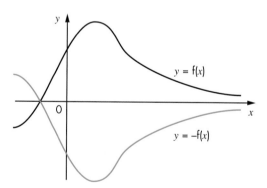

Rule 6 The graph of $y = f(-x)$ is the reflection of the graph $y = f(x)$ in the y-axis.

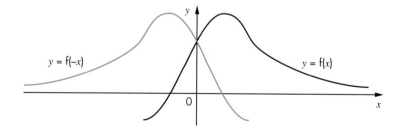

EXAMPLE 1

Sketch the following graphs.

a $y = x^2$ **b** $y = 5x^2$ **c** $y = x^2 - 5$

d $y = -x^2$ **e** $y = (x - 5)^2$ **f** $y = 2x^2 + 3$

Describe the transformation(s) that change(s) graph **a** to each of the other graphs.

Graph **a** is the basic graph to which we apply the rules to make the necessary transformations: graph **b** uses Rule 3, graph **c** uses Rule 1, graph **d** uses Rule 5, graph **e** uses Rule 2, and graph **f** uses Rules 3 and 1.

The graphs are

a

$y = x^2$

b

$y = 5x^2$

c

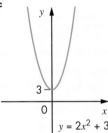

$y = x^2 - 5$

d

$y = -x^2$

e

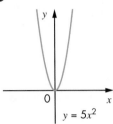

$y = (x - 5)^2$

f

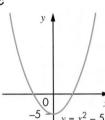

$y = 2x^2 + 3$

The transformations are:

graph **b** is a stretch of scale factor 5 in the y-direction,

graph **c** is a translation of $\begin{pmatrix} 0 \\ -5 \end{pmatrix}$,

graph **d** is a reflection in the x-axis,

graph **e** is a translation of $\begin{pmatrix} 5 \\ 0 \end{pmatrix}$,

graph **f** is a stretch of scale factor 2 in the y-direction, followed by a translation of $\begin{pmatrix} 0 \\ 3 \end{pmatrix}$.

Note that two of the transformations cause problems because they seem to do the opposite of what is expected. These are:

$y = f(x + a)$ (Rule 2)

The translation is $\begin{pmatrix} -a \\ 0 \end{pmatrix}$, so the sign of the constant inside the bracket changes in the vector (see part **e** in Example 1).

$y = f(ax)$ (Rule 4)

This is not a stretch. It actually closes the graph up. Just like an enlargement (see Chapter 8) can make something smaller, a stretch can make it squeeze closer to the axes.

EXERCISE 26A

1 On the same axes sketch the following graphs.

    a $y = x^2$ **b** $y = 3x^2$ **c** $y = \frac{1}{2}x^2$ **d** $y = 10x^2$

    e Describe the transformation(s) that take(s) the graph in part **a** to each of the graphs in parts **b** to **d**.

2 On the same axes sketch the following graphs.

    a $y = x^2$ **b** $y = x^2 + 3$ **c** $y = x^2 - 1$ **d** $y = 2x^2 + 1$

    e Describe the transformation(s) that take(s) the graph in part **a** to each of the graphs in parts **b** to **d**.

3 On the same axes sketch the following graphs.

    a $y = x^2$ **b** $y = (x + 3)^2$ **c** $y = (x - 1)^2$ **d** $y = 2(x - 2)^2$

    e Describe the transformation(s) that take(s) the graph in part **a** to each of the graphs in parts **b** to **d**.

4 On the same axes sketch the following graphs.

    a $y = x^2$ **b** $y = (x + 3)^2 - 1$ **c** $y = 4(x - 1)^2 + 3$

    d Describe the transformation(s) that take(s) the graph in part **a** to each of the graphs in parts **b** and **c**.

5 On the same axes sketch the following graphs.

    a $y = x^2$ **b** $y = -x^2 + 3$ **c** $y = -3x^2$ **d** $y = -2x^2 + 1$

    e Describe the transformation(s) that take(s) the graph in part **a** to each of the graphs in parts **b** to **d**.

6 On the same axes sketch the following graphs.

    a $y = \sin x$ **b** $y = 2\sin x$ **c** $y = \frac{1}{2}\sin x$ **d** $y = 10\sin x$

    e Describe the transformation(s) that take(s) the graph in part **a** to each of the graphs in parts **b** to **d**.

7 On the same axes sketch the following graphs.

    a $y = \sin x$ **b** $y = \sin 3x$ **c** $y = \sin \dfrac{x}{2}$ **d** $y = 5\sin 2x$

    e Describe the transformation(s) that take(s) the graph in part **a** to each of the graphs in parts **b** to **d**.

8 On the same axes sketch the following graphs.

    a $y = \sin x$ **b** $y = \sin (x + 90°)$ **c** $y = \sin (x - 45°)$ **d** $y = 2\sin (x - 90°)$

    e Describe the transformation(s) that take(s) the graph in part **a** to the graphs in parts **b** to **d**.

9 On the same axes sketch the following graphs.

   a $y = \sin x$
   b $y = \sin x + 2$
   c $y = \sin x - 3$
   d $y = 2\sin x + 1$

   e Describe the transformation(s) that take(s) the graph in part **a** to each of the graphs parts **b** to **d**.

10 On the same axes sketch the following graphs.

   a $y = \sin x$
   b $y = -\sin x$
   c $y = \sin(-x)$
   d $y = -\sin(-x)$

   e Describe the transformation(s) that take(s) the graph in part **a** to each of the graphs in parts **b** to **d**.

11 On the same axes sketch the following graphs.

   a $y = \cos x$
   b $y = 2\cos x$
   c $y = \cos(x - 60°)$
   d $y = \cos x + 2$

   e Describe the transformation(s) that take(s) the graph in part **a** to each of the graphs in parts **b** to **d**.

12 **a** Describe the transformations of the graph of $y = x^2$ needed to obtain these graphs.

     i $y = 4x^2$
     ii $y = 9x^2$
     iii $y = 16x^2$

   b Describe the transformations of the graph of $y = x^2$ needed to obtain these graphs.

     i $y = (2x)^2$
     ii $y = (3x)^2$
     iii $y = (4x)^2$

   c Describe two different transformations that take the graph of $y = x^2$ to the graph of $y = (ax)^2$, where a is a positive number.

13 On the right is a sketch of the function $y = f(x)$. Use this to sketch the following.

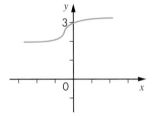

   a $y = f(x) + 2$
       b $y = 2f(x)$

   c $y = f(x - 3)$
     d $y = -f(x)$

   e $y = 2f(x) + 3$
    f $y = -f(x) - 2$

14 What is the equation of the graph obtained when the following transformations are performed on the graph of $y = x^2$?

   a stretch by a factor of 5 in the y-direction

   b translation of $\begin{pmatrix} 0 \\ 7 \end{pmatrix}$

   c translation of $\begin{pmatrix} -3 \\ 0 \end{pmatrix}$

   d translation of $\begin{pmatrix} -2 \\ -3 \end{pmatrix}$

   e stretch by a factor of 3 in the y-direction followed by a translation of $\begin{pmatrix} 0 \\ 4 \end{pmatrix}$

   f reflection in the x-axis, followed by a stretch, scale factor 3, in the y-direction

15 What is the equation of the graph obtained when the following transformations are performed on the graph of $y = \cos x$?

a stretch by a factor of 6 in the y-direction

b translation of $\begin{pmatrix} 0 \\ 3 \end{pmatrix}$

c translation of $\begin{pmatrix} -30 \\ 0 \end{pmatrix}$

d translation of $\begin{pmatrix} 45 \\ -2 \end{pmatrix}$

e stretch by a factor of 3 in the y-direction followed by a translation of $\begin{pmatrix} 0 \\ -2 \end{pmatrix}$

16 a Sketch the graph $y = x^3$.

b Use your sketch in part **a** to draw the graphs obtained after $y = x^3$ is transformed as follows.

   i   reflection in the x-axis

   ii translation of $\begin{pmatrix} 0 \\ -2 \end{pmatrix}$

   iii stretch by a scale factor of 3 in the y-direction

   iv translation of $\begin{pmatrix} -2 \\ 0 \end{pmatrix}$

c Give the equation of each of the graphs obtained in part **b**.

17 a Sketch the graph of $y = \dfrac{1}{x}$.

b Use your sketch in part **a** to draw the graphs obtained after $y = \dfrac{1}{x}$ is transformed as follows.

   i   translation of $\begin{pmatrix} 0 \\ 4 \end{pmatrix}$

   ii translation of $\begin{pmatrix} 4 \\ 0 \end{pmatrix}$

   iii stretch, scale factor 3 in the y-direction

   iv stretch, scale factor $\frac{1}{2}$ in the x-direction

c Give the equation of each of the graphs obtained in part **b**.

18 The graphs below are all transformations of $y = x^2$. Two points through which each graph passes are indicated. Use this information to work out the equation of each graph.

a

b

c

d

19 The graphs below are all transformations of $y = \sin x$. Two points through which each graph passes are indicated. Use this information to work out the equation of each graph.

a
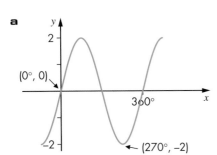
$(0°, 0)$
$360°$
$(270°, -2)$

b
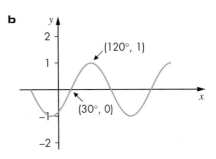
$(120°, 1)$
$(30°, 0)$

c
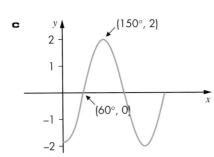
$(150°, 2)$
$(60°, 0)$

d
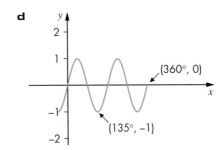
$(360°, 0)$
$(135°, -1)$

20 Below are the graphs of $y = \sin x$ and $y = \cos x$.

$y = \sin x$

$y = \cos x$

a Describe a series of transformations that would take the first graph to the second.

b Which of these is equivalent to $y = \cos x$?

  i $y = \sin (x + 90°)$ **ii** $y = -\sin (x - 90°)$ **iii** $y = 2\cos \dfrac{x}{2}$

21 **A**

B

4

C

-2 0

D

3

E
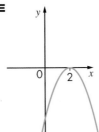
2

Match each of the graphs **A**, **B**, **C**, **D** and **E** to one of these equations.

  i $y = x^2$ **ii** $y = -x^2 + 3$ **iii** $y = -(x - 2)^2$ **iv** $y = (x + 2)^2$ **v** $y = x^2 + 4$

1 The diagrams, which are not drawn to scale, show the graph of $y = x^2$ and four other graphs A, B, C and D.

A, B, C and D represent four different transformations of $y = x^2$.

Find the equation of each of the graphs A, B, C and D.

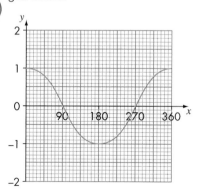

AQA, Question 18, Paper 1 Higher, November 2003

2 The sketch to the right is of the graph of $y = x^2$

Copy these axes and sketch the following graphs.

a $y = x^2 + 2$

b $y = (x - 2)^2$

c $y = \frac{1}{2}x^2$

AQA, Question 21, Paper 1 Higher, November 2004

3 A sketch of $y = f(x)$ for $0° \leqslant x \leqslant 360°$ is shown on the grid below.

a Choose the correct equation for $y = f(x)$.

$y = \sin x$ $y = \cos x$ $y = \tan x$

b Grids **i**, **ii** and **iii** show sketches of transformations of the function $y = f(x)$. For each sketch, write down the equation of the transformed function.

i

ii

iii

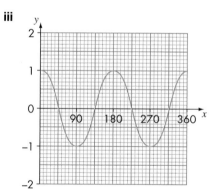

AQA, Question 15, Paper 1 Higher, June 2001

4 The graph of $y = \sin x$ for $0° \leqslant x \leqslant 360°$ is shown on the grid below. The point $P(90, 1)$ lies on the curve.

On a copy of the grid, sketch the graphs of:

a $y = \sin (x - 45)$

b $y = 2 \sin x$

AQA, Question 20, Paper 1 Higher, June 2003

WORKED EXAM QUESTION

The sketch shows the graph $y = x^3$.

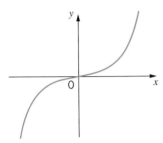

On the axes below sketch the graphs indicated.
p is a positive integer greater than 1.
(The graph $y = x^3$ is shown dotted to help you.)

a $y = x^3 - p$

b $y = (x + p)^3$

c $y = \dfrac{x^3}{p}$

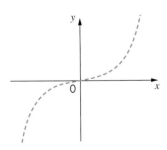

AQA, Question 22, Paper 2 Higher, November 2000

Solution

a   This is a translation of $y = x^3$ by the vector $\begin{pmatrix} 0 \\ -p \end{pmatrix}$

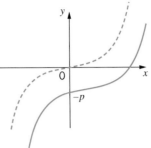

b   This is a translation of $y = x^3$ by the vector $\begin{pmatrix} -p \\ 0 \end{pmatrix}$.

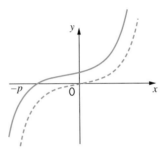

c   This is a stretch of $y = x^3$ by a scale factor of $\dfrac{1}{p}$ in the y-direction.

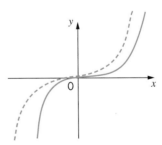

You do not know what the actual value of p is so make sure that the translation is clear. Alternatively, make a value for p up, say 2.

GRADE YOURSELF

(A*) Able to transform the graph of a given function

(A*) Able to identify the equation of a function from its graph, which has been formed by a transformation on a known function

What you should know now

- How to sketch the graphs of functions such as $y = f(ax)$ and $y = f(x + a)$ from the known graph of $y = f(x)$

- How to describe from their graphs the transformation of one function into another

- How to identify equations from the graphs of transformations of known graphs

Proof

1 Proving standard results

2 Algebraic proof

This chapter will show you ...

- the meaning of "a counter-example"
- the difference between a numerical demonstration and a proof
- how to prove results using rigorous and logical mathematical arguments

Visual overview

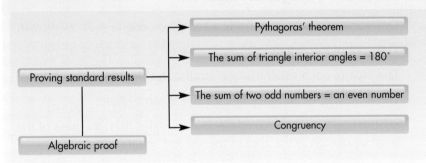

Proving standard results → Pythagoras' theorem

The sum of triangle interior angles = 180°

The sum of two odd numbers = an even number

Congruency

Algebraic proof

What you should already know

The mathematical results in this book, such as:

- The interior angles in a triangle add up to 180°
- The sum of any two odd numbers is always an even number
- The theorems concerning circles
- Pythagoras' theorem

Quick check

1 Give the value of the angle marked z in terms of x and y.

2 Write down a relationship between p, q and r.

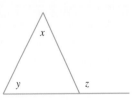

3 Complete this table.

+	even	odd
even	even	
odd		

Can you **prove** any of the mathematical results listed on the previous page?

The method of mathematical **proof** is to proceed in logical steps, establishing a series of mathematical statements by using facts which are already known to be true. With few exceptions, a proof will also require the use of algebraic manipulation.

In the next pages, we prove four standard results: Pythagoras' theorem, the sum of the interior angles of a triangle is 180°, the sum of any two odd numbers is always an even number, and congruency. Follow them through, making sure that you understand each step in the process.

Proof of Pythagoras' theorem

Draw a square of side c inside a square of side $(a + b)$, as shown.

The area of the exterior square is $(a + b)^2 = a^2 + 2ab + b^2$.

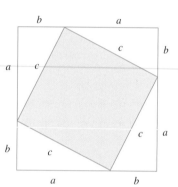

The area of each small triangle around the shaded square is $\frac{1}{2}ab$.

The total area of all four triangles is $4 \times \frac{1}{2}ab = 2ab$.

Subtracting the total area of the four triangles from the area of the large square gives the area of the shaded square:

$$a^2 + 2ab + b^2 - 2ab = a^2 + b^2$$

But the area of the shaded square is c^2, so

$$c^2 = a^2 + b^2$$

which is Pythagoras' theorem.

The sum of the interior angles of a triangle is 180°

One of your earlier activities in geometry may have been to draw a triangle, to cut off its corners and to stick them down to **show that** they make a straight line.

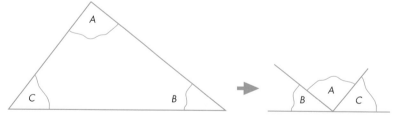

Does this prove that the interior angles make 180° or were you just lucky and picked a triangle that worked? Was the fact that everyone else in the class managed to pick a triangle that worked also a lucky coincidence?

Of course not! But this was a **demonstration**, not a proof. You would have to show that this method worked for *all* possible triangles (there is an infinite number!) to say that you have proved this result.

Your proof must establish that the result is true for *all* triangles.

Look at the following proof.

Start with triangle ABC with angles α, β and γ (figure **i**).

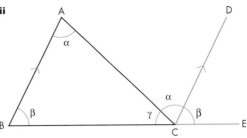

On figure **i** draw a line CD parallel to side AB and extend BC to E, to give figure **ii**.

Since AB is parallel to CD

∠ACD = ∠BAC = α (alternate angles)   ∠DCE = ∠ABC = β (corresponding angles)

BCE is a straight line, so γ + α + β = 180°. Therefore the interior angles of a triangle = 180°.

This proof assumes that alternate angles are equal and that corresponding angles are equal. Strictly speaking, we should prove these results, but we have to accept certain results as true. These are based on Euclid's axioms from which all geometric proofs are derived.

The sum of any two odd numbers is always an even number

If you try this with numbers, you can see that the result is true. For example, 3 + 5 = 8, 11 + 17 = 28. But this is not a proof. Once again, we may have been lucky and found some results that work. Until we have tried an infinite number of different pairs, we cannot be sure.

Look at the following algebraic proof.

Let n be any whole number.

Whatever whole number is represented by n, $2n$ has to be even. So, $2n + 1$ represents any odd number.

Let one odd number be $2n + 1$, and let the other odd number be $2m + 1$.

The sum of these is

$$(2n + 1) + (2m + 1) = 2n + 2m + 1 + 1 = 2n + 2m + 2 = 2(n + m + 1),$$ which must be even.

Congruency

There are four conditions to prove congruency. These are commonly known as SSS (three sides the same), SAS (two sides and the included angle the same), ASA (or AAS) (two angles and one side the same) and RHS (right-angled triangle, hypotenuse, and one short side the same). **Note:** AAA (three angles the same) is not a condition for congruency.

When you prove a result, you must explain or justify every statement or line. Proofs have to be rigorous and logical.

EXAMPLE 1

ABCD is a parallelogram. X is the point where the diagonals meet.

Prove that triangles AXB and CXD are congruent.

∠BAX = ∠DCX (alternate angles)

∠ABX = ∠CDX (alternate angles)

AB = CD (opposite sides in a parallelogram)

Hence ΔAXB is congruent to ΔCXD (ASA).

Note that you could have used ∠AXB = ∠CXD (vertically opposite angles) as the second line but whichever approach is used you *must* give a reason for each statement.

In some questions, a numerical example is used to give you a clue which will help you to write down an algebraic proof.

1 **a** Choose any odd number and any even number. Add these together. Is the result odd or even? Does this always work for any odd number and even number you choose?

b Let any odd number be represented by $2n + 1$. Let any even number be represented by $2m$, where m and n are integers. Prove that the sum of an odd number and an even number always gives an odd number.

2 Prove the following results.

a the sum of two even numbers is even

b the product of two even numbers is even

c the product of an odd number and an even number is even

d the product of two odd numbers is odd

e the sum of four consecutive numbers is always even

f half the sum of four consecutive numbers is always odd

3 **a** Show that the triangle ABC (figure **i**) is isosceles.

b Prove that the triangle DEF (figure **ii**) with one angle of $x°$ and an exterior angle of $90°$ + $\dfrac{x°}{2}$ is isosceles.

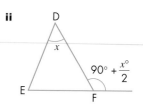

4 Prove that a triangle with an interior angle of $\dfrac{x°}{2}$ and an exterior angle of $x°$ is isosceles.

5 **a** Using the theorem that the angle subtended by an arc at the centre of a circle is twice the angle subtended by the same arc at the circumference, find the values of angles DAB and ACB in the circle shown in figure **i**.

b Prove that the sum of the opposite angles of a cyclic quadrilateral is $180°$. (You may find figure **ii** useful.)

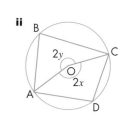

6 A Fibonacci sequence is formed by adding the previous two terms to get the next term. For example, if we start with 3 and 4, the series is

3, 4, 7, 11, 18, 29, 47, 76, 123, 199, ...

a Continue the Fibonacci sequence up to 10 terms. 1, 1, 2, ...

b Continue the Fibonacci sequence up to 10 terms. a, b, $a + b$, $a + 2b$, $2a + 3b$, ...

c Prove that the difference between the 8th term and the 5th term of any Fibonacci sequence is twice the sixth term.

7 The nth term in the sequence of triangular numbers 1, 3, 6, 10, 15, 21, 28, ... is given by

$\frac{1}{2}n(n + 1)$.

a Show that the sum of the 11th and 12th terms is a perfect square.

b Explain why the $(n + 1)$th term of the triangular number sequence is given by
$\frac{1}{2}(n + 1)(n + 2)$.

c Prove that the sum of any two consecutive triangular numbers is always a square number.

8 a The triangle ABC is isosceles.
BCD and AED are straight lines.
Find the value of the angle
CED, marked x, in figure **i**.

i

ii

b Prove that angle ACB = angle
CED in figure **ii**.

9 The diagram shows part of a 10 × 10 "hundred square".

a One 2 × 2 square is marked.

12	13	14	15
22	23	24	25
32	33	34	35
42	43	44	45

i Work out the difference between the product of the bottom-left
and top-right values and the product of the top-left and
bottom-right values:

$22 \times 13 - 12 \times 23$

ii Repeat this for any other 2 × 2 square of your choosing.

b Prove that this will always give an answer of 10 for any 2 × 2 square chosen.

c The diagram shows a calendar square
(where the numbers are arranged in rows of seven).

Prove that you always get a value of 7 if you repeat
the procedure in part **a i**.

1	2	3	4	5	6	7
8	9	10	11	12	13	14
15	16	17	18	19	20	21
22	23	24	25	26	27	28
29	30	31				

d Prove that in a number square that is arranged in
rows of n numbers then the difference is always n if
you repeat the procedure in part **a i**.

10 Prove that if you add any two-digit number from the 9 times table to the reverse of itself
(that is, swap the tens digit and units digit), the result will always be 99.

27.2 Algebraic proof

In this section you will learn how to:
• give a rigorous and logical algebraic proof

Key words
area
length
width

There are three levels of "proof": **Verify** that…, **Show** that…, and **Prove** that… .

• At the lowest level (verification), all you have to do is to substitute numbers into the result to
show that it works.

• At the middle level, you have to show that both sides of the result are the same algebraically.

• At the highest level (proof), you have to manipulate the left-hand side of the result to become
its right-hand side.

The following example demonstrates these three different procedures.

EXAMPLE 2

You are given that $n^2 + (n + 1)^2 - (n + 2)^2 = (n - 3)(n + 1)$

a Verify that this result is true.

b Show that this result is true.

c Prove that this result is true.

a Choose a number for n, say $n = 5$. Put this value into both sides of the expression, which gives:

$5^2 + (5 + 1)^2 - (5 + 2)^2 = (5 - 3)(5 + 1)$

$25 + 36 - 49 = 2 \times 6$

$12 = 12$

Hence, the result is true.

b Expand the LHS and the RHS of the expression to get:

$n^2 + n^2 + 2n + 1 - (n^2 + 4n + 4) = n^2 - 2n - 3$

Collect like terms on each side, which gives:

$n^2 + n^2 - n^2 + 2n - 4n + 1 - 4 = n^2 - 2n - 3$

$n^2 - 2n - 3 = n^2 - 2n - 3$

That is, both sides are algebraically the same.

c Expand the LHS of the expression to get: $n^2 + n^2 + 2n + 1 - (n^2 + 4n + 4)$

Collect like terms, which gives: $n^2 + n^2 - n^2 + 2n - 4n + 1 - 4 = n^2 - 2n - 3$

Factorise the collected result: $n^2 - 2n - 3 = (n - 3)(n + 1)$ which is the RHS of the original expression.

EXERCISE 27B

1 Speed Cabs charges 45 pence per kilometre for each journey. Evans Taxis has a fixed charge of 90p plus 30p per kilometre.

a i Verify that Speed Cabs is cheaper for a journey of 5 km.

ii Verify that Evans Taxis is cheaper for a journey of 7 km.

b Show clearly why both companies charge the same for a journey of 6 km.

c Show that if Speed Cabs charges a pence per kilometre, and Evans Taxis has a fixed charge of £b plus a charge of c pence per kilometre, both companies charge the same for a journey of $\frac{100b}{(a - c)}$ kilometres.

2 You are given that:

$(a + b)^2 + (a - b)^2 = 2(a^2 + b^2)$

a Verify that this result is true for $a = 3$ and $b = 4$.

b Show that the LHS is the same as the RHS.

c Prove that the LHS can be simplified to the RHS.

3 Prove that $(a + b)^2 - (a - b)^2 = 4ab$.

4 The rule for converting from degrees Fahrenheit to degrees Celsius is to subtract 32° and then to multiply by $\frac{5}{9}$.

Prove that the temperature that has the same value in both scales is –40°.

5 The sum of the series $1 + 2 + 3 + 4 + \dots + (n - 2) + (n - 1) + n$ is given by $\frac{1}{2}n(n + 1)$.

a Verify that this result is true for $n = 6$.

b Write down a simplified value, in terms of n, for the sum of these two series.

$$1 + 2 + 3 + \dots + (n - 2) + (n - 1) + n$$

and $\quad n + (n - 1) + (n - 2) + \dots + 3 + 2 + 1$

c Prove that the sum of the first n integers is $\frac{1}{2}n(n + 1)$.

> **HINTS AND TIPS**
>
> Add together the first terms in each series, the second terms in each series, and so on.

6 The following is a "think of a number" trick.

- Think of a number. $\quad\longrightarrow\quad$ • Multiply it by 2.
- Add 10. $\quad\longrightarrow\quad$ • Divide the result by 2.
- Subtract the original number.

The result is always 5.

a Verify that the trick works when you pick 7 as the original number.

b Prove why the trick *always* works.

7 You are told that "when two numbers have a difference of 2, the difference of their squares is twice the sum of the two numbers".

a Verify that this is true for 5 and 7.

b Prove that the result is true.

c Prove that when two numbers have a difference of n, the difference of their squares is n times the sum of the two numbers.

> **HINTS AND TIPS**
>
> Use a and $a + 2$ as the numbers.

8 Four consecutive numbers are 4, 5, 6 and 7.

a Verify that their product plus 1 is a perfect square.

b Complete the multiplication square and use it to show that

$$(n^2 - n - 1)^2 = n^4 - 2n^3 - n^2 + 2n + 1$$

	n^2	$-n$	-1
n^2	n^4		$-n^2$
$-n$		n^2	
-1			

c Let four consecutive numbers be $(n - 2)$, $(n - 1)$, n, $(n + 1)$. Prove that the product of four consecutive numbers plus 1 is a perfect square.

9 Here is another mathematical trick to try on a friend.

- Think of two single-digit numbers.
- Multiply one number (your choice) by 2.
- Add 5 to this answer.
- Multiply this answer by 5.
- Add the second number.
- Subtract 4.
- Ask your friend to state his or her final answer.
- Mentally subtract 21 from his or her answer.

The two digits you get are the two digits your friend first thought of.

Prove why this works.

EXERCISE 27C

A*

You may not be able algebraically to prove all of these results. Some of them can be disproved by a counter-example. You should first try to verify each result, then attempt to prove it – or at least try to demonstrate that the result is probably true by trying lots of examples.

1 T represents any triangular number. Prove the following.

    a $8T + 1$ is always a square number

    b $9T + 1$ is always another triangular number

2 Lewis Carroll, who wrote *Alice in Wonderland*, was also a mathematician. In 1890, he suggested the following results.

    a For any pair of numbers, x and y, if $x^2 + y^2$ is even, then $\frac{1}{2}(x^2 + y^2)$ is the sum of two squares.

    b For any pair of numbers, x and y, $2(x^2 + y^2)$ is always the sum of two squares.

    c Any number whose square is the sum of two squares is itself the sum of two squares.

    Can you prove these statements to be true or false?

3 For all values of n, $n^2 - n + 41$ gives a prime number. True or false?

4 For any integer n, $2n$, $n^2 - 1$ and $n^2 + 1$ form three numbers that obey Pythagoras' theorem. Can you prove this?

5 Waring's theorem states that: "Any whole number can be written as the sum of not more than four square numbers."

For example, $27 = 3^2 + 3^2 + 3^2$ and $23 = 3^2 + 3^2 + 2^2 + 1^2$.

Is this always true?

6 Take a three-digit multiple of 37, for example, $7 \times 37 = 259$. Write these digits in a cycle.

Take all possible three-digit numbers from the cycle, for example, 259, 592 and 925.

Divide each of these numbers by 37 to find that

    $259 = 7 \times 37 \qquad 592 = 16 \times 37 \qquad 925 = 25 \times 37.$

Is this true for all three-digit multiples of 37?

Is it true for a five-digit multiple of 41?

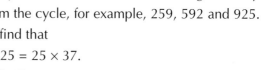

7 Prove that the sum of the squares of two consecutive integers is an odd number.

8 PQRS is a parallelogram. Prove that triangles PQS and RQS are congruent.

9 OB is a radius of a circle, centre O. C is the point where the perpendicular bisector of OB meets the circumference. Prove that triangle OBC is equilateral.

10 In the following grid, $\overrightarrow{OA} = \mathbf{a}$ and $\overrightarrow{OB} = \mathbf{b}$.
Prove that AB is parallel to EF.

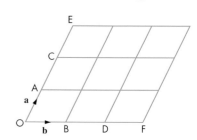

1 Show that the sum of any three consecutive integers is always a multiple of 3.

AQA, Question 9, Paper 2 Higher, November 2003

2 a This is a page from Zoe's exercise book.

> $2^3 - 1^3 = 7$ (prime)   The difference between
> $3^3 - 2^3 = 19$ (prime)   consecutive cube
> $4^3 - 3^3 = 37$ (prime)   numbers is always a
>   prime number.

Give a counter example to show that Zoe is wrong. Justify your answer.

b Prove that $(n + 5)^2 - (n + 3)^2 = 4(n + 4)$

AQA, Question 16, Paper 2 Higher, June 2005

3 In the diagram, the lines AC and BD intersect at E. AB and DC are parallel and AB = CD.

Prove that triangles ABE and CDE are congruent.

AQA, Question 15, Paper 2 Higher, June 2003

4 Annie, Bert and Charu are investigating the number sequence

21, 40, 65, 96, 133, …

a Annie has found the following pattern.

1st term	$1 \times 2 + 3^2 + 2 \times 5 =$	21
2nd term	$2 \times 3 + 4^2 + 3 \times 6 =$	40
3rd term	$3 \times 4 + 5^2 + 4 \times 7 =$	65
4th term	$4 \times 5 + 6^2 + 5 \times 8 =$	96
5th term	$5 \times 6 + 7^2 + 6 \times 9 =$	133

Complete the nth term for Annie's pattern.

nth term $n \times (n + 1) + \ldots\ldots + \ldots\ldots \times \ldots\ldots$

b Bert has found this formula for the nth term

$(3n + 1)(n + 3) + 5$

Charu has found this formula for the nth term

$(2n + 3)^2 - (n + 1)^2$

Prove that these two formulae are equivalent.

AQA, Question 14, Paper 2 Higher, November 2004

WORKED EXAM QUESTION

a n is a positive integer.
  i Explain why $n(n + 1)$ must be an even number.
  ii Explain why $2n + 1$ must be an odd number.
b Expand and simplify $(2n + 1)^2$
c Prove that the square of any odd number is always 1 more than a multiple of 8.

Solution

a i If n is odd, $n + 1$ is even

  If n is even, $n + 1$ is odd

  Even times odd is always even

> This is a lead in to the rest of the task. An explanation in words is good enough. Keep the words to a minimum.

  ii $2n$ must be even so $2n + 1$ must be odd

> An explanation in words is good enough.

b $(2n + 1)^2 = (2n + 1)(2n + 1) = 4n^2 + 2n + 2n + 1 = 4n^2 + 4n + 1$

> Always write down a squared bracket twice then expand it by whichever method you prefer.

c $(2n + 1)^2 = 4n^2 + 4n + 1$

> Use the fact that $2n + 1$ is odd, and it has been "squared" in part **b**.

  $4n^2 + 4n + 1 = 4n(n + 1) + 1$

> The "one more than" is taken care of with the +1.

  $4 \times n(n + 1) + 1 = 4 \times$ even $+ 1$,
  which must be a multiple of 8 plus 1.

> Show that the $4n^2 + 4n$ is a multiple of 8 using the result in part **a i**.

GRADE YOURSELF

B Able to verify results by substituting numbers into them

B Able to understand the proofs of simple theorems such as an exterior angle of a triangle is the sum of the two opposite interior angles

A Able to show that an algebraic statement is true, using both sides of the statement to justify your answer

A* Able to prove algebraic and geometric results with rigorous and logical mathematical arguments

What you should know now

- The meaning of the terms "verify that", "show that" and "prove"

- How to prove some standard results in mathematics, such as Pythagoras' theorem

- How to use your knowledge of proof to answer the questions throughout the book that are flagged with the proof icon

Coursework guidance

During your GCSE course, you will need to do two coursework tasks. One of the tasks will cover the content from Number and Algebra and/or Shape and Space (AO1 task), and the other will cover the content from Handling Data (AO4 task). The tasks will be assessed and marked by your teacher or by the examination board. Each task will carry 10% of the total marks for the examination. Each task has three strands, with a maximum mark of 8 in each strand. The two tables, which follow, will give you some idea of what each strand means and what you need to do in order to obtain a particular mark in each strand.

AO1 task
- **Strand i**: Decisions. This is about how you decide to solve a particular problem and then how you ask your own questions in order to extend the problem.
- **Strand ii**: Presentation. This is about how you present your work mathematically. It involves making tables of results, drawing graphs, using algebraic notation or using computer software.
- **Strand iii**: Reasons. This is about finding solutions to problems and drawing conclusions. You need to find patterns, rules or formulae and to explain how you obtained them.

Mark	Strand i: Making and monitoring decisions to solve problems	Strand ii: Communicating mathematically	Strand iii: Developing skills of mathematical reasoning
1	You should show that you understand the problem by giving an example.	You should explain how you intend to solve the problem by giving an example or by drawing a diagram.	You should find an easy example that fits the problem.
2	You should plan a suitable method to help solve the problem further by giving at least three examples.	You should write out your results clearly and carefully in a list or show them on diagrams.	You should look for any patterns in your results.
3	You should identify the information needed to solve the problem and check that your results are correct.	You should show your results in a clearly labelled table or by using diagrams and symbols.	You should explain the pattern, or find a rule for your results.
4	You should break down the problem into easier and more manageable stages.	You should link your tables, diagrams or graphs with a clear explanation.	You should test a different example to show that your pattern or rule works and comment on the outcome.
5	You should introduce some questions of your own in order to extend the problem to give a further solution.	You should find an algebraic formula to explain the rule and show by substitution that the formula works.	You should explain why your rule or formula works by using simple algebra, graphs or computer software.
6	You should develop the problem further by using algebra, graphs or trigonometry.	You should introduce more difficult algebra or trigonometry on at least three occasions.	You should comment constructively on your solution to show that you have fully understood the problem.
7	You should analyse a more complex problem by considering approaches which manipulate three variables.	You should show you can present an accurate and convincing mathematical solution or proof.	You should give reasons why you are considering using approaches which use three variables.
8	You should introduce new content or an area of mathematics that is unfamiliar into a more complex problem.	You should use mathematical techniques efficiently to give a complete and concise solution or proof.	You should provide an accurate proof to a more complex problem and explain the conditions under which it remains valid.

Coursework guidance (continued)

AO4 task

- **Strand i**: Planning. This is about how you decide to design the problem by specifying your aims and hypotheses and planning an overall strategy.
- **Strand ii**: Collection and presentation of data. This is about the methods you use to collect the data for the problem and how you use statistical calculations, diagrams or computer software to illustrate the data.

- **Strand iii**: Interpretation. This is about how you interpret and summarise the results based on your statistical calculations and diagrams. It also involves evaluating your strategy and how you could make improvements.

Mark	Strand i: Specify and plan	Strand ii: Process and represent	Strand iii: Interpret and discuss
1–2	Collect data relevant to the problem. State your overall plan and aims.	Present your results on diagrams such as bar charts or pictograms. Use the mode and range for the data.	Make a comment on the data. Attempt to summarise any results you notice in the data.
3–4	Your plan should include a suitable hypothesis relevant to the problem. Decide how to collect your data and use an appropriate sample size.	Use relevant statistical calculations for the problem, such as mode, median, mean and range. Present your data in a variety of forms, such as stem-and-leaf diagrams, scatter graphs or pie charts, and link them with a relevant explanation.	Interpret any graphs and statistical calculations used and draw sensible conclusions, which relate to your original hypothesis.. Comment on how you could improve your work.
5–6	In a more complex problem, you should develop hypotheses that are linked and where comparisons can be made. Consider how to overcome any practical problems when choosing your sample.	Ensure that your data is relevant, and use more complex statistical calculations, such as the mean for grouped data. Use appropriate diagrams, such as cumulative frequency graphs, box plots or lines of best fit, and give clear reasons for your choice of presentation.	Summarise and correctly interpret your diagrams and statistical calculations. Make relevant comparisons and show that the nature of the sampling method used may have some significance on your results. Evaluate the effectiveness of your strategy.
7–8	In a more demanding problem, you should plan and look for practical problems that you might encounter and consider how to avoid bias, modifying your method of data collection in light of this. Use other suitable data collection techniques and refine these to enhance the problem.	You should ensure that all practical problems are dealt with, and use effectively a wide range of more advanced statistical calculations to present a convincing argument. Use a range of diagrams, such as histograms, to help you to summarise the data and show how the variables are related.	All diagrams and calculations should be correctly interpreted in order to appreciate the significance of the results. You should explain why any possible bias might affect your conclusions, and make suggestions on how you could make an improvement. Comment on any limitations in your work.

Really Useful Maths!

Chapter 2
Really Useful Maths!: Sheep Farmer

Date	Number of lambs	Total live weight in kg	Mean live weight in kg	Total weight of meat in kg	Meat as % of live weight	Total price paid for meat	Price paid per kg of meat
1st April	13	468	36	211	45.1% ✓	£812.56	£3.85
15th April	8	290	36	134	46.2% ✓	£451.91	£3.37
22nd April	18	672	37	312	46.4% ✓	£1105.31	£3.54
29th April	11	398	36	179	45.0% ✓	£625.04	£3.49
6th May	18	657	37	291	44.3% ✓	£907.89	£3.12
20th May	8	309	39	130	42.1% ✓	£386.15	£2.97
3rd June	10	416	42	171	41.1% ✗	£480.46	£2.81
17th June	4	174	44	72	41.4% ✗	£196.54	£2.73

The mean weight per lamb has increased from 36 kg to 44 kg. This is an increase of 22%. However the price per kg of lamb has fallen from £3.85 to £2.73, a decrease of 29%.

The only two weeks when the condition of the lambs fell below 42% were 3rd June and 17th June.

Comment: There were only 3 weeks when Mrs Woolman earned less than the average lamb price. The trend of both Mrs Woolman's prices and the average prices were decreasing from April to June.

Chapter 4
Really Useful Maths!: Water recycling

	Daily water usage		
	Litres used each: flush/shower/load	Frequency used	Total litres per day
Toilet	13.16	12 times a day	157.92
Shower	91	2 times a day	182
Washing machine	113.75	3 times a week	48.75
Dishwasher	40.95	once every 2 days	20.475
Total:			409.145

They can collect 300 litres from the roof in 1 day.
It will take $4\frac{1}{2}$ days to fill the tank.

Chapter 5
Really Useful Maths!: Riding stables

Horse	Weight in kg	Feed in kg	Worming paste in tubes
Summer	850	6.1	1.5
Sally	400	4.0	0.75
Skip	550	5.4	1
Simon	500	4.0	1
Barney	350	2.8	0.75
Teddy	650	6.2	1.25

Cost per adult: £28.50

Cost per child: £25.50

Chapter 9
Really Useful Maths!: The street

Roof area for one block of 5 bungalows	711 m²
Roof area of whole street	14,227 m²
Number of slates needed	247,552 slates
Total cost of slates	£59,412.48
Total weight of slates	594,124.8 kg

Chapter 10
Really Useful Maths!: Oil

Country	Oil produced, barrels per person per year	Oil consumed, barrels per person per year	Difference produced − consumed	Rank order production	Consumption as a % of production
Algeria	13.5	2.3	11.2	3	17%
Australia	9.8	14.5	−4.7	7	148%
Chile	0.4	5.5	−5.1	8	1297%
Indonesia	1.5	1.8	−0.3	6	122%
Japan	0.05	15.2	−15.15	10	30 525%
Nigeria	6.7	0.8	5.9	4	12%
Saudi Arabia	124.6	21.4	103.2	1	17%
UK	11.8	10.2	1.6	5	86%
USA	9.6	24.3	−14.7	9	252%
Venezuela	37.4	7.2	30.2	2	19%

Year	World population	World oil production, barrels per day	World oil production, barrels per person per day
1984	4.77×10^9	5.45×10^7	4.2
1989	5.19×10^9	5.99×10^7	4.2
1994	5.61×10^9	6.10×10^7	4.0
1999	6.01×10^9	6.58×10^7	4.0
2004	6.38×10^9	7.25×10^7	4.1

Chapter 11
Really Useful Maths!: Dairy farm

	3-month moving average for milk production in thousands of litres											
	Jan	Feb	Mar	Apr	May	Jun	Jul	Aug	Sep	Oct	Nov	Dec
2004		53	54.7	58.3	64	68.7	72.3	69.7	67.7	63.3	61.3	69.7
2005	61.7	63	64.7	67	74	78.7	83.3	80.7	78	72.7	70.3	

Comments on line graphs: Each year, January has the lowest production. It rises steadily towards July, then decreases again towards the following January. 2005 production is about 10,000 litres more per month than 2004.

Comments on Scatter graphs: Monthly sunshine/milk production: positive correlation. Monthly rainfall/milk production: negative correlation.

Chapter 12
Really Useful Maths!: Garden design

Perimeter of patio	56.55 m	Area of patio	254.47 m²
Perimeter of play area	45.13 m	Area of play area	130.27 m²
Perimeter of one flower bed	13.83 m	Area of one flower bed	7.5 m²
Dimensions of top pond	length = 4 m width = 2 m	Area of top pond	8 m²
Dimensions of second pond	length = 5 m width = 3 m	Area of second pond	15 m²
Dimensions of third pond	length = 6 m width = 4 m	Area of third pond	24 m²
Dimensions of bottom pond	length = 7 m width = 5 m	Area of bottom pond Area of lawn	35 m² 703.26 m²

Chapter 14
Really Useful Maths!: Bright ideas

Volume of stem	164.9 cm³	Length of x	7.5 cm
Weight of stem	1649 g	Length of L	9 cm
Volume of base	88.3 cm³	Length of L	27 cm
Weight of base	883 g	Surface area of small cone	141 cm²
Total weight	2532 g	Surface area of large cone	1272 cm²
		Surface area of lampshade	1131 cm²

$\theta = 200°$.
Total length of trim = 125.66 cm.

Chapter 18
Really Useful Maths!: Are we living longer?

Age distribution in the UK (numbers in millions)			
Age (a) in years	1976	2001	% change
$0 \leqslant a < 15$	12.9	11.1	−14%
$15 \leqslant a < 25$	8.1	7.2	−11%
$25 \leqslant a < 35$	7.9	8.4	6%
$35 \leqslant a < 45$	6.4	8.8	38%
$45 \leqslant a < 55$	9.8	7.8	−20%
$55 \leqslant a < 65$	3.1	6.2	100%
$65 \leqslant a < 75$	5.1	4.9	−4%
$75 \leqslant a < 85$	2.3	3.3	43%
$85 \leqslant a < 105$	0.5	1.1	120%

Midpoint of ages	1976 frequency (millions)	Midpoint × frequency	2001 frequency (millions)	Midpoint × frequency
7.5	12.9	96.75	11.1	83.25
20	8.1	162	7.2	144
30	7.9	237	8.4	252
40	6.4	256	8.8	352
50	9.8	490	7.8	390
60	3.1	186	6.2	372
70	5.1	357	4.9	343
80	2.3	184	3.3	264
95	0.5	47.5	1.1	104.5
Totals	56.1	2016.25	58.8	2304.75
Mean age		35.94		39.20

Cumulative frequencies for age distributions (in millions)									
	<15	<25	<35	<45	<55	<65	<75	<85	<105
1976	12.9	21	28.9	35.3	45.1	48.2	53.3	55.6	56.1
2001	11.1	18.3	26.7	35.5	43.3	49.5	54.4	57.7	58.8

	1976	2001
Mean	36	39
Median	34	38
Upper quartile	52	56
Lower quartile	16	20
IQR	36	36

The missing numbers from the article are:
2.7, $85 \leqslant a < 105$,
120, 20, $45 \leqslant a < 55$,
36, 39, 3, 34, 38, 4, 4

Chapter 20
Really Useful Maths!: Walking holiday

Day	Distance in km	Height climbed in metres	Time in minutes	Time in hours and minutes	Start time	Time allowed for breaks	Finish time
1	16	270	267	4 h 27 m	9:30 am	2 hours	3:57pm
2	20	210	321	5 h 21 m	9:00 am	$2\frac{3}{4}$ hours	5:06pm
3	15	80	233	3 h 53 m	10:00 am	$2\frac{1}{2}$ hours	4:23pm
4	17	210	276	4h 36 m	10:30 am	$2\frac{1}{4}$ hours	5:21pm
5	18	120	282	4 h 42 m	10:00 am	$2\frac{1}{2}$ hours	5:12pm
6	17	290	284	4 h 44 m	10:30 am	2 hours	5:14pm
7	22	90	339	5 h 39 m	10:00 am	$2\frac{3}{4}$ hours	6:24pm
8	12	300	210	3 h 30 m	10:30 am	$2\frac{1}{4}$ hours	4:15pm

Chapter 22
Really Useful Maths!: Windpower

Distance of turbine out to sea	Angle of elevation from shore
3 km	2.29°
4 km	1.72°
5 km	1.37°
6 km	1.15°
7 km	0.98°
8 km	0.86°

Wind speed (m/s)	Available power (W/m²)
6	132.34
7	210
8	313.47
9	446.33
10	612.24
11	814.90
12	1057.96

Wind speed (m/s)	Available power (W/m²)	Rotor area for 50 m blade (m²)	Power (MW)	Rotor area for 60 m blade (m²)	Power (MW)	Rotor area for 70 m blade (m²)	Power (MW)
7	210	7854	1.65	11310	2.38	15394	3.23
8	313.47	7854	2.46	11310	3.55	15394	4.83
9	446.33	7854	3.51	11310	5.05	15394	6.87
10	612.24	7854	4.81	11310	6.92	15394	9.42

Chapter 23
Really Useful Maths!: A new floor

Oak effect Room	Maximum floor area (m²)	Maximum edging needed (m)
Lounge	61.24	32.35
Sitting room	29.8275	21.25
Kitchen/diner	45.175	27.5
Conservatory	12.4425	11.95
Total:	148.685	93.05

Beech effect Room	Maximum floor area (m²)	Maximum edging needed (m)
Hall	15.8025	15.25
Bathroom	9.5875	11.65
Total:	25.39	26.9

The area of the lounge and kitchen/diner may be calculated in several ways.
Other possible answers are:

Lounge: 61.07 m² and 61.13 m²   Kitchen/Diner: 44.9675 m²
(if this alternative answer is given, total maximum floor area for oak effect becomes 148.4775 m², the numbers of packs of flooring required is unaffected)

Similarly, the edging required for the Kitchen/Diner could be calculated as 27.35 m (if this alternative answer is given, total maximum edging needed for oak effect becomes 92.9 m, numbers of packs required is unaffected)

	Number of packs	Price per pack	Total cost
Beech flooring	13	£56.40	£733.20
Beech edging	3	£21.15	£63.45
Oak flooring	75	£61.10	£4582.50
Oak edging	8	£25.85	£206.80
		Total:	£5585.95

Total price exclusive of VAT is: £4754.00

Quick check

1 a 3841 **b** 41 **c** 625

2 a any multiple of 7, e.g. 7, 14, 21, ..., 70...
  b 11, 13, 17 or 19
  c 1, 4, 9 ,16, 25 ,36 ,49 or 64
  d 1, 3, 9

3 a 17 **b** 25 **c** 5

Exercise 1A
1 a 6000
  b 5 cans cost £1.95, so 6 cans cost £1.95.
    32 = 5 × 6 + 2. cost is £10.53.
2 a 288 **b** 16
3 a 38
  b coach price for adults = £8, coach price for juniors = £4,
    money for coaches raised by tickets = £12 400, cost of
    coaches = £12 160, profit = £240
4 £68.70
5 (18.81...) Kirsty can buy 18 models.
6 (7.58...) Eunice must work for 8 weeks.
7 £8.40
8 £450

Exercise 1B
1 a 18 **b** 140 **c** 1.4 **d** 12 **e** 21.3
  f 6.9 **g** 2790 **h** 12.1 **i** 18.9
2 a 280 **b** 12 **c** 0.18 **d** 450 **e** 0.62
  f 380 **g** 0.26 **h** 240 **i** 12
3 750
4 300

Exercise 1C
1 a 50 000 **b** 60 000 **c** 30 000 **d** 90 000
  e 90 000 **f** 0.5 **g** 0.3 **h** 0.006
  i 0.05 **j** 0.0009 **k** 10 **l** 90
  m 90 **n** 200 **o** 1000
2 a 56 000 **b** 27 000 **c** 80 000 **d** 31 000
  e 14 000 **f** 1.7 **g** 4.1 **h** 2.7
  i 8.0 **j** 42 **k** 0.80 **l** 0.46
  m 0.066 **n** 1.0 **o** 0.0098
3 a 60 000 **b** 5300 **c** 89.7 **d** 110
  e 9 **f** 1.1 **g** 0.3 **h** 0.7
  i 0.4 **j** 0.8 **k** 0.2 **l** 0.7
4 a 65, 74 **b** 95, 149 **c** 950, 1499
5 Elsecar 750, 849, Hoyland 1150, 1249,
  Barnsley 164 500, 165 400

Exercise 1D
1 a 60 000 **b** 120 000 **c** 10 000 **d** 15 **e** 140
   f 100   **g** 200 **h** 0.028
  i 0.09 **j** 400 **k** 8000 **l** 0.16
  m 45 **n** 0.08 **o** 0.25
  p 4 000 000 **q** 360 000

2 a 5 **b** 50 **c** 25 **d** 600 **e** 3000
  f 5000 **g** 2000 **h** 2000 **i** 400 **j** 8000
k 4 000 000 **l** 3 200 000

Exercise 1E
The answers will depend on the approximations made. Your
answers should be to the same order as these.
1 a 35 000 **b** 15 000 **c** 960 **d** 5
  e 1200 **f** 500
2 a 39 700 **b** 17 000 **c** 933 **d** 4.44
  e 1130 **f** 550
3 a 4000 **b** 10 **c** 1 **d** 19 **e** 3 **f** 18
4 a 4190 **b** 8.79 **c** 1.01 **d** 20.7 **e** 3.07 **f** 18.5
5 a £3000 **b** £2000 **c** £1500 **d** £700
6 a £15 000 **b** £18 000 **c** £17 500
7 £20 000
8 8p
9 a 40 miles per hour **b** 10 gallons **c** £70
10 a 80 000 **b** 2000 **c** 1000 **d** 30 000
  e 5000 **f** 200 000 **g** 75 **h** 140
  i 100 **j** 3000
11 a 86 900 **b** 1760 **c** 1030 **d** 29 100
  e 3930 **f** 237 000 **g** 84.8 **h** 163
  i 96.9 **j** 2440
12 approx. 500
13 a i 27.57142857 **ii** 27.6
  b i 16.89651639 **ii** 16.9
  c i 704.4198895 **ii** 704

Exercise 1F
You may not have the same approximations. Can you justify
your answers?
1 a 1.74 m **b** 5 minutes **c** 240 g **d** 82°C
  e 35 000 people **f** 15 miles **g** 14 m^2
2 82°F, $5\frac{1}{2}$ km, 110 min, 43 000 people, 6.2 seconds, 67th,
  1788, 15 practice walks, 5 seconds
  The answers will depend on the approximations made.
  Your answers should be to the same order as these.
3 40
4 40 minutes
5 60 stamps
6 70 mph
7 270 fans
8 80 000 kg (80 tonnes)

Exercise 1G
1 a 12 **b** 9 **c** 6 **d** 13 **e** 15 **f** 14
  g 16 **h** 10 **i** 18 **j** 17 **k** 8 (or 16) **l** 21
2 4 packs of sausages and 5 packs of buns (or multiples of
  these)
3 24 seconds
4 30 seconds
5 1 + 3 + 5 + 7 + 9 = 25, 1 + 3 + 5 + 7 + 9 + 11 = 36, 1 +
  3 + 5 + 7 + 9 + 11 + 13 = 49,
  1 + 3 + 5 + 7 + 9 + 11 + 13 + 15 = 64

6 a −2   **b** −5   **c** −7   **d** −1   **e** −9
  f −11   **g** −12   **h** −20   **i** −30   **j** −13
7 a 1   **b** 3   **c** 4   **d** 2   **e** 10
  f −2   **g** −1   **h** 20   **i** 40   **j** −4
8 a 1, 3, 6, 10, 15, 21, 28, 36, 45, 55, 66, 78, 91, 105
  b Adding consecutive pairs gives you square numbers.
9 a 1, 64, 729, 4096, 15 625
  b 1, 8, 27, 64, 125
  c $\sqrt{a^3} = a \times \sqrt{a}$
  d square numbers
10 a 0.2   **b** 0.5   **c** 0.6   **d** 0.9   **e** 1.2
  f 0.8   **g** 1.1   **h** 1.5
11 The answers will depend on the approximations made.
  Your answers should be to the same order as these.
  a 60   **b** 1500   **c** 180

Exercise 1H

1 a $84 = 2 \times 2 \times 3 \times 7$ **b** $100 = 2 \times 2 \times 5 \times 5$
  c $180 = 2 \times 2 \times 3 \times 3 \times 5$
  d $220 = 2 \times 2 \times 5 \times 11$
  e $280 = 2 \times 2 \times 2 \times 5 \times 7$
  f $128 = 2 \times 2 \times 2 \times 2 \times 2 \times 2 \times 2$
  g $50 = 2 \times 5 \times 5$
2 a $84 = 2^2 \times 3 \times 7$ **b** $100 = 2^2 \times 5^2$
  c $180 = 2^2 \times 3^2 \times 5$ **d** $220 = 2^2 \times 5 \times 11$
  e $280 = 2^3 \times 5 \times 7$ **f** $128 = 2^7$
  g $50 = 2 \times 5^2$ **h** $1000 = 2^3 \times 5^3$
  i $576 = 2^6 \times 3^2$ **j** $650 = 2 \times 5^2 \times 13$
3 1, 2, 3, 2^2, 5, 2×3, 7, 2^3, 3^2, 2×5, 11, $2^2 \times 3$, 13, 2×7,
  3×5, 2^4, 17, 2×3^2, 19, $2^2 \times 5$, 3×7, 2×11, 23, $2^3 \times 3$,
  5^2, 2×13, 3^3, $2^2 \times 7$, 29, $2 \times 3 \times 5$, 31, 2^5, 3×11, $2 \times$
  17, 5×7, $2^2 \times 3^2$, 37, 2×19, 3×13, $2^3 \times 5$, 41, $2 \times 3 \times$
  7, 43, $2^2 \times 11$, $3^3 \times 5$, 2×23, 47, $2^4 \times 3$, 7^2, 2×5^2
4 a Double each time
  b 64, 128
  c 81, 243
  d 256, 1024, 4096
  e 3, 3^2, 3^3, 3^4, 3^5, 3^6, 4, 4^2, 4^3, 4^4, 4^5

Exercise 1I

1 a 20   **b** 56   **c** 6   **d** 28   **e** 10   **f** 15
  g 24   **h** 30
2 They are the two numbers multiplied together.
3 a 8   **b** 18   **c** 12   **d** 30
4 No. The numbers have a common factor. Multiplying them
  together would mean using this factor twice, thus
  increasing the size of the common multiple. It would not
  be the lowest common multiple.
5 a 168   **b** 105   **c** 84   **d** 168   **e** 48
  f 54   **g** 75   **h** 144
6 a 8   **b** 7   **c** 4   **d** 14   **e** 12   **f** 9
  g 5   **h** 4   **i** 3   **j** 16   **k** 5   **l** 18
7 a ii and iii   **b** iii

Exercise 1J

1 a −15   **b** −14   **c** −24   **d** 6   **e** 14
  f 2   **g** −2   **h** −8   **i** −4   **j** 3
  k −24   **l** −10   **m** −18   **n** 16   **o** 36
2 a −9   **b** 16   **c** −3   **d** −32   **e** 18
  f 18   **g** 6   **h** −4   **i** 20   **j** 16
  k 8   **l** −48   **m** 13   **n** −13   **o** −8
3 a −2   **b** 30   **c** 15   **d** −27   **e** −7
4 a −9   **b** 3   **c** 1
5 a 16   **b** −2   **c** −12
6 Any appropriate divisions.

Exercise 1K

1 a −4   **b** −6   **c** 4   **d** 45   **e** 6   **f** 6
2 a 38   **b** 24   **c** −3   **d** −6   **e** −1   **f** 2
  g −25   **h** 25   **i** 0   **j** −20   **k** 4   **l** 0
3 a $(3 \times -4) + 1 = -11$ **b** $-6 \div (-2 + 1) = 6$
  c $(-6 \div -2) + 1 = 4$ **d** $4 + (-4 \div 4) = 3$
  e $(4 + -4) \div 4 = 0$ **f** $(16 - -4) \div 2 = 10$
4 a 49   **b** −1   **c** −5   **d** −12

ANSWERS TO CHAPTER 2

Quick check

1 a $\frac{2}{5}$ **b** $\frac{3}{8}$ **c** $\frac{3}{7}$

2

Fraction	Percentage	Decimal
$\frac{3}{4}$	75%	0.75
$\frac{2}{5}$	40%	0.4
$\frac{11}{20}$	55%	0.55

3 a £23   **b** £4.60   **c** 23p

Exercise 2A

1 a $\frac{1}{3}$ **b** $\frac{1}{5}$ **c** $\frac{2}{5}$ **d** $\frac{5}{24}$ **e** $\frac{2}{5}$ **f** $\frac{1}{6}$ **g** $\frac{2}{7}$ **h** $\frac{1}{3}$
2 $\frac{3}{5}$ **3** $\frac{12}{31}$ **4** $\frac{7}{12}$
5 $\frac{1}{8}$ **6** $\frac{5}{12}$ **7** $\frac{1}{5}$
8 $\frac{3}{20}$

Exercise 2B

1 a $\frac{8}{15}$ **b** $\frac{7}{12}$ **c** $\frac{3}{10}$ **d** $\frac{11}{12}$ **e** $\frac{1}{10}$ **f** $\frac{1}{8}$
  g $\frac{1}{12}$ **h** $\frac{1}{3}$
2 a $\frac{7}{9}$ **b** $\frac{5}{8}$ **c** $\frac{3}{8}$ **d** $\frac{1}{15}$ **e** $3\frac{31}{45}$ **f** $4\frac{47}{60}$
  g $\frac{41}{72}$ **h** $\frac{29}{48}$ **i** $1\frac{43}{48}$ **j** $1\frac{109}{120}$ **k** $1\frac{23}{30}$ **l** $1\frac{31}{84}$

3 $\frac{1}{20}$　　　　　　　　　**4** $\frac{1}{6}$
5 $\frac{1}{3}$　　　　　　　　　**6** 260
7 three-quarters of 68　　　**8** £51
9 10 minutes

Exercise 2C
1 a $\frac{1}{6}$　**b** $\frac{1}{10}$　**c** $\frac{3}{8}$　**d** $\frac{3}{14}$　**e** $\frac{7}{20}$　**f** $\frac{16}{45}$
　g $\frac{3}{5}$　**h** $\frac{5}{8}$
2 a $\frac{5}{12}$　**b** $2\frac{1}{12}$　**c** $6\frac{1}{4}$　**d** $2\frac{11}{12}$　**e** $3\frac{9}{10}$
　f $3\frac{1}{3}$　**g** $12\frac{1}{2}$　**h** 30
3 21 tonnes　　　　　　**4** $\frac{3}{8}$
5 $\frac{3}{8}$　　　　　　　　**6** $\frac{2}{5}$ of $6\frac{1}{2}$
7 £5　　　　　　　　　**8** £10.40

Exercise 2D
1 a $\frac{3}{4}$　**b** $1\frac{2}{5}$　**c** $1\frac{1}{15}$　**d** $1\frac{1}{14}$　**e** 4　**f** 4
　g 5　**h** $1\frac{5}{7}$　**i** $\frac{4}{9}$　**j** $1\frac{3}{5}$
2 40
3 15
4 16
5 a $2\frac{2}{15}$　**b** 38　**c** $1\frac{7}{8}$　**d** $\frac{9}{32}$　**e** $\frac{1}{16}$　**f** $\frac{256}{625}$

Exercise 2E
1 a 1.1　**b** 1.03　**c** 1.2　**d** 1.07　**e** 1.12
2 a £62.40　　**b** 12.96 kg　**c** 472.5 g
　d 599.5 m　**e** £38.08　　**f** £90
　g 391 kg　　**h** 824.1 cm　**i** 253.5 g
　j £143.50　**k** 736 m　　**l** £30.24
3 1 690 200
4 Bob £17 325, Jean £20 475, Anne £18 165, Brian £26 565
5 575 g
6 60 girls
7 £287.88, £84.60, £135.13, £34.66
8 £540.96
9 Calculate the VAT on certain amounts, and $\frac{1}{6}$ of that amount. Show the error grows as the amount increases. After £600 the error is greater than £5, so the method works to within £5 with prices up to £600.

Exercise 2F
1 a 0.92　**b** 0.85　**c** 0.75　**d** 0.91　**e** 0.88
2 a £9.40　　**b** 23 kg　**c** 212.4 g　**d** 339.5 m
　e £4.90　　**f** 39.6 m　**g** 731 m　　**h** 83.52 g
　i 360 cm
3 £5525　　　　　　**4** 448 people

5 705 pupils　　　　　**6** £18 975
7 a 66.5 mph　**b** 73.5 mph
8 £39.60　　　　　　**9** 524.8 units
10 £765　　　　　　**11** 1.10 × 0.9 = 0.99 (99%)

Exercise 2G
1 a 25%　**b** 60.6%　**c** 46.3%　**d** 12.5%
　e 41.7%　**f** 60%　　**g** 20.8%　**h** 10%
　i 1.9%　**j** 8.3%　　**k** 45.5%　**l** 10.5%
2 32%　　　　**3** 6.49%　　　　**4** 33.7%
5 a 49.2%　**b** 64.5%　**c** 10.6%
6 17.9%　　　**7** 7.4%　　　　**8** 90.5%
9 a Commonwealth 20.9%, USA 26.5%, France 10.3%, Other 42.3%
　b 100%, because this is all imports.

Exercise 2H
1 a i 10.5 kg　**ii** 11.03 kg　**iii** 12.16 kg　**iv** 14.07 kg
　b 9 days
2 12 years　**3 a** £14272.27　**b** 20 years
4 a i 2550　**ii** 2168　**iii** 1331　**b** 7 years
5 a £6800　**b** £5440　**c** £3481.60
6 a i 1.9 million litres　**ii** 1.6 million litres
　iii 1.2 million litres
　b 10th August
7 a i 51 980　**ii** 84 752　**iii** 138 186
　b 2010
8 a 21 years　**b** 21 years
9 3 years　　**10** 30 years
11 1.1 × 1.1 = 1.21 (21% increase)

Exercise 2I
1 a 800 g　**b** 250 m　**c** 60 cm　**d** £3075
　e £200　**f** £400
2 80
3 T shirt £8.40, Tights £1.20, Shorts £5.20, Sweater £10.74, Trainers £24.80, Boots £32.40
4 £833.33
5 £300
6 240
7 £350
8 4750 blue bottles
9 £22
10 less by $\frac{1}{4}$%
11 Calculate the pre-VAT price for certain amounts, and $\frac{5}{6}$ of that amount. Show the error grows as the amount increases. Up to £280 the error is less than £5.

ANSWERS TO CHAPTER 3

Quick check
1 a $\frac{3}{5}$　**b** $\frac{1}{5}$　**c** $\frac{1}{3}$　**d** $\frac{16}{25}$　**e** $\frac{2}{5}$　**f** $\frac{3}{4}$　**g** $\frac{1}{3}$
2 a £12　**b** £33　**c** 175 litres　**d** 15 kg
　e 40 m　**f** £35　**g** 135 g　**h** 1.05 litres

Exercise 3A
1 $\frac{7}{10}$　　　　　　　　**2** $\frac{2}{5}$
3 a $\frac{2}{5}$　**b** $\frac{3}{5}$　　　　**4 a** $\frac{7}{10}$　**b** $\frac{3}{10}$
5 a $\frac{2}{9}$　**b** $\frac{1}{3}$　**c** $\frac{2}{9}$
6 sugar $\frac{5}{22}$, flour $\frac{3}{11}$, margarine $\frac{2}{11}$, fruit $\frac{7}{22}$

Exercise 3B

1 a 160 g : 240 g   **b** 80 kg : 200 kg
   c 150 : 350   **d** 950 m : 50 m
   e 175 min : 125 min   **f** £20 : £30 : £50
   g £36 : £60 : £144   **h** 50 g : 250 g : 300 g
2 a 160   **b** 37.5%
3 a 28.6%   **b** 250 kg
4 a 21 horses   **b** 94% (2 sf)
5 a 1 : 400 000   **b** 1 : 125 000   **c** 1 : 250 000
   d 1 : 25 000   **e** 1 : 20 000   **f** 1 : 40 000
6 a 1 : 1 000 000   **b** 47 km   **c** 0.8 cm
7 a 1 : 250 000   **b** 2 km   **c** 4.8 cm
8 a 1 : 1.6   **b** 1 : 3.25   **c** 1 : 1.125
   d 1 : 1.44   **e** 1 : 5.4   **f** 1 : 1.5
   g 1 : 4.8   **h** 1 : 42   **i** 1 : 1.25

Exercise 3C

1 a 3 : 2   **b** 32   **c** 80
2 a 100   **b** 160
3 1000 g Assam tea   **4** 10 125 people
5 5.5 l of tea   **6 a** 11 pages   **b** 32%
7 Kevin £2040, John £2720
8 20 l lemonade, 0.5 l ginger
9 a 14% (2sf)   **b** 75 good apples

Exercise 3D

1 18 mph   **2** 52.5 mph   **3** 11:50 am

4

	Distance	Time	Av speed
a	150 miles	2 hr	75 mph
b	260 miles	6 hr 30 min	40 mph
c	175 miles	5 hr	35 mph
d	240 km	3 hr	80 km/h
e	544 km	8 hr 30 min	64 km/h
f	325 km	3 hr 15 min	100 km/h
g	215 km	4 hr 18 min	50 km/h

5 a 120 km   **b** 48 km/h
6 a 30 min   **b** 6 mph
7 a 2.25 h   **b** 99 miles
8 a 1.25 h   **b** 1 h 15 min
9 a 48 mph   **b** 6 h 40 min

10 a 10 m/s   **b** $3\frac{1}{3}$ m/s   **c** $16\frac{2}{3}$ m/s
   d $41\frac{2}{3}$ m/s   **e** $20\frac{5}{6}$ m/s
11 a 90 km/h   **b** 43.2 km/h   **c** 14.4 km/h
   d 108 km/h   **e** 1.8 km/h
12 a 64.8 km/h   **b** 27.8 sec (1dp)
   c 8:07 (nearest minute)

Exercise 3E

1 60 g
2 £5.22
3 45 trees
4 a £312.50   **b** 8 textbooks
5 a 56 l   **b** 350 miles
6 a 300 kg   **b** 9 weeks
7 40 sec

Exercise 3F

1 a large jar as more g per £
   b 600 g tin as more g per p
   c 5 kg bag as more kg per £
   d 75 ml tube as more ml per £
   e large box as more g per £
   f large box as more g per £
   g 400 ml bottle as more ml per £
2 large tin (small £5.11/l, medium £4.80/l, large £4.47/l)
3 a 95p   **b** Family size
4 Bashir's
5 Mary
6 Kelly

Exercise 3G

1 a 0.75 g/cm^3
2 $8\frac{1}{3}$ g/cm^3
3 32 g
4 120 cm^3
5 156.8 g
6 3200 cm^3
7 2.72 g/cm^3
8 36 800 kg
9 1.79 g/cm^3 (3 sf)
10 1.6 g/cm^3

ANSWERS TO CHAPTER 4

Quick check

1 a 90 mm^2 **b** 40 cm^2 **c** 21 m^2

2 120 cm^3

Exercise 4A

1 a 8 cm, 25.1 cm, 50.3 cm^2 **b** 5.2 m, 16.3 m, 21.2 m^2
   c 6 cm, 37.7 cm, 113 cm^2 **d** 1.6 m, 10.1 m, 8.04 m^2
2 a 5π cm   **b** 8π cm   **c** 18π m   **d** 12π cm
3 a 25π cm^2 **b** 36π cm^2 **c** 100π cm^2 **d** 0.25π m^2
4 8.80 m

5 a 440 cm   **b** 4
6 1p : 3.1 cm^2, 2p : 5.3 cm^2, 5p : 2.3 cm^2, 10p : 4.5 cm^2
7 7.96 cm
8 38.6 cm
9 (14π + 14) cm
10 a 18π cm^2 **b** 4π cm^2 **c** 48π cm^2
11 a 16π m^2 **b** 21π cm^2 **c** 9π cm^2
12 a Sue 62.8 cm, Julie 69.1 cm, Dave 75.4 cm, Brian 81.7 cm
   b the difference between the distances round the waists of two people is 2π times the difference between their radii
   c 6.28 m

Exercise 4B
1 **a** 30 cm²   **b** 77 cm²   **c** 24 cm²   **d** 42 cm²
  e 40 m²   **f** 6 cm   **g** 3 cm   **h** 10 cm
2 **a** 27.5 cm, 36.25 cm²   **b** 33.4 cm, 61.2 cm²
  c 38.5 m, 90 m²
3 **a** 57 m²   **b** 702.5 cm²   **c** 84 m²
4 **a** 47 m²   **b** 51 m²   **c** 86 m²
5 Any five pairs of lengths that add up to 10 cm.
  For example: 1 cm, 9 cm; 2 cm, 8 cm; 3 cm, 7 cm; 4
  cm, 6 cm; 4.5 cm, 5.5 cm
6 80.2%   7 1 100 000 km²

Exercise 4C
1 **a i** 5.59 cm   **ii** 22.3 cm²
  b i 8.29 cm   **ii** 20.7 cm²
  c i 16.3 cm   **ii** 98.0 cm²
  d i 15.9 cm   **ii** 55.6 cm²
2 2π cm, 6π cm²
3 **a** 73.8 cm   **b** 20.3 cm
4 **a** 107 cm²   **b** 173 cm²   **c** 18.8 cm²   **d** 34.9 cm²
5 (36π − 72) cm²   6 36.5 cm²   7 6π cm
8 **i** 13.9 cm   **ii** 7.07 cm²

Exercise 4D
1 **i**   **a**   **b**   **c**

  ii **a** 21 cm²   **b** 48 cm²   **c** 36 m²
  iii **a** 63 cm³   **b** 432 cm³   **c** 324 m³
2 **a** 432 m³   **b** 225 m³   **c** 1332 m³
3 525 000 litres   4 7650 litres
5 **a** 21 cm³, 210 cm³   **b** 54 cm², 270 cm²
6 146 cm³   7 19 600 m³
8 327 litres   9 1.02 tonnes

Exercise 4E
1 **a i** 226 cm³   **ii** 207 cm²
  b i 14.9 cm³   **ii** 61.3 cm²
  c i 346 cm³   **ii** 275 cm²
  d i 1060 cm³   **ii** 636 cm²

2 **a i** 72π cm³   **ii** 48π cm²
  b i 112π cm³   **ii** 56π cm²
  c i 180π cm³   **ii** 60π cm²
  d i 600π m³   **ii** 120π m²
3 £80   4 1.23 tonnes
5 5 cm   6 10 cm
7 3 cm   8 332 litres
9 1.71 g/cm³   10 7.78 g/cm³
11 905 g

Exercise 4F
1 **a** 56 cm³   **b** 168 cm³   **c** 1040 cm³
  d 84 cm³   **e** 160 cm³
2 270 cm³
3 **a** 73.3 m³   **b** 45 m³   **c** 3250 cm³
4 208 g
5 1.5 g/cm³
6 **a** 202 g   **b** 441 g   **c** 47.25 g
7 **a** 9 cm   **b** 6 cm
8 260 cm³

Exercise 4G
1 **a i** 3560 cm³   **ii** 1430 cm²
  b i 314 cm³   **ii** 283 cm²
  c i 1020 cm³   **ii** 679 cm²
2 935 g
3 24π cm²
4 283 cm²
5 **a** 816π cm³   **b** 720π mm³
6 140 g
7 2.81 cm

Exercise 4H
1 **a** 36π cm³   **b** 288π cm³   **c** 1330π cm³
2 **a** 36π cm²   **b** 100π cm²   **c** 196π cm²
3 65 400 cm³, 7850 cm²
4 **i** 1960 cm²   **ii** 8180 cm³
5 125 cm
6 6231
7 **a** 3.5 cm   **b** 3.3 cm

ANSWERS TO CHAPTER 5

Quick check

1 **a** 2x + 12   **b** 4x − 12   **c** 12x − 6

2 **a** 5y   **b** 4x − 3   **c** −x − 4

3 **a** 6x   **b** 8y²   **c** 2c³

4 **a** x = 1   **b** x = 3   **c** x = 9
  d x = 8   **e** x = 24   **f** x = 15

Exercise 5A
1 **a** 13   **b** −3   **c** 5
2 **a** 2   **b** 8   **c** −10
3 **a** 6   **b** 3   **c** −2
4 **a** −7   **b** −10   **c** 6.5
5 **a** −4.8   **b** 48   **c** 32
6 **a** 1.4   **b** 1.4   **c** −0.4
7 **a** 13   **b** 74   **c** 17
8 **a** 75   **b** 22.5   **c** −135
9 **a** 2.5   **b** −20   **c** 2.5

Exercise 5B

1 $6 + 2m$	**2** $10 + 5l$	**3** $12 - 3y$
4 $20 + 8k$	**5** $6 - 12f$	**6** $10 - 6w$
7 $10k + 15m$	**8** $12d - 8n$	**9** $t^2 + 3t$
10 $k^2 - 3k$	**11** $4t^2 - 4t$	**12** $8k - 2k^2$
13 $8g^2 + 20g$	**14** $15h^2 - 10h$	**15** $y^3 + 5y$
16 $h^4 + 7h$	**17** $k^3 - 5k$	**18** $3t^3 + 12t$
19 $15d^3 - 3d^4$	**20** $6w^3 + 3wt$	**21** $15a^3 - 10ab$
22 $12p^4 - 15mp$	**23** $12h^3 + 8h^2g$	**24** $8m^3 + 2m^4$

Exercise 5C

1 a $7t$ **b** $9d$ **c** $3e$ **d** $2t$ **e** $5t^2$
  f $4y^2$ **g** $5ab$ **h** $3a^2d$

2 a $22 + 5t$ **b** $21 + 19k$
  c $22 + 2f$ **d** $14 + 3g$

3 a $2 + 2h$ **b** $9g + 5$
  c $17k + 16$ **d** $6e + 20$

4 a $4m + 3p + 2mp$ **b** $3k + 4h + 5hk$
  c $12r + 24p + 13pr$ **d** $19km + 20k - 6m$

5 a $9t^2 + 13t$ **b** $13y^2 + 5y$
  c $10e^2 - 6e$ **d** $14k^2 - 3kp$

6 a $17ab + 12ac + 6bc$ **b** $18yw + 6yt - 8wt$
  c $14mn - 15mp - 6np$ **d** $8r^3 - 6r^2$

Exercise 5D

1 $6(m + 2t)$	**2** $3(3t + p)$	**3** $4(2m + 3k)$
4 $4(r + 2t)$	**5** $m(n + 3)$	**6** $g(5g + 3)$
7 $2(2w - 3t)$	**8** $y(3y + 2)$	**9** $t(4t - 3)$
10 $3m(m - p)$	**11** $3p(2p + 3t)$	**12** $2p(4t + 3m)$
13 $4b(2a - c)$	**14** $5bc(b - 2)$	**15** $2b(4ac + 3ed)$
16 $2(2a^2 + 3a + 4)$		**17** $3b(2a + 3c + d)$
18 $t(5t + 4 + a)$		**19** $3mt(2t - 1 + 3m)$
20 $2ab(4b + 1 - 2a)$		**21** $5pt(2t + 3 + p)$

22 a, **d**, **f** and **h** do not factorise   **b** $m(5 + 2p)$
  c $t(t - 7)$ **e** $2m(2m - 3p)$ **g** $a(4a - 5b)$ **i** $b(5a - 3bc)$

Exercise 5E

1 30	**2** 21	**3** 72	**4** 12	**5** 6
6 $10\frac{1}{2}$	**7** -10	**8** 7	**9** 11	**10** -4
11 7	**12** $2\frac{4}{5}$	**13** 1	**14** $11\frac{1}{2}$	**15** $\frac{1}{5}$

Exercise 5F

1 3	**2** 7	**3** 5	**4** 3	**5** 4
6 6	**7** 8	**8** 1	**9** $1\frac{1}{2}$	**10** $2\frac{1}{2}$
11 $\frac{1}{2}$	**12** $1\frac{1}{5}$	**13** 2	**14** -2	**15** -1
16 -2	**17** -2	**18** -1		

Exercise 5G

1 $x = 2$	**2** $y = 1$	**3** $a = 7$	**4** $t = 4$
5 $p = 2$	**6** $k = -1$	**7** $m = 3$	**8** $s = -2$
9 $d = 6$	**10** $x = 11$	**11** $y = 1$	**12** $h = 4$
13 $b = 9$	**14** $c = 6$		

Exercise 5H

1 55p   **2 a** $1\frac{1}{2}$ **b** 2   **3 a** $1\frac{1}{2}$ cm   **b** 6.75 cm^2
4 17 sweets   **5** 3 years old   **6** 9 years old
7 3 cm   **8** 5

Exercise 5I

1 a 4 and 5   **b** 4 and 5   **c** 2 and 3
2 3.5   **3** 3.7   **4** 2.5   **5** 1.5 (or -2)
6 a 2.4   **b** 2.8   **c** 3.2
7 b 7.8 cm by 12.8 cm   **8** 5 (or -6)

Exercise 5J

1 $x = 4, y = 1$ **2** $x = 1, y = 4$ **3** $x = 3, y = 1$
4 $x = 5, y = -2$ **5** $x = 7, y = 1$ **6** $x = 5, y = \frac{1}{2}$
7 $x = 4\frac{1}{2}, y = 1\frac{1}{2}$ **8** $x = -2, y = 4$ **9** $x = 2\frac{1}{2}, y = -1\frac{1}{2}$
10 $x = 2\frac{1}{4}, y = 6\frac{1}{2}$ **11** $x = 4, y = 3$ **12** $x = 5, y = 3$

Exercise 5K

1 $x = 2, y = -3$ **2** $x = 7, y = 3$ **3** $x = 4, y = 1$
4 $x = 2, y = 5$ **5** $x = 4, y = -3$ **6** $x = 1, y = 7$
7 $x = 2\frac{1}{2}, y = 1\frac{1}{2}$ **8** $x = -1, y = 2\frac{1}{2}$ **9** $x = 6, y = 3$
10 $x = \frac{1}{2}, y = -\frac{3}{4}$ **11** $x = -1, y = 5$ **12** $x = 1\frac{1}{2}, y = \frac{3}{4}$

Exercise 5L

1 $x = 5, y = 1$ **2** $x = 3, y = 8$ **3** $x = 9, y = 1$
4 $x = 7, y = 3$ **5** $x = 4, y = 2$ **6** $x = 6, y = 5$
7 $x = 3, y = -2$ **8** $x = 2, y = \frac{1}{2}$ **9** $x = -2, y = -3$
10 $x = -1, y = 2\frac{1}{2}$ **11** $x = 2\frac{1}{2}, y = -\frac{1}{2}$ **12** $x = -1\frac{1}{2}, y = 4\frac{1}{2}$
13 $x = -\frac{1}{2}, y = -6\frac{1}{2}$ **14** $x = 3\frac{1}{2}, y = 1\frac{1}{2}$ **15** $x = -2\frac{1}{2}, y = -3\frac{1}{2}$

Exercise 5M

1 Amul £7.20, Kim £3.50
2 a $10x + 5y = 3.45, 8x + 10y = 4.38$ **b** £1.71
3 a $6x + 3y = 4.35, 11x + 7y = 8.80$ **b** £5.55
4 84p   **5** 10.3 kg   **6** £4.40
7 £62   **8** £195   **9** 2 hr 10 min

Exercise 5N

1 $k = \dfrac{T}{3}$ **2** $y = X + 1$ **3** $p = 3Q$

4 $r = \dfrac{A - 9}{4}$ **5** $n = \dfrac{W + 1}{3}$

6 a $m = p - t$ **b** $t = p - m$ **7** $m = gv$

8 $m = \sqrt{t}$ **9** $r = \dfrac{C}{2\pi}$ **10** $b = \dfrac{A}{h}$

11 $l = \dfrac{P - 2w}{2}$ **12** $p = \sqrt{m - 2}$

13 a $a = \dfrac{v - u}{t}$ **b** $t = \dfrac{v - u}{a}$ **14** $d = \sqrt{\dfrac{4A}{\pi}}$

15 a $n = \dfrac{W - t}{3}$ **b** $t = W - 3n$

16 a $y = \dfrac{x + w}{5}$ **b** $w = 5y - x$ **17** $p = \sqrt{\dfrac{k}{2}}$

18 a $t = u^2 - v$ **b** $u = \sqrt{v + t}$

19 a $m = k - n^2$ **b** $n = \sqrt{k - m}$ **20** $r = \sqrt{\dfrac{T}{5}}$

21 a $w = K - 5n^2$ **b** $n = \sqrt{\dfrac{K - w}{5}}$

Quick check

1 5.3   **2** 246.5

3 0.6   **4** 2.8

5 16.1   **6** 0.7

Exercise 6A

1 10.3 cm   **2** 5.9 cm

3 8.5 cm   **4** 20.6 cm

5 18.6 cm   **6** 17.5 cm

7 5 cm   **8** 13 cm

9 10 cm

Exercise 6B

1 a 15 cm   **b** 14.7 cm   **c** 6.3 cm   **d** 18.3 cm

2 a 20.8 m   **b** 15.5 cm   **c** 15.5 m   **d** 12.4 cm

3 a 5 m   **b** 6 m   **c** 3 m   **d** 50 cm

Exercise 6C

1 6.63 m   **2** 2.06 m

3 11.3 m   **4** 19.2 km

5 a 127 m   **b** 99.6 m   **c** 27.4 m

6 4.58 m

7 a 3.87 m   **b** 1.74 m

8 3.16 m   **9** 13 units

10 a 4.74 m   **b** 4.54 m

11 16.5 cm^2 **12** 12.1 m

13 $25^2 = 24^2 + 7^2$: therefore, right-angled

14 7.21 units

Exercise 6D

1 a 32.2 cm^2 **b** 2.83 cm^2 **c** 50.0 cm^2

2 22.2 cm^2

3 15.6 cm^2

4 a

b The areas are 12 cm^2 and 13.6 cm^2 respectively, so triangle with 6 cm, 6 cm, 5 cm sides has the greater area

5 a   **b** 166.3 cm^2

6 259.8 cm^2

7 a 10 cm   **b** 26 cm   **c** 9.6 cm

Exercise 6E

1 a i 14.4 cm   **ii** 13 cm   **iii** 9.4 cm   **b** 15.2 cm

2 No, 6.6 m is longest length

3 a 24 cm and 20.6 cm   **b** 15.0 cm

4 21.3 cm

5 a 8.49 m   **b** 9 m

6 a 11.3 cm   **b** 7 cm   **c** 8.06 cm

7 a 50.0 cm   **b** 54.8 cm   **c** 48.3 cm   **d** 27.0 cm

Exercise 6F

1 a 0.682   **b** 0.829   **c** 0.922   **d** 1   **e** 0.707

    f 0.342   **g** 0.375   **h** 0

2 a 0.731   **b** 0.559   **c** 0.388   **d** 0   **e** 0.707

    f 0.940   **g** 0.927   **h** 1

3 45°

4 a i 0.574   **ii** 0.574   **b i** 0.208   **ii** 0.208

   c i 0.391   **ii** 0.391   **d** Same

   e i sin 15° is the same as cos 75°

     ii cos 82° is the same as sin 8°

     iii sin x is the same as cos $(90° - x)$

5 a 0.933   **b** 1.48   **c** 2.38   **d** Infinite   **e** 1

    f 0.364   **g** 0.404   **h** 0

6 a 0.956   **b** 0.899   **c** 2.16   **d** 0.999

    e 0.819   **f** 0.577   **g** 0.469   **h** 0.996

7 Has values > 1

8 a 4.53   **b** 4.46   **c** 6   **d** 0

9 a 10.7   **b** 5.40   **c** Infinite   **d** 0

10 a 3.56   **b** 8.96   **c** 28.4   **d** 8.91

11 a 5.61   **b** 7.08   **c** 6   **d** 10

12 a 1.46   **b** 7.77   **c** 0.087   **d** 7.15

13 a 7.73   **b** 48.6   **c** 2.28   **d** 15.2

14 a 29.9   **b** 44.8   **c** 20.3   **d** 2.38

15 a $\frac{4}{5}, \frac{3}{5}, \frac{4}{3}$ **b** $\frac{5}{13}, \frac{12}{13}, \frac{5}{12}$ **c** $\frac{7}{25}, \frac{24}{25}, \frac{7}{24}$

Exercise 6G

1 a 30°   **b** 51.7°   **c** 39.8°   **d** 61.3°

    e 87.4°   **f** 45.0°

2 a 60°   **b** 50.2°   **c** 2.6°   **d** 45.0

    e 78.5°   **f** 45.6°

3 a 31.0°   **b** 20.8°   **c** 41.8°   **d** 46.4°

    e 69.5°   **f** 77.1°

4 a 53.1°   **b** 41.8°   **c** 44.4°   **d** 56.4°

    e 2.4°   **f** 22.6°

5 a 36.9°   **b** 48.2°   **c** 45.6°   **d** 33.6°

    e 87.6°   **f** 67.4°

6 a 31.0°   **b** 37.9°   **c** 15.9°   **d** 60.9°

    e 57.5°   **f** 50.2°

7 Error message, largest value 1, smallest value −1

8 a i 17.5°   **ii** 72.5°   **iii** 90°   **b** Yes

Exercise 6H

1 a 17.5°   **b** 22.0°   **c** 32.2°

2 a 5.29 cm   **b** 5.75 cm   **c** 13.2 cm

3 a 4.57 cm   **b** 6.86 cm   **c** 100 cm

4 a 5.12 cm   **b** 9.77 cm   **c** 11.7 cm   **d** 15.5 cm

5 a 47.2°   **b** 5.42 cm   **c** 13.7 cm   **d** 38.0°

6 a 6   **b** 15   **c** 30

Exercise 6I

1 a 51.3°   **b** 75.5°   **c** 51.3°

2 a 6.47 cm   **b** 32.6 cm   **c** 137 cm

3 a 7.32 cm   **b** 39.1 cm   **c** 135 cm

4 a 5.35 cm **b** 14.8 cm **c** 12.0 cm **d** 8.62 cm
5 a 5.59 cm **b** 46.6° **c** 9.91 cm **d** 40.1°
6 a 10 **b** 39 **c** 2.5

Exercise 6J
1 a 33.7° **b** 36.9° **c** 52.1°
2 a 5.09 cm **b** 30.4 cm **c** 1120 cm
3 a 8.24 cm **b** 62.0 cm **c** 72.8 cm
4 a 9.02 cm **b** 7.51 cm **c** 7.14 cm **d** 8.90 cm
5 a 13.7 cm **b** 48.4° **c** 7.03 cm **d** 41.2°
6 12, 12, 2

Exercise 6K
1 a 12.6 **b** 59.6 **c** 74.7 **d** 16.0 **e** 67.9 **f** 20.1
2 a 44.4° **b** 39.8° **c** 44.4° **d** 49.5°
  e 58.7° **f** 38.7°
3 a 67.4° **b** 11.3 **c** 134 **d** 28.1° **e** 39.7
  f 263 **g** 50.2° **h** 51.3° **i** 138 **j** 22.8
4 b $\sin\theta \div \cos\theta = \frac{b}{c} \div \frac{a}{c} = \frac{b}{a} = \tan\theta$

Exercise 6L
1 a 65° **2** 2.05–3.00 m
3 44° **4** 6.82 m

5 31° **6 a** 25° **b** 2.10 m
7 a 20° **b** 4.78 m **8** 42.4 m
9 21.1 m **10 a** 4 **b** $\frac{4}{5}, \frac{3}{4}$ **c i** 1.5 **ii** 20 **iii** 30

Exercise 6M
1 10.1 km **2** 22°
3 429 m **4** 156 m
5 a 222 m **b** 42° **6 a** 21.5 m **b** 17.8 m
7 13.4 m **8** 19°

Exercise 6N
1 a 73.4 km **b** 15.6 km
2 a 14.7 miles **b** 8.5 miles
3 120° **4 a** 59.4 km **b** 8.4 km
5 a 15.9 km **b** 24.1 km **c** 31.2 km **d** 052°
6 2.28 km
7 a 66.2 km **b** 11.7 km **c** 13.1 km **d** 170°
8 48.4 km, 100°

Exercise 6P
1 5.79 cm **2** 48.2° **3** 7.42 cm **4** 81.6 cm **5** 9.86 m
6 a 36.4 cm² **b** 115 cm² **c** 90.6 cm² **d** 160 cm²

ANSWERS TO CHAPTER 7

Quick check

1 $a = 50°$

2 $b = 140°$

3 $c = d = 65°$

Exercise 7A
1 $a = b = 70°, c = 50°, d = 80°, e = 55°, f = 70°,$
  $g = h = 57.5°$
2

3 a $a = 110°, b = 55°$ **b** $c = e = 105°, d = 75°$
  c $f = 135°, g = 25°$ **d** $e = f = 94°$
  e $f = l = 105°, k = 75°$ **f** $m = o = 49°, n = 131°$
4 40°, 40°, 100°
5 $a = b = 65°, c = d = 115°, e = f = 65°, g = 80°,$
  $h = 60°, i = 60°, j = 60°, k = 20°$
6 a $x = 25°, y = 15°$ **b** $x = 7°, y = 31°$
  c $x = 60°, y = 30°$
7 a $x = 50°$: 60°, 70°, 120°, 110° – possibly trapezium
  b $x = 60°$: 50°, 130°, 50°, 130° – parallelogram or
    isosceles trapezium
  c $x = 30°$: 20°, 60°, 140°, 140° – possibly kite
  d $x = 20°$: 90°, 90°, 90°, 90° – square or rectangle

Exercise 7B
1 a 1440° **b** 2340° **c** 17 640° **d** 7740°
2 a 150° **b** 162° **c** 140° **d** 174°
3 a 9 **b** 15 **c** 102 **d** 50
4 a 15 **b** 36 **c** 24 **d** 72
5 a 12 **b** 9 **c** 20 **d** 40
6 a 130° **b** 95° **c** 130°
7 a 50° **b** 40° **c** 59°
8 Hexagon
9 a Octagon **b** 89°
10 a i 71° **ii** 109° **iii** Equal
  b If S = sum of the two opposite interior angles,
    then $S + I = 180$ (angles in a triangle), and we know E
    $+ I = 180$ (angles on a straight line),
    so $S + I = E + I$, therefore $S = E$

Exercise 7C
1 a 56° **b** 62° **c** 105° **d** 55° **e** 45°
  f 30° **g** 60° **h** 145°
2 a 55° **b** 52° **c** 50° **d** 24° **e** 39°
  f 80° **g** 34° **h** 30°
3 a 41° **b** 49° **c** 41°
4 a 72° **b** 37° **c** 72°
5 a $x = y = 40°$ **b** $x = 131°, y = 111°$
  c $x = 134°, y = 23°$ **d** $x = 32°, y = 19°$
  e $x = 59°, y = 121°$ **f** $x = 155°, y = 12.5°$
6 68°
7 a x **b** $2x$
  c $\angle ABC = (x + y)$ and $\angle AOC = 2(x + y)$

Exercise 7D

1 a $a = 50°, b = 95°$ **b** $c = 92°, x = 90°$
c $d = 110°, e = 110°, f = 70°$
d $g = 105°, h = 99°$ **e** $j = 89°, k = 89°, l = 91°$
f $m = 120°, n = 40°$ **g** $p = 44°, q = 68°$
h $x = 40°, y = 34°$

2 a $x = 26°, y = 128°$ **b** $x = 48°, y = 78°$
c $x = 133°, y = 47°$ **d** $x = 36°, y = 72°$
e $x = 55°, y = 125°$ **f** $x = 35°$
g $x = 48°, y = 45°$ **h** $x = 66°, y = 52°$

3 a $x = 49°, y = 49°$ **b** $x = 70°, y = 20°$
c $x = 80°, y = 100°$ **d** $x = 100°, y = 75°$

4 a $x = 50°, y = 62°$ **b** $x = 92°, y = 88°$
c $x = 93°, y = 42°$ **d** $x = 55°, y = 75°$

5 a $x = 95°, y = 138°$ **b** $x = 14°, y = 62°$
c $x = 32°, y = 48°$ **d** $52°$

6 a $71°$ **b** $125.5°$ **c** $54.5°$

7 a x **b** $360° - 2x$
c $\angle ADC = \frac{1}{2}$ reflex $\angle AOC = 180° - x$,
so $\angle ADC + \angle ABC = 180°$

Exercise 7E

1 a $38°$ **b** $110°$ **c** $15°$ **d** $45°$

2 a 6 cm **b** 10.8 cm **c** 3.21 cm **d** 8 cm
3 a $x = 12°, y = 156°$ **b** $x = 100°, y = 50°$
c $x = 62°, y = 28°$ **d** $x = 30°, y = 60°$
4 a $62°$ **b** $66°$ **c** $19°$ **d** $20°$
5 19.5 cm
6 a $\angle AOB = \cos^{-1}\dfrac{OA}{OB} = \cos^{-1}\dfrac{OC}{OB} = \angle COB$

  b As $\angle AOB = \angle COB$, so $\angle ABO = \angle CBO$, so OB bisects $\angle ABC$

Exercise 7F

1 a $a = 65°, b = 75°, c = 40°$
  b $d = 79°, e = 58°, f = 43°$
  c $g = 41°, h = 76°, i = 76°$
  d $k = 80°, m = 52°, n = 80°$

2 a $a = 75°, b = 75°, c = 75°, d = 30°$
  b $a = 47°, b = 86°, c = 86°, d = 47°$
  c $a = 53°, b = 53°$ **d** $a = 55°$

3 a $36°$ **b** $70°$

4 a $x = 25°$ **b** $x = 46°, y = 69°, z = 65°$
  c $x = 38°, y = 70°, z = 20°$ **d** $x = 48°, y = 42°$

5 a $2x$ **b** $90° - x$ **c** $\angle OPT = 90°$, so $\angle APT = x$

ANSWERS TO CHAPTER 8

Quick check

Trace shape **a** and check whether it fits exactly on top of the others. You should find that shape **b** is not congruent to the others.

Exercise 8A

1 a Yes, SAS **b** Yes, SSS **c** No **d** No
  e Yes, ASA **f** Yes, RHS **g** Yes, SSS
  h Yes, ASA

2 a Yes, SSS. A to R, B to P, C to Q **b** No
  c Yes, SAS. A to R, B to Q, C to P **d** No

3 i $60°$ **ii** $80°$ **iii** $40°$ **iv** 5 cm

4 i $110°$ **ii** $55°$ **iii** $85°$ **iv** $110°$ **v** 4 cm

5 SSS or RHS

6 SSS or SAS or RHS

Exercise 8B

1 a i $\begin{pmatrix} 1 \\ 3 \end{pmatrix}$ **ii** $\begin{pmatrix} 4 \\ 2 \end{pmatrix}$ **iii** $\begin{pmatrix} 2 \\ -1 \end{pmatrix}$ **iv** $\begin{pmatrix} 5 \\ 1 \end{pmatrix}$

   v $\begin{pmatrix} -1 \\ 6 \end{pmatrix}$ **vi** $\begin{pmatrix} 4 \\ 6 \end{pmatrix}$

  b i $\begin{pmatrix} -1 \\ -3 \end{pmatrix}$ **ii** $\begin{pmatrix} 3 \\ -1 \end{pmatrix}$ **iii** $\begin{pmatrix} 1 \\ -4 \end{pmatrix}$ **iv** $\begin{pmatrix} 4 \\ -2 \end{pmatrix}$

   v $\begin{pmatrix} -2 \\ 3 \end{pmatrix}$ **vi** $\begin{pmatrix} 3 \\ 3 \end{pmatrix}$

  c i $\begin{pmatrix} -4 \\ -2 \end{pmatrix}$ **ii** $\begin{pmatrix} -3 \\ 1 \end{pmatrix}$ **iii** $\begin{pmatrix} -2 \\ -3 \end{pmatrix}$ **iv** $\begin{pmatrix} 1 \\ -1 \end{pmatrix}$

   v $\begin{pmatrix} -5 \\ 4 \end{pmatrix}$ **vi** $\begin{pmatrix} 0 \\ 4 \end{pmatrix}$

  d i $\begin{pmatrix} 3 \\ 2 \end{pmatrix}$ **ii** $\begin{pmatrix} -4 \\ 2 \end{pmatrix}$ **iii** $\begin{pmatrix} 5 \\ -4 \end{pmatrix}$ **iv** $\begin{pmatrix} -2 \\ -7 \end{pmatrix}$

   v $\begin{pmatrix} 5 \\ 0 \end{pmatrix}$ **vi** $\begin{pmatrix} 1 \\ -5 \end{pmatrix}$

2

3 a $\begin{pmatrix} -3 \\ -1 \end{pmatrix}$ **b** $\begin{pmatrix} 4 \\ -4 \end{pmatrix}$ **c** $\begin{pmatrix} -5 \\ -2 \end{pmatrix}$ **d** $\begin{pmatrix} 4 \\ 7 \end{pmatrix}$ **e** $\begin{pmatrix} -1 \\ 5 \end{pmatrix}$

  f $\begin{pmatrix} 1 \\ 6 \end{pmatrix}$ **g** $\begin{pmatrix} -4 \\ 4 \end{pmatrix}$ **h** $\begin{pmatrix} -4 \\ -7 \end{pmatrix}$

4 $10 \times 10 = 100$ (including $\begin{pmatrix} 0 \\ 0 \end{pmatrix}$)

Exercise 8C

1

2 a–e

f Reflection in the
 y-axis

3 b A′(2, –1), B′(5, 0), C′(–3, –3), D′(3, 2)
 c *y*-value changes sign   **d** (*a*, –*b*)

4 b A′(–2, 1), B′(0, 5), C′(–3, –2), D′(4, –3)
 c *x*-value changes sign   **d** (–*a*, *b*)

5

6 a–i

7

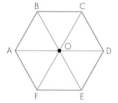

 j A reflection in *y* = *x*

8 c A′(1, 2), B′(0, 5), C′(2, –3), D′(–4, –2)
 d Coordinates are reversed: *x* becomes *y* and
  y becomes *x*   **e** (*b*, *a*)

9 c A′(–1, –2), B′(–5, 0), C′(2, –3) D′(3, 4)
 d Coordinates are reversed and change sign,
  x becomes –*y* and *y* becomes –*x*   **e** (–*b*, –*a*)

Exercise 8D

1 a

 b i Rotation 90° anticlockwise
  ii Rotation 180°

2

3 a 90° anticlockwise
 b 270° anticlockwise
 c 300° clockwise
 d 260° clockwise

4 c ii A′(2, –1), B′(4, –2), C′(1, –4)
 c iii Original coordinates (*x*, *y*) become (*y*, –*x*)   **iv** Yes
5 ii A′(–1, –2), B′(–2, –4), C′(–4, –1)
 iii Original coordinates (*x*, *y*) become (–*x*, –*y*)   **iv** Yes
6 ii A′(–2, 1), B′(–4, 2), C′(–1, 4)
 iii Original coordinates (*x*, *y*) become (–*y*, *x*)   **iv** Yes
7 Show by drawing a shape or use the fact that (*a*, *b*)
 becomes (*a*, –*b*) after reflection in the *x*-axis, and
 (*a*, –*b*) becomes (–*a*, –*b*) after reflection in the *y*-axis,
 which is equivalent to a single rotation of 180°
8 Show by drawing a shape or use the fact that (*a*, *b*)
 becomes (*b*, *a*) after reflection in the line *y* = *x*, and (*b*, *a*)
 becomes (–*a*, –*b*) after reflection in the line
 y = –*x*, which is equivalent to a single rotation of 180°

9 a

 b i Rotation 60° clockwise about O
  ii Rotation 120° clockwise about O
  iii Rotation 180° about O
  iv Rotation 240° clockwise about O
 c i Rotation 60° clockwise about O
  ii Rotation 180° about O

Exercise 8E

1

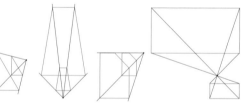

2 d All shapes are the same.

3

4 a

 b 3:1
 c 3:1
 d 9:1

5 a–c

d Scale factor $-\frac{1}{2}$, centre (1, 3)
e Scale factor –2, centre (1, 3)
f Scale factor –1, centre (–2.5, –1.5)
g Scale factor –1, centre (–2.5, –1.5)
h Same centres, and the scale factor are reciprocals of each other

Exercise 8F

1 A translation $\begin{pmatrix} 1 \\ -2 \end{pmatrix}$, B reflection in y-axis,
C rotation 90° clockwise about (0, 0),
D reflection in $x = 3$, E reflection in $y = 4$,
F enlargement by scale factor 2, centre (0, 1)
2 a T_1 to T_2: rotation 90° clockwise about (0, 0)
b T_1 to T_6: rotation 90° anticlockwise about (0, 0)
c T_2 to T_3: translation $\begin{pmatrix} 2 \\ 2 \end{pmatrix}$
d T_6 to T_2: rotation 180° about (0, 0)
e T_6 to T_5: reflection in y-axis
f T_5 to T_4: translation $\begin{pmatrix} 4 \\ 0 \end{pmatrix}$

3 a–d

e T_d to T: rotation 90° anticlockwise about (0,0)

4 (–4, –3)
5 a (–5, 2) **b** Reflection in y-axis
6 (3, 1)
7 Reflection in x-axis, translation $\begin{pmatrix} 0 \\ -5 \end{pmatrix}$, rotation 90° clockwise about (0, 0)
8 Translation $\begin{pmatrix} 0 \\ -8 \end{pmatrix}$, reflection in x-axis, rotation 90° clockwise about (0, 0)
9 Rotation 180° clockwise or anticlockwise about (0, 0)

ANSWERS TO CHAPTER 9

Exercise 9B

4 a i Construct 60° angle and bisect it
ii Bisect 30° angle
iii Construct 90° angle and bisect it to get 45°, then bisect 45° angle
iv Construct 45° angle on upper arm of 30° angle
8 b AC = 5.1 cm, BC = 6.3 cm
9 b PR = 5.9 cm, RQ = 4.1 cm

Exercise 9C

1 a Circle with radius 2 cm
b Circle with radius 4 cm
c Circle with radius 5 cm
2 a **b**
c
3 Circle with radius 4 m
4
5 a **b** **c**

d **e** **f**
6
7

Exercise 9D

1 **2**
3 **4**
5 **6**

7

Stake

8 a Sketch should show a circle of radius 6 cm around London and one of radius 4cm around Glasgow.
   b No   **c** Yes
9 a Yes
   b Sketch should show a circle of radius 4 cm around Leeds and one of radius 4cm around Exeter. The area where they overlap should be shaded.
10 a This is the perpendicular bisector of the line from York to Birmingham. It should pass just below Manchester and just through the top of Norwich.
   b Sketch should show a circle of radius 7cm around Glasgow and one of radius 5 cm around London.
   c The transmitter can be built anywhere on line constructed in part **a** that is within the area shown in part **b**.
11 Sketch should show two circles around Birmingham, one of radius 3 cm and one of radius 5cm. The area of good reception is the area between the two circles.

12 Sketch should show a circle of radius 6 cm around Glasgow, 2 circles around York, one of radius 4 cm and one of radius 6 cm and a circle around London of radius 8 cm. The small area in the Irish sea that is between the 2 circles around York and inside both the circle around Glasgow and the circle around London is where the boat can be.
13 Sketch should show 2 circles around Newcastle upon Tyne, one of radius 4 cm and one of radius 6 cm, and two circles around Bristol, one of radius 3 cm and one of radius 5 cm. The area that is between both pairs of circles is the area that should be shaded.
14 Sketch should show the perpendicular bisector of the line running from Newcastle upon Tyne to Manchester and that of the line running from Sheffield to Norwich. Where the lines cross is where the oil rig is located.
15 Sketch should show the perpendicular bisector of the line running from Glasgow to Norwich and that of the line running from Norwich to Exeter. Where the lines cross is where Fred's house is.
16 Sketch should show the bisectors of the angles made by the piers and the sea wall at points A and B. These are the paths of each boat.

ANSWERS TO CHAPTER 10

Quick check

1 a 0.6   **b** 0.44   **c** 0.375
2 a $\frac{17}{100}$ **b** $\frac{16}{25}$ **c** $\frac{429}{500}$
3 a $\frac{13}{15}$ **b** $\frac{9}{40}$
4 a 5   **b** 4

Exercise 10A

1 a 2^4 **b** 3^5 **c** 7^2 **d** 5^3 **e** 10^7 **f** 6^4
   g 4^1 **h** 1^7 **i** 0.5^4 **j** 100^3
2 a $3 \times 3 \times 3 \times 3$ **b** $9 \times 9 \times 9$ **c** 6×6
   d $10 \times 10 \times 10 \times 10 \times 10$
   e $2 \times 2 \times 2 \times 2 \times 2 \times 2 \times 2 \times 2 \times 2 \times 2$
   f 8   **g** $0.1 \times 0.1 \times 0.1$ **h** 2.5×2.5
   i $0.7 \times 0.7 \times 0.7$ **j** 1000×1000
3 a 16   **b** 243   **c** 49   **d** 125   **e** 10 000 000
   f 1296   **g** 4   **h** 1   **i** 0.0625   **j** 1 000 000
4 a 81   **b** 729   **c** 36   **d** 100 000   **e** 1024
   f 8   **g** 0.001   **h** 6.25   **i** 0.343   **j** 1 000 000
5 a 1   **b** 4   **c** 1   **d** 1   **e** 1
6 Any power of 1 is equal to 1.
7 10^6
8 10^6
9 a 1   **b** −1   **c** 1   **d** 1   **e** −1
10 a 1   **b** −1   **c** −1   **d** 1   **e** 1

Exercise 10B

1 a $\frac{1}{5^3}$ **b** $\frac{1}{6}$ **c** $\frac{1}{10^5}$ **d** $\frac{1}{3^2}$ **e** $\frac{1}{8^2}$
   f $\frac{1}{9}$ **g** $\frac{1}{w^2}$ **h** $\frac{1}{t}$ **i** $\frac{1}{x^m}$ **j** $\frac{4}{m^3}$

2 a 3^{-2} **b** 5^{-1} **c** 10^{-3} **d** m^{-1} **e** t^{-n}
3 a i 2^4 **ii** 2^{-1} **iii** 2^{-4} **iv** -2^3
   b i 10^3 **ii** 10^{-1} **iii** 10^{-2} **iv** 10^6
   c i 5^3 **ii** 5^{-1} **iii** 5^{-2} **iv** 5^{-4}
   d i 3^2 **ii** 3^{-3} **iii** 3^{-4} **iv** -3^5
4 a $\frac{5}{x^3}$ **b** $\frac{6}{t}$ **c** $\frac{7}{m^2}$ **d** $\frac{4}{q^4}$ **e** $\frac{10}{y^5}$
   f $\frac{1}{2x^3}$ **g** $\frac{1}{2m}$ **h** $\frac{3}{4t^4}$ **i** $\frac{4}{5y^3}$ **j** $\frac{7}{8x^5}$
5 a $7x^{-3}$ **b** $10p^{-1}$ **c** $5t^{-2}$ **d** $8m^{-5}$ **e** $3y^{-1}$
6 a i 25   **ii** $\frac{1}{125}$ **iii** $\frac{4}{5}$ **b i** 64   **ii** $\frac{1}{16}$ **iii** $\frac{5}{256}$
   c i 8   **ii** $\frac{1}{32}$ **iii** $4\frac{1}{2}$ **d** 1 000 000   **ii** $\frac{1}{1000}$ **iii** $\frac{1}{4}$

Exercise 10C

1 a 5^4 **b** 5^3 **c** 5^2 **d** 5^3 **e** 5^{-5}
2 a 6^3 **b** 6^0 **c** 6^6 **d** 6^{-7} **e** 6^2
3 a a^3 **b** a^5 **c** a^7 **d** a^4 **e** a^2 **f** a^1
4 a 4^6 **b** 4^{15} **c** 4^6 **d** 4^{-6} **e** 4^6 **f** 4^0
5 a $6a^5$ **b** $9a^2$ **c** $8a^6$ **d** $-6a^4$ **e** $8a^8$
   f $-10a^{-3}$
6 a $3a$ **b** $4a^3$ **c** $3a^4$ **d** $6a^{-1}$ **e** $4a^7$ **f** $5a^{-4}$
7 a $8a^5b^4$ **b** $10a^3b$ **c** $30a^{-2}b^{-2}$ **d** $2ab^3$
   e $8a^{-5}b^7$
8 a $3a^3b^2$ **b** $3a^2c^4$ **c** $8a^2b^2c^3$
9 $1 = \dfrac{a^x}{a^x} = a^x \div a^x = a^{x-x} = a^0$

Exercise 10D

1 5	**2** 10	**3** 8	**4** 9	**5** 25	**6** 3
7 4	**8** 10	**9** 5	**10** 8	**11** 12	**12** 20
13 5	**14** 3	**15** 10	**16** 3	**17** 2	**18** 2

19 6 **20** 6 **21** $\frac{1}{4}$ **22** $\frac{1}{2}$ **23** $\frac{1}{3}$ **24** $\frac{1}{5}$

25 $\frac{1}{10}$ **26** $\frac{5}{6}$ **27** $1\frac{2}{3}$ **28** $\frac{8}{3}$ **29** $1\frac{4}{5}$ **30** $\frac{5}{8}$

31 $\frac{3}{5}$ **32** $\frac{1}{4}$ **33** $2\frac{1}{2}$ **34** $\frac{4}{5}$ **35** $1\frac{1}{7}$

36 $(x^{\frac{1}{n}})^n = x^{\frac{1}{n} \times n} = x^1 = x$, but
$(\sqrt[n]{x})^n = \sqrt[n]{x} \times \sqrt[n]{x} \ldots n$ times $= x$, so $x^{\frac{1}{n}} = \sqrt[n]{x}$

Exercise 10E

1 a 16 **b** 25 **c** 216 **d** 81
2 a $t^{\frac{2}{3}}$ **b** $m^{\frac{3}{4}}$ **c** $k^{\frac{2}{5}}$ **d** $x^{\frac{3}{2}}$
3 a 4 **b** 9 **c** 64 **d** 3125
4 a $\frac{1}{5}$ **b** $\frac{1}{6}$ **c** $\frac{1}{2}$ **d** $\frac{1}{3}$ **e** $\frac{1}{4}$ **f** $\frac{1}{2}$ **g** $\frac{1}{2}$ **h** $\frac{1}{3}$
5 a $\frac{1}{125}$ **b** $\frac{1}{216}$ **c** $\frac{1}{8}$ **d** $\frac{1}{27}$ **e** $\frac{1}{64}$ **f** $\frac{1}{4}$ **g** $\frac{1}{256}$ **h** $\frac{1}{9}$
6 a $\frac{1}{100\,000}$ **b** $\frac{1}{12}$ **c** $\frac{1}{25}$ **d** $\frac{1}{27}$ **e** $\frac{1}{32}$ **f** $\frac{1}{32}$ **g** $\frac{1}{81}$ **h** $\frac{1}{13}$

Exercise 10F

1 a 31 **b** 310 **c** 3100 **d** 31 000
2 a 65 **b** 650 **c** 6500 **d** 65 000
3 a 0.31 **b** 0.031 **c** 0.0031 **d** 0.000 31
4 a 0.65 **b** 0.065 **c** 0.0065 **d** 0.000 65
5 a 250 **b** 34.5 **c** 4670 **d** 346
 e 207.89 **f** 56 780 **g** 246 **h** 0.76
 i 999 000 **j** 23 456 **k** 98 765.4 **l** 43 230 000
 m 345.78 **n** 6000 **o** 56.7 **p** 560 045
6 a 0.025 **b** 0.345 **c** 0.00467
 d 3.46 **e** 0.207 89 **f** 0.056 78
 g 0.0246 **h** 0.0076 **i** 0.000 000 999
 j 2.3456 **k** 0.098 765 4 **l** 0.000 043 23
 m 0.000 000 034 578 **n** 0.000 000 000 06
 o 0.000 000 567 **p** 0.005 600 45
7 a 230 **b** 578 900 **c** 4790 **d** 57 000 000
 e 216 **f** 10 500 **g** 0.000 32 **h** 9870
8 a, b and c

Exercise 10G

1 a 0.31 **b** 0.031 **c** 0.0031 **d** 0.000 31
2 a 0.65 **b** 0.065 **c** 0.0065 **d** 0.000 65
3 a $9\,999\,999\,999 \times 10^{99}$
 b $0.000\,000\,001 \times 10^{-99}$ (depending on number of digits displayed)
4 a 31 **b** 310 **c** 3100 **d** 31 000
5 a 65 **b** 650 **c** 6500 **d** 65 000
6 a 250 **b** 34.5 **c** 0.004 67
 d 34.6 **e** 0.020 789 **f** 5678
 g 246 **h** 7600 **i** 89 700
 j 0.008 65 **k** 60 000 000 **l** 0.000 567
7 a 2.5×10^2 **b** 3.45×10^{-1} **c** 4.67×10^4
 d 3.4×10^9 **e** 2.078×10^{10} **f** 5.678×10^{-4}
 g 2.46×10^3 **h** 7.6×10^{-2} **i** 7.6×10^{-4}
 j 9.99×10^{-1} **k** 2.3456×10^2
 l $9.876\,54 \times 10^1$ **m** 6×10^{-4}
 n 5.67×10^{-3} **o** $5.600 45 \times 10^1$
8 2.7797×10^4
9 $2.815\,81 \times 10^5$, 3×10^1, $1.382\,101 \times 10^6$
10 1.298×10^7, 2.997×10^9, 9.3×10^4

Exercise 10H

1 a 5.67×10^3 **b** 6×10^2 **c** 3.46×10^{-1}
 d 7×10^{-4} **e** 5.6×10^2 **f** 6×10^5
 g 7×10^3 **h** 1.6 **i** 2.3×10^7
 j 3×10^{-6} **k** 2.56×10^6 **l** 4.8×10^2
 m 1.12×10^2 **n** 6×10^5 **o** 2.8×10^6
2 a 1.08×10^8 **b** 4.8×10^6 **c** 1.2×10^9
 d 1.08 **e** 6.4×10^2 **f** 1.2×10^1
 g 2.88 **h** 2.5×10^7 **i** 8×10^{-6}
3 a 1.1×10^8 **b** 6.1×10^6 **c** 1.6×10^9
 d 3.9×10^{-2} **e** 9.6×10^8 **f** 4.6×10^{-7}
 g 2.1×10^3 **h** 3.6×10^7 **i** 1.5×10^2
 j 3.5×10^9 **k** 1.6×10^4
4 a 2.7×10^7 **b** 1.6×10^6 **c** 2×10^7
 d 4×10^{-2} **e** 2×10^1 **f** 6×10^{-2}
 g 2×10^{-1} **h** 5×10^8 **i** 2×10^5
5 a 5.4×10^5 **b** 2.9×10^9 **c** 1.1×10^{-2}
 d 6.3×10^{-4} **e** 2.8×10^2 **f** 5.5×10^{-2}
 g 4.9×10^8 **h** 8.6×10^2
6 2×10^{13}, 1×10^{-10}, mass $= 2 \times 10^3$ g (2 kg)
7 a (2^{63}) 9.2×10^{18} grains
 b $(1 + 9.2 \times 10^{18}) \times 32 = 3 \times 10^{20}$ grains
8 a 6×10^7 sq miles **b** 30%
9 1.5×10^7 sq miles **10** 5×10^4
11 2.3×10^5 **12** 3.2×10^8 kg
13 250 **14** 9.41×10^4

Exercise 10I

1 a 0.5 **b** $0.\dot{3}$ **c** 0.25 **d** 0.2 **e** $0.1\dot{6}$
 f $0.\dot{1}42857\dot{}$ **g** 0.125 **h** $0.\dot{1}$ **i** 0.1
 j $0.\dot{0}76923\dot{}$
2 b They all contain the same pattern of digits, starting at a different point in the pattern.
3 $0.\dot{1}$, $0.\dot{2}$, $0.\dot{3}$, etc. Digit in decimal fraction same as numerator.
4 $0.\dot{0}\dot{9}$, $0.\dot{1}\dot{8}$, $0.\dot{2}\dot{7}$, etc. Sum of digits in recurring pattern = 9. First digit is one less than numerator.
5 0.444 ..., 0.454 ..., 0.428 ..., 0.409 ..., 0.432 ..., 0.461 ..., $\frac{9}{22}$, $\frac{3}{7}$, $\frac{16}{37}$, $\frac{4}{9}$, $\frac{5}{11}$, $\frac{6}{13}$
6 $\frac{38}{120}$, $\frac{35}{120}$, $\frac{36}{120}$, $\frac{48}{120}$, $\frac{50}{120}$, $\frac{7}{24}$, $\frac{3}{10}$, $\frac{19}{60}$, $\frac{2}{5}$, $\frac{5}{12}$
7 a $\frac{1}{8}$ **b** $\frac{17}{50}$ **c** $\frac{29}{40}$ **d** $\frac{5}{16}$ **e** $\frac{89}{100}$ **f** $\frac{1}{20}$
 g $\frac{27}{20}$ **h** $\frac{7}{32}$
8 a $0.08\dot{3}$ **b** 0.0625 **c** 0.05 **d** 0.04 **e** 0.02
9 a $\frac{4}{3}$ **b** $\frac{6}{5}$ **c** $\frac{5}{2}$ **d** $\frac{10}{7}$ **e** $\frac{20}{11}$ **f** $\frac{15}{4}$
10 a 0.75, $1.\dot{3}$; $0.8\dot{3}$, 1.2; 0.4, 2.5; 0.7, $1.\dot{4}2857\dot{}$; 0.55, $1.\dot{8}\dot{1}$; $0.2\dot{6}$, 3.75
 b no
11 1
12 a 24.242 42 ... **b** 24 **c** $\frac{24}{99}$
13 a $\frac{8}{9}$ **b** $\frac{34}{99}$ **c** $\frac{5}{11}$ **d** $\frac{21}{37}$ **e** $\frac{4}{9}$ **f** $\frac{2}{45}$
 g $\frac{13}{90}$ **h** $\frac{1}{22}$ **i** $2\frac{7}{9}$ **j** $7\frac{7}{11}$ **k** $3\frac{1}{3}$ **l** $2\frac{2}{33}$
14 a true **b** true **c** recurring
15 a $\frac{9}{9}$ **b** $\frac{45}{90} = \frac{1}{2} = 0.5$

Exercise 10J

1 a $\sqrt{6}$ **b** $\sqrt{15}$ **c** 2 **d** 4 **e** $2\sqrt{10}$
 f 3 **g** $2\sqrt{3}$ **h** $\sqrt{21}$ **i** $\sqrt{14}$ **j** 6
 k 6 **l** $\sqrt{30}$

2 a 2   **b** $\sqrt{5}$ **c** $\sqrt{6}$ **d** $\sqrt{3}$ **e** $\sqrt{5}$
   f 1   **g** $\sqrt{3}$ **h** $\sqrt{7}$ **i** 2   **j** $\sqrt{6}$
   k 1   **l** 3

3 a $2\sqrt{3}$ **b** 15   **c** $4\sqrt{2}$ **d** $4\sqrt{3}$ **e** $8\sqrt{5}$
   f $3\sqrt{3}$ **g** 24   **h** $3\sqrt{7}$ **i** $2\sqrt{7}$ **j** $6\sqrt{5}$
   k $6\sqrt{3}$ **l** 30

4 a $\sqrt{3}$ **b** 1   **c** $2\sqrt{2}$ **d** $\sqrt{2}$ **e** $\sqrt{5}$
   f $\sqrt{3}$ **g** $\sqrt{2}$ **h** $\sqrt{7}$ **i** $\sqrt{7}$ **j** $2\sqrt{3}$
   k $2\sqrt{3}$ **l** 1

5 a a **b** 1   **c** $\sqrt{a}$

6 a $3\sqrt{2}$ **b** $2\sqrt{6}$ **c** $2\sqrt{3}$ **d** $5\sqrt{2}$ **e** $2\sqrt{2}$
   f $3\sqrt{3}$ **g** $4\sqrt{3}$ **h** $5\sqrt{3}$ **i** $3\sqrt{5}$ **j** $3\sqrt{7}$
   k $4\sqrt{2}$ **l** $10\sqrt{2}$ **m** $10\sqrt{10}$ **n** $5\sqrt{10}$ **o** $7\sqrt{2}$
   p $9\sqrt{3}$

7 a 36   **b** $16\sqrt{30}$ **c** 54   **d** 32   **e** $48\sqrt{6}$
   f $48\sqrt{6}$ **g** $18\sqrt{15}$ **h** 84   **i** 64   **j** 100
   k 50   **l** 56

8 a $20\sqrt{6}$ **b** $6\sqrt{15}$ **c** 24   **d** 16   **e** $12\sqrt{10}$
   f 18   **g** $20\sqrt{3}$ **h** $10\sqrt{21}$ **i** $6\sqrt{14}$ **j** 36
   k 24   **l** $12\sqrt{30}$

9 a 6   **b** $3\sqrt{5}$ **c** $6\sqrt{6}$ **d** $2\sqrt{3}$ **e** $4\sqrt{5}$
   f 5   **g** $7\sqrt{3}$ **h** $2\sqrt{7}$ **i** 6   **j** $2\sqrt{7}$
   k 5   **l** 24

10 a $2\sqrt{3}$ **b** 4   **c** $6\sqrt{2}$ **d** $4\sqrt{2}$ **e** $6\sqrt{5}$
   f $24\sqrt{3}$ **g** $3\sqrt{2}$ **h** $\sqrt{7}$ **i** $10\sqrt{7}$ **j** $8\sqrt{3}$
   k $10\sqrt{3}$ **l** 6

11 a abc **b** $\frac{a}{c}$ **c** $c\sqrt{b}$

12 a 20   **b** 24   **c** 10   **d** 24   **e** 3   **f** 6
13 a $\frac{3}{4}$ **b** $8\frac{1}{3}$ **c** $\frac{5}{16}$ **d** 12   **e** 2

Exercise 10K

1 $11 + 6\sqrt{2}$

2 a $2\sqrt{3} - 3$ **b** $3\sqrt{2} - 8$ **c** $10 + 4\sqrt{5}$
   d $12\sqrt{7} - 42$ **e** $15\sqrt{2} - 24$ **f** $9 - \sqrt{3}$

3 a $2\sqrt{3}$ **b** $1 + \sqrt{5}$ **c** $-1 - \sqrt{2}$ **d** $\sqrt{7} - 30$
   e -41 **f** $7 + 3\sqrt{6}$ **g** $9 + 4\sqrt{5}$ **h** $3 - 2\sqrt{2}$
   i $11 + 6\sqrt{2}$

4 a $3\sqrt{2}$ cm   **b** $2\sqrt{3}$ cm   **c** $2\sqrt{10}$ cm

5 a $\sqrt{3} - 1$ cm^2 **b** $2\sqrt{5} + 5\sqrt{2}$ cm^2
   c $2\sqrt{3} + 18$ cm^2

6 a $\dfrac{\sqrt{3}}{3}$ **b** $\dfrac{\sqrt{2}}{2}$ **c** $\dfrac{\sqrt{5}}{5}$ **d** $\dfrac{\sqrt{3}}{6}$

   e $\sqrt{3}$ **f** $\dfrac{5\sqrt{2}}{2}$ **g** $\dfrac{3}{2}$ **h** $\dfrac{5\sqrt{2}}{2}$

   i $\dfrac{\sqrt{21}}{3}$ **j** $\dfrac{\sqrt{2} + 2}{2}$ **k** $\dfrac{2\sqrt{3} - 3}{3}$ **l** $\dfrac{5\sqrt{3} + 6}{3}$

7 a i 1   **ii** -4 **iii** 2   **iv** 17   **v** -44
   b They become whole numbers. Difference of two squares makes the 'middle terms' (and surds) disappear.

   c i $\dfrac{5 + 5\sqrt{5}}{-4}$ **ii** $\dfrac{5 + 3\sqrt{3}}{2}$

ANSWERS TO CHAPTER 11

Quick check

1 a 7   **b** 6   **c** 8   **d** 6

Exercise 11A

1 Mode

2 Three possible answers: 12, 14, 14, 16, 18, 20, 24; or 12, 14, 14, 16, 18, 22, 24; or 12, 14, 14, 16, 20, 22, 24

3 53

4 a median (mean could be unduly influenced by results of very able and/or very poor candidates)
   b median (mean could be unduly influenced by pocket money of students with very rich or generous parents)
   c mode (numerical value of shoe sizes irrelevant, just want most common size)
   d median (mean could be distorted by one or two extremely short or tall performers)
   e mode (the only way to get an "average" of non-numerical values)
   f median (mean could be unduly influenced by very low weights of premature babies)

5 The mean is 31.5 which rounds up to 32, so the statement is correct (though the mode and median are 31)

6 a i £18 000   **ii** £24 000   **iii** £23 778
   b A 6% rise would increase the mean salary to £25 204, a £1500 pay increase would produce a mean of £25 278

7 a Median   **b** Mode   **c** Mean
8 11.6   **9** 42.7 kg   **10** 24

Exercise 11B

1 a i 7   **ii** 6   **iii** 6.4   **b i** 8   **ii** 8.5   **iii** 8.2
2 a 668   **b** 1.9   **c** 0   **d** 328
3 a 2.2, 1.7, 1.3   **b** Better dental care
4 a 50   **b** 2   **c** 2.8
5 a Roger 5, Brian 4   **b** Roger 3, Brian 8
   c Roger 5, Brian 4   **d** Roger 5.4, Brian 4.5
   e Roger, smaller range   **f** Brian, better mean
6 a 40   **b** 7   **c** 3   **d** 2   **e** 2.5   **f** 2.5
   g 2.4
7 a 34   **b** $x + 80 + 3y + 104 = 266$,
      so $x + 3y = 266 - 184 = 82$
   c $x = 10, y = 24$ **d** 2.5

Exercise 11C

1 a i $30 < x \leqslant 40$ **ii** 29.5   **b i** $0 < y \leqslant 100$ **ii** 158.3
   c i $5 < z \leqslant 10$ **ii** 9.43   **d i** 7–9   **ii** 8.41
2 a 100 g $< w \leqslant$ 120 g   **b** 10.86 kg   **c** 108.6 g
3 a $175 < h \leqslant 200$ **b** 31%   **c** 193.3 hours   **d** No
4 a Yes, average distance is 11.7 miles per day
   b Because shorter runs will be done faster which will affect the average.
   c Yes because the shortest could be 1 mile, the longest 25 miles
5 24
6 Soundbuy; average increases are Soundbuy 17.7p, Springfields 18.7p, Setco 18.2p

Exercise 11D
1 b 1.7
2 b 2.8
3 a i 17, 13, 6, 3, 1   **ii** £1.45
 b ii £5.35
 c Much higher mean. Early morning, people just want a paper or a few sweets, later people are buying food for the day.
4 c 140.4 cm
5 b Monday 28.4 min, Tuesday 20.9 min, Wednesday 21.3 min
 c There are more patients on a Monday, and so longer waiting times, because the surgery is closed at the weekend

Exercise 11E
1 The respective frequency densities on which each histogram should be based are
 a 2.5, 6.5, 6, 2, 1, 1.5   **b** 4, 27, 15, 3   **c** 17, 18, 12, 6.67   **d** 0.4, 1.2, 2.8, 1   **e** 9, 21, 13.5, 9

4 a 775   **b** 400
5 a i

Age, y (years)	$9 < y \leq 10$	$10 < y \leq 12$	$12 < y \leq 14$	$14 < y \leq 17$	$17 < y \leq 19$	$19 < y \leq 20$
Frequency	4	12	8	9	5	1

 ii 10–12   **iii** 13   **iv** 11, 16, 5   **v** 13.4
 b i

Temperature, t (°C)	$10 < t \leq 11$	$11 < t \leq 12$	$12 < t \leq 14$	$14 < t \leq 16$	$16 < t \leq 19$	$19 < t \leq 21$
Frequency	15	15	50	40	45	15

 ii 12–14°C   **iii** 14.5°C   **iv** 12°C, 17°C, 5°C   **v** 14.8°C
 c i

Weight, w (kg)	$50 < w \leq 70$	$70 < w \leq 90$	$90 < w \leq 100$	$100 < w \leq 120$	$120 < w \leq 170$
Frequency	160	200	120	120	200

 ii 70–90 kg and 120–170 kg   **iii** 93.33 kg   **iv** 74 kg, 120 kg, 46 kg   **v** 99.0 kg
6 a 7.33 hours   **b** 8.44 hours   **c** 7 hours
7 b 14.3 kg   **c** 14.7 kg   **d** 33 plants
8 a

Speed, v (mph)	$0 < v \leq 40$	$40 < v \leq 50$	$50 < v \leq 60$	$60 < v \leq 70$	$70 < v \leq 80$	$80 < v \leq 100$
Frequency	80	10	40	110	60	60

 b 360   **c** 64.5 mph   **d** 59.2 mph

Exercise 11F
1 Moving averages are: 9.3, 9.1, 9.0, 9.1, 8.7, 8.6, 9.1, 9.0, 9.4, 9.7, 9.7, 9.9, 10.1, 9.7, 9.9, 9.4, 9.9, 10.0, 10.0, 9.9, 10.1, 10.7
2 a Moving averages are: 44.5, 42.3, 41.0, 41.3, 42.3, 44.5, 45.8
 b Amounts raised dip in the middle of the collection period
3 a Moving averages are: 108.10, 107.24, 108.39, 105.89, 109.54, 111.40, 112.55, 118.70, 118.50, 119.80, 120.30, 123.18, 124.33
 b Gradually rises
 c Trend suggests next moving average about £125.50, so estimated first quarter 2006 bill is £137.29
4 b Moving averages are: 80, 81, 82, 83, 82, 85, 87, 90, 94, 92, 91, 89, 86
 c Recent fall may be due to moving to cheaper provider or using e-mail rather than making calls
 d Trend suggests next moving average about 83.5, so first quarter 2006 bill is £78
5 a Moving averages are: 12.3, 13.0, 13.0, 10.0, 10.3, 10.0, 13.7, 13.0, 13.7, 13.0, 13.0, 13.0, 13.3, 13.0, 13.7, 13.3, 13.3, 13.7, 14.3, 15.0, 14.7
 b Apart from a blip in June 2004, sales showing slight improvement
 c Trend suggests next moving average about 14.6, so January 2006 sales estimate is 15

2 a
 b
 c Girls £4.36, boys £4.81

3

6 b Moving averages are: (videos) 3.7, 3.6, 3.3, 2.8, 2.5; (DVDs) 0.6, 1.1, 1.4, 2.1, 2.8
 c Sales of DVD players increasingly strongly, video recorder sales falling
 d Trend suggests next moving averages about 2.3 (videos) and 3.5 (DVDs), so 2006 sales estimates are 2.1 (videos) and 4.0 (DVDs)

Exercise 11H
1 a It is a leading question, and there is no option to disagree with the statement
 b Unbiased, and the responses do not overlap
2 a Responses overlap
 b Give as options: up to £2, more than £2 and up to £5, more than £5 and up to £10, more than £10

Exercise 11I
1 Price 78p, 80.3p, 84.2p, 85p, 87.4p, 93.6p
2 a £1 = $1.80   **b** Greatest drop was from June to July
 c There is no trend in the data
3 a 9.7 million   **b** 4.5 years   **c** 12 million   **d** 10 million
4 £74.73
5 a Holiday month   **b i** 138–144 thousand
 ii 200–210 thousand

ANSWERS TO CHAPTER 12

Quick check

1 a $-3x$ **b** $2x$ **c** $-3x$ **d** $6m^2$
e $-6x^2$ **f** $-12p^2$

2 a -6 **b** $-\frac{1}{2}$ **c** $\frac{2}{3}$

Exercise 12A

1 $x^2 + 5x + 6$ **2** $t^2 + 7t + 12$ **3** $w^2 + 4w + 3$
4 $m^2 + 6m + 5$ **5** $k^2 + 8k + 15$ **6** $a^2 + 5a + 4$
7 $x^2 + 2x - 8$ **8** $t^2 + 2t - 15$ **9** $w^2 + 2w - 3$
10 $f^2 - f - 6$ **11** $g^2 - 3g - 4$ **12** $y^2 + y - 12$
13 $x^2 + x - 12$ **14** $p^2 - p - 2$ **15** $k^2 - 2k - 8$
16 $y^2 + 3y - 10$ **17** $a^2 + 2a - 3$ **18** $t^2 + t - 12$
19 $x^2 - 9$ **20** $t^2 - 25$ **21** $m^2 - 16$
22 $t^2 - 4$ **23** $y^2 - 64$ **24** $p^2 - 1$
25 $25 - x^2$ **26** $49 - g^2$ **27** $x^2 - 36$

Exercise 12B

1 $6x^2 + 11x + 3$ **2** $12y^2 + 17y + 6$ **3** $6t^2 + 17t + 5$
4 $8t^2 + 2t - 3$ **5** $10m^2 - 11m - 6$ **6** $12k^2 - 11k - 15$
7 $6p^2 + 11p - 10$ **8** $10w^2 + 19w + 6$ **9** $6a^2 - 7a - 3$
10 $8r^2 - 10r + 3$ **11** $15g^2 - 16g + 4$ **12** $12d^2 + 5d - 2$
13 $8p^2 + 26p + 15$ **14** $6t^2 + 7t + 2$ **15** $6p^2 + 11p + 4$
16 $6 - 7t - 10t^2$ **17** $12 + n - 6n^2$ **18** $6f^2 - 5f - 6$
19 $12 + 7q - 10q^2$ **20** $3 - 7p - 6p^2$ **21** $4 + 10t - 6t^2$

Exercise 12C

1 $4x^2 - 1$ **2** $9t^2 - 4$ **3** $25y^2 - 9$
4 $16m^2 - 9$ **5** $4k^2 - 9$ **6** $16h^2 - 1$
7 $4 - 9x^2$ **8** $25 - 4t^2$ **9** $36 - 25y^2$
10 $a^2 - b^2$ **11** $9t^2 - k^2$ **12** $4m^2 - 9p^2$
13 $25k^2 - g^2$ **14** $a^2b^2 - c^2d^2$ **15** $a^4 - b^4$

Exercise 12D

1 $x^2 + 10x + 25$ **2** $m^2 + 8m + 16$ **3** $t^2 + 12t + 36$
4 $p^2 + 6p + 9$ **5** $m^2 - 6m + 9$ **6** $t^2 - 10t + 25$
7 $m^2 - 8m + 16$ **8** $k^2 - 14k + 49$ **9** $9x^2 + 6x + 1$
10 $16t^2 + 24t + 9$ **11** $25y^2 + 20y + 4$ **12** $4m^2 + 12m + 9$
13 $16t^2 - 24t + 9$ **14** $9x^2 - 12x + 4$ **15** $25t^2 - 20t + 4$
16 $25r^2 - 60r + 36$ **17** $x^2 + 2xy + y^2$ **18** $m^2 - 2mn + n^2$
19 $4t^2 + 4ty + y^2$ **20** $m^2 - 6mn + 9n^2$ **21** $x^2 + 4x$
22 $x^2 - 10x$ **23** $x^2 + 12x$ **24** $x^2 - 4x$

Exercise 12E

1 $(x + 2)(x + 3)$ **2** $(t + 1)(t + 4)$ **3** $(m + 2)(m + 5)$
4 $(k + 4)(k + 6)$ **5** $(p + 2)(p + 12)$ **6** $(r + 3)(r + 6)$
7 $(w + 2)(w + 9)$ **8** $(x + 3)(x + 4)$ **9** $(a + 2)(a + 6)$
10 $(k + 3)(k + 7)$ **11** $(f + 1)(f + 21)$ **12** $(b + 8)(b + 12)$
13 $(t - 2)(t - 3)$ **14** $(d - 4)(d - 1)$ **15** $(g - 2)(g - 5)$
16 $(x - 3)(x - 12)$ **17** $(c - 2)(c - 16)$ **18** $(t - 4)(t - 9)$
19 $(y - 4)(y - 12)$ **20** $(j - 6)(j - 8)$ **21** $(p - 3)(p - 5)$
22 $(y + 6)(y - 1)$ **23** $(t + 4)(t - 2)$ **24** $(x + 5)(x - 2)$
25 $(m + 2)(m - 6)$ **26** $(r + 1)(r - 7)$ **27** $(n + 3)(n - 6)$
28 $(m + 4)(m - 11)$ **29** $(w + 4)(w - 6)$ **30** $(t + 9)(t - 10)$
31 $(h + 8)(h - 9)$ **32** $(t + 7)(t - 9)$ **33** $(d + 1)^2$
34 $(y + 10)^2$ **35** $(t - 4)^2$ **36** $(m - 9)^2$
37 $(x - 12)^2$ **38** $(d + 3)(d - 4)$ **39** $(t + 4)(t - 5)$
40 $(q + 7)(q - 8)$

Exercise 12F

1 $(x + 3)(x - 3)$ **2** $(t + 5)(t - 5)$ **3** $(m + 4)(m - 4)$
4 $(3 + x)(3 - x)$ **5** $(7 + t)(7 - t)$ **6** $(k + 10)(k - 10)$
7 $(2 + y)(2 - y)$ **8** $(x + 8)(x - 8)$ **9** $(t + 9)(t - 9)$
10 $(x + y)(x - y)$ **11** $(x + 2y)(x - 2y)$ **12** $(x + 3y)(x - 3y)$
13 $(3x + 1)(3x - 1)$ **14** $(4x + 3)(4x - 3)$ **15** $(5x + 8)(5x - 8)$
16 $(2x + 3y)(2x - 3y)$ **17** $(3t + 2w)(3t - 2w)$ **18** $(4y + 5x)(4y - 5x)$

Exercise 12G

1 $(2x + 1)(x + 2)$ **2** $(7x + 1)(x + 1)$ **3** $(4x + 7)(x - 1)$
4 $(3t + 2)(8t + 1)$ **5** $(3t + 1)(5t - 1)$ **6** $(4x - 1)^2$
7 $3(y + 7)(2y - 3)$ **8** $4(y + 6)(y - 4)$ **9** $(2x + 3)(4x - 1)$
10 $(2t + 1)(3t + 5)$ **11** $(x - 6)(3x + 2)$ **12** $(x - 5)(7x - 2)$

Exercise 12H

1 $-2, -5$ **2** $-3, -1$ **3** $-6, -4$ **4** $-3, 2$
5 $-1, 3$ **6** $-4, 5$ **7** $1, -2$ **8** $2, -5$
9 $7, -4$ **10** $3, 2$ **11** $1, 5$ **12** $4, 3$
13 $-4, -1$ **14** $-9, -2$ **15** $2, 4$ **16** $3, 5$
17 $-2, 5$ **18** $-3, 5$ **19** $-6, 2$ **20** $-6, 3$
21 $-1, 2$ **22** -2 **23** -5 **24** 4
25 $-2, -6$ **26** $5, -3$ **27** 7 **28** $-6, -4$
29 $2, 16$ **30** $-6, 4$ **31** $-9, 6$ **32** $-10, 3$
33 $-4, 11$ **34** $-8, 9$ **35** $8, 9$ **36** 1

Exercise 12I

1 a $\frac{1}{3}, -3$ **b** $1\frac{1}{3}, -\frac{1}{2}$ **c** $-\frac{1}{5}, 2$ **d** $-2\frac{1}{2}, 3\frac{1}{2}$
e $-\frac{1}{6}, -\frac{1}{3}$ **f** $\frac{2}{3}, 4$ **g** $\frac{1}{2}, -3$ **h** $\frac{5}{2}, -\frac{7}{6}$
i $-1\frac{2}{3}, 1\frac{1}{5}$ **j** $1\frac{3}{4}, 1\frac{1}{7}$ **k** $\frac{2}{3}, \frac{1}{8}$ **l** $\pm\frac{1}{4}$
m $-2\frac{1}{4}, 0$ **n** $\pm 1\frac{1}{5}$ **p** $-\frac{1}{3}, 3$

2 a $7, -6$ **b** $-2\frac{1}{2}, 1\frac{1}{2}$ **c** $7, -6$ **d** $-1, \frac{11}{13}$
e $3, -2$ **f** $-\frac{2}{5}, \frac{1}{2}$ **g** $-\frac{1}{3}, -\frac{1}{4}$ **h** $\frac{1}{5}, -2$
i 4 **j** $-2, \frac{1}{8}$ **k** $-\frac{1}{3}, 0$ **l** ± 5
m $-1\frac{2}{3}$ **n** $\pm 3\frac{1}{2}$ **p** $-2\frac{1}{2}, 3$

Exercise 12J

1 $1.77, -2.27$ **2** $-0.23, -1.43$ **3** $3.70, -2.70$
4 $0.29, -0.69$ **5** $-0.19, -1.53$ **6** $-1.23, -2.43$
7 $-0.41, -1.84$ **8** $-1.39, -2.27$ **9** $1.37, -4.37$
10 $2.18, 0.15$ **11** $-0.39, -5.11$ **12** $0.44, -1.69$
13 $1.64, 0.61$ **14** $0.36, -0.79$ **15** $1.89, 0.11$

Exercise 12K

1 a $(x + 2)^2 - 4$ **b** $(x + 7)^2 - 49$ **c** $(x - 3)^2 - 9$
d $(x + 3)^2 - 9$ **e** $(x - 2)^2 - 4$ **f** $(x + 1.5)^2 - 2.25$
g $(x - 2.5)^2 - 6.25$ **h** $(x + 0.5)^2 - 0.25$ **i** $(x + 5)^2 - 25$
j $(x + 3.5)^2 - 12.25$ **k** $(x - 1)^2 - 1$ **l** $(x + 1)^2 - 1$
2 a $(x + 2)^2 - 5$ **b** $(x + 7)^2 - 54$ **c** $(x - 3)^2 - 6$
d $(x + 3)^2 - 2$ **e** $(x - 2)^2 - 5$ **f** $(x + 1.5)^2 + 0.75$
g $(x - 2.5)^2 - 11.25$ **h** $(x + 0.5)^2 - 1.25$ **i** $(x + 5)^2 - 25$
j $(x + 1)^2 - 2$ **k** $(x - 1)^2 - 8$ **l** $(x + 1)^2 - 10$
3 a $-2 \pm \sqrt{5}$ **b** $-7 \pm 3\sqrt{6}$ **c** $3 \pm \sqrt{6}$ **d** $-3 \pm \sqrt{2}$
e $2 \pm \sqrt{5}$ **f** $-1.5 \pm \sqrt{0.75}$ **g** $2.5 \pm \sqrt{11.25}$
h $-0.5 \pm \sqrt{1.25}$ **i** $-4 \pm \sqrt{22}$
j $-1 \pm \sqrt{2}$ **k** $1 \pm 2\sqrt{2}$ **l** $-1 \pm \sqrt{10}$
4 a $1.45, -3.45$ **b** $5.32, -1.32$ **c** $-4.16, 2.16$

Exercise 12L

1 $52, 2$ **2** $65, 2$ **3** $24, 2$ **4** $85, 2$
5 $145, 2$ **6** $68, 2$ **7** $-35, 0$ **8** $-23, 0$
9 $41, 2$ **10** $40, 2$ **11** $-135, 0$ **12** $37, 2$

Exercise 12M

1 a $1 \pm \sqrt{5}$ **b** $-1 \pm 2\sqrt{2}$ **c** $-2 \pm 4\sqrt{3}$
   d $-1 \pm \sqrt{7}$ **e** $4 \pm \sqrt{14}$ **f** $2 \pm \sqrt{2}$

2 a $-1 \pm \dfrac{\sqrt{14}}{2}$ **b** $-1 \pm \dfrac{3\sqrt{2}}{2}$ **c** $\dfrac{-3 \pm \sqrt{19}}{2}$

   d $\dfrac{5 \pm \sqrt{89}}{4}$ **e** $\dfrac{-1 \pm \sqrt{61}}{10}$ **f** $\dfrac{-3 \pm \sqrt{33}}{4}$

Exercise 12N

1 6, 8, 10   **2** 15 m, 20 m   **3** 29   **4** 6.54, 0.46
5 5, 0.5   **6** 16 m by 14 m   **7** 48 km/h   **8** 45, 47
9 2.54 m, 3.54 m   **10** 6 cm   **11** 30 km/h   **12** 10p
13 1.25, 0.8   **14** 10   **15** 5 h   **16** 0.75 m

ANSWERS TO CHAPTER 13

Quick check

1 A (3, 0), B ((1, 4), C (4, 5)

2 a 18   **b** 145

Exercise 13A

1 a i 9 am   **ii** 10 am   **iii** 12 noon
   b i 40 km/h   **ii** 120 km/h   **iii** 40 km/h
2 a i 125 km   **ii** 125 km/h
   b i between 2 pm and 3 pm   **ii** about $12\frac{1}{2}$ km/h
3 a i 263 m/min (3 sf)   **ii** 15.8 km/h (3 sf)
   b i 500 m/min   **ii** Paul by 1 minute
4 a Patrick ran quickly at first, then had a slow middle section but he won the race with a final sprint. Araf ran steadily all the way and came second. Sean set off the slowest, speeded up towards the end but still came in third.
   b i 1.67 m/s   **ii** 6 km/h

Exercise 13B

1 a $\frac{15}{2}$ **b** $\frac{25}{8}$ **c** $\frac{15}{16}$ **d** $\frac{2}{25}$ **e** $\frac{6}{35}$ **f** $\frac{1}{2}$ **g** $-\frac{4}{5}$
2 a $2\frac{1}{2}$ km/h   **b** 3.75 m/s   **c** $2\frac{1}{2}$ km/h
3 a AB: 30 km/h, BC: 6 km/h, CD: 0 km/h, DE: 36 km/h (in opposite direction)
   b FG: 4 m/s, GH: 16 m/s, HI: 2 m/s (in opposite direction), IJ: 16 m/s (in opposite direction)

Exercise 13C

1 a 20 m/s^2 **b** 7.1 m/s
2 a 3.5 m/s^2 **b** 3.5 m/s^2
3 a between 2 and 4 hours, and between 8 and 10 hours
   b 10 km/h^2, 0 km/h^2, 5 km/h^2, 0 km/h^2, -6.25 km/h^2, -3.75 km/h^2

4

5 a

     b 3 m/s^2

Exercise 13D

1

2 a

   b

3 a

End of year	Amount owing (£)	End of year	Amount owing (£)	End of year	Amount owing (£)
1	52 500	6	34 356	11	17 324
2	50 085	7	31 273	12	13 391
3	42 749	8	28 037	13	9260
4	40 087	9	24 639	14	4923
5	37 291	10	21 071	15	369

b

Quick check

1 Triangles a, c and d are congruent to the triangle in the question

2 a 28   **b** 14

Exercise 14A

1 2, 3
2 a Yes, 4
   b No, corresponding sides have different ratios
3 a PQR is an enlargement of ABC   **b** 1 : 3
   c Angle R   **d** BA
4 a Sides in same ratio   **b** Angle P   **c** PR
5 a Same angles   **b** Angle Q   **c** AR
6 a 8 cm   **b** 7.5 cm   **c** $x = 6.67$ cm, $y = 13.5$ cm
   d $x = 24$ cm, $y = 13$ cm   **e** AB = 10 cm, PQ = 6 cm
   f 4.2 cm
7 a Sides in same ratio   **b** 1 : 3   **c** 13 cm   **d** 39 cm
8 4.8 m

Exercise 14B

1 a 9 cm   **b** 12 cm
2 a 5 cm   **b** 5 cm   **c** $x = 60$ cm, $y = 75$ cm
   d $x = 45$ cm, $y = 60$ cm   **e** DC = 10 cm, EB = 8 cm
3 82 m   **4** 220 feet   **5** 15 m
6 3.09 m   **7** 6 m

Exercise 14C

1 5 cm
2 6 cm
3 10 cm
4 $x = 6$ cm, $y = 7.5$ cm
5 $x = 15$ cm, $y = 21$ cm
6 $x = 3$ cm, $y = 2.4$ cm

Exercise 14D

1 a 4 : 25   **b** 8 : 125
2 a 16 : 49   **b** 64 : 343
3 Linear scale factor 2, 3, $\frac{1}{4}$, 5, $\frac{1}{10}$, 7, $\frac{1}{5}$, $\frac{1}{2}$;
   linear ratio 1 : 2, 1 : 3, 4 : 1, 1: 5, 10 : 1, 1 : 7, 5 : 1, 2 : 1;
   linear fraction $\frac{2}{1}$, $\frac{3}{1}$, $\frac{1}{4}$, $\frac{5}{1}$, $\frac{1}{10}$, $\frac{7}{1}$, $\frac{1}{5}$, $\frac{1}{2}$; area scale factor 4, 9, $\frac{1}{16}$,
   25, $\frac{1}{100}$, 49, $\frac{1}{25}$, $\frac{1}{4}$; volume scale factor 8, 27, $\frac{1}{64}$, 125, $\frac{1}{1000}$,
   343, $\frac{1}{125}$, $\frac{1}{8}$
4 a 1 : 2   **b** 1 : 8   **c** 8 pints   **d** No
5 135 cm^2
6 a 56 cm^2 **b** 126 cm^2
7 a 48 ft^2 **b** 3 ft^2
8 a 2400 cm^3 **b** 8100 cm^3
9 a 3750 cm^3 **b** 3.75 cm^3
10 4 litres
11 91.125 litres
12 a 5.0625 litres   **b** The height of the can
13 a 5.4 m^2 **b** 1.35 m^2
14 1.38 m^3
15 £6
16 6 cm, 8 cm, 10 cm
17 $3r$ cm
18 a 9, 36   **b** 16, 80   **c** 9, 45   **d** 36, 270   **e** Solids b and d

Exercise 14E

1 6.2 cm, 10.1 cm   **2** 4.26 cm, 6.74 cm
3 9.56 cm   **4** 3.38 m
5 35 mins   **6** 8.39 cm
7 26.5 cm   **8** 16.9 cm
9 a 4.33 cm, 7.81 cm   **10** 2478 ml
   b 143 g, 839 g
11 53.8 kg   **12** 1.73 kg
13 92.8 cm   **14** 1.30 m^2, 4.42 m^2

Quick check

1 12.96 cm

2 21.6°

Exercise 15A

1 13.1 cm
2 73.7°
3 9.81 cm
4 33.5 m
5 a 10.0 cm   **b** 11.5°   **c** 4.69 cm
6 63.0°

Exercise 15B

1 a 58.6°   **b** 20.5 cm   **c** 2049 cm^3 **d** 64.0°
2 a 3.46 m   **b** 75.5°   **c** 73.2°   **d** 60.3 m^2
3 a 24.0°   **b** 48.0°   **c** 13.5 cm   **d** 16.6°
4 a 32.0°   **b** 35.8°
5 a 3.46 m   **b** 70.5°

Exercise 15C

1 36.9°, 143.1°   **2** 53.1°, 126.9°
3 48.6°, 131.4°   **4** 224.4°, 315.6°
5 194.5°, 345.5°   **6** 198.7°, 341.3°
7 190.1°, 349.9°   **8** 234.5°, 305.5°
9 28.1°, 151.9°   **10** 185.6°, 354.4°
11 33.6°, 146.4°   **12** 210°, 330°

Exercise 15D

1 53.1°, 306.9°   **2** 54.5°, 305.5°
3 62.7°, 297.3°   **4** 54.9°, 305.1°
5 79.3°, 280.7°   **6** 143.1°, 216.9°
7 104.5°, 255.5°   **8** 100.1°, 259.9°
9 111.2°, 248.8°   **10** 166.9°, 193.1°
11 78.7°, 281.3°   **12** 44.4°, 315.6°

Exercise 15E

1 a 0.707   **b** −1 (−0.9998)   **c** −0.819   **d** 0.731
2 a −0.629   **b** −0.875   **c** −0.087   **d** 0.999

3 a 21.2°, 158.8°   **b** 209.1°, 330.9°
  c 50.1°, 309.9°   **d** 150.0°, 210.0°
  e 60.9°, 119.1°   **f** 29.1°, 330.9°
4 30°, 150°
5 −0.755
6 a 1.41   **b** −1.37   **c** −0.0367   **d** −0.138
  e 1.41   **f** −0.492
7 True
8 a cos 65°   **b** cos 40°
9 a 10°, 130°   **b** 12.7°, 59.3°
10 38.2°, 141.8°

Exercise 15F
1 14.5°, 194.5°   **2** 38.1°, 218.1°
3 50.0°, 230.0°   **4** 61.9°, 241.9°
5 68.6°, 248.6°   **6** 160.3°, 340.3°
7 147.6°, 327.6°   **8** 135.4°, 315.4°
9 120.9°, 300.9°   **10** 105.2°, 285.2°
11 54.4°, 234.4°   **12** 42.2°, 222.2°
13 160.5°, 340.5°   **14** 130.9°, 310.9°
15 76.5°, 256.5°   **16** 116.0°, 296.0°
17 174.4°, 354.4°   **18** 44.9°, 224.9°
19 50.4°, 230.4°   **20** 111.8°, 291.8°

Exercise 15G
1 a 3.64 m   **b** 8.05 cm   **c** 19.4 cm
2 a 46.6°   **b** 112.0°   **c** 36.2°
3 50.3°, 129.7°
4 2.88 cm, 20.9 cm
5 a i 30°   **ii** 40°   **b** 19.4 m
6 36.5 m
7 a 36.8 m   **b** 22.2 m
8 3.47 m
9 767 m
10 26.8 km/h

Exercise 15H
1 a 7.71 m   **b** 29.1 cm   **c** 27.4 cm
2 a 76.2°   **b** 125.1°   **c** 90°   **d** Right-angled triangle
3 5.16 cm
4 65.5 cm

5 a 10.7 cm   **b** 41.7°   **c** 38.3°   **d** 6.69 cm
  e 54.4 cm^2
6 72.3°
7 25.4 cm, 38.6 cm
8 58.4 km at 092.5°
9 21.8°
10 a 82.8°   **b** 8.89 cm

Exercise 15I
1 a 8.60 m   **b** 90°   **c** 27.2 cm   **d** 26.9°
  e 41.0°   **f** 62.4 cm   **g** 90.0°   **h** 866 cm
  i 86.6 cm
2 7 cm
3 11.1 km
4 19.9 knots
5 a 27.8 miles   **b** 262°

Exercise 15J
1 $\dfrac{3}{5}$ **2** $\sqrt{\dfrac{2}{5}}$

3 $\sqrt{19}$, $\sin x = \dfrac{\sqrt{6}}{\sqrt{19}}$, $\cos x = \dfrac{\sqrt{13}}{\sqrt{19}}$, $\tan x = \dfrac{\sqrt{6}}{\sqrt{13}}$

4 a $\sqrt{157}$ **b** $\sin A = \dfrac{6}{\sqrt{157}}$, $\cos A = \dfrac{11}{\sqrt{157}}$

5 $9\sqrt{3}$ cm^2
6 400 cm^2

Exercise 15K
1 a 24.0 cm^2 **b** 26.7 cm^2 **c** 243 cm^2
  d 21 097 cm^2 **e** 1224 cm^2
2 4.26 cm
3 a 42.3°   **b** 49.6°
4 103 cm^2
5 2033 cm^2
6 21.0 cm^2
7 a 33.2°   **b** 25.3 cm^2
9 a $\dfrac{1}{\sqrt{2}}$ **b** 21 cm^2

ANSWERS TO CHAPTER 16

Quick check

1 a 13   **b**

Exercise 16A
1

2

3

4

5

6

 b (3, 7)

7

 b (4, 11)

8

 b (6, 1)

9

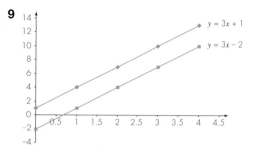

b No, because the lines are parallel.

10

x	0	1	2	3	4	5
y	5	4	3	2	1	0

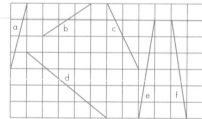

Exercise 16B

1 **a** 2 **b** $\frac{1}{3}$ **c** −3 **d** 1 **e** −2 **f** $-\frac{1}{3}$ **g** 5 **h** −5 **i** $\frac{1}{5}$ **j** $-\frac{3}{4}$

2

3 **a** 1 **b** −1 They are perpendicular and symmetrical about the axes.

4 **a** 0.5 **b** 0.4 **c** 0.2 **d** 0.1 **e** 0

5 **a** $1\frac{2}{3}$ **b** 2 **c** $3\frac{1}{3}$ **d** 10 **e** ∞

Exercise 16C

1

$y = 2x + 6, y = 3x − 4, y = \frac{1}{2}x + 5, y = x + 7$

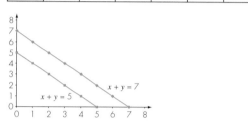

$y = 4x − 3, y = 2x − 7, y = \frac{1}{4}x − 3, y = \frac{2}{3}x + 4$

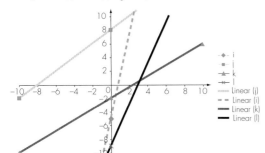

$y = 6x - 5, y = x + 8, y = \frac{4}{3}x - 2, y = 3x - 9$

- i
- j
- k
- l
- Linear (j)
- Linear (i)
- Linear (k)
- Linear (l)

2 a

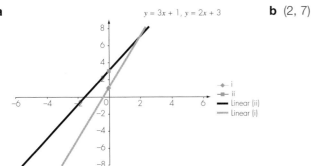

$y = 3x + 1, y = 2x + 3$

- i
- ii
- Linear (ii)
- Linear (i)

b (2, 7)

$3x - 2y = 18, x - y = 4, 5x - 2y = 15, 2x - 3y = 15$

- e
- f
- g
- h
- Linear (f)
- Linear (e)
- Linear (g)
- Linear (h)

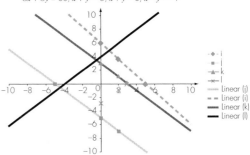

$6x + 5y = 30, x + y = -5, x + y = 3, x - y = -4$

- i
- j
- k
- l
- Linear (j)
- Linear (i)
- Linear (k)
- Linear (l)

3 a

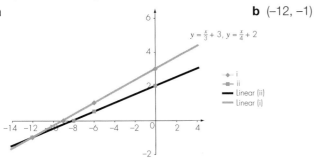

$y = \frac{x}{3} + 3, y = \frac{x}{4} + 2$

- i
- ii
- Linear (ii)
- Linear (i)

b (−12, −1)

2 a

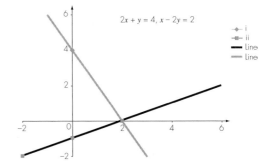

$2x + y = 4, x - 2y = 2$

- i
- ii
- Line
- Line

b (2, 0)

3 a

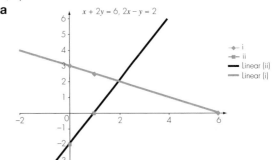

$x + 2y = 6, 2x - y = 2$

- i
- ii
- Linear (ii)
- Linear (i)

b (2, 2)

4 a

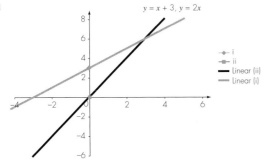

$y = x + 3, y = 2x$

- i
- ii
- Linear (ii)
- Linear (i)

b (3, 6)

Exercise 16D

1 $3x + 2y = 6, 4x + 3y = 12, 4x - 5y = 20, x + y = 10$

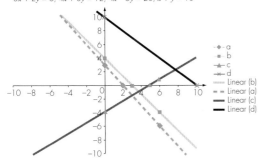

- a
- b
- c
- d
- Linear (b)
- Linear (a)
- Linear (c)
- Linear (d)

4 a

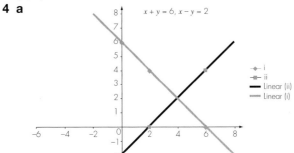

$x + y = 6, x - y = 2$

- i
- ii
- Linear (ii)
- Linear (i)

b (4, 2)

Exercise 16E

1 **a** $y = \frac{4}{3}x - 2$ or $3y = 4x - 6$ **b** $y = x + 1$ **c** $y = 2x - 3$ **d** $2y = x + 6$ **e** $y = x$ **f** $y = 2x$
2 **a i** $y = 2x + 1, y = -2x + 1$ **ii** reflection in y-axis (and $y = 1$) **iii** different sign
b i $5y = 2x - 5, 5y = -2x - 5$ **ii** reflection in y-axis (and $y = -1$) **iii** different sign
c i $y = x + 1, y = -x + 1$ **ii** reflection in y-axis (and $y = 1$) **iii** different sign
3 **a** $y = -2x + 1$ **b** $2y = -x$ **c** $y = -x + 1$ **d** $5y = -2x - 5$ **e** $y = \frac{3}{2}x - 3$
4 **a i** $2y = -x + 1, y = -2x + 1$ **ii** reflection in $x = y$ **iii** reciprocal of each other
b i $2y = 5x + 5, 5y = 2x - 5$ **ii** reflection in $x = y$ **iii** reciprocal of each other
c i $y = 2, x = 2$ **ii** reflection in $x = y$ **iii** reciprocal of each other (reciprocal of zero is infinity)

Exercise 16F

1 **a** 32°F **b** $\frac{9}{5}$ (Take gradient at C =10° and 30°.) **c** $F = \frac{9}{5}C + 32$
2 **a** 0.07 (Take gradient at U = 0 and 500.) **b** £10 **c** C = £(10 + 0.07U) or Charge = £10 + 7p/unit
3 **a** $\frac{5}{2}$ (Take gradient at D = 0 and 40.) **b** £20 **c** C = £(20 + $\frac{5D}{2}$) or Charge = £20 + £2.50/day
4 **a** $\frac{1}{2}$ (Take gradient at N = 0 and 500.) **b** £50 **c** C = £(50 + $\frac{N}{2}$) or £50 + 50p/person
5 **a** $\frac{4}{10}$ **b** 24.5 cm **c** 0.1 cm or 1 mm **d** $\angle = 24.5 + \frac{W}{10}$ or Length = 24.5 + 1 mm/kg

Exercise 16G

1 (4, 1)
2 (2, 3)
3 (3, 10)
4 (5, 5)
5 (1, 5)
6 (3, 16)
7 (−2, 6)
8 (−6, −9)
9 (1, −1)
10 (2, 6)
11 (2, 8)
12 $(7\frac{1}{2}, 3\frac{1}{2})$

Exercise 16H

1 **a** $-\frac{1}{2}$ **b** $\frac{1}{3}$ **c** $-\frac{1}{5}$ **d** 1 **e** −2 **f** −4
g 3 **h** $\frac{3}{2}$ **i** $-\frac{2}{3}$ **j** $-\frac{1}{10}$ **k** $\frac{1}{6}$ **l** $-\frac{3}{4}$
2 **a** $y = -\frac{1}{2}x - 1$ **b** $y = \frac{1}{3}x + 1$ **c** $y = -x + 2$ **d** $y = x + 2$
e $y = -2x + 3$ **f** $y = -4x - 3$ **g** $y = 3x$ **h** $y = 1.5x - 5$
3 **a** $y = 4x + 1$ **b** $y = \frac{1}{2}x - 2$ **c** $y = -x + 3$

4 **a** $y = -\frac{1}{3}x - 1$ **b** $y = 3x + 5$ **c** $y = -x + 1$
5 **a** $y = -x + 14$ **b** $y = x + 2$
6 $y = 2x + 6$
7 $y = -\frac{1}{4}x + 2$
8 **a** (0, −20) **b** $y = -\frac{1}{5}x + 6$ **c** $y = 5x - 20$
9 $y = -\frac{1}{2}x + 5$
10 **a** $y = 3x - 6$
b Bisector of AB is $y = -2x + 9$, bisector of AC is $y = \frac{x}{2} + \frac{3}{2}$, solving these equations shows the lines intersect at (3, 3)
c (3, 3) lies on $y = 3x - 6$ because $(3 \times 3) - 6 = 3$

ANSWERS TO CHAPTER 17

Quick check

1
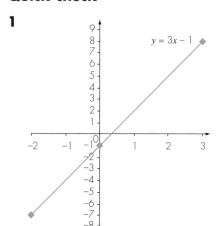
2 $y = 3x + 1$

Exercise 17A

1 **a** Values of y: 27, 12, 3, 0, 3, 12, 27
b 6.8 **c** 1.8 or −1.8
2 **a** Values of y: 27, 18, 11, 6, 3, 2, 3, 6, 11, 18, 27
b 8.3 **c** 3.5 or −3.5
3 **a** Values of y: 27, 16, 7, 0, −5, −8, −9, −8, −5, 0, 7
b −8.8 **c** 3.4 or −1.4

4 **a** Values of y: 2, −1, −2, −1, 2, 7, 14 **b** 0.25
c 0.7 or −2.7 **e** (1.1, 2.6) and (−2.6, 0.7)
5 **a** Values of y: 18, 12, 8, 6, 6, 8, 12 **b** 9.75 **c** 2 or −1
d Values of y: 14, 9, 6, 5, 6, 9, 14 **e** (1, 6)
6 **a** Values of y: 4, 1, 0, 1, 4, 9, 16 **b** 7.3 **c** 0.4 or −2.4
e (1, 4) and (−1, 0)
7 **a** Values of y: 15, 9, 4, 0, −3, −5, −6, −6, −5, −3, 0, 4, 9
b −0.5 and 3

Exercise 17B

1 **a** Values of y: 12, 5, 0, −3, −4, −3, 0, 5, 12 **b** 2 and −2
2 **a** Values of y: 7, 0, −5, −8, −9, −8, −5, 0, 7 **b** 3 and −3
3 **c** Values of y: 15, 8, 3, 0, −1, 0, 3, 8, 15
d Values of y: 11, 4, −1, −4, −5, −4, −1, 4, 11
e 1 and −1, 2.2 and −2.2
4 **a** Values of y: 5, 0, −3, −4, −3, 0, 5, 12 **b** −4 and 0
5 **a** Values of y: 16, 7, 0, −5, −8, −9, −8, −5, 0, 7, 16
b 0 and 6
6 **a** Values of y: 10, 4, 0, −2, −2, 0, 4, 10, 18 **b** −3 and 0
7 **c** Values of y: 10, 4, 0, −2, −2, 0, 4, 10
d Values of y: 6, 0, −4, −6, −6, −4, 0, 6, 14
e 0 and 3, −5 and 0
8 **a** Values of y: 9, 4, 1, 0, 1, 4, 9 **b** +2 **c** Only 1 root
9 **a** Values of y: 10, 3, −2, −5, −6, −5, −2, 3, 10
b 0.6 and 5.4

10 a Values of y: 19, 6, –3, –8, –9, –6, 1, 12   **b** 0.9 and –3.4

11 a –4, –9, –1, –5, 0, 0, 0, 0, 0

  b (0, –4), (0, –9), (0, –1), (0, –5), (–2, –4), (3, –9), (–1.5, –2.25), (1.5, –2.25), (–2.5, –6.25)

12 a $y = (x - 2)^2$ **b** 0

13 a $y = (x - 3)^2 - 6$ **b** –6

14 a $y = (x - 4)^2 - 14$ **b** –14

15 a $y = -(x - 1)^2 - 5$ **b** –5

Exercise 17C

1 a Values of y: 10, 5, 4, 2.5, 2, 1.33, 1, 0.67, 0.5

  b i 0.8   **ii** –1.6

2 a Values of $5\sqrt{x}$: 0, 5 and –5, 7.1 and –7.1, 8.7 and –8.7, 10 and –10, 11.2 and –11.2

  b i 9.4 and –9.4   **ii** 2.6

3 a Values of $\frac{1}{2}\sqrt{x}$: 0, $\frac{1}{2}$ and $-\frac{1}{2}$, 0.71 and –0.71, 0.87 and –0.87, 1 and –1, 1.1 and –1.1

  b i 0.8 and –0.8   **ii** 2.25

4 a Values of y: 10, 5, 2.5, 2, 1, 0.5, 0.4, 0.25, 0.2

  c 4.8 and 0.2

5 a Values of y: 25, 12.5, 10, 5, 2.5, 1, 0.5, 0.33, 0.25

  c 0.48 and –10.48

Exercise 17D

1 a Values of y: –24, –12.63, –5, –0.38, 2, 2.9, 3, 3.13, 4, 6.38, 11, 18.63, 30   **b** 4.7

2 a Values of y: –54, –31.25, –16, –6.75, –2, –0.25, 0, 0.25, 2, 6.75, 16, 31.25, 54   **b** 39.4

3 a Values of y: 27, 15.63, 8, 3.38, 1, 0.13, 0, –0.13, –1, –3.38, –8, –15.63, –27   **b** 0.2

4 a Values of y: –36, –23.13, –14, –7.88, –4, –1.63, 0, 1.63, 4, 7.88, 14, 23.13, 36   **b** 0.6

5 a Values of y: –45, –26.88, –14, –5.63, –1, 0.63, 0, –2.13, –5, –7.88, –10, –10.63, –9   **b** –9.3

6 a Values of y: –16, –5.63, 1, 4.63, 6, 5.88, 5, 4.13, 4, 5.38, 9, 15.63, 26   **c** –1.6, –0.4, 1.9

7 a Values of y: –20, –9.63, –3, 0.63, 2, 1.88, 1, 0.13, 0, 1.38, 5, 11.63, 22   **c** –1.9, 0.4, 1.5

8 a Quadratic   **b** Linear   **c** None

  d Reciprocal   **e** None   **f** Cubic

  g Linear   **h** None   **i** Quadratic

Exercise 17E

1 a Values of y: 0.01, 0.04, 0.11, 0.33, 1, 3, 9, 27

  c 15.6   **d** –0.63

2 a Values of y: 32, 16, 8, 4, 2, 1, 0.5, 0.25, 0.13, 0.06, 0.03

  c 0.18   **d** 0.42

3 b Values of y: 1, 2, 4, 8, 16, 32, 64, 128, 256, 512

  c 9.2×10^{18} **d** £4.61 × 10^{14}

4 a Number of pieces: 2, 4, 8, 16, 32, 64, 128, 256

  b number of pieces = 2^n **c** 1.1×10^{15} pieces

  d 1.1×10^8 km

Exercise 17F

1 115°   **2** 327°

3 324°   **4** 195°

5 210°, 330°   **6** 135°, 225°

7 a 64°   **b** 206°, 334°   **c** 116°, 244°

Exercise 17G

1 a i –1.4, 4.4   **ii** –2, 5   **iii** –0.6, 3.6   **b** 2.6, 0.4

2 a –5, 1   **b i** –5.3, 1.3   **ii** –4.8, 0.8   **iii** –3.4, –0.6

3 a i 0, 6   **ii** 4.3, 0.7   **b i** 4.8, 0.2   **ii** 5.4, –0.4

4 a i –1.6, 2.6   **ii** 1.4, –1.4   **b i** 2.3, –2.3   **ii** 2, –2

5 a 0, 2   **b** 2.5   **c** –0.6, 1, 1.6   **d** 2.8   **e** –0.8, 0.6, 2.2

6

  a –0.4, 4.4

  b –1, 5

7

  a 1.6, –1.6

  b –1.2, 1.2

8

  a 2.2, –2.2

  b –1.8, 2.8

9

  a 3.3, –0.3

  b 4.8, 0.2

10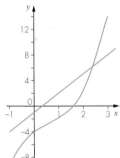

  a 2   **b** 2.5

ANSWERS TO CHAPTER 18

Quick check

1 29.0

Exercise 18A

1 b About 328 million   **c** Between 1980 and 1985

  d Rising living standards

2 b Smallest difference Wednesday (7°), greatest difference Friday (10°)

Exercise 18B

1 a

2	8 9
3	4 5 6 8 8 9
4	1 1 3 3 3 8 8

  b 43 cm   **c** 39 cm   **d** 20 cm

2 a

0	2 8 9 9 9
1	2 3 7 7 8
2	0 1 2 3

  b 9 messages   **c** 15 messages

Exercise 18C

1 a Positive correlation, reaction time increases with amount of alcohol drunk.
 b Negative correlation, you drink less alcohol as you get older.
 c No correlation, speed of cars on MI is not related to the temperature.
 d Weak, positive correlation, older people generally have more money saved in the bank.

2 c ≈ 19 cm/s **d** ≈ 34 cm
3 c Greta **d** ≈ 67 **e** ≈ 72
4 b Yes, usually (good correlation)
5 b No correlation, so cannot draw a line of best fit

Exercise 18D

1 a cumulative frequency 1, 4, 10, 22, 25, 28, 30
 c 54 secs, 16 secs
2 a cumulative frequency 1, 3, 5, 14, 31, 44, 47, 49, 50
 c 56 secs, 17 secs **d** Pensioners, median closer to 60 secs
3 a cumulative frequency 12, 30, 63, 113, 176, 250, 314, 349, 360
 c 605 pupils, 280 pupils **d** 46–47 schools
4 a cumulative frequency 2, 5, 10, 16, 22, 31, 39, 45, 50
 c 20.5°C, 10°C
5 a cumulative frequency 9, 22, 45, 60, 71, 78, 80
 c 56, 43 **d** 17.5%
6 a cumulative frequency 6, 16, 36, 64, 82, 93, 98, 100
 c 225p, 110p
7 a cumulative frequency 8, 22, 47, 82, 96, 100
 c £1605, £85 **d** 13%

Exercise 18E

1 a

 b The students are much slower than the pensioners. Although both distributions have the same inter-quartile range, the students' median and upper quartile are 1 minute, 35 seconds higher. The fastest person to compete the calculations was a student, but so was the slowest

2 a

 b Schools are much larger in Rotherham than Dorset. The Dorset distribution is symmetrical, but the Rotherham distribution is negatively skewed. This means that most schools in Rotherham are large.

3 a The resorts have similar median temperatures, but Resort B has a much wider temperature range. The greatest extremes of temperature are recorded in Resort B
 b Resort A is probably a better choice as the weather seems more consistent

4 a

 b Both distributions have a similar inter-quartile range, and there is little difference between the upper quartile values. Men have a wider range of salaries, but the higher men's median and the fact that the men's distribution is negatively skewed and the women's distribution is positively skewed indicates that men are better paid than women.

5 b £1605, £85
 c ii symmetric
6 a Symmetric **b** Negatively skewed
 c Negatively skewed **d** Symmetric
 e Negatively skewed **f** Positively skewed
 g Negatively skewed **h** Positively skewed
 i Positively skewed **j** Symmetric

Exercise 18F

1 a Mean 6, standard deviation 2.45 **b** 11.6, 3.77
 c 108, 4.43 **d** 203, 1.41 **e** 73.65, 3.57
 f 1, 2.51 **g** 77.2, 5.19 **h** 35, 3.98
2 a 6 **b** 1.41
3 a 8, 2.61 **b** 18, 2.61 **c** 28, 2.61
4 a 8, 1.94 **b** 8, 4.73
 c Paula because she is more consistent, although Rose occasionally gets high scores

Exercise 18G

1

Time of call	2	3	4	5	6	7	8	9	10	12
Frequency	5	1	1	5	1	3	1	1	1	1

mean 5.4, standard deviation 2.82
2 a Mean 2.15, standard deviation 1.19
 b 24.3, 1.51 **c** 102.15, 1.19 **d** 7.79, 0.47
 e 3.55, 0.88 **f** 0.166, 0.066
3 a i 3.49, 1.73 **ii** 3.0
 b i 6.96, 2.42 **ii** 5.85
 c The mean and the square of the standard deviation is about double that of the result in part a
 d Mean about 10.45, standard deviation about 3
4 a 135.2, 7.44
 b 2.84, 1.49 **i** 135.2 **ii** 7.44
 c Same
 d Smaller numbers

ANSWERS TO CHAPTER 19

Quick check

1 a Perhaps around 0.6 **b** Very close to 1
 c Very close to 0 **d** 1 **e** 1

Exercise 19A

1 a $\frac{1}{5}$, $\frac{2}{25}$, $\frac{1}{10}$, $\frac{21}{200}$, $\frac{37}{250}$, $\frac{163}{1000}$, $\frac{329}{2000}$ **b** 6 **c** 1
 d $\frac{1}{6}$ **e** 1000
2 a $\frac{19}{200}$, $\frac{27}{200}$, $\frac{4}{25}$, $\frac{53}{200}$, $\frac{69}{200}$ **b** 40
 c No, it is weighted towards the side with numbers 4 and 5

3 a 32 is too high, 20 of the 50 throws between 50 and 100 unlikely to be 5

   b Yes

4 a $\frac{1}{5}, \frac{1}{4}, \frac{38}{100}, \frac{21}{50}, \frac{77}{200}, \frac{1987}{5000}$ **b** 8

5 a 0.346, 0.326, 0.294, 0.305, 0.303, 0.306

   b 0.231, 0.168, 0.190, 0.16, 0.202, 0.201

   c Red 0.5, white 0.3, blue 0.2

   d 1

   e Red 10, white 6, blue 4

6 b 20

7 a 6

8 a Caryl, most throws   **b** $\frac{107}{275}, \frac{169}{550}, \frac{91}{550}, \frac{38}{275}$ **c** Yes

9 a Method B   **b** B   **c** C   **d** A   **e** B   **f** A   **g** B   **h** B

10 a Not likely   **b** Impossible   **c** Not likely

   d Certain   **e** Impossible   **f** 50–50 chance

   g 50–50 chance   **h** Certain   **i** Quite likely

Exercise 19B

1 a Yes   **b** Yes   **c** No   **d** Yes   **e** Yes   **f** Yes

2 Events a and f

3 $\frac{3}{5}$

4 a i $\frac{3}{10}$ **ii** $\frac{3}{10}$ **iii** $\frac{3}{10}$ **b** All except iii   **c** Event iv

5 b i $\frac{1}{10}$ **ii** $\frac{3}{10}$ **iii** $\frac{3}{10}$ **iv** $\frac{7}{10}$ **c** All except iii   **d** Event ii

6 a $\frac{3}{8}$ **b** $\frac{1}{8}$ **c** All except ii   **d** Outcomes overlap

7 $\frac{3}{20}$

8 Not mutually exclusive events

9 a i 0.25   **ii** 0.4   **iii** 0.7

   b Events not mutually exclusive

   c Man/woman, American man/American woman

   d Man/woman

Exercise 19C

1 25

2 1000

3 a 260   **b** 40   **c** 130   **d** 10

4 5

5 a 150   **b** 100   **c** 250   **d** 0

6 167   **b** 833

7 1050

8 a Each score expected 10 times   **b** 3.5

   c Find the average of the scores, which is 21 (1 + 2 + 3 + 4 + 5 + 6) divided by 6

9 400

Exercise 19D

1 a 23   **b** 20%   **c** $\frac{4}{25}$ **d** 480

2 a 10   **b** 7   **c** 14%   **d** 15%

3 b 4   **c i** $\frac{1}{4}$ **ii** $\frac{3}{16}$ **iii** $\frac{1}{4}$

4 a 16   **b** 16   **c** 73   **d** $\frac{51}{73}$

5 b 3   **c** $\frac{1}{4}$

6 a The greenhouse sunflowers are bigger on average

   b The garden sunflowers have a more consistent size (smaller range)

7 a 40%   **b** 45%

   c No as you don't know how much the people who get over £350 actually earn

Exercise 19E

1 a $\frac{1}{6}$ **b** $\frac{1}{6}$ **c** $\frac{1}{3}$

2 a $\frac{1}{4}$ **b** $\frac{1}{4}$ **c** $\frac{1}{2}$

3 a $\frac{1}{13}$ **b** $\frac{1}{13}$ **c** $\frac{2}{13}$

4 a $\frac{2}{11}$ **b** $\frac{4}{11}$ **c** $\frac{6}{11}$

5 a $\frac{1}{3}$ **b** $\frac{2}{5}$ **c** $\frac{11}{15}$ **d** $\frac{11}{15}$ **e** $\frac{1}{3}$

6 a 0.6   **b** 120

7 a 0.8   **b** 0.2

8 a 0.75   **b** 0.6   **c** 0.5   **d** 0.6

   e i Cannot add P(red) and P(1) as events are not mutually exclusive   **ii** 0.75

9 a $\frac{17}{20}$ **b** $\frac{2}{5}$ **c** $\frac{3}{4}$

10 Probability cannot exceed 1, and probabilities cannot be summed in this way as events are not mutually exclusive

Exercise 19F

1 a 7   **b** 2, 12

   c $P(2) = \frac{1}{36}$, $P(3) = \frac{1}{18}$, $P(4) = \frac{1}{12}$, $P(5) = \frac{1}{9}$, $P(6) = \frac{5}{36}$, $P(7) = \frac{1}{6}$, $P(8) = \frac{5}{36}$, $P(9) = \frac{1}{9}$, $P(10) = \frac{1}{12}$, $P(11) = \frac{1}{18}$, $P(12) = \frac{1}{36}$

   d i $\frac{1}{12}$ **ii** $\frac{1}{3}$ **iii** $\frac{1}{2}$ **iv** $\frac{7}{36}$ **v** $\frac{5}{12}$ **vi** $\frac{5}{18}$

2 a $\frac{1}{12}$ **b** $\frac{11}{36}$ **c** $\frac{1}{6}$ **d** $\frac{5}{9}$

3 a $\frac{1}{36}$ **b** $\frac{11}{36}$ **c** $\frac{5}{18}$

4 a $\frac{5}{18}$ **b** $\frac{1}{6}$ **c** $\frac{1}{9}$ **d** 0   **e** $\frac{1}{2}$

5 a $\frac{1}{4}$ **b** $\frac{1}{2}$ **c** $\frac{3}{4}$ **d** $\frac{1}{4}$

6 a 6   **b i** $\frac{4}{25}$ **ii** $\frac{13}{25}$ **iii** $\frac{1}{5}$ **iv** $\frac{3}{5}$

7 a $\frac{1}{8}$ **b** $\frac{3}{8}$ **c** $\frac{7}{8}$ **d** $\frac{1}{8}$

8 a 16   **b** 32   **c** 1024   **d** 2^n

9 a $\frac{1}{12}$ **b** $\frac{1}{4}$ **c** $\frac{1}{6}$

Exercise 19G

1 a $\frac{1}{4}$ **b** $\frac{1}{2}$ **c** $\frac{3}{4}$

2 a $\frac{1}{13}$ **b** $\frac{12}{13}$ **c i** $\frac{1}{169}$ **ii** $\frac{25}{169}$

3 a $\frac{2}{3}$ **b** $\frac{1}{2}$ **d i** $\frac{1}{6}$ **ii** $\frac{1}{2}$ **iii** $\frac{5}{6}$ **e** 15 days

4 a $\frac{2}{5}$ **b i** $\frac{4}{25}$ **ii** $\frac{12}{25}$

5 a $\frac{1}{8}$ **b** $\frac{3}{8}$ **c** $\frac{7}{8}$

6 a 0.14   **b** 0.41   **c** 0.09

7 a $\frac{3}{5}$ **c i** $\frac{1}{3}$ **ii** $\frac{7}{15}$ **iii** $\frac{8}{15}$

8 a 1   **b** 1   **c**

	$\frac{1}{4}$		$\frac{1}{4}$	$\frac{1}{10}$
$\frac{3}{5}$	$\frac{1}{3}$	$\frac{3}{5} \times \frac{1}{3}$	
$\frac{2}{3}$	$\frac{3}{5} \times \frac{2}{3}$	$\frac{2}{3}$	

Exercise 19H

1 a $\frac{4}{9}$ **b** $\frac{4}{9}$

2 a $\frac{1}{169}$ **b** $\frac{2}{169}$

3 a $\frac{1}{4}$ **b** $\frac{1}{2}$

4 $\frac{1}{216}$

5 a $\frac{4}{25}$ **b** $\frac{12}{25}$

6 a 0.08   **b** 0.32   **c** 0.48

7 a 0.336   **b** 0.452   **c** 0.024

Exercise 19I

1 a $\frac{125}{216}$ (0.579)   **b** $\frac{91}{216}$ (0.421)

2 a $\frac{1}{16}$ **b** $\frac{15}{16}$

3 a 0.378   **b** 0.162   **c** 0.012   **d** 0.988

4 a $\frac{4}{25}$ **b** $\frac{9}{25}$ **c** $\frac{16}{25}$

5 a i $\frac{1}{216}$ (0.005)   **ii** $\frac{125}{216}$ (0.579)   **iii** $\frac{91}{216}$ (0.421)

   b i $\frac{1}{1296}$ (0.00077)   **ii** $\frac{625}{1296}$ (0.482)   **iii** $\frac{671}{1296}$ (0.518)

   c i $\frac{1}{7776}$ (0.00013)   **ii** $\frac{3125}{7776}$ (0.402)   **iii** $\frac{4651}{7776}$ (0.598)

   d i $\frac{1}{6^n}$ **ii** $\frac{5^n}{6^n}$ **iii** $1 - \frac{5^n}{6^n}$

6 a $\frac{32}{243}$ (0.132)   **b** $\frac{1}{243}$ (0.004)   **c** $\frac{242}{243}$ (0.996)

7 a $\frac{3}{8}$ **b** $\frac{1}{120}$ **c** $\frac{119}{120}$

Exercise 19J

1 a $\frac{27}{1000}$ **b** $\frac{189}{1000}$ **c** $\frac{441}{1000}$ **d** $\frac{343}{1000}$

2 a $\frac{1}{1296}$ (0.00077)   **b** $\frac{625}{1296}$ (0.482)   **c** $\frac{125}{324}$

3 a $\frac{1}{9}$ **b** $\frac{7}{18}$ **c** $\frac{7}{18}$ **d** $\frac{1}{9}$ **e** $\frac{8}{9}$

4 a 0.154   **b** 0.456

5 a 0.3024   **b** 0.4404   **c** 0.7428

6 a 0.9   **b** 0.6   **c** 0.54   **d** 0.216

7 a 0.6   **b** 0.6   **c** 0.432   **d** Independent events

8 a $\frac{1}{9}$ **b** $\frac{1}{9}$ **c** $\frac{7}{27}$ **d** $\frac{1}{27}$

9 a 0.126   **b** 0.4   **c** 0.42   **d** 0.054

Exercise 19K

1 a $\frac{1}{60}$ **b** 50

2 a $\frac{1}{6}$ **b** 0   **c i** $\frac{2}{3}$ **ii** $\frac{1}{3}$ **iii** 0

3 a i $\frac{3}{8}$ **ii** $\frac{5}{8}$ **b i** $\frac{5}{12}$ **b ii** $\frac{7}{12}$

4 a i $\frac{5}{13}$ **ii** $\frac{8}{13}$ **b i** $\frac{15}{91}$ **ii** $\frac{4}{13}$

5 a i $\frac{1}{3}$ **ii** $\frac{2}{15}$ **b** $\frac{4}{15}$ **c** $\frac{1}{6}$ **d** 1

6 Both events are independent

7 a $\frac{1}{120}$ **b** $\frac{7}{40}$ **c** $\frac{21}{40}$ **d** $\frac{7}{24}$

8 a $\frac{1}{9}$ **b** $\frac{2}{9}$ **c** $\frac{2}{3}$ **d** $\frac{7}{9}$

9 a 0.000495   **b** 0.00198   **c** 0.000018   **d** 0.00024

10 a 0.54   **b** 0.38   **c** 0.08   **d** 1

11 a RFC, FRC, CFC, CRC   **b** $\frac{1}{3}$ **c** $\frac{1}{3}$ **d** $\frac{1}{3}$ **e**
Probability is the same regardless of which day he chooses

ANSWERS TO CHAPTER 20

Quick check

1 a 17, 20, 23 **b** 28, 36, 45   **c** 15, 10, 5
  d 49, 64, 81

2 a 1   **b** 4   **c** 7

3 a $2(x + 3)$ **b** $x(x - 1)$ **c** $2x(5x + 1)$

4 a $x^2 + 8x + 12$ **b** $2x^2 - 5x - 3$ **c** $x^2 - 4x + 4$

5 a $x = 3 - 2y$ **b** $x = 4 + 3y$ **c** $x = 4y - 3$

Exercise 20A

1 a $\frac{5x}{6}$ **b** $\frac{19x}{20}$ **c** $\frac{23x}{20}$ **d** $\frac{3x + 2y}{6}$ **e** $\frac{x^2y + 8}{4x}$

  f $\frac{5x + 7}{6}$ **g** $\frac{7x - 3}{4}$ **h** $\frac{13x - 5}{15}$ **i** $\frac{3x - 1}{4}$

  j $\frac{12x - 23}{10}$

2 a $\frac{x}{6}$ **b** $\frac{11x}{20}$ **c** $\frac{7x}{20}$ **d** $\frac{3x - 2y}{6}$ **e** $\frac{xy^2 - 8}{4y}$

  f $\frac{x - 1}{6}$ **g** $\frac{x - 1}{4}$ **h** $\frac{-7x - 5}{15}$

  i $\frac{x - 1}{4}$ **j** $\frac{-8x + 7}{10}$

3 a 3   **b** 6   **c** 2   **d** 5   **e** 0.75   **f** 3

4 a $\frac{x^2}{6}$ **b** $\frac{3xy}{14}$ **c** $\frac{8}{3}$ **d** $\frac{2xy}{3}$ **e** $\frac{x^2 - 2x}{10}$

  f $\frac{1}{6}$ **g** $\frac{6x^2 + 5x + 1}{8}$

  h $\frac{2x^2 + x}{15}$ **i** $\frac{2x - 4}{x - 3}$ **j** $\frac{1}{2x}$

5 a $\frac{3}{2}$ **b** $\frac{x}{y}$ **c** $\frac{8}{3}$ **d** $\frac{2xy}{3}$ **e** $\frac{5x}{2x - 4}$

  f $\frac{2x^2 - 12x + 18}{75}$ **g** 1   **h** $\frac{1}{4x + 2}$

  i $\frac{x^2 - 5x + 6}{48}$ **j** $\frac{1}{2x}$

6 a x **b** $\frac{x}{2}$ **c** $\frac{3x^2}{16}$ **d** 3

  e $\frac{17x + 1}{10}$ **f** $\frac{13x + 9}{10}$ **g** $\frac{3x^2 - 5x - 2}{10}$

  h $\frac{x + 3}{2}$ **i** $\frac{2}{3}$ **j** $\frac{2x^2 - 6y^2}{9}$

8 a 3, −1.5   **b** 4, −1.25   **c** 3, −2.5   **d** 0, 1
  i $\frac{x - 1}{4}$ **j** $\frac{-8x + 7}{10}$

9 a $\frac{x - 1}{2x + 1}$ **b** $\frac{2x + 1}{x + 3}$ **c** $\frac{2x - 1}{3x - 2}$

  d $\frac{x + 1}{x - 1}$ **e** $\frac{2x + 5}{4x - 1}$

Exercise 20B

1 a (5, −1)   **b** (4, 1)   **c** (8, −1)

2 a (1, 2) and (−2, −1)   **b** $x = -4, y = 1; x = -2, y = 2$

3 a (3, 4) and (4, 3)   **b** (0, 3) and (−3, 0)   **c** (3, 2) and (−2, 3)

4 a (2, 5) and (−2, −3)   **b** (−1, −2) and (4, 3)   **c** (3, 3) and (1, −1)

5 a (2, 4)   **b** (1, 0)   **c** The line is a tangent to the curve

Exercise 20C

1 a 21, 34: add previous 2 terms   **b** 49, 64: next square number   **c** 47, 76: add previous 2 terms

2 15, 21, 28, 36

3 61, 91, 127

4 $\frac{1}{2}, \frac{3}{5}, \frac{2}{3}, \frac{5}{7}, \frac{3}{4}$

5 a 6, 10, 15, 21, 28   **b** It is the sums of the natural numbers, or the numbers in Pascal's Triangle.

6 a 2, 6, 24, 720   **b** 69!

Exercise 20D

1   a 13, 15, $2n + 1$ **b** 25, 29, $4n + 1$
  c 33, 38, $5n + 3$ **d** 32, 38, $6n - 4$
  e 20, 23, $3n + 2$ **f** 37, 44, $7n - 5$
  g 21, 25, $4n - 3$ **h** 23, 27, $4n - 1$
  i 17, 20, $3n - 1$ **j** 42, 52, $10n - 8$
  k 24, 28, $4n + 4$ **l** 29, 34, $5n - 1$

2 a $3n + 1$, 151   **b** $2n + 5$, 105   **c** $5n - 2$, 248
   d $4n - 3$, 197   **e** $8n - 6$, 394   **f** $n + 4$, 54
   g $5n + 1$, 251   **h** $8n - 5$, 395   **i** $3n - 2$, 148
   j $3n + 18$, 168   **k** $7n + 5$, 355   **l** $8n - 7$, 393
3 a 33rd   **b** 30th   **c** 100th = 499
4 a i $4n + 1$ **ii** 401   **iii** 101, 25th
   b i $2n + 1$ **ii** 201   **iii** 99 or 101, 49th and 50th
   c i $3n + 1$ **ii** 301   **iii** 100, 33rd
   d i $2n + 6$ **ii** 206   **iii** 100, 47th
   e i $4n + 5$ **ii** 405   **iii** 101, 24th
   f i $5n + 1$ **ii** 501   **iii** 101, 20th
   g i $3n - 3$ **ii** 297   **iii** 99, 34th
   h i $6n - 4$ **ii** 596   **iii** 98, 17th
   i i $8n - 1$ **ii** 799   **iii** 103, 13th
   j i $2n + 23$ **ii** 223   **iii** 99 or 101, 38th and 39th

5 a $\dfrac{2n + 1}{3n + 1}$ **b** Getting closer to $\frac{2}{3}$ $(0.\dot{6})$
   c i 0.667 774 (6dp)   **ii** 0.666 778 (6dp)
   d 0.666 678 (6dp), 0.666 667 (6dp)

6 a $\dfrac{4n - 1}{5n + 1}$ **b** Getting closer to $\frac{4}{5}$ (0.8)
   c i 0.796 407 (6dp)   **ii** 0.799 640 (6dp)
   d 0.799 964 (6dp), 0.799 9996 (7dp)

7 a 64, 128, 256, 512, 1024   **b i** $2^n - 1$ **ii** $2^n + 1$ **iii** 3×2^n
8 a The number of zeros equals the power.   **b** 6
   c i $10^n - 1$ **ii** 2×10^n
9 a Even,   **b** Odd,

+	Odd	Even
Odd	Even	Odd
Even	Odd	Even

×	Odd	Even
Odd	Odd	Even
Even	Even	Even

10 a 36, 49, 64, 81, 100   **b i** $n^2 + 1$ **ii** $2n^2$ **iii** $n^2 - 1$
11 $1 + 3 + 5 + 7 = 16 = 4^2$, $1 + 3 + 5 + 7 + 9 = 25 = 5^2$
12 a 28, 36, 45, 55, 66   **b i** 210 **ii** 5050   **c** You get the square numbers.
13 a Even   **b** Odd   **c** Odd   **d** Odd   **e** Odd
   f Odd   **g** Even   **h** Odd   **i** Odd
14 a Odd or even   **b** Odd or even   **c** Odd or even
   d Odd   **e** Odd or even   **f** Even

Exercise 20E
1 b $4n - 3$ **c** 97   **d** 50th diagram
2 b $2n + 1$ **c** 121   **d** 49th set

3 a 18   **b** $4n + 2$ **c** 12
4 a i 24   **ii** $5n - 1$ **iii** 224   **b** 25
5 a i 20 cm   **ii** $(3n + 2)$ cm   **iii** 152 cm   **b** 332
6 a i 20   **ii** 162   **b** 79.8 km
7 a i 14   **ii** $3n + 2$ **iii** 41   **b** 66
8 a i 5   **ii** n **iii** 18   **b** 20
9 a 2^n **b i** $100 \times 2^{n-1}$ ml   **ii** 1600 ml

Exercise 20F
1 a i 35, 48   **ii** $n^2 - 1$ **b i** 38, 51   **ii** $n^2 + 2$ **c i** 39, 52   **ii** $n^2 + 3$ **d i** 34, 47   **ii** $n^2 - 2$
   e i 35, 46   **ii** $n^2 + 10$
2 a i 37, 50   **ii** $(n + 1)^2 + 1$ **b i** 35, 48   **ii** $(n + 1)^2 - 1$ **c i** 41, 54   **ii** $(n + 1)^2 + 5$
   d i 50, 65   **ii** $(n + 2)^2 + 1$ **e i** 48, 63   **ii** $(n + 2)^2 - 1$
3 a i $n^2 + 4$ **ii** 2504   **b i** $3n + 2$ **ii** 152   **c i** $(n + 1)^2 - 1$ **ii** 2600   **d i** $n(n + 4)$ **ii** 2700
   e i $n^2 + 2$ **ii** 2502   **f i** $5n - 4$ **ii** 246
4 a $2n^2 - 3n + 2$ **b** $3n^2 + 2n - 3$ **c** $\frac{1}{2}n^2 + \frac{5}{2}n + 1$

Exercise 20G
1 $-8y$ **2** $\dfrac{-x}{8}$ **3** $\dfrac{b + 5c}{4}$

4 $\dfrac{b(q + p)}{q - p}$ **5** $\dfrac{a(q - p)}{q + p}$ **6** $\dfrac{A}{\pi(2h + k)}$

7 $\dfrac{u}{\sqrt{(1 - a)}}$ **8** $\dfrac{3 + st}{2 + s}$ **9** $\dfrac{6 + st}{2 + s}$

10 $\dfrac{2R - 3}{R - 1}$ **11 a** $\dfrac{P}{\pi + 2k}$ **b** $\sqrt{\dfrac{2A}{\pi + \sqrt{(k^2 - 1)}}}$

12 $\dfrac{100A}{100 + RY}$ **13 a** $b = \dfrac{Ra}{a - R}$ **b** $a = \dfrac{Rb}{b - R}$

14 a $\dfrac{2 + 2y}{y - 1}$ **c** $x = \dfrac{2W + 2zy}{z + y}$
   d Same formula as in **a**
15 a Cannot factorise the expression.
   b $\dfrac{3V}{r^2(2r + 3h)}$ **c** Yes, $\sqrt[3]{\dfrac{3V}{5\pi}}$
16 $x = \dfrac{2W - 2zy}{z + y}$

ANSWERS TO CHAPTER 21

Quick check

1 $P = 4l$ **2** $C = \pi d$ **3** $A = \frac{1}{2}bh$
4 $A = \pi r^2$ **5** $V = l^3$ **6** $V = \pi r^2 h$

Exercise 21A
1 $P = 2a + 2b$ **2** $P = a + b + c + d$
3 $P = 4x$ **4** $P = p + 2q$
5 $P = 4x + 4y$ **6** $P = a + 3b$
7 $P = 5x + 2y + 2z$ **8** $P = 2\pi r$
9 $P = 2h + (2 + \pi)r$ **10** $P = 2l + \pi d$

Exercise 21B
1 $A = a^2 + ab$ **2** $A = \frac{1}{2}bh$
3 $A = bh$ **4** $A = \frac{1}{2}(a + b)h$
5 $A = \pi r^2$ **6** $A = 2ad - a^2$
7 $A = \frac{1}{2}bh + \frac{1}{2}bw$ **8** $A = 2rh + \pi r^2$
9 $A = \frac{1}{8}\pi d^2 + \frac{1}{2}dh$ **10** $A = \frac{1}{8}\pi D^2 + \frac{1}{2}(b + D)w$

Exercise 21C
1 $V = 6p^3$ **2** $V = \pi r^2 h$
3 $V = \frac{1}{2}bhw$ **4** $V = \frac{1}{2}bhl$
5 $V = aqt + bpt - apt$ **6** $V = abl + adl + 2cdl$

Exercise 21D

1　a A　b L　c L　d A　e V　f V　g V
　h A　i L　j V　k A　l L　m V　n A
　o V　p A　q V　r A　s A　t A　u L
　v A　w A　x A　y V　z V

2　a C　b I　c C　d I　e C　f I　g C
　h I　i C　j I　k C　l C　m C　n C
　o C　p I　q C　r C　s I　t C　u C
　v C　w C　x C　y C

3　a C, L　b I　c C, V　d C, L　e I
　f I　g C, V　h C, V　i C, V　j C, V
　k C, L　l I　m C, V

4　a 2　b 2, 3　c 2　d 2, 2

5　Inconsistent

6　a A is F_2, B is F_4, C is F_3
　b F_1 is the total length of the curved edges

ANSWERS TO CHAPTER 22

Quick check

1　a 25　b 9　c 27　d 4　2　a 48　b $\frac{1}{2}$

Exercise 22A

1　a 15　　　b 2
2　a 75　　　b 6
3　a 150　　b 6
4　a 22.5　　b 12
5　a 175 miles　b 8 hours
6　a £66.50　b 175 kg
7　a 44　　　b 84 m^2

Exercise 22B

1　a 100　b 10
2　a 27　b 5
3　a 56　b 1.69
4　a 192　b 2.25
5　a 25.6　b 5

6　a £50　　　b 225
7　a 3.2 °C　b 10 atm
8　a 388.8 g　b 3 mm
9　a 2 J　　b 40 m/s
10　a £78　　b 400 miles

Exercise 22C

1　$Tm = 12$　a 3　b 2.5
2　$Wx = 60$　a 20　b 6
3　$Q(5 - t) = 16$　a −3.2　b 4
4　$Mt^2 = 36$　a 4　b 5
5　$W\sqrt{T} = 24$　a 4.8　b 100
6　$gp = 1800$　a £15　b 36
7　$td = 24$　a 3 °C　b 12 km
8　$ds^2 = 432$　a 1.92 km　b 8 m/s
9　$p\sqrt{h} = 7.2$　c 2.4 atm　b 100 m
10　$W\sqrt{F} = 0.5$　a 5 t/h　b 0.58 t/h

ANSWERS TO CHAPTER 23

Quick check

1　a 6370　b 6400　c 6000

2　a 2.4　b 2.39

3　a 50　b 47.3

Exercise 23A

1　a $6.5 \leqslant 7 < 7.5$　　b $115 \leqslant 120 < 125$
　c $3350 \leqslant 3400 < 3450$　d $49.5 \leqslant 50 < 50.5$
　e $5.50 \leqslant 6 < 6.49$　f $16.75 \leqslant 16.8 < 16.85$
　g $15.5 \leqslant 16 < 16.5$　h $14\,450 \leqslant 14\,500 < 14\,549$
　i $54.5 \leqslant 55 < 55.5$　j $52.5 \leqslant 55 < 57.5$

2　a $5.5 \leqslant 6 < 6.5$　　b $16.5 \leqslant 17 < 17.5$
　c $31.5 \leqslant 32 < 32.5$　d $237.5 \leqslant 238 < 238.5$
　e $7.25 \leqslant 7.3 < 7.35$　f $25.75 \leqslant 25.8 < 25.85$
　g $3.35 \leqslant 3.4 < 3.45$　h $86.5 \leqslant 87 < 87.5$
　i $4.225 \leqslant 4.23 < 4.235$　j $2.185 \leqslant 2.19 < 2.195$
　k $12.665 \leqslant 12.67 < 12.675$　l $24.5 \leqslant 25 < 25.5$
　m $35 \leqslant 40 < 45$　　n $595 \leqslant 600 < 605$
　o $25 \leqslant 30 < 35$　　p $995 \leqslant 1000 < 1050$
　q $3.95 \leqslant 4.0 < 4.05$　r $7.035 \leqslant 7.04 < 7.045$
　s $11.95 \leqslant 12.0 < 12.05$　t $6.995 \leqslant 7.00 < 7.005$

Exercise 23B

1　a 7.5, 8.5　b 25.5, 26.5　c 24.5, 25.5
　d 84.5, 85.5　e 2.395, 2.405　f 0.15, 0.25
　g 0.055, 0.065　h 250 g, 350 g　i 0.65, 0.75
　j 365.5, 366.5　k 165, 175　l 205, 215

2　a <65.5 g　b 64.5 g　c <2620 g　d 2580 g

Exercise 23C

1　a $38.25 \text{ cm}^2 \leqslant \text{area} < 52.25 \text{ cm}^2$
　b $37.1575 \text{ cm}^2 \leqslant \text{area} < 38.4475 \text{ cm}^2$
　c $135.625 \text{ cm}^2 \leqslant \text{area} < 145.225 \text{ cm}^2$

2　a $5.5 \text{ m} \leqslant \text{length} < 6.5 \text{ m}, 3.5 \text{ m} \leqslant \text{width} < 4.5 \text{ m}$
　b 29.25 m^2　c 18 m

3　$79.75 \text{ m}^2 \leqslant \text{area} < 100.75 \text{ m}^2$

4　$216.125 \text{ m}^3 \leqslant \text{volume} < 354.375 \text{ m}^3$

5　$20.9 \text{ m} \leqslant \text{length} < 22.9 \text{ m}$ (3 sf)

6　$16.4 \text{ cm}^2 \leqslant \text{area} < 21.7 \text{ cm}^2$ (3 sf)

7　a i $64.1 \text{ cm}^3 \leqslant \text{volume} < 69.6 \text{ cm}^3$ (3 sf)
　　ii £22 569 $\leqslant$ price < £24 506 (nearest £)
　b 23 643 $\leqslant$ price < 23 661 (nearest £)
　c Errors in length are compounded by being used 3 times
　　in **a**, but errors in weight are only used once in **b**.

8　a $14.65 \text{ s} \leqslant \text{time} < 14.75 \text{ s}$
　b $99.5 \text{ m} \leqslant \text{length} < 100.5 \text{ m}$
　c 6.86 m/s (3 sf)

9　a +2.53% (3 sf)　b +3.82% (3 sf)

10　$3.41 \text{ cm} \leqslant \text{length} < 3.43 \text{ cm}$ (3 sf)

11　$5.80 \text{ cm} \leqslant \text{length} < 5.90 \text{ cm}$ (3 sf)

12　$14 \text{ s} \leqslant \text{time} < 30 \text{ s}$

Quick check

1 a 8 **b** 10

2 a

b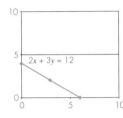

1 a $x < 3$ **b** $t > 8$ **c** $p \geqslant 10$ **d** $x < 5$
e $y \leqslant 3$ **f** $t > 5$ **g** $x < 6$ **h** $y \leqslant 15$
i $t \geqslant 18$ **j** $x < 7$ **k** $x \leqslant 3$ **l** $t \geqslant 5$

2 a 8 **b** 6 **c** 16 **d** 3 **e** 7

3 a 11 **b** 16 **c** 16

4 a $x \geqslant -6$ **b** $t \leqslant \frac{8}{3}$ **c** $y \leqslant 4$ **d** $x \geqslant -2$
e $w \leqslant 5.5$ **f** $x \leqslant \frac{14}{5}$

5 a $x \leqslant 2$ **b** $x > 38$ **c** $x < 6\frac{1}{2}$ **d** $x \geqslant 7$
e $t > 10$ **f** $y \leqslant \frac{7}{5}$

6 a $3 < x < 6$ **b** $2 < x < 5$ **c** $-1 < x \leqslant 3$
d $1 \leqslant x < 4$ **e** $2 \leqslant x < 4$ **f** $0 \leqslant x \leqslant 5$

Exercise 24B

1 a $x > 1$ **b** $x \leqslant 3$ **c** $x < 2$ **d** $x \geqslant -1$ **e** $x \leqslant -1$ **f** $x \geqslant 1$

2 a **b** **c** **d**

e **f** **g** **h**

3 a $x \geqslant 4$ **b** $x < -2$

c $x \geqslant 3\frac{1}{2}$ **d** $x < -1$

e $x < 1\frac{1}{2}$ **f** $x \leqslant -2$

g $x > 50$ **h** $x \geqslant -6$

4 a $x > 2$ **b** $x \geqslant 6$

c $x \leqslant -1$ **d** $x \geqslant -4$

Exercise 24C

1 $-2 \leqslant x \leqslant 2$

2 $x > 5, x < -5$

3 $-7 < x < 7$

4 $x \geqslant 1, x \leqslant -1$

5 $x \geqslant 3, x \leqslant -3$

6 $x > 3, x < -3$

7 $-2 \leqslant x \leqslant 2$

8 $-4 < x < 4$

9 $x > 1, x < -1$

10 $x \geqslant 3, x \leqslant -3$

11 $x > 2, x < -2$

12 $-3 < x < 3$

13 $-1 \leq x \leq 1$

14 $-4 < x < 4$

15 $x \geq 5, x \leq -5$

16 $x \geq 10, x \leq -10$

17 $-1.5 < x < 1.5$

18 $x \geq \frac{1}{2}, x \leq -\frac{1}{2}$

19 $-9 \leq x \leq 9$

20 $x > 0, x < 0$

Exercise 24D

1

2

3

4

5 a

b i Yes   **ii** Yes   **iii** No

6

7

8

9

10 a–d   **11 a–f**   **12**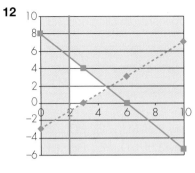

e i No **ii** No **iii** Yes   **g i** No **ii** No **iii** Yes   **b i** No **ii** Yes **iii** No **iv** No

Exercise 24E

1 a £148x **b** £125y **c** £(148x + 125y)

2 a £(Ax + By) **b** £(Ax + 2Bx) **c** £(9A + (9 + y)B)

3 a May be true **b** Must be false **c** May be true, e.g. $x = 30$, $y = 20$ **d** May be true, e.g. $x = 3$, $y = 40$

4 a May be true **b** May be true **c** Must be false

5 E Excels hold 40E; S Storms hold 50S. There must be at least 1500 seats, so $40E + 50S \geqslant 1500$. Cancelling through by 10 gives $4E + 5S \geqslant 150$

6 a W rides cost £1.50W. This cannot exceed £6.00, so $1.50W \leqslant 6.00$. Cancelling through by 1.5 gives $W \leqslant 4$

   b Likewise $2D \leqslant 6$, giving $D \leqslant 3$

   c Total cost is $1.50W + 2D \leqslant 6.00$. Multiplying through by 2 gives $3W + 4D \leqslant 12$

   d $D \leqslant 2$ **e i** Yes **ii** No **iii** No **iv** Yes

7 a $45x + 25y \leqslant 200 \Rightarrow 9x + 5y \leqslant 40$ **b** $y \geqslant x + 2$

8 a i Cost $30x + 40y \leqslant 300 \Rightarrow 3x + 4y \leqslant 30$ **ii** At least 2 apples, so $x \geqslant 2$ **iii** At least 3 pears, so $y \geqslant 3$

   iv At least 7 fruits, so $x + y \geqslant 7$

   b i No **ii** No **iii** No **iv** Yes

9 a i Space $4x + 3y \leqslant 48$ **ii** Cost $300x + 500y \leqslant 6000 \Rightarrow 3x + 5y \leqslant 60$ **b i** Yes **ii** No **iii** No **iv** Yes

10 a i Number of seats required is $40x + 50y \geqslant 300 \Rightarrow 4x + 5y \geqslant 30$ **ii** Number of 40-seaters $x \leqslant 6$

   iii Number of 50-seaters $y \leqslant 5$

   b i Yes **ii** Yes **iii** Yes **iv** Yes

   c Combination iii, which costs £760

   d Five 40-seaters and two 50-seaters cost £740

ANSWERS TO CHAPTER 25

Quick check

a $\begin{pmatrix} 1 \\ 3 \end{pmatrix}$ **b** $\begin{pmatrix} 3 \\ 0 \end{pmatrix}$ **c** $\begin{pmatrix} 2 \\ -1 \end{pmatrix}$ **d** $\begin{pmatrix} -1 \\ -2 \end{pmatrix}$

Exercise 25A

1 a Any 3 of $\overrightarrow{AC}$, $\overrightarrow{CF}$, $\overrightarrow{BD}$, $\overrightarrow{DG}$, $\overrightarrow{GI}$, $\overrightarrow{EH}$, $\overrightarrow{HJ}$, $\overrightarrow{JK}$ **b** Any 3 of $\overrightarrow{BE}$, $\overrightarrow{AD}$, $\overrightarrow{DH}$, $\overrightarrow{CG}$, $\overrightarrow{GJ}$, $\overrightarrow{FI}$, $\overrightarrow{IK}$

   c Any 3 of $\overrightarrow{AO}$, $\overrightarrow{CA}$, $\overrightarrow{FC}$, $\overrightarrow{IG}$, $\overrightarrow{GD}$, $\overrightarrow{DB}$, $\overrightarrow{KJ}$, $\overrightarrow{JH}$, $\overrightarrow{HE}$ **d** Any 3 of $\overrightarrow{BO}$, $\overrightarrow{EB}$, $\overrightarrow{HD}$, $\overrightarrow{DA}$, $\overrightarrow{JG}$, $\overrightarrow{GC}$, $\overrightarrow{KI}$, $\overrightarrow{IF}$

2 a 2**a** **b** 2**b** **c** **a** + **b** **d** 2**a** + **b** **e** 2**a** + 2**b** **f** **a** + 2**b** **g** **a** + **b** **h** 2**a** + 2**b** **i** 3**a** + **b**

   j 2**a** **k** **b** **l** 2**a** + **b**

3 a Equal **b** $\overrightarrow{AI}$, $\overrightarrow{BJ}$, $\overrightarrow{DK}$

4 a $\overrightarrow{OJ} = 2\overrightarrow{OD}$ and parallel **b** $\overrightarrow{AK}$ **c** $\overrightarrow{OF}$, $\overrightarrow{BI}$, $\overrightarrow{EK}$ **5**

6 a Lie on same straight line **b** All multiples of **a** + **b** and start at O **c** H **d i** $\overrightarrow{OQ}$ = **a** + $\frac{1}{2}$**b** **ii** $\overrightarrow{OR}$ = 3**a** + $\frac{3}{2}$**b**

   e n**a** + $\frac{n}{2}$**b**

7 a – **b** **b** 3**a** – **b** **c** 2**a** – **b** **d** **a** – **b** **e** **a** + **b** **f** –**a** – **b** **g** 2**a** – **b** **h** –**a** – 2**b** **i** **a** + 2**b**

   j –**a** + **b** **k** 2**a** – 2**b** **l** **a** – 2**b**

8 a Equal but in opposite directions   **b** Any 3 of $\overrightarrow{DA}$, $\overrightarrow{EF}$, $\overrightarrow{GJ}$, $\overrightarrow{FI}$, $\overrightarrow{AH}$

9 a Opposite direction and $\overrightarrow{AB} = -\frac{1}{2}\overrightarrow{CK}$ **b** $\overrightarrow{BJ}$, $\overrightarrow{CK}$ **c** $\overrightarrow{EB}$, $\overrightarrow{GO}$, $\overrightarrow{KH}$

10 a

11 a Any 3 of $\overrightarrow{MJ}$, $\overrightarrow{AG}$, $\overrightarrow{HC}$, $\overrightarrow{BD}$, $\overrightarrow{OH}$, $\overrightarrow{NA}$, $\overrightarrow{PO}$, $\overrightarrow{KB}$, $\overrightarrow{IE}$ **b** Any 3 of $\overrightarrow{DG}$, $\overrightarrow{HJ}$, $\overrightarrow{AL}$, $\overrightarrow{EH}$, $\overrightarrow{BA}$, $\overrightarrow{OM}$, $\overrightarrow{FB}$, $\overrightarrow{IO}$, $\overrightarrow{KN}$

  c Any 3 of $\overrightarrow{GD}$, $\overrightarrow{HE}$, $\overrightarrow{BF}$, $\overrightarrow{JH}$, $\overrightarrow{AB}$, $\overrightarrow{OI}$, $\overrightarrow{LA}$, $\overrightarrow{MO}$, $\overrightarrow{NK}$ **d** Any 3 of $\overrightarrow{CH}$, $\overrightarrow{DB}$, $\overrightarrow{EI}$, $\overrightarrow{GA}$, $\overrightarrow{HO}$, $\overrightarrow{BK}$, $\overrightarrow{JM}$, $\overrightarrow{AN}$, $\overrightarrow{OP}$

  e Any 3 of $\overrightarrow{FH}$, $\overrightarrow{EG}$, $\overrightarrow{IA}$, $\overrightarrow{BJ}$, $\overrightarrow{KM}$, $\overrightarrow{OL}$ **f** Any 3 of $\overrightarrow{JD}$, $\overrightarrow{AE}$, $\overrightarrow{OF}$, $\overrightarrow{LH}$, $\overrightarrow{MB}$, $\overrightarrow{NI}$

  g i $\overrightarrow{FG}$, $\overrightarrow{IJ}$ or $\overrightarrow{KL}$ **ii** $\overrightarrow{OC}$, $\overrightarrow{KD}$, $\overrightarrow{NG}$, $\overrightarrow{PH}$ **iii** $\overrightarrow{FJ}$ or $\overrightarrow{IL}$ **iv** $\overrightarrow{FL}$ **v** $\overrightarrow{LF}$ **vi** $\overrightarrow{PC}$ **vii** $\overrightarrow{CP}$

  viii Same as part **d**   **ix** Same as part **a**

12 Parts **b** and **d** could be, parts **a** and **c** could not be

13 a Any multiple (positive or negative) of 3**a**–**b**   **b** Will be a multiple of 3**a**–**b**

Exercise 25B

1 a i –**a** + **b**   **ii** $\frac{1}{2}$(–**a** + **b**)   **iii**

  iv $\frac{1}{2}$**a** + $\frac{1}{2}$**b**   **b i a** – **b**   **ii** $\frac{1}{2}$**a** – $\frac{1}{2}$**b**   **iii**

  iv $\frac{1}{2}$**a** + $\frac{1}{2}$**b**   **c**

  d M is midpoint of parallelogram of which OA and OB are two sides

2 a i –**a** – **b**   **ii** $-\frac{1}{2}$**a** – $\frac{1}{2}$**b**   **iii**

  iv $\frac{1}{2}$**a** – $\frac{1}{2}$**b**   **b i b** + **a**   **ii** $\frac{1}{2}$**b** + $\frac{1}{2}$**a**   **iii**

  iv $\frac{1}{2}$**a** – $\frac{1}{2}$**b**   **c**

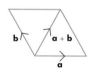

  d N is midpoint of parallelogram of which OA and OC are two sides

3 a

  b

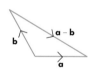

4 a i –**a** + **b**   **ii** $\frac{1}{3}$(–**a** + **b**)   **iii** $\frac{2}{3}$**a** + $\frac{1}{3}$**b**   **b** $\frac{3}{4}$**a** + $\frac{1}{4}$**b**

5 a i $\frac{2}{3}$**b**   **ii** $\frac{1}{2}$**a** + $\frac{1}{2}$**b**   **iii** $-\frac{2}{3}$**b**   **b** $\frac{1}{2}$**a** – $\frac{1}{6}$**b**   **c** $\overrightarrow{DE} = \overrightarrow{DO} + \overrightarrow{OE} = \frac{3}{2}$**a** – $\frac{1}{2}$**b**

  d $\overrightarrow{DE}$ parallel to $\overrightarrow{CD}$ (multiple of $\overrightarrow{CD}$) and D is a common point

6 a

  $\overrightarrow{CD}$ = –**a** + **b** = **b** – **a**   **b i** –**a**   **ii** –**b**   **iii a** – **b**   **c** 0, vectors return to starting point

  d i 2**b**   **ii** 2**b** – 2**a**   **iii** –2**a**   **iv** 2**b** – **a**   **v** –**a** – **b**

7 a

  $\overrightarrow{CX} = \sqrt{1^2 + 1^2}$**b** = $\sqrt{2}$**b**   **b** $\overrightarrow{YE} = \sqrt{1^2 + 1^2}$**a** = $\sqrt{2}$**a**.

  $\overrightarrow{CD} = \overrightarrow{CX} + \overrightarrow{XD} = \sqrt{2}$**b** – **a** $\overrightarrow{DE} = \overrightarrow{DY} + \overrightarrow{YE} =$ **b** – $\sqrt{2}$**a**

  c i –**a**   **ii** –**b**   **iii a** – $\sqrt{2}$**b**   **iv** $\sqrt{2}$**a** – **b**   **v** $\sqrt{2}$**a** + **a**   **vi** $\sqrt{2}$**b** + **b**   **vii** 2**b** + $\sqrt{2}$**b** – **a** – $\sqrt{2}$**a**

  viii 2**b** + $\sqrt{2}$**b** – 2**a** – $\sqrt{2}$**a**

8 a i –**a** + **b**   **ii** $\frac{1}{2}$(–**a** + **b**) = $-\frac{1}{2}$**a** + $\frac{1}{2}$**b**   **iii** $\frac{1}{2}$**a** + $\frac{1}{2}$**b**   **b i** $\frac{1}{2}$**b** + $\frac{1}{2}$**c**   **ii** $-\frac{1}{2}$**a** + $\frac{1}{2}$**c**   **c i** $-\frac{1}{2}$**a** + $\frac{1}{2}$**c**

  ii Equal   **iii** Parallelogram

9 a i $\frac{1}{2}$**a**   **ii c** – **a**   **iii** $\frac{1}{2}$**a** + $\frac{1}{2}$**c**   **iv** $\frac{1}{2}$**c**   **b i** $-\frac{1}{2}$**a** + $\frac{1}{2}$**b**   **ii** $-\frac{1}{2}$**a** + $\frac{1}{2}$**b**

  c Opposite sides are equal and parallel   **d** NMRQ and PNLR

Quick check

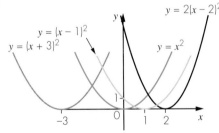

Exercise 26A

1 a–d

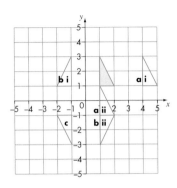

$y = 10x^2$
$y = 3x^2$
$y = x^2$
$y = \frac{1}{2}x^2$

e Stretch sf in y-direction: 3, $\frac{1}{2}$, 10

2 a–d

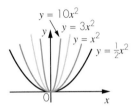

$y = x^2 + 3$
$y = 2x^2 + 1$
$y = x^2$
$y = x^2 - 1$

e *b* Translation $\begin{pmatrix} 0 \\ 3 \end{pmatrix}$ *c* Translation $\begin{pmatrix} 0 \\ -1 \end{pmatrix}$

d Stretch sf 2 in y-direction, followed by translation $\begin{pmatrix} 0 \\ 1 \end{pmatrix}$

3 a–d

$y = 2(x - 2)^2$
$y = (x - 1)^2$
$y = (x + 3)^2$
$y = x^2$

e *b* Translation $\begin{pmatrix} -3 \\ 0 \end{pmatrix}$ *c* Translation $\begin{pmatrix} 1 \\ 0 \end{pmatrix}$

d Stretch sf 2 in y-direction, followed by translation $\begin{pmatrix} 2 \\ 0 \end{pmatrix}$

4 a–c

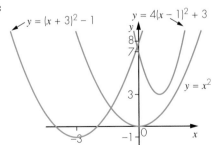

$y = (x + 3)^2 - 1$
$y = 4(x - 1)^2 + 3$
$y = x^2$

d *b* Translation $\begin{pmatrix} -3 \\ -1 \end{pmatrix}$

c Translation $\begin{pmatrix} 1 \\ 3 \end{pmatrix}$ followed by stretch sf 4 in y-direction

5 a–d

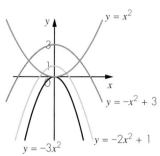

$y = x^2$

$y = -x^2 + 3$

$y = -2x^2 + 1$

$y = -3x^2$

e *b* Reflection in *x*-axis, followed by translation $\begin{pmatrix} 0 \\ 3 \end{pmatrix}$

c Reflection in the *x*-axis, followed by stretch sf 3 in *y*-direction

d Reflection in *x*-axis, followed by stretch sf 2 in *y*-direction and translation $\begin{pmatrix} 0 \\ 1 \end{pmatrix}$

6 a–d

$y = 10 \sin x$

$y = 2 \sin x$

$y = \sin x$

$y = \frac{1}{2} \sin x$

7 a–d

$y = 5 \sin 2x$

$y = \sin 3x$

$y = \sin \frac{x}{2}$

$y = \sin x$

e *b* Stretch sf $\frac{1}{3}$ in *x*-direction

c Stretch sf 2 in *x*-direction

d Stretch sf 5 in *y*-direction, followed by stretch sf $\frac{1}{2}$ in *x*-direction

e Stretch sf in *y*-direction: 2, $\frac{1}{2}$, 10

8 a–d

$y = \sin x$

$y = 2 \sin (x - 90)$

$y = \sin (x + 90)$

$y = \sin (x - 45)$

e *b* Translation $\begin{pmatrix} -90 \\ 0 \end{pmatrix}$ *c* Translation $\begin{pmatrix} 40 \\ 0 \end{pmatrix}$

d Stretch sf 2 in *y*-direction followed by

translation $\begin{pmatrix} 90 \\ 0 \end{pmatrix}$

9 a–d

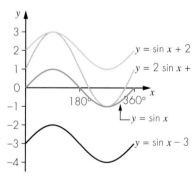

$y = \sin x + 2$

$y = 2 \sin x +$

$y = \sin x$

$y = \sin x - 3$

e *b* Translation $\begin{pmatrix} 0 \\ 2 \end{pmatrix}$ *c* Translation $\begin{pmatrix} 0 \\ -3 \end{pmatrix}$

d Stretch sf 2 in *y*-direction followed by translation $\begin{pmatrix} 0 \\ 1 \end{pmatrix}$

10 a–d

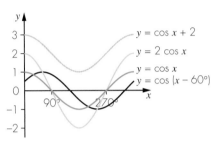

e *b* Reflection in *x*-axis   *c* Reflection in *y*-axis
  d This leaves the graph in the same place and is the identity transform

11 a–d

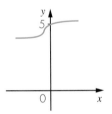

e *b* Stretch sf 2 in *y*-direction   *c* Translation $\begin{pmatrix} 60 \\ 0 \end{pmatrix}$

  d Translation $\begin{pmatrix} 0 \\ 2 \end{pmatrix}$

12 a i Stretch sf 4 in *y*-direction   **ii** Stretch sf 9 in *y*-direction   **iii** Stretch sf 16 in *y*-direction
  b i Stretch sf $\frac{1}{2}$ in *x*-direction   **ii** Stretch sf $\frac{1}{3}$ in *x*-direction   **iii** Stretch sf $\frac{1}{4}$ in *x*-direction

  c Stretch sf a^2 in *y*-direction, or stretch sf $\dfrac{1}{a}$ in *x*-direction

13 a

b

c

d

e

f

14 a $y = 5x^2$ **b** $y = x^2 + 7$ **c** $y = (x + 3)^2$
  d $y = 3x^2 + 4$ **e** $y = (x + 2)^2 - 3$ **f** $y = -3x^2$
15 a $y = 6\cos x$ **b** $y = \cos x + 3$ **c** $y = \cos (x + 30°)$ **d**
  $y = 3\cos x - 2$ **e** $y = \cos (x - 45°) - 2$

16 a

b i

ii

iii

iv

  c i $y = -x^3$ **ii** $y = x^3 - 2$ **iii** $y = 3x^3$ **iv** $y = (x + 2)^3$

17 a

b i

ii

iii   **iv**

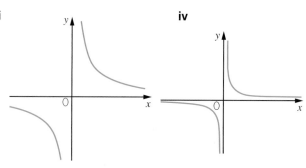

c i $y = \dfrac{1}{x} + 4$ **ii** $y = \dfrac{1}{x - 4}$

   iii $y = \dfrac{3}{x}$ **iv** $y = \dfrac{1}{2x}$

18 a $y = x^2 + 2$ **b** $y = (x - 2)^2$
   c $y = 2x^2$ **d** $y = -x^2 + 4$

19 a $y = 2 \sin x$ **b** $y = \sin(x - 30°)$
   c $y = 2 \sin(x - 60°)$ **d** $y = \sin 2x$

20 a Translation $\begin{pmatrix} 0 \\ -90 \end{pmatrix}$

   b i Equivalent   **ii** Equivalent   **iii** Not equivalent

21 i A   **ii** D   **iii** E   **iv** C   **v** B

ANSWERS TO CHAPTER 27

Quick check

1 $z = x + y$

2 $p^2 = q^2 + r^2$

3

+	**Even**	**Odd**
even	even	odd
odd	odd	even

Exercise 27A

6 a 3, 5, 8, 13, 21, 34, 55
   b $3a + 5b$, $5a + 8b$, $8a + 13b$, $13a + 21b$, $21a + 34b$
8 a i $40°$
9 a i 10

Index